The Biology of Mental Health and Disease

The Biology of Mental Health and Disease

The Twenty-seventh Annual Conference
of the Milbank Memorial Fund

WITH 108 CONTRIBUTORS

Foreword by Stanley Cobb, M.D.

PAUL B. HOEBER, Inc.

MEDICAL BOOK DEPARTMENT OF HARPER & BROTHERS

The report of the Twenty-seventh Annual Conference of the Milbank Memorial Fund: A Symposium on Biological Aspects of Mental Health and Disease. Held at the New York Academy of Medicine, New York City, November 13-16, 1950.

CONTENTS

PARTICIPANTS

CHAIRMEN OF SESSIONS

BARD, PHILIP, PH.D.
Professor of Physiology, The Johns Hopkins University School of Medicine

CARMICHAEL, LEONARD, PH.D.
President, Tufts College and Director of Research Laboratory of Sensory Psychology and Physiology

COBB, STANLEY, M.D.
Psychiatrist-in-Chief, Massachusetts General Hospital; Bullard Professor of Neuropathology, Harvard Medical School

CORI, CARL F., M.D.
Professor of Biochemistry, Washington University School of Medicine

GERARD, RALPH W., M.D., PH.D.
Professor of Physiology, University of Chicago

LEWIS, NOLAN D. C., M.D.
Professor of Psychiatry, College of Physicians and Surgeons, Columbia University; Director, New York State Psychiatric Institute

PENFIELD, WILDER, M.D.
Director, Montreal Neurological Institute

WHITEHORN, JOHN C., M.D.
Henry Phipps Professor of Psychiatry, The Johns Hopkins University School of Medicine

---

ALTSCHULE, MARK D., M.D.
Director, Internal Medicine and Research in Clinical Physiology, McLean Hospital, Waverly, Mass.; Assistant Professor of Medicine, Harvard Medical School

ASHBY, WINIFRED M., PH.D.
Guest Research Worker, St. Elizabeth's Hospital, Washington, D. C.

BAILEY, PERCIVAL, M.D.
Director of the Illinois State Psychopathic Institute; and Distinguished Professor of Neurology and Neurological Surgery and Clinical Professor of Psychiatry, University of Illinois College of Medicine

BALL, ERIC G., PH.D.
Professor of Biological Chemistry, Harvard Medical School

BARACH, ALVAN L., M.D.
Associate Professor of Clinical Medicine, College of Physicians and Surgeons, Columbia University

BARRON, DONALD H., PH.D.
Professor of Physiology, Yale University School of Medicine

BENDA, CLEMENS E., M.D.
Clinical Director and Director of Research, Walter E. Fernald School; Instructor, Department of Neuropathology, Harvard Medical School

BERNHEIM, FREDERICK, PH.D.
Professor of Pharmacology, Duke University School of Medicine

BISHOP, GEORGE H., PH.D.
Professor of Neurophysiology, Department of Neuropsychiatry, Washington University School of Medicine

BÖÖK, JAN A., M.D.
Department of Medical Genetics, University of Lund, Sweden

BOUDREAU, FRANK G., M.D.
Executive Director, Milbank Memorial Fund

BRANCALE, RALPH, M.D.
Director, New Jersey Diagnostic Center, Menlo Park

BRAZIER, MARY, A. B., PH.D.
Neurophysiologist, Massachusetts General Hospital; Research Associate in Neuropathology, Harvard Medical School

BRUETSCH, WALTER L., M.D.
Clinical Professor of Psychiatry and Neurology, Indiana University School of Medicine; Clinical Director and Head of the Research Department, Central State Hospital, Indianapolis

CHANG, H.-T., PH.D.
Assistant Professor of Physiology, Yale University School of Medicine

CLEGHORN, ROBERT A., M.D.
Associate Professor of Psychiatry, Allan Memorial Institute, McGill University

CONEL, J. LEROY, PH.D.
Research Associate in Pathology, The Children's Medical Center, Boston; Professor of Anatomy, Emeritus, Boston University School of Medicine

COWEN, DAVID, M.D.
Assistant Professor of Neuropathology, College of Physicians and Surgeons, Columbia University

CRAIGIE, E. HORNE, PH.D.
Professor of Comparative Anatomy and Neurology, University of Toronto

ELLIOTT, K. A. C., PH.D., SC.D.
Research Neurochemist, Montreal Neurological Institute; Associate Professor of Experimental Neurology and Biochemistry, McGill University

FELIX, ROBERT H., M.D.
Director, National Institute of Mental Health, Public Health Service

FERRARO, A., M.D.
Principal Research Scientist, New York State Psychiatric Institute; Clinical Professor of Psychiatry, Columbia University

FINESINGER, JACOB E., M.D.
Professor of Psychiatry, University of Maryland School of Medicine

FLEXNER, LOUIS B., M.D.
Professor of Anatomy and Chairman, Department of Anatomy, School of Medicine, University of Pennsylvania; Research Associate, Department of Embryology, Carnegie Institution of Washington

FOLCH-PI, J., M.D.
Director of Scientific Research, McLean Hospital, Waverly, Mass.; Assistant Professor of Biological Chemistry, Harvard Medical School

FÖLLING, ASBJÖRN, DR. MED.
Professor of Physiology, The Veterinary School, University of Oslo

GALDSTON, IAGO, M.D.
Executive Secretary, Medical Information Bureau, The New York Academy of Medicine

GANTT, W. HORSLEY, M.D.
Associate Professor of Psychiatry, The Johns Hopkins University School of Medicine

GATES, R. RUGGLES, D.SC.
Biological Laboratories, Harvard University

GIBBS, FREDERIC A., M.D.
Professor of Neurology, University of Illinois College of Medicine

GILDEA, EDWIN F., M.D.
Professor of Psychiatry, Washington University School of Medicine

GREGG, ALAN, M.D.
Vice President, The Rockefeller Foundation

GRUENBERG, ERNEST M., M.D.
Executive Director, Mental Health Commission, New York State Department of Mental Hygiene

HARGREAVES, G. R., M.R.C.S., L.R.C.P.
Chief, Mental Health Section, World Health Organization

HARLOW, HARRY F., PH.D.
Professor of Psychology, University of Wisconsin; Scientific Advisor, Human Resources, U. S. Army

HEBB, DONALD O., PH.D.
Professor of Psychology, McGill University

HIMWICH, HAROLD E., M.D.
Director, Research Division, Galesburg State Research Hospital, Galesburg, Illinois

HOAGLAND, HUDSON, PH.D.
Executive Director, Worcester Foundation for Experimental Biology, Shrewsbury, Mass.

HOCH, PAUL H., M.D.
Principal Research Scientist in Charge of Department of Research Psychiatry, New York State Psychiatric Institute; Assistant Professor of Psychiatry, College of Physicians and Surgeons, Columbia University

HOOKER, DAVENPORT, PH.D.
Professor of Anatomy and Head of the Department, University of Pittsburgh School of Medicine

HUME, DAVID M., M.D.
Instructor in Surgery and Director, Laboratory for Surgical Research, Harvard Medical School

INGALLS, THEODORE, H., M.D.
Associate Professor of Epidemiology, Harvard School of Public Health

JASPER, HERBERT H., M.D.
Professor of Experimental Neurology, McGill University; Montreal Neurological Institute

JERVIS, GEORGE A., M.D.
Neuropathologist, Letchworth Village, Thiells, N. Y.

KALINOWSKY, LOTHAR B., M.D.
Research Associate, Department of Psychiatry, College of Physicians and Surgeons, Columbia University

KALLMANN, FRANZ J., M.D.
Associate Research Scientist, Department of Medical Genetics, New York State Psychiatric Institute

KATZENELBOGEN, SOLOMON, M.D.
Director of Laboratory and Research, St. Elizabeths Hospital, Washington, D. C.; Clinical Professor of Psychiatry, George Washington University School of Medicine, Washington, D. C.

KETY, SEYMOUR S., M.D.
Scientific Director, National Institutes of Mental Health, Neurological Diseases and Blindness, National Institutes of Health. Professor of Physiology, Graduate School of Medicine, University of Pennsylvania.

KEYS, ANCEL, PH.D.
Director, Laboratory of Physiological Hygiene, University of Minnesota

KLÜVER, HEINRICH, PH.D.
Professor of Experimental Psychology, Division of the Biological Sciences, University of Chicago

KRUSE, H. D., M.D.
Milbank Memorial Fund

LANDIS, CARNEY, PH.D., D.SC.
Principal Research Psychologist, New York State Psychiatric Institute; Professor of Psychology, Columbia University

LARRABEE, MARTIN G., PH.D.
Associate Professor of Biophysics, The Johns Hopkins University

LEHMANN, H., M.D.
Clinical Director, Verdun Protestant Hospital, Montreal; Lecturer in Psychiatry, McGill University

LEIGHTON, ALEXANDER H., M.D.
Department of Sociology and Anthropology, Cornell University

LIDDELL, HOWARD S., PH.D.
Professor of Psychobiology, Cornell University

LIDZ, THEODORE, M.D.
Professor of Psychiatry, Yale University School of Medicine

LILIENTHAL, JOSEPH L., JR., M.D.
Professor of Environmental Medicine, Associate Professor of Medicine, The Johns Hopkins University

LILLY, JOHN C., M.D.
Assistant Professor of Biophysics, The Eldridge Reeves Johnson Foundation for Medical Physics; University of Pennsylvania School of Medicine

LLOYD, DAVID P. C., D.PHIL.
Member, The Rockefeller Institute for Medical Research

LORENZ, WILLIAM F., M.D.
Professor of Neuropsychiatry, University of Wisconsin Medical School

MAGOUN, HORACE W., PH.D.
Chairman, Department of Anatomy, University of California Medical School, Los Angeles

MALAMUD, WILLIAM, M.D.
Professor of Psychiatry, Boston University School of Medicine

MANERY, JEANNE F., PH.D.
Research Scientist, D.R.N.L., Fort Churchill; Assistant Professor, Department of Biochemistry, University of Toronto

MARRAZZI, AMEDEO S., M.D.
Chief, Clinical Research Division, Medical Laboratories, Army Chemical Center, Maryland

McCULLOCH, WARREN S., M.D.
Professor of Psychiatry and Physiology, University of Illinois College of Medicine

McFARLAND, ROSS A., PH.D.
Associate Professor of Industrial Hygiene, Harvard School of Public Health

MEDUNA, L. J., M.D.
Professor of Psychiatry, Illinois Neuropsychiatric Institute

METTLER, FRED A., M.D.
Professor of Anatomy, College of Physicians and Surgeons, Columbia University

† MEYERHOF, OTTO, M.D.
Research Professor of Biochemistry, University of Pennsylvania School of Medicine

† Doctor Meyerhof died on October 13, 1951.

MUSTARD, H. S., M.D.
Executive Director, State Charities Aid Association, New York City

NEEL, JAMES V., M.D., PH.D.
Associate Geneticist, Institute of Human Biology; and Associate Professor of Medical Genetics, University of Michigan Medical School

NIMS, LESLIE F., PH.D.
Senior Physiologist, Brookhaven National Laboratory

NURNBERGER, JOHN I., M.D.
Research Associate in Clinical Psychiatry and Cell Research, The Institute of Living, Hartford, Conn.

OCHOA, SEVERO, M.D.
Professor of Pharmacology, New York University College of Medicine

PARRAN, THOMAS, M.D.
Dean, Graduate School of Public Health, University of Pittsburgh

PINCUS, GREGORY, SC.D.
Director of Laboratories, Worcester Foundation for Experimental Biology, Shrewsbury, Mass.

POPE, ALFRED, M.D.
Research Associate in Neuropathology, McLean Hospital, Waverley, Mass.; Associate in Neuropathology, Harvard Medical School.

QUASTEL, J. H., D.SC., F.R.S.
Professor of Biochemistry, McGill University, Montreal; Director, Research Institute, Montreal General Hospital

RACKER, EFRAIM, M.D.
Assistant Professor of Microbiology, New York University College of Medicine

REED, SHELDON CLARK, PH.D.
Director of Dight Institute, University of Minnesota

RITTENBERG, DAVID, PH.D
Associate Professor of Biochemistry, College of Physicians and Surgeons, Columbia University

ROIZIN, LEON, M.D.
Associate Research Scientist (Neuropathology), New York State Psychiatric Institute; Associate in Psychiatry, Columbia University

ROSSEN, RALPH, M.D.
Commissioner of Mental Health, State of Minnesota

SELYE, HANS, M.D., PH.D., D.SC., F.R.S.(C.)
  Professor and Director of the Institut de Médecine et de Chirurgie
  expérimentales, Université de Montréal

SOLOMON, HARRY C., M.D.
  Medical Director, Boston Psychopathic Hospital; Professor of Psychiatry, Harvard Medical School

SPERRY, WARREN M., PH.D.,
  Principal Research Scientist (Biochemistry), New York State Psychiatric Institute

STEVENSON, GEORGE S., M.D.
  Medical Director, The National Association for Mental Health

STONE, WILLIAM E., PH.D.
  Associate Professor of Physiology, University of Wisconsin

TAYLOR, REGINALD M., M.D.
  Associate Research Psychiatrist, New York State Psychiatric Institute;
  Department of Psychiatry, Columbia University

TEUBER, HANS-LUKAS, PH.D.
  Assistant Professor of Experimental Psychology, New York University
  College of Medicine

THOMPSON, LLOYD J., M.D.
  Professor and Director of Department of Psychiatry and Neurology,
  Bowman Gray School of Medicine of Wake Forest College

TSCHIRGI, ROBERT D., M.D., PH.D.
  Assistant Professor of Physiology, University of Chicago

WAELSCH, HEINRICH B., M.D., SC.D.
  Associate Professor of Biochemistry, Columbia University; Associate
  Research Scientist (Biochemistry), New York State Psychiatric In-
  stitute

WILDER, RUSSELL M., M.D.
  Director, National Institute of Arthritis and Metabolic Diseases, Na-
  tional Institutes of Health, Federal Security Agency, U.S. Public Health
  Service

WINDLE, WILLIAM F., PH.D.
  Professor and Chairman, Department of Anatomy, University of Pennsylvania School of Medicine

WINKELMAN, N. W., M.D.
  Professor of Neuropathology, Graduate School of Medicine, University
  of Pennsylvania; Medical Director, Philadelphia Psychiatric Hospital

WOLF, ABNER, M.D.
 Professor of Neuropathology, College of Physicians and Surgeons, Columbia University

WOLFF, HAROLD G., M.D.
 Professor of Medicine (Neurology), Cornell University Medical College

WOOLSEY, CLINTON N., M.D.
 Charles Sumner Slichter Research Professor of Neurophysiology, University of Wisconsin Medical School

FOREWORD

ALL investigators and practitioners who are interested in how the brain works, normally or abnormally, owe a debt of gratitude to the Milbank Memorial Fund for bringing together this conference. The academic, technical and geographic diversity of the participants made the conference much more valuable than if it had been a neuropsychiatric or neurophysiological meeting. The list of participants included anatomists, physiologists, geneticists, chemists, neuropathologists, neurologists, neurosurgeons, psychologists, and psychiatrists—to name only the principal disciplines represented. They came from sixteen states of the United States and three foreign countries. Naturally they represented many points of view. Disagreements were common. Therein lies the effectiveness of these conferences. They bring together experts, working with different techniques but with the same general goals, and no need to compromise.

This was a conference on "Mental Health and Disease." Obviously a field so broad could not be covered in a week or a month. It had to be limited in scope, with emphasis on certain aspects at the expense of others. This delimitation was accomplished partly by adding to the title: "Biological Aspects of" but more by critical choosing of the speakers. The emphasis was evidently brought about by asking men who work in the preclinical or "basic" medical sciences, rather than clinicians. Of the principal speakers ten were chemists, six were physiologists, five psychiatrists, four neuropathologists, three anatomists, three psychologists, two geneticists and one internist, one epidemiologist and one electroencephalographer. These men were skillfully chosen to give weight and balance to the discussions. The psychiatrists and psychologists were mostly men interested in laboratory investigation rather than in the clinical fields.

Many of the disagreements at the conference were from semantic difficulties. Some words were used by different speakers to mean different things. This is clearly shown in the published discussions. Even the term "biological" as used in the title is ambiguous with a suggestion that it rules out sociology and personology. But some well-known psychiatrists have defined Psychiatry as the science of interpersonal relations. Surely the behavior of groups of organisms is one of the most important parts of biology. One realizes that the word "biological" is commonly used to denote the laboratory approach as opposed to the human approach. One often hears psychiatrists speak of the "biological aspects" as if they referred only to "lower animals" as opposed to the psychological or personality approach. I for one cannot accept this. Sociology and psychology are parts of the mother science, Biology—the study of living organisms singly and in group relationships.

Another semantic difficulty that kept cropping up during the Conference was the confusion consequent upon the use of such terms as "organic," "functional," "mental," "physical," and "purely psychological." This confusion was enhanced by the apparently irresistible temptation of even superior scientists to dichotomize phenomena into "organic *or* functional," "mental *or* physical." This is historically a most primitive type of classification with little approximation to fact. Yet the cliche seems to stick in our minds and befuddle our thinking on important points. At the risk of being pedantic, and with the assurance that I am repetitive and perhaps a bore (for I have been fighting this battle for fifteen years) I am again going to point out the need for definition and clarity. In this conference phrases like the following were repeatedly heard: "Organic pathology will be found"—"Clinically, organic mental changes do occur"—"Psychogenic, or without structural change"—"Chronic organic states"—"Functional organic states"—"Functional psychoses"—"Psychoses are diseases of the brain and not of the mind."

Here the term "functional" is misused to mean "psychogenic," a barbarism of the clinic but now almost routine out-patient department slang. "Functional" is a useful word in physiology and architecture. It should not be spoiled by other and less acceptable usages. "Organic" is used in a hazy way to mean that since the "organs" are involved there is something "really wrong." More specifically the users of "organic" usually mean in psychiatry that there is a lesion of the brain. ("Lesion" being a visible abnormality.) If they mean this, why not say definitely what organ is meant and speak of "cerebral lesions"? To talk of "organic states" without specifying what "organ" is and what "state" is sloppy, about on a par with those devoted horticulturists who practice "organic gardening" and refuse to use "chemicals"! As a matter of fact we are in an "organic state" from conception to crematorium.

I would like to make three assumptions, which I believe can be upheld by scientific data in 1951:

First: No biological process goes on without change of structure.

Second: Whenever the brain functions there is organic change.

Third: The brain is the organ of mind.

If we accept these three we must admit that "organic" change takes place whenever a person has a thought. This is an important function of the brain. All function is organic, so the slang use of the terms "organic" or "functional" is meaningless. The same argument can be repeated substituting the terms "physical" and "mental."

These are some of the more conspicuous semantic troubles that showed up in the conference. One interested in the subject could pick out many others more subtle and perhaps just as much of a drag on psychiatric progress. Fortunately when men-of-good-will meet together they try to understand each other, even if they speak different tongues. This earnest will to understand and appreciate each other was conspicuous at the conference, and contributed largely to its success.

Many fields were remarkably well covered in this Conference by interesting contributions of talented men. What, then, was left out? Obviously the great areas of psychiatry that have to do with sociology, interpersonal relations, psychotherapy, psychoanalysis, the learning process, pedagogy, public health, etc. It is hoped that at a later date a conference including these subjects may be brought together. The publication of this volume gives a solid basis from which the next conference might take off.

STANLEY COBB

Boston, Massachusetts

PREFACE

THAT mental health and disease have biologic aspects is a proposition not easily denied. At one time, it was the predominant if not the sole prevailing point of view on the etiology of mental disorders. This approach suffered from overnarrowness, overeagerness, overenthusiasm, and overestimation. Too much was expected too early from too little. Then when the Freudian concept took hold, the pendulum swung to psychodynamics; in consequence, the biologic doctrine went into eclipse.

Actually there was nothing wrong with the fundamental tenet that biologic processes have some relationship to the mental realm. During the past decade the new methods, observations, and increments to knowledge in this area have been truly impressive. Yet the conditions under which this very progress has been achieved have created their own problems. In the evolution of medical science, the dictates of convenience if not necessity have led to a division of labor in this field as in others. With separate approaches specialists from many divisions have been working on different aspects of the common problem of the relation between biology and mental health. All this has occurred in an atmosphere of virtual segregation of each professional specialization. Each division and indeed subdivision has its own organization, meets separately at scientific meetings, and publishes its observations in its own journal. Each has its intricate technics, its special vocabulary, and its own ever-increasing subject matter.

To the bystander some implications of this situation for research on the biological aspects of mental health and disease are plain. The data that have accumulated are, for the most part, unassembled and unorganized. There is little or no opportunity to cross professional lines, to meet together and trade experience. Hence, there is too little chance to broaden or sharpen individual research projects through inclusion of technics and viewpoints from allied specialties.

Conceived and designed to take a first step towards amending this situation, the Symposium on the Biological Aspects of Mental Health and Disease was frankly an experiment in cross-fertilization. Representatives of all disciplines bearing upon the subject were brought together and given the opportunity to cover it in full scope. The aim was to have the members of each discipline become acquainted with the progress and future plans of other departments. Such an arrangement could widen the horizon of each special division in its views and plan of research and could encourage the application of combined technics from the various disciplines. Furthermore, it would bring about the assembling of the salient facts, views and technics of each topic, and would promote the organization of all the material as a preparatory step toward its integration.

The recorded proceedings form the contents of this volume. It will be observed that several authorities have contributed to each topic. In each instance, the first contributor presents its background and current status including the essentials of new developments. Other contributors to the topic have sections of equal significance. Their function was not to discuss in the conventional sense. Rather they rounded out the subject matter, aired the basis of a rival view, or reviewed the essence of their own investigations without any constraint of referring to the preceding presentation. It should be especially noted that each contributor has realized that he is writing, not primarily for his confreres in his subgroup with its own technical parlance, but for his fellow scientists in the various other disciplines. Limitations of time greatly curtailed extemporaneous discussion, but what did occur is included in this published account.

The biology of normal mental activity is the subject of the first half of the book. The cerebral structure is viewed in both its histologic and chemical aspects. The transport system of the brain is presented in discussions confined largely to the vascular network, the newer measurements of cerebral circulation, and the blood-brain barrier.

Against this background of structure and transport, the metabolism and function of neural tissue are described. These topics include the formation, activity, and degradation of substances in carbohydrate, protein, lipid, and inorganic metabolism; biologic oxidations for energy production with their three fundamental types of reactions; and the role of the enzyme systems. The activity of the individual neuron is studied through its electrical and chemical manifestations.

Next come a group of observations on the patterns of localization areas of the cerebral cortex, comprising mechanisms of cortical projection. Even higher than the level of integration found in the cerebral cortex is the central integrative mechanism, and here a newly formulated concept is presented, based on evidence from the electrical behavior of nerve. To elucidate the functional organization of the brain, the effects of loss of particular parts on mental functions and states are observed. Finally, the endocrine influence on personality and behavior and the contribution of genetic endowment to mental performance are discussed.

The second half of the book is given to mental disorders, both natural and experimental. Of the natural form, both etiology and morbid alterations are presented. On the causation of mental disorders, two factors in particular are considered, organic disease and genetics, the latter particularly through the study of twins.

Similarly, structural and functional alterations are described for experimentally induced disorders. Observations on behavior in this group also become highly important in classifying the nature of the disorders and in ascertaining whether they are analogues of naturally occurring forms. Then too, the mode of production is significant for its revelations on the etiology of mental disease. For example, it is enlightening to know that different drugs can produce qualitatively different mental effects in the same person. For the production of abnormal reactions, drugs, hypoxia, starvation, athiaminosis, and conditioning have been found to be effective.

Considerable attention is given to biochemotherapy. Hypoglycemic coma, the convulsants, metrazol and electroshock, inhalation of carbon dioxide and nitrous oxide are discussed. Also reported are preliminary results on the effectiveness of niacin in the treatment of depressive states, and ACTH or cortisone in depressive or schizophrenic psychoses.

Besides the expositions on mental disease, there are chapters containing past and newly-gained knowledge of mental deficiencies. The types of aberrant metabolism associated with various kinds of mental deficiency are covered. That this area is in a state of ferment was indicated by the presentation of a new and broad concept of the etiology of mongolism.

In arranging the Symposium the planners were under no misconception about the manifold influences on mental health and the multiple conditions in the etiology of mental disease. The subject, limited as it was specifically to the biologic aspects, was envisioned without prejudice to psychodynamic and psychobiologic concepts. A conference on mental health and disease in a holistic framework would have had to sacrifice much detail that was in need of assembling and organization or would have been impracticably lengthy. An immediately pressing and preceding need was the organization of the biologic data. This is a desirable preliminary step in preparation for relating and intermeshing the biologic and psychodynamic aspects.

The Milbank Memorial Fund extends its deep appreciation to the distinguished investigators who entered into the spirit of the undertaking and contributed so magnificently to it. It was their Symposium. To them should go whatever favorable comment the published material draws. For any actual or seeming oversight of topics that should have been included in the program, the planners accept responsibility and plead in extenuation the vast ground to be covered.

The Biology of Mental
Health and Disease

CHAPTER 1

Histologic Development of the Cerebral Cortex

J. LEROY CONEL, PH.D.

PRIOR TO THE prenatal age of five months the neurons of the cortex of the human fetus are packed closely together with no suggestion of horizontal lamination. At five months the arrangement of the nerve cells in horizontal layers begins. By age of six months the definitive six layers are clearly apparent, and there is no change in the arrangement of the bodies of the nerve cells during the course of subsequent development. No mitosis has been observed in any cells in the cortex of the full-term fetus; therefore it is presumed that the neurons do not increase in number by the method of cell division after this period of development.

At as early an age as three months intrauterine life the vast majority of the cells throughout the entire length and breadth of the cortex are pyramidal in shape, with a short apical dendrite directed toward the external surface of the cortex. Many of the cells in the deepest part of the cortex are spindle-shaped. At the age of three months there is but little difference in the size of the cells in all parts of the cortex. Some of the cells in the inner part of the cortex are larger than the others. At this age, as demonstrated by the cresyl violet stain, each nerve cell consists of a nucleus only, with a slight rim of darkly stained chromophil substance on the external surface of the nuclear membrane. A very short apical dendrite is present on most of the cells, but there is no indication of basal dendrites.

I have been concerned chiefly with the postnatal development of the neurons in the cortex, and thus far have studied them at the following stages of development: in the newborn, at one month, three months, and six months. During the course of the investigation it became apparent that as the cortex advances in age progressive changes occur in the following microscopic features, and they may serve as criteria of development: (1) width of the entire cortex and of each horizontal layer, (2) number of nerve cells, (3) size of nerve cells, (4) condition of the chromophil substance, (5) neurofibrils, (6) size, compactness of structure, and length of the processes of nerve cells, (7) pedunculated bulbs, (8) size and number of exogenous fibers, and (9) state of myelination. These nine criteria are discussed in the order in which they are listed.

1. The width of the cortex increases with advancing age. Increase in width is interpreted as an indication of activity in growth. The cortex increases in breadth more rapidly in some areas than in others. According to this criterion, up to the postnatal age of six months the entire primary motor area FAγ is active in growth, and during the period between three and six months the functional regions of the lower extremities, trunk, and arm are especially active. Proceeding anteriorly to area FAγ there is a gradual diminution in growth activity, and it is least in the most anterior regions of the frontal lobe. It is more active in the orbital gyri than at the frontal pole.

In the parietal lobe, growth is the most active in area PB, the primary afferent center. Next in order with reference to growth activity follow areas PG, PF, PE, PC, and PH. Growth activity is less in PB than in FAγ.

In the occipital lobe, growth is more active in the primary afferent area OC than in areas OA and OB, but in OC it is less than in the primary somesthetic area PB.

In the temporal lobe, growth is more active in the primary afferent area TC and in the temporal pole than in the other regions in this lobe.

Up to the age of six months the cortex of the insula shows little activity in growth. Activity is also slight in gyrus cinguli.

Growth is not very active in the cortex of the hippocampal regions up to the age of six months.

In all areas of the cortex in which growth is occurring as indicated by the criterion of width, it is the most active in the two pyramidal and the inner granular layers (III, V, and IV), is less active in the molecular and polymorphic layers (I and VI), and is least active in the outer granular layer (II).

2. The unit for counting nerve cells is the same as that used by Economo, namely, 0.1 cu. mm. The number of cells per unit in the cortex decreases as development proceeds. This is probably because the nerve cells are pushed farther and farther apart by the increase in growth of various structures, e.g., length and size of the processes of the nerve and glial cells, number and size of exogenous nerve fibers, number and size of blood vessels, and possibly an increase in the quantity of intercellular fluids. According to this criterion, up to six months growth is active in all parts of the frontal lobe, but is much more active in area FAγ than elsewhere. In this area, growth is especially active in the giant pyramidal cells of Betz and the cells in lamina IIIc. Throughout the frontal lobe, growth is more active in laminae IIIb and IIIc, and in layers IV and VI than in any other layers.

In the parietal lobe, growth is greater in area PB than in any other part of the lobe. Growth is more active in the two granular layers and in layer III than in area FAγ.

In the occipital lobe, growth is more active in layers IV and VI than in the other layers, and is least active in layers III and V. Growth in layer IV is less active than it is in this layer in area PB.

Growth is more active in the primary afferent area TC than in any other area in the temporal lobe, and is more active in TC than in the primary visual area OC. In area TC, growth is the most active in layer IV, and is quite active in laminae IIIb and IIIc. Growth is least active in layer V.

In the insula, growth is more active in layer IV and laminae IIIb and IIIc than in any other layers. It is least active in layer V.

Growth is conspicuously less active in the various areas of gyrus cinguli than in any other area in the isocortex.

3. At the fetal age of three months the bodies of the nerve cells are approximately the same size throughout the entire width and length of the cortex. By the age of five months differences in the size of cells have appeared. A few cells in each unit in layer V throughout the entire cortex, both isocortex and allocortex, are larger than any other cells, and they retain this supremacy in size even to the adult stage. These cells are designated in this investigation as the extra-large pyramidal cells. They are especially large in the primary motor area FAγ where they are the well-known giant pyramidal cells of Betz. Up to the oldest postnatal age studied there is no sharp distinction between Betz cells in area FAγ and extra-large pyramidal cells in the adjoining cortex in the posterior region of the frontal gyri. Throughout the entire isocortex (all of the cortex excepting the hippocampal areas, or allocortex) in all stages of development from the newborn to the six-month infant the nerve cells fall into the following sequence as to the size of their bodies revealed in the cresyl violet staining: (1) the extra-large pyramidal cells in layer V, (2) the large cells in lamina IIIc, (3) the large cells in IIIb and the large ordinary and special pyramidal and spindle cells in layers V and VI, (4) the large cells in lamina IIIa, (5) the small cells in III, V, and VI, (6) the cells of layer IV, and (7) the cells of layer II. This order obtains throughout the entire isocortex in all stages of development from the newborn to and including the six-month infant. During this entire period of development all the nerve cells in the frontal lobe, excepting those in layer II, are largest in area FAγ and smallest in the anterior part of the lobe. The decrease in size posteroanteriorly is gradual. During this period there has been in general a slight increase in the size of all cells, and a marked increase in the size of the cells in lamina IIIc. The increase in the latter cells occurs principally between the third and sixth months of development.

In the parietal lobe the cells of the various categories are of about the same size in all parts of the lobe. All of them increase in size during the period between birth and six months, and the increase is the most marked during the interim between the one-month and three-month stages. During the latter period the large pyramidal cells in lamina IIIc increase considerably. There is but little, if any, increase in size of cells in this lobe between the third and sixth months. The cells in the parietal lobe are about the same size as the cells in the middle region of the frontal lobe.

The cells in the occipital lobe increase but slightly in the interim between birth and the first month, but there is a marked increase in size during the period between the first and third months. The increase is especially noticeable in the large cells of layer V and lamina IIIc. There is a little increase in the size of the cells in the occipital lobe betwen the third and sixth months. In general, the cells in the occipital lobe are smaller than the corresponding cells in the parietal lobe.

In the temporal lobe there is a small increase in the size of all cells between birth and one month of age, and a decided increase in the period between the one-month and three-month stages. This increase is especially marked in the extra-large pyramidal cells of layer V and the large pyramidal cells in lamina IIIc. There is a definite increase in size of the cells in lamina IIIc during the period between the three-month and six-month stages, but all other cells in the temporal cortex increase slightly, if at all.

The cells in the cortex of the insula increase in size but slightly during the first six months of postnatal life.

The cells in gyrus cinguli also increase but slightly during this period, excepting that the pyramidal cells in lamina IIIc show a marked increase in the interim between the one-month and three-month stages of development.

Increase in size of the cells in the hippocampal areas is gradual but slight during the first six months of postnatal development.

4. The chromophil substance in nerve cells steadily increases in quantity as the cortex advances in age. Also there seems to be a progressive differentiation in this substance. The chromophil substance invades the apical dendrite sooner and always in greater quantity than it does the basal dendrites. The amount and extent of chromophil substance in the dendrites gradually increases with advancing age. The chromophil substance does not enter the axons.

At all stages of development from the newborn to the six-month infant the cells in all parts of the isocortex fall into the following sequence as to differentiation of the chromophil substance: (a) the extra-large pyramidal cells in layer V, (b) the large ordinary and special pyramidal and spindle cells in layers V and VI, (c) the large cells in IIIc, (d) the large cells in IIIb, (e) the large cells in IIIa, (f) the small cells in V and VI, (g) the cells of layer IV, (h) the small cells of layer III, and (i) the cells of layer II.

According to this criterion the giant pyramidal cells of Betz are more advanced in development than any other cells in the entire cortex in any stage of development from the newborn to the six-month infant, inclusive. In all stages of development there is a gradual decrease in the degree of differentiation of the chromophil substance in all nerve cells in the cortex of the frontal lobe in a posteroanterior direction.

In all stages from birth to six months the various areas in the cortex of the parietal lobe fall into the following sequence as to the differentiation of the chromophil substance: (a) PB, (b) PC, (c) PE, PF, and PG, (d) PH.

Differentiation is less advanced in the cells in PB than in corresponding cells in area FAγ.

In the occipital lobe, differentiation is more advanced in area OC than in areas OA and OB. It is less advanced in OC than in area FAγ.

In the temporal lobe, differentiation is more advanced in the primary acoustic center TC, and the adjoining areas TA and TB than in the more distant areas TE, TF, and TG. Differentiation is less advanced in area TC than in area OC, the primary visual center.

The advanced state of differentiation of the chromophil substance in the large pyramidal cells of lamina IIIc is a conspicuous feature in all areas of the cortex in the six-month infant, but especially in and near the primary motor and sensory areas.

5. The state of differentiation of neurofibrils in the nerve cells is studied in sections prepared by a modification of the silver method of Cajal. The cells in each area of the isocortex fall into the same sequence with reference to the differentiation of neurofibrils as they do in regard to the differentiation of the chromophil substance. Also the order of differentiation as to areas in the cortex is the same as in the case of the differentiation of the chromophil substance. There is a steady progression in the differentiation of neurofibrils from the birth to the six-month stage of development. The advanced degree of differentiation of neurofibrils in the cells of lamina IIIc is a conspicuous feature in all areas of the isocortex in the six-month infant, but especially in the primary motor and sensory areas.

6. The dendrites of all nerve cells in the cortex increase in size, length, and compactness of structure with advancing age. There is no increase in the number of dendrites or of their branches during development from birth to the six-month stage, excepting in the case of terminal branches of the apical dendrites. The latter do increase in number.

The axons of the nerve cells in the cortex also increase in size, length, and compactness of structure with advancing age. The amount of myelin deposited on axons also increases.

With reference to these criteria the nerve cells in each area of the isocortex fall into the same sequence as in the differentiation of the chromophil substance.

In all stages of development the dendrites and axons of cells in the primary motor area FAγ are more advanced in development than those of any other cells in the cortex. There is a gradual decrease in the degree of development of the processes of cells in the frontal lobe in a posteroanterior direction.

The cells in the primary sensory area PB are more advanced than any other cells in the parietal lobe, but are less advanced than the cells in area FAγ. The cells in area PC are less advanced than those in PB, but are more advanced than those in PE, PF, and PG. Development of the processes of the cells in area PH is less advanced than in area PG.

In the occipital lobe, area OC is more advanced than areas OA, and OB, but is less advanced than area PB.

The cells in the primary acoustic area TC are in about the same state of development as those in the primary visual area OC, and are less advanced than those in area PB. The other areas in the temporal lobe are less advanced than area TC.

In the six-month cortex the advanced degree of development of the processes of the large pyramidal cells in lamina IIIc is especially noticeable in and near the primary motor and sensory areas, viz., FAγ, PB, OC, and TC.

7. Small structures which I have named "pedunculated bulbs" are present on the dendrites of nerve cells in the cortex. Each one is a small bulb attached to the dendrite by a slender stalk. These structures are not present on axons. The pedunculated bulbs increase in number and in extent of distribution on dendrites as the cortex advances in age. In all stages of development from the newborn to the six-month infant the bulbs are the most numerous on the apical dendrite of a nerve cell, are much less in quantity on the basal dendrites and collateral branches of the apical dendrite, and considerably less in number on the terminal branches of the apical dendrite. According to this criterion the nerve cells in each area of the isocortex fall into the same sequence as in the case of development of the dendrites and axons of the cells. Also, the various areas in the isocortex fall into the same order as in regard to the degree of development of the dendrites and axons.

8. The exogenous fibers increase in number and size with advancing age. These are the tangential fibers in the molecular layer, horizontal fibers in layers II to VI, inclusive, the subcortical association fibers, and the vertical fibers. All four of these categories of fibers are present in all areas of the cortex. The fibers of each category fall into three groups as to size, viz., small, intermediate, and large.

With advancing age of the cortex there is a gradual increase in the number and size of the fibers of all four categories, but in each stage of development there are differences between areas as to both the number and size. In each area of the isocortex at any stage of development the horizontal exogenous fibers are smallest in size and least in number in layer II. Proceeding inwardly in the cortex the horizontal fibers gradually increase in size, and are largest in lamina VIb. The horizontal fibers gradually increase in number from layer II to a maximum in layer IV. They decrease in layer V, then increase slightly in layer VI. By the criterion of number and size of the exogenous fibers the primary motor area FAγ is more advanced in development than any other area at all ages from birth to six months. Proceeding anteriorly from this area the exogenous fibers gradually decrease in quantity and size, and are fewest in number and smallest in size in the most anterior areas of the frontal lobe.

In the parietal lobe the exogenous fibers are of about the same size and number in area PB as in area FAγ. Proceeding posteriorly in the parietal lobe from area PB the fibers decrease gradually in quantity and size, reaching a minimum for this lobe in area PH.

The exogenous fibers in the primary visual area OC are slightly less numerous than those in area PB but are about the same size as in the latter area.

In the temporal lobe the exogenous fibers are more numerous and larger in the primary acoustic area TC than in any other area in this lobe, and are about the same in both these respects as those in area OC. The fibers gradually decrease in size and number distal to this area, being fewest in quantity and smallest in area TF.

The distance to which the vertical exogenous fibers invade the cortex likewise increases gradually with advancing age.

9. There is a gradual increase in the amount of myelin on the nerve fibers with advancing age. In each area of the isocortex at each stage of development there is a gradual increase in the number of myelinated fibers and in the quantity of myelin on the fibers from layer II to layer VI. Throughout the entire cortex at each stage of development myelination is more advanced on the vertical exogenous fibers in the subcortical white substance than on the horizontal and vertical exogenous fibers inside the cortex. There are differences between various areas as to the degree of myelination, and these differences are the same as those in the case of the size and number of exogenous fibers. There are also differences in the degree of myelination in the brains at any one age of development.

All nine of these criteria support the following statements. (a) At all stages from birth to six months, inclusive, histologic development in the human cerebral cortex is the most advanced in layers IV, V, and VI, and the other strata follow in this order: lamina IIIc, lamina IIIb, lamina IIIa, layer II. (b) At all stages, development is the most advanced in the primary motor area FAγ; the primary somesthetic area PB is next; the primary visual area OC is next, followed closely by the primary acoustic area TC. (c) In the frontal, parietal, occipital, and temporal lobes the primary areas FAγ, PB, OC, and TC are foci in which development is more advanced at all ages than in other areas in their respective lobes. In each lobe the degree of development gradually diminishes with increase in distance from the focus of maximum development. (d) Similarity in microscopic structure throughout the entire isocortex is much more impressive than any differences. The allocortex in the hippocampal areas bears some resemblance to the isocortex. The great density of the mesh of fibers formed in layer IV by the axons of Golgi type II cells in the primary afferent areas is one of the most noticeable features of microscopic structure. This is not a difference in structure, however, for this mesh is present in some degree in all areas of the cortex, including the primary motor area FAγ.

The cortex is a thin mantle of homogeneous structure, and of fairly uniform thickness at any given stage of development. It seems probable that function in it is determined by distribution of the fibers rather than by specificity of cells. The minute parceling of the cortex into subdivisions is not justified by any significant differences in microscopical structure.

Neurovascular Relations in the Central Nervous Organs*

E. HORNE CRAIGIE, PH.D.

It is a very old truism which we hammer into students in comparative anatomy that all the organ systems of the body are mutually dependent; yet the important relations of the blood vessels to the central nervous organs are usually given somewhat scant consideration in any discussion of the development, structure, or functioning of the brain or the spinal cord.

In development, whether phylogenetic or ontogenetic, the neural tube is first supplied only with a superficial vascular network enveloping it intimately but not penetrating its substance. This is seen in *Amphioxus* and in the spinal cord of the adult lamprey as well as in the early embryos of higher vertebrates.

Soon, however, minute twigs grow inward from this superficial net, branch within the substance of the wall of the neural tube, and connect up with each other so that blood may flow through them and be brought very near to every nervous element. This has already occurred in the brain of the adult lamprey and takes place early in the development of both brain and spinal cord in every higher vertebrate. Even at this stage, however, there appears a peculiar difference among vertebrates, a difference which does not correspond with their stage of advancement but cuts right through the taxonomic series.

Among cyclostomes, the most primitive living vertebrates, the vessels penetrating the brain substance of a lamprey lie close together in pairs and form simple, hairpin loops each supplying a tiny irregular cylinder of brain tissue and spaced so that collectively they provide for diffusion of essential substances between the blood and all parts of the brain. In a hagfish, on the other hand, the twigs from the superficial vascular net penetrate singly, not in pairs, and connect internally with several neighbors so as to constitute a spongy, three-dimensional net within the nervous tissue. This net being completely continuous, there is a diffuse spreading of blood in all directions within the neural organs.

Such a dichotomy of the vascular morphology is found not only in the cyclostomes but also in amphibians, in reptiles, and in mammals, and a very few intermediate conditions have been observed. Only, in reptiles and mammals which have the vascular loops, each loop is branched in a tree-like fashion instead of remaining so simple as in lampreys or salamanders.

* For a more extensive review with a bibliography up to 1944 see: CRAIGIE, E. HORNE: The Architecture of the Cerebral Capillary Bed. *Biological Reviews*, 1945, 20, pp. 133-146.

Scharrer has shown experimentally that the distance of diffusion of essential substances through the tissue around each loop is approximately half the distance between adjoining loops.

Thus the arterial limb of each loop is an absolute end artery and the tissue supplied by it has no other source for substances brought by the blood.

Many decades ago, however, Cohnheim pointed out that in higher mammals, which all have a spongy reticular vascular mechanism, the arteries entering the brain function as end arteries, a concept which has roused much discussion. It is obvious now that the spongy capillary network is perfectly continuous throughout the brain and spinal cord. However, this continuous network is composed almost entirely of vessels of capillary or precapillary size. It is connected with innumerable small arteries and veins but these have few direct connections by anastomoses of vessels larger than capillaries. Apparently the resistance in the capillaries is too great to permit adequate supply of any considerable area of tissue by spread of blood through the capillary net alone and thus most cerebral arteries function as end arteries despite the continuity of the capillaries.

It is found that in this way specific arteries supply definite centers within the brain or precisely circumscribed parts of such centers. Larger arteries also supply through their branches more or less precisely delimited regions, such as specific areas of the cerebral cortex, and the distribution of individual vessels is so constant that it has important morphologic as well as physiologic significance. It may throw decisive light upon unsettled problems of homology or of the developmental origin of particular parts, and its relation to physiologic disturbances or pathologic conditions needs no demonstration.

One other point is that the continuous capillary reticulum is not uniform in density but varies greatly in this respect, the denser or less dense regions corresponding precisely with differentiated histologic areas. It has been pointed out by Gerard that the differences in capillary density are very much less than the differences in metabolic activity in various parts. Nevertheless, it seems unquestionable that these two features are intimately related. The rate of flow of blood in any region is regulated by active changes in the caliber of the arteries supplying it, but the availability of materials to the individual neurons and the readiness of removal of their material products are determined not only by the rate of flow of the blood but also by the volume of the blood within a unit volume of brain tissue, by the total areas of the capillary walls, and by the distance between these walls and the neurons, assuming that they are equally permeable in all cases.

In cold-blooded vertebrates the vascular supply is everywhere less rich than in warm-blooded vertebrates and the differences in richness of supply of various parts of the brain are less great. In general, the relative richness of corresponding parts remains comparable, however, exceptions to this statement often being explicable by known differences in functional importance. For example, the cochlear nuclei are the richest parts of the brain except the supraoptic and paraventricular nuclei in reptiles, birds, and mammals, and even in the frog. In tailed amphibians, fishes, and cyclostomes, however, the cochlear mechanism is not differentiated. The hypoglossal nucleus is notably more vascular in snakes and lizards, which have highly mobile tongues, than in turtles or alligators in which the tongue is less active. In the rat the marked differences in vascularity among different parts are not conspicuous at birth but develop before the time of weaning. Finally, it may be noted that no general differences in quantitative vascular richness have so far been demonstrated between animals possessing the loop-type of vascular mechanism and their relatives possessing capillary reticula.

An additional point which may be of interest in connection with the present symposium is that there is a perivascular space round the intracerebral vessels, the outer boundary of which space is a delicate pia-glial membrane. In mammals which have a reticular cerebral capillary bed, however, the pia-glial membrane appears to end with the arterioles and venules and not to continue round the capillaries. Around the independent capillary loops in an amphibian (*Necturus*), on the other hand, the pia-glial membrane is continuous.

CHAPTER 2

Chemical Constituents of Brain
During Development and in Maturity

J. FOLCH-PI, M.D.

It is obvious that this presentation cannot include a comprehensive discussion of all the material encompassed by the title. Therefore, I will limit myself to a few main topics. These will fall under three headings: chemical composition of adult brain, changes in brain composition in the course of development, and finally, presentation of some of the most recent results of our own work.

Chemical Composition of Adult Brain

This discussion will be limited to what is known about brain lipids and brain proteins. Carbohydrates will only be mentioned insofar as they are constituents of lipids and proteins, because brain tissue is relatively poor in glycogen, and such glycogen as is present appears to have a purely metabolic significance. Enzymes and electrolytes will be left out because they will be authoritatively covered by other participants in this Symposium.

Lipids are the main constituents of brain tissue.[13] They represent from 65 to 75 per cent of solids in different areas of white matter and about 40 per cent of solids in gray matter. They have been the subject of work on the part of many chemists for the last century and a half. It is an illustration of the difficulties involved in work in neurochemistry, that after all this time our knowledge of them is far from complete and full of wide gaps. Brain lipids are cholesterol, which is present mostly, if not exclusively, as free cholesterol; phosphatides, which are compounds containing P and fatty acids. The following ones are well known: the phosphoglycerides, which contain glycerophosphoric acid as central constituent, the phosphosphingosides, which contain phosphoric acid and sphingosine, and the phospho-inositides, which have phosphoric acid and inositol as constituents. The phosphoglycerides are lecithin,[10] which is diacyl-glyceryl-phosphoryl choline; phosphatidyl ethanolamine,[4] which is diacyl-glyceryl-phosphoryl ethanolamine; phosphatidyl serine,[3, 4] which is diacyl-glyceryl-phosphoryl

11

serine; and the acetal phospholipids, which appear to be for the most part palmital and stearal-glyceryl-phosphoryl ethanolamine.[15] As to whether glycerophosphoric acid in phosphoglycerides is alpha or beta, or a mixture of both, the presence in nature of the alpha structure is well established;[1,14] no reliable evidence has yet been obtained as to the occurrence or absence of the beta structure. Only one phosphosphingoside has been described. This is sphingomyelin,[16] the structure of which is that of monoacyl-sphingocyl-phosphoryl choline. Finally, one phosphoinositide is well recognized. This is diphosphoinositide,[6] the central constituent of which is inositol meta diphosphate. One glycerol radical and one fatty acid radical complete the molecule, but the exact structure has not yet been established.

Cerebrosides or galactolipids[13] are another group of brain lipids. They contain as constituents galactose, sphingosine, and a fatty acid. Finally, a number of less well-known compounds have been recognized, such as sulfatides (lipids containing S), and gangliosides,[11] which are complex substances akin to cerebrosides. One sulfatide has been isolated and well studied by Blix, the cerebron sulfuric acid.[2]

In the case of brain proteins the span of our knowledge was comprehensively reviewed in the book, *Chemistry of the Brain*,[13] by I. H. Page in 1937. One-half page was devoted to the subject out of a total of 430 pages. This is about as much as we knew about brain proteins at the time. From that old work and from some more recent work, our knowledge can be summarized in a few short sentences. Brain contains nucleoproteins, both of the DPN and PNA types. They are present in the tissue in combination with lipids, as liponucleoproteins.[9] It contains trypsin-resistant and pepsin-resistant protein or proteins and this fraction is usually described as neuro-keratin[12] since Kühne and Chittenden isolated and studied it. It contains several proteins of the globulin and albumin types. Finally, a large amount of brain proteins belong to a fraction which is insoluble in water and saline solutions, but which, contrariwise to neurokeratin, is digestible by proteolytic enzymes. I will deal later with another group of brain proteins, the proteolipids, when I discuss some of our own work.

Changes of Brain Tissue in Course of Development

Brain tissue exhibits marked changes in composition in the course of its development from neural tube to adult brain.[5, 13] This is a fascinating subject of study and such work as has already been done promises it to be a rich and rewarding field of research for future biochemists. Most of our present knowledge has unfortunately been gathered by methods that have become obsolete, and most of the results obtained had been evaluated by criteria that are considered no longer tenable. Therefore, our present knowledge can only be stated in the most general terms. It appears that the neural tube contains very little, if any, lipid material. The amount of lipids increases with successive stages of development. The timetable of deposition of lipids varies from one type of lipid to the other. Thus, phosphatides increase steadily in concentration. Cholesterol increases both steadily and in spurts. Finally, cerebrosides and sulfatides are deposited rather massively at the time that myelinization takes place. The amount of phosphatides and of cholesterol also increases greatly at the time of myelinization, but, as already stated, there is also a steady deposition of both of them that goes on throughout the whole process of development. Much less is known about the rate of deposition of proteins, but such evidence as is available shows a steady increase with time in the amount of proteins present in the tissue. It would be very interesting to try to correlate the changes in chemical pattern with changes in functional pattern but at the present time this would be largely hypothetical.

Current Research

About four years ago we embarked on a program of study of exactly the field described by the title of this presentation. The first problem we were faced with was the lack of adequate methods both for the analyses of brain tissue and for the isolation of most brain components. Eventually we were successful in developing a satisfactory method for the preparation of total pure brain lipids. It was then found that only three-fourths of the lipids thus isolated could be accounted for in terms of already known compounds. We then started working towards the isolation and identification of the unknown substances that accounted for that unidentified one-fourth of total brain lipids. This work is by no means completed, but already two new types of compounds have been isolated and partly identified. The first one is a new lipid to which the name "strandin"[7] has been given. The second one is a group of lipoproteins to which the name "proteolipids"[8] has been given because these substances are soluble in chloroform-methanol mixtures and insoluble in water and salt solutions, contrariwise to other known lipoproteins which are soluble in water or salt solutions and insoluble in organic solvents. In order to present this material in a form as clear as possible, I will not describe our work as it progressed, but will simply discuss succinctly the evidence for the foregoing statements.

Brain tissue is homogenized with a chloroform-methanol mixture 2:1 by volume in the proportions of 20 cc. of solvent mixture per gram of tissue. The homogenate is filtered. The filtrate is a total extract which contains, besides lipids, a certain amount of non-lipid contaminants. The lipid contaminants can be removed by taking the extract to dryness, emulsifying the residue in water, and dialyzing the emulsion against distilled water. The emulsion is then lyophilized. It is this preparation that represents total pure lipids. When those total pure lipids are analyzed, it is found that (a) only about three-fourths of the material can be accounted for in terms of known lipids; (b) these total lipids contain much more N and NH_2-N than could be expected from the amount of phosphatides and cerebrosides that are present; and (c) some of the lyophilized material is now insoluble in the same chloroform-methanol mixture that was criginally used to prepare the extract from the tissue. In the follow-up study it was established that this part of the lyophilized material that had become insoluble, in the course of the procedure, was protein material. This was a rather unexpected finding. There are no known proteins that will go into solution in chloroform. Therefore it became necessary to postulate that this protein had not been extracted from the tissue as a free protein, but that it must have been present in combination with lipids, the hypothetical compound or compounds being of such configuration that the outside surface would be of lipid nature and the resulting compound would exhibit the solubilities of lipids. According to this way of thinking, somewhere along the process of drying the extract, emulsifying the residue in water, dialyzing the emulsion, and lyophilizing it, the linkage between constituent lipid and protein moieties in the postulated compounds would be broken, and then the protein moiety would, of course, be insoluble in a chloroform-methanol mixture.

The proof of such a hypothesis had to be the isolation of the postulated compounds in native form, that is to say, in a form in which the constituent lipid and protein moieties would remain linked with each other, and the complex would still be soluble in chloroform-methanol. This we have succeeded in doing as follows: The crude chloroform-methanol extract from the tissue is placed in contact with at least fivefold its volume of water. Methyl alcohol diffuses from the extract into the water. The resulting water-methanol mixture, being lighter than water, flows upward and is replaced by pure water at the interphase. Concomitantly, the chloroform, that has been left behind by the diffusion of methanol into the water, flows downward into the mass of the extract because it is heavier than the extract. Fresh extract replaces the chloroform at the interphase. Thus, water and extract are coming into contact continuously and this pumping mechanism goes on for as long as there is methanol left in the extract. Non-lipid substances in the extract diffuse quantitatively into the water phase, along with the methanol. When the system reaches equilibrium it has the following appearance: There is an upper water-methanol phase, a lower chloroform phase, and a fluff floating at the interphase. Without going into unnecessary detail, let it be stated that fluff and chloroform contain essentially all of the lipids and all of the proteins from the original extract, and that all the non-lipid contaminants have passed into the water-methanol phase. The latter is removed, and the fluff and chloroform are collected separately. From the fluff, by a procedure the details of which are not pertinent to this presentation, a crystalline compound can be isolated, proteolipid B. This proteolipid contains 50 per cent proteins and 50 per cent lipids. It is freely soluble in chloroform-methanol and it can be re-crystallized without change in chemical composition. It thus appears to represent a fairly pure compound, although the possibility must be kept in mind that the crystals obtained may be isomorphic crystals of closely related compounds.

From the chloroformic solution, by a rather simple fractionation procedure, a substance is obtained, proteolipid C. It consists of 75 per cent protein and 25 per cent lipid. It is freely soluble in chloroform and chloroform-methanol and insoluble in water. It is birefringent but does not show well-formed crystals. From the nature of its lipid moiety and from its solubilities, it appears to be different from proteolipid B.

The bond between lipid and protein moieties in both proteolipids B and C can be split by the simple process of drying their solutions in chloroform-methanol mixtures saturated, or nearly saturated, with water. In absence of water no splitting occurs during drying. The isolated protein moieties, from both proteolipids B and C, contain 1.7–1.8 per cent S and are resistant to the action of proteolytic enzymes.

The proteolipids represent major components of brain tissue. They account for about 20 per cent of solids in white matter and 6–8 per cent of solids in gray matter. They represent a type of compound of properties at variance with properties of any other tissue components that have been known hitherto.

Strandin: Due to the limitation of time, I will make a statement of the properties and composition of strandin, and otherwise refer you to papers that will be published shortly. Strandin is a lipid constituted by fatty acids, sphingosine or a sphingosine-like substance, a carbohydrate (presumably galactose), a primary amine (which may be glucosamine), and a chromogenic radical different from the other radicals that have been enumerated. The presence of this chromogenic radical has made possible the development of a method for the quantitative estimation of strandin in tissues. By means of this method it has been found that strandin is present in gray matter at a concentration of 6 to 7 mg. per gram of tissue and is absent from all other normal tissues except white matter, which contains it at a concentration of about one-tenth its concentration in gray matter. Strandin is freely soluble in chloroform and water and has been obtained as a crystalline substance which is homogeneous in the electrophoretic field and 80 per cent homogeneous in the ultracentrifugal field. From the study of its physical properties, it has been found to have a minimal possible molecular weight of 250,000. It is present in the tissue in combination with some other component, presumably a protein. It is quite likely that strandin in the tissue is part of a complex of really enormous molecular size. The fact that it is essentially present only in gray matter encourages us to work towards establishing its physiologic significance.

Summary and Conclusion

From all this work, and from older work, a pattern appears in spite of the still large areas of confusion. This pattern is that most, if not all, of brain proteins are linked with lipids in the form of lipoproteins. These lipoproteins are of the water-soluble type such as the liponucleoproteins that we have isolated and studied in preliminary fashion; they are of the water-insoluble type, such as proteolipids, which, as stated above, constitute a radically new type of lipoproteins. There are other types that I have not discussed in detail. For instance, let it be stated that neurokeratin itself has been found to be a lipoprotein. Thus the conclusion is warranted that the real living tissue of brain is constituted by lipoproteins and that these are closer to the living protoplasm than either the free proteins or the free lipids that have been studied in the past.

I would like to conclude this presentation by stating emphatically the need of further work on this subject. I feel that knowledge of the type here described holds promise of throwing light on the physiology of brain, both in health and in disease. With modern technics this type of work is now open to all comers, and it is most desirable that more people devote to this field their energies and their enthusiasm.

REFERENCES

1. BAER, E., and KATES, M. *Journal of Biological Chemistry*, 1948, 175, p. 79.
2. BLIX, G. *Zeitschrift für Physiologische Chemie*, 1933, 219, p. 82.
3. FOLCH, J. *Journal of Biological Chemistry*, 1948, 174, p. 439.
4. FOLCH, J. *Journal of Biological Chemistry*, 1942, 146, p. 35.
5. FOLCH, J. in Psychiatric Research, Cambridge, Mass., Harvard University Press, 1947, p. 17.
6. FOLCH, J. *Journal of Biological Chemistry*, 1949, 177, p. 505.
7. FOLCH, J., and ARSOVE, S. *Federation Proceedings*, 1949, 8, p. 198.
8. FOLCH, J., and LEES, M. *Federation Proceedings*, 1950, 9, p. 171.
9. FOLCH, J., and UZMAN, L. L. *Federation Proceedings*, 1948, 7, p. 155.
10. GOBLEY, M. *Comptes rendus hebdomadaires des séances de l'Academie des sciences*, 1845, 21, p. 766; 1846, 22, p. 464; 1847, 23, p. 654.
11. KLENK, E. *Zeitschrift für physiologische Chemie*, 1942, 273, p. 76.
12. KÜHNE, W., and CHITTENDEN, R. H. *Zeitschrift für Biologie*, 1890, 26, p. 291.
13. PAGE, I. H. Chemistry of the Brain. Springfield, Ill., Charles C Thomas, 1937.
14. SCHMIDT, G.; HERSHMAN, B.; and THANNHAUSER, S. J. *Journal of Biological Chemistry*, 1945, 161, p. 523.
15. THANNHAUSER, S. J.; BONCODDO, N. F.; and SCHMIDT, G. *Federation Proceedings*, 1950, 9, p. 238.
16. THUDICHUM, J. L. W. A Treatise on the Chemical Constitution of Brain. London, Bailliere, Tindall, and Cox, 1884, 262 pp.

Discussion

WARREN M. SPERRY, PH.D.

Having recently reviewed the literature on the biochemistry of the brain during early development, and having managed to amass a manuscript of something over sixty pages on that topic, I marveled somewhat at Dr.

Folch-Pi's temerity in attempting to cover not only that subject, but also the chemistry of the adult brain, in the time he had available. Of course, as he said, it was an impossible task, and he quite properly confined his attention largely to his own very interesting and very important work. I understand that the discussers in this symposium have been encouraged to add to the speakers' comments, where they have anything to add, and so I shall take the time I have to say a few words based on the review to which I have referred.

My feeling, after going over that literature, was that I had had a tantalizing glimpse, as through a glass darkly, of a very complex mechanism which was undergoing a series of intricate and involved changes. The difficulty in reviewing the subject, and at the same time the reason for the unseemly length of the manuscript, was that, whereas there is quite a lot of information scattered through the literature on most phases of the subject, there is too little to justify broad, generalizing conclusions. Furthermore, when more than one author has published data on a given subject, there are usually some discrepancies in the results.

Let me give you just two examples. The first one I shall take partly from my own experience. Some years ago Mrs. Brand and I carried out a study of the distribution of cholesterol in the cat's brain. We determined the cholesterol fractions in some twenty-odd different areas and structures of the brain in quite a large number of cats. We have never published the findings, and probably never shall, because we found a defect in the work after we had almost completed it. We discovered that the tissue slices which we were analyzing, and which we were dunking in saline according to the usual technic, were apparently taking up water at a very rapid rate; at least, they were increasing in weight. Dr. Elliott does not quite agree with our interpretation, but in any event, whatever the reason, the fact was that we could not calculate our results back to the original tissue. But that defect did not interfere with the evaluation of the results in terms of the proportion between the cholesterol fractions, and we found that in the great majority of our results the total cholesterol concentration exceeded the free cholesterol concentration. The difference was usually very small, probably within the error of the method, but since the great majority of the values were in the same direction, one had to conclude that there seemed to be a trace at least of combined cholesterol in the brain. It is possible that that came from residual blood serum, although we tried to minimize that possibility by exsanguinating the cats as well as we could before we did the analysis.

There is nothing particularly new in this finding. Other investigators have reported that cholesterol esters are either absent from the brain or present there in very small amounts. But, in going over the literature on the early development of the brain, I found that three recent investigators, and very good ones, who have presented quite elaborate studies, reported quite considerable amounts of cholesterol esters. Brante, in particular, who published a monograph concerning the results of an extensive study, reported values up to as much as 30 per cent of cholesterol ester, i.e., 30 per cent of total cholesterol in the combined form, in young brains. Rossiter and his colleagues, and Macy and Williams and their colleagues, also reported quantities which, although not nearly as large as those formed by Brante, were larger than could be reasonably explained on the basis of the usual error of the method. It would be very interesting if it were established that there is cholesterol ester in appreciable quantity in the young, developing brain, but unfortunately the data are not consistent. In going over those values, especially of Brante, one will find that there is at one age a value of zero and at the next age 15 per cent or 30 per cent; thus it is impossible to draw any conclusions.

My second example is as follows: Several investigators have reported the absence of sphingolipids from the embryonic brain, and it has been concluded by some that these sphingolipids (cerebrosides and sphingomyelin, or, as I prefer to call them, glycosphingosides and phosphosphingosides) are present largely if not entirely in the myelin, since they appear during myelination, as Dr. Folch-Pi has said. On the other hand, there have been at least two or three recent investigators, particularly Brante again, and I think Rossiter, who have found quite large quantities of sphingolipids in the embryonic brain before there was any appreciable amount of myelination. So here again the evidence is not clear-cut.

I wish I had time to expand on the chemistry of myelination. Dr. Waelsch and I reviewed it at some length two years ago at another symposium, and there isn't time to go into it now, except to say that Dr. Waelsch and I found that the deposition of lipids in the brain during the period of early development is not entirely by any means in myelin. A large part of it, perhaps 50 per cent or more during certain phases of the process, is deposited in other structures. I summarized the situation, after going over the literature on myelin, in these words: "Although it is true that many of the changes in chemical composition of the brain appear to be correlated fairly closely in point of time with myelination, there is considerable evidence which suggests that myelination is only one of many processes which are taking place more or less simultaneously in the developing brain."

There was one phase of the subject which it was a pleasure to review, and that was the recent work on enzymes in the developing brain. Dr. Flexner and Dr. Ashby, in particular, have furnished very fine work in that field, but since they are both going to talk on this program, I will not say anything more about that. I shall look forward with much interest to hearing what they have to say.

I will conclude on a positive note. There is one constituent of the brain for which there are excellent data. Many investigators have presented evidence on this constituent, and the data are, for the most part, in excellent agreement. I refer to the major constituent of the brain, though one doesn't often think of it as such, and that is water.

I should like to congratulate Dr. Folch-Pi for the excellent work which he has been doing in this field.

CHAPTER 3

Cerebral Circulation and Metabolism

SEYMOUR S. KETY, M.D.

It is not possible to exaggerate the importance of studies of brain metabolism *in vitro*, because only by careful control of all the multitudinous factors which influence these complex chemical reactions can one appreciate their separate contributions to this most complex field.

It is occasionally of interest, however, to study the over-all metabolism of the brain, undisturbed in structure and function, and to this end we must conduct studies of cerebral metabolism *in vivo*, a field which is comparatively new. In fact, it was only in 1943 that Dumke and Schmidt[2] made the first quantitative measurements on a living brain which approached the normal physiological state; this brain was that of the rhesus monkey.

If we are to approach the brain in a state as undisturbed as possible in structure and function or wish to include in our observation various types of clinical disease, then we must go to the human brain because it is only in the human brain that observations can be made without anesthesia or surgical interference and because it is not always possible to simulate human disease in lower animals.

Determination of Blood Flow through the Brain

In order to observe the metabolism or to measure it in terms of oxygen consumption it is necessary first to determine the blood flow through the brain. Methods for the estimation of cerebral blood flow are comparatively new. The Fick principle which has served so well in estimations of cardiac output, renal blood flow, and hepatic blood flow, has also been utilized in an approach to the cerebral circulation.[4, 10]

It will be recalled that the Fick principle states that if only two factors are known, the blood flow to an organ can be calculated. We can write that the blood flow through any organ is equal to the quantity of some substance which is utilized per minute by that organ divided by the arteriovenous difference in concentration of that substance in the blood going to and coming from the organ.

Lennox and Gibbs[14] applied this principle to a study of the human cerebral circulation, utilizing oxygen as the tracer substance. Unfortunately, they were not able independently to calculate the oxygen consumption of the brain; it was possible, however, to obtain the arteriovenous oxygen difference in the case of the human brain, and they were able to make the assumption that, in the conditions which they studied, oxygen consumption by the brain could be considered constant. Under those circumstances the cerebral blood flow varied inversely with the arteriovenous oxygen difference, and, on the basis of that rather astute assumption in limited conditions, it was possible for them to gather a comparatively interesting group of data on cerebral circulation. But obviously, if one is going to study conditions in which the metabolism may be expected to change, one can no longer make such an assumption.

However, if instead of using oxygen, one were to use an inert gas which is taken up by the brain, not by its metabolic processes but simply in physical solution, then it might be possible to apply the same Fick principle, that is, to obtain both the numerator and the denominator of the expression for this substance since they would both be independent of complex metabolic processes and more predictable in terms of simple physicochemical laws.

To this end, we applied nitrous oxide to a study of the cerebral circulation and studied the uptake of nitrous oxide in the brain. In the experimental setup a needle was inserted into the internal jugular vein at its superior bulb just as it leaves the cranium, and another needle into any artery—the femoral seemed to be a convenient one. From these needles plastic tubes were led to a sampling manifold. The subject breathed a gas mixture containing 15 per cent nitrous oxide, 21 per cent oxygen, and 64 per cent nitrogen. While the subject breathed this gas mixture, blood samples were taken from artery and vein and analyzed subsequently for their content of nitrous oxide.

In a typical pair of curves which result, the arterial blood takes the gas up very rapidly in the first few minutes and tends to level off after a while. The venous blood coming from the brain has a lower concentration of nitrous oxide, since the brain also absorbs the gas; but the venous concentration tends to approach equilibrium in a period of about ten minutes.

From these two curves, by the application of elementary calculus instead of elementary arithmetic, it is possible to obtain the denominator of the Fick equation. This becomes now the integral of the arteriovenous difference over a certain period of time or simply the area between the arterial and venous curves over a period of about ten minutes.

We have some ancillary data which suggest very strongly that blood obtained from one internal jugular vein is representative of venous blood from the brain as a whole[10] and is also insignificantly contaminated with blood from the face and scalp.[15] Therefore we feel that the arteriovenous difference obtained here really arises from the brain.

The problem of the quantity of nitrous oxide taken up by the brain in a certain period of time can be answered by the realization that at some time or other the venous blood leaving the brain must be in equilibrium with the brain itself as far as nitrous oxide tension goes. The problem is, how long does that equilibrium take?

In experiments in dogs it was possible to demonstrate that equilibrium takes place in about ten minutes.[6] Dogs were allowed to breathe nitrous oxide mixtures and were electrocuted at varying time intervals from about two minutes to two hours. Parts of their brain were removed anaerobically and analyzed for nitrous oxide. At the same time, venous blood obtained from the brain just before death was also analyzed for nitrous oxide. We found that in the early minutes of inhalation the brain was not quite in equilibrium with the venous blood; but, after about ten minutes, equilibrium was established, and then, even though the experiments went on for another two hours, there was no further increase in the nitrous oxide tension in the brain.

These studies in dogs we have confirmed by studies in human beings in which radioactive krypton was used instead of nitrous oxide. By means of the penetrating gamma rays from this gas the concentration in the brain could be measured without the necessity of removing parts of the brain and analyzing them.

Therefore it can be said that at the end of ten minutes the brain content of nitrous oxide is represented very well by the content of nitrous oxide in the blood which leaves the brain, and therefore the numerator of the Fick expression is obtained. Since the denominator is the arteriovenous integrated difference, both of the factors necessary for calculation of cerebral blood flow are available. Once cerebral blood flow has been calculated, then it is possible by rearranging the Fick formula to calculate the oxygen or glucose consumption of the brain at the same time by obtaining arteriovenous oxygen or glucose difference.

TABLE 1.   CEREBRAL CIRCULATION AND METABOLISM
NORMAL VALUES IN HEALTHY YOUNG MEN

	Per 100 Gm. Per Minute	For Whole Brain Per Minute
Blood flow	54 ml.	750 ml.
Oxygen consumption	3.3 ml.	46 ml.
Glucose consumption	5.4 mg.	76 mg.

In Table 1 is a summary of normal values obtained in a series of observations on healthy young men by this procedure.[10] These are calculated both per 100 grams of brain and for the entire brain of average weight (1400 Gm.).

The cerebral vascular resistance is a measure of the over-all hindrance which blood suffers in its passage through the brain. The units are not absolute, but are expressed rather as millimeters of mercury pressure necessary to produce a flow of 1 cc. of blood per hundred grams of brain per minute.

Factors Appearing to Influence Cerebral Blood Flow

Let us turn to a brief examination of the factors which appear to influence the cerebral blood flow in unanesthetized man (Table 2). By a process of hyperventilation, it is possible to lower the CO_2 tension of the blood from values of 40 mm. normally to about 25 mm. of mercury at the end of a ten-minute period. This results in a marked constriction of cerebral vessels, producing a marked reduction of cerebral blood flow, amounting to 35 per cent. On the other hand, inhalations of low concentrations of CO_2 produce marked cerebral vasodilation and a marked increase in cerebral blood flow from 53 to 94 ml. per 100 Gm. per minute. The inhalation of 100 per cent oxygen produces a mild constriction of cerebral vessels, and a 13 per cent reduction in cerebral blood flow; while the inhalation of 10 per cent oxygen produces about a 35 per cent increase[11] in flow.

These changes in cerebral blood flow, I might say, are all reflections of changes in the state of constriction or dilatation of the blood vessels, as can be demonstrated by a calculation of the cerebrovascular resistance.

It is apparent from our data that as the CO_2 tension increases, the cerebral blood flow increases at an accelerated rate. One can also depict the effect of pH upon cerebral blood flow from the same experiments. Here as the pH decreases, cerebral blood flow increases. It is difficult, on the basis of these experiments, to distinguish between CO_2 and hydrogen ion as to the effect on cerebral blood flow. However, we have other data in diabetic acidosis in which, in the face of a marked reduction in CO_2 tension, there is nonetheless an acidosis; and in these patients again the cerebral blood flow appears to be correlated with the arterial pH. I think it is fair to say that arterial pH and/or carbon dioxide appear to be very potent regulators of the vascular bed of the brain.

A number of drugs have been studied in their effect upon cerebral circulation and metabolism. I have selected just one, aminophylline, to report at this time. This drug produces, strangely enough, a decrease in cerebral blood flow which is due to a constriction of cerebral vessels. The oxygen consumption by the brain does not change.[18] This decrease in cerebral blood flow is reflected in a fairly marked decrease in the oxygen content and saturation of the venous blood from the brain, suggesting that aminophylline produces a mild degree of cerebral anoxia. These results with aminophylline are also common to other xanthine drugs. Caffeine produces a constriction of cerebral vessels in contradiction to some earlier results from animals.

In patients with brain tumors we have studied the effect of cerebrospinal

TABLE 2. PHYSIOLOGICAL AND PATHOLOGICAL STATES INVOLVING
ALTERATIONS IN CEREBROVASCULAR RESISTANCE AND BLOOD FLOW

Condition	Mean Arterial Blood Pressure (mm. Hg)	Cerebral Blood Flow (ml./100Gm./min.)	Cerebral O_2 Consumption (ml./100Gm./min.)	Cerebrovascular Resistance $\left(\dfrac{\text{mm. Hg}}{\text{ml./100Gm./min.}}\right)$
Normal	85	54	3.3	1.6
Hyperventilation	98	34	3.7	2.9
CO_2 (5–7%)	93	93	3.3	1.1
O_2 (85–100%)	98	45	3.2	2.2
O_2 (10%)	78	73	3.2	1.1
Increased intracranial pressure	118	34	2.8	3.5
Primary polycythemia	108	25	3.0	4.3
Anemia	78	79	3.3	1.0
Cerebral arteriosclerosis	121	41	2.8	3.0
Cerebral hemangioma	75	164	3.3	0.5
Essential hypertension	159	54	3.4	3.0

fluid pressure upon cerebrovascular resistance and cerebral blood flow.[12] There was quite a high degree of correlation between the cerebrospinal fluid pressure and cerebrovascular resistance. If one plots the cerebral blood flow against the cerebrospinal pressure, one sees again a correlation except that up to a pressure of about 400 mm. of water or so, the correlation is rather poor and there does not appear to be any systematic change in the cerebral blood flow. Above 400 mm. of water pressure, however, there is a profound and consistent decrease in cerebral blood flow.

The explanation for the interesting fact that cerebral blood flow is not reduced in the early stages of increased intracranial pressure despite the fact that cerebrovascular resistance is increased from the initial stages onward lies in the fact that the blood pressure also rises, as was noticed by Cushing many years ago. This rise in blood pressure is sufficient in the early stages of increased intracranial pressure to maintain a normal cerebral blood flow.

Essential hypertension offers an interesting challenge to study its effect upon cerebral circulation. We have recorded in Table 2 the results of the first dozen or so studies which we performed.[5] The mean arterial blood pressure is markedly elevated, nearly double the normal value. Nevertheless, the cerebral blood flow is exactly normal. This is evidence, as can be more clearly demonstrated by calculation of the cerebrovascular resistance, that the cerebral vessels in essential hypertension are markedly constricted, and thus maintain a normal cerebral blood flow in the face of a nearly double perfusion pressure.

These observations in the brain exactly conform with observations which have been made by other groups on practically every other vascular bed in the body in which it is demonstrated that in hypertension there is a generalized increase in vascular tone throughout the body.

It was of interest to study the effect on cerebral blood flow of a sudden drop in blood pressure in hypertensive patients.[7] Should this increase in tone of cerebral vessels be organic and irreversible, then it would not be wise to drop the blood pressure of patients with hypertension because, under those circumstances, the hypertension would be necessary to force a normal amount of blood through constricted vessels. On the other hand, if this were a functional phenomenon, then a drop in blood pressure would not affect the cerebral blood flow since one would expect this constriction to be released. As a matter of fact, one finds that with quite a considerable drop in blood pressure obtained by sympathetic blockade of the trunk and lower extremities, there is only a moderate reduction in cerebral blood flow; although it is significant, it is not nearly as great as the reduction in blood pressure. This is due to the fact that there is a significant relaxation of cerebral vessels from a control value of 3.1 resistance units to 2.6 resistance units, which suggests that this increase in tone of cerebral vessels in hypertension is not organic but at least to a great extent is functional and capable

TABLE 3. CONDITIONS INVOLVING ALTERATIONS IN MENTAL STATE OR CEREBRAL METABOLISM

Condition	Mental State	Mean Arterial Blood Pressure (mm. Hg)	Cerebral Blood Flow (ml./100Gm./min.)	Cerebral O_2 Consumption (ml./100Gm./min.)	Cerebrovascular Resistance $\left(\dfrac{\text{mm. Hg}}{\text{ml./100Gm./min.}}\right)$
Normal	Alert	85	54	3.3	1.6
Schizophrenics	Alert-inaccessible	95	54	3.3	1.7
Schizophrenics, narcosynthesis	Alert-more accessible	95	54	3.3	1.8
Cerebral arteriosclerosis	Confused	121	41	2.8	3.0
Diabetic acidosis	Confused	86	45	2.7	2.1
Insulin hypoglycemia	Confused	86	61	2.6	1.4
Brain tumor	Comatose	122	34	2.5	3.6
Pentothal anesthesia	Comatose	78	60	2.1	1.3
Insulin coma	Comatose	93	63	1.9	1.5
Diabetic coma	Comatose	66	65	1.7	1.1

of release. It also suggests that it is safe to lower the blood pressure of hypertensive persons since cerebral blood flow will not be as markedly reduced as will the blood pressure.

Now we turn to a group of conditions which may be characterized by a primary change in cerebral oxygen consumption (Table 3). The first of these studies were some which were made at Philadelphia General Hospital on patients in diabetic acidosis and coma.[9] We have studied the cerebral blood flow and oxygen consumption of the brains of these patients, and have tested a number of possible correlations. The first of these is a correlation between cerebral metabolic rate in terms of oxygen, compared with the mental state of the individual, 3.3 ml. of O_2 per 100 Gm. of brain per minute representing the normal cerebral oxygen consumption of healthy young men. Those patients in diabetic acidosis before or after treatment who were alert had a total metabolism which was comparable to the normal. Those who were confused at the time of the study had a moderate reduction in the oxygen consumption of the brain, and those who were unconscious had quite a marked reduction in this function.

The decrease in the cerebral oxygen consumption which is associated with diabetic coma amounts to about a 40 per cent reduction from the normal value. This reduction in oxygen consumption by the brain is not, however, due to a decrease in cerebral blood flow. If we plot the cerebral metabolic rate against the cerebral blood flow, we find there is no correlation whatever. As a matter of fact, the cerebral blood flow in most patients with diabetic coma is actually above the normal value. These patients are not suffering from a lack of cerebral circulation. They are suffering from an intrinsic defect in their oxygen uptake by the cells of the brain. What this defect is due to can be surmised by some other correlations.

If one plots the oxygen consumption of the brain against the arterial pH, one finds the very crudest kind of correlation which suggests that the pH of the environment of the neurons may in some way affect the metabolism, although not very strongly. If one plots the blood ketone level against the cerebral oxygen consumption, one finds a better correlation. As the ketones rise, the oxygen consumption falls. This is only a correlation, and, of course, there is no real evidence of a cause and effect relationship in these observations.

On the other side of the coin are some studies that were made on the effect of insulin hypoglycemia upon the metabolism of the intact brain.[8] We studied schizophrenic patients who were being subjected to insulin shock therapy. It was found that the arterial glucose concentration showed a profound fall from 74 mg. per 100 ml. at the normal fasting level, to 19 in hypoglycemia, to 8 mg. per cent in deep insulin coma. The oxygen content of the arterial blood was not markedly interfered with, and the blood pressure stayed remarkably constant as did the cerebral blood flow throughout the entire procedure. The oxygen consumption of the brain, however, showed a profound change from a value of 3.4 ml. O_2 per 100 Gm. per minute resting, to 2.6 in hypoglycemia, to 1.9 in deep insulin coma. We were also able to calculate the glucose consumption, and this was found to show again a marked reduction as the blood glucose level fell.

One should point out that the glucose consumption represents the consumption of glucose from the blood and does not tell us what consumption is going on from the stores of carbohydrate which are in the brain. If one assumes that the brain continues to burn glucose even at the very low level of coma, and the respiratory quotient which we obtained suggests that that is the case, one can calculate how much glucose is required to utilize 1.9 ml. of oxygen. One can demonstrate that the utilization of this quantity of blood glucose is not nearly enough to provide the substrate for this degree of oxidization. Therefore there is evidence that the brain is turning to its own carbohydrate sources in this process as Kerr and Ganthus found some time ago in experiments on dogs. On the basis of their data, it is possible to calculate how long the carbohydrate stores of the brain will last at such a rate of oxygen consumption, and one arrives at a value of about ninety minutes, which represents about the length of time that one can keep a patient in insulin coma without irreversible changes taking place.

We turn next to the effect of surgical anesthesia upon cerebral metabolism.[17] We have studied thiopental or pentothal which was given to patients at operation. The oxygen saturation fell somewhat, as did the blood pressure, probably as the result of a depression of the respective medullary centers. Cerebral blood flow during pentothal anesthesia was somewhat increased above normal, undoubtedly a result of the marked increase in CO_2 tension, but the oxygen consumption of the brain fell from a normal value of 3.3 to 2.1 ml. per 100 Gm. of brain per minute.

In the case of ether, we have made a few observations to the present date which confirm the same phenomenon. There is a reduction of cerebral metabolism of about 35 or 40 per cent from the normal with surgical anesthesia.

Effect of Hyperthyroidism upon Cerebral Metabolism

Some interesting studies were done in our laboratory recently on the effect of hyperthyroidism upon cerebral metabolism.[16] A group of nine patients with hyperthyroidism were studied, whose basal metabolic rate varied from +30 per cent to +88 per cent. The interesting fact uncovered by these studies is that the oxygen consumption of the brain in hyperthyroidism is perfectly normal, even though the oxygen consumption by the body as a whole is markedly increased. This represents, I think, one of the first indications that hyperthyroidism may not be a general change in metabolism throughout the body but may be confined to certain organs. At least it seems to exempt a very important organ, namely, the brain.

Effect of Mental Disease upon Cerebral Metabolism

In Table 3 are shown examples of two types of mental disease. One has classically been considered an "organic" psychosis, the psychosis of senility associated with cerebral arteriosclerosis, and one is regarded as a "functional" psychosis, schizophrenia. We can compare the functions which we were able to study in these patients with normal values. The oxygen content of the blood is not markedly different among the three groups. The blood pressure is somewhat higher in the senile psychotics because there is also arteriosclerosis present and a mild degree of hypertension. In senile psychosis, there is a considerable reduction in cerebral blood flow from a normal figure of 54, to 41 ml. of blood per 100 Gm. of brain per minute.[3] This reduction in cerebral blood flow is undoubtedly associated with an increase in cerebrovascular resistance which is about double the normal value, and this increase in resistance also confirms the observations of countless pathologists who have observed these narrow vessels in the brain of patients dying with senile psychosis.

It is interesting that this increase in resistance in the brain of cerebral arteriosclerotics is of the same magnitude as that which occurs in essential hypertension, but the blood pressure in patients with psychosis is only 121 as opposed to a much higher level in hypertension. It is tempting to speculate that if these patients could produce a blood pressure which was increased in proportion to the increase in vascular resistance, they might in that way maintain a normal cerebral blood flow. At any rate, their oxygen consumption is also significantly reduced below the normal. It is suggested that this reduction in oxygen consumption is on the basis of a reduction in blood flow and that the oxygen consumption change is responsible for, or in some way associated with, the mental changes in this disease.

Conversely, schizophrenia shows none of these changes.[13] There is no significant difference between the schizophrenic brain and the normal brain with respect to blood flow, vascular resistance, or oxygen consumption. These schizophrenics encompassed all types of the disease, from the earliest simple schizophrenics to patients with very severely deteriorated mentalities or affects.

Of course, one can use this as comfort to that school of psychiatry which believes that schizophrenia is not a disease of the brain but a disease of the mind. On the other hand, one can simply say that this proves that it takes just as much oxygen to think an irrational thought as it does to think a rational one.

The mere fact that one has not observed any difference in metabolism on the basis of gross over-all oxygen consumption does not mean that much more subtle distinctions may not exist. It would be something like trying to tell the difference between a Cadillac and a Packard on the basis of the gasoline consumption per mile.

Even though we cannot tell the difference between schizophrenia and normal thinking, there is a definite correlation between the oxygen consumption of the brain and gross mental state. I have taken a number of our observations at random and classified them simply according to the mental state which the patient had at the time of the study, and I have grouped them as alert, mentally obtunded, or comatose. The alert group contained the group of normal young men, schizophrenics (I am assured by psychiatrists that schizophrenics are alert but simply thinking in different directions from the normal), and patients with hypertension. The mentally obtunded are those with brain tumor, diabetic acidosis, hypoglycemia, or senile psychosis. The comatose are those with brain tumor, diabetic coma, insulin coma, or under anesthesia.

There is an interesting correlation which is statistically significant among these three groups. A normal value of 3.3 ml. of oxygen per 100 Gm. per minute has fallen in the mentally obtunded patients to 2.8, and in the comatose patients to the very low value of 2.0. There does appear to be some relationship between the mind and the brain on the basis even of these scant data.

Limitation of Study

It would not be fair if I finished without pointing out some of the limitations of this procedure. I need hardly say that this method measures only the over-all blood flow and the over-all oxygen consumption of the brain, and is not capable of identifying localized changes in oxygen consumption. The studies of Davies[1] on local oxygen consumption of cortex should be very interesting as complementary information to these *in vivo* studies. Furthermore, this method is capable of studying phenomena only over a period of ten minutes, and is not capable of estimations of blood flow and metabolism in rapidly changing conditions such as syncope and convulsions. Until such specialized technics are generally available, however, there is still much to be learned from a study of the whole brain in health and disease and under circumstances where the functions studied can be held reasonably constant for several minutes.

REFERENCES

1. DAVIES, P. W. *Proceedings of the Association for Research in Nervous and Mental Disease*, 1948, 26, p. 205.
2. DUMKE, P. R., and SCHMIDT, C. F. *American Journal of Physiology*, 1943, 138, p. 421.
3. FREYHAN, F. A.; WOODFORD, R. B.; and KETY, S. S. *Journal of Nervous and Mental Disease*, 1951, 113, p. 511.
4. KETY, S. S. "The Quantitative Determination of Cerebral Blood Flow in Man." Methods in Medical Research, Vol. I. Chicago, Year Book Publishers, 1948.

5. KETY, S. S.; HAFKENSCHIEL, J. H.; JEFFERS, W. A.; LEOPOLD, I. H.; and SHEN-
   KIN, H. A.   *Journal of Clinical Investigation*, 1948, 27, p. 511.
6. KETY, S. S.; HARMEL, M. H.; BROOMELL, H. T.; and RHODE, C. B. *Journal
   of Biological Chemistry*, 1948, 173, p. 478.
7. KETY, S. S.; KING, B. D.; HORVATH, S. H.; JEFFERS, W. A.; and HAFKEN-
   SCHIEL, J. H.   *Journal of Clinical Investigation*, 1950, 29, p. 402.
8. KETY, S. S.; LUKENS, F. D. W.; WOODFORD, R. B.; HARMEL, M. H.; FREYHAN,
   F. A; and SCHMIDT, C. F.   *Federation Proceedings*, 1948, 7, p. 64.
9. KETY, S. S.; POLIS, B. D.; NADLER, C. S.; and SCHMIDT, C. F.   *Journal of
   Clinical Investigation*, 1948, 27, p. 500.
10. KETY, S. S., and SCHMIDT, C. F.   *Journal of Clinical Investigation.* 1948, 27,
    p. 476.
11. KETY, S. S., and SCHMIDT, C. F.   *Journal of Clinical Investigation*, 1948, 27,
    p. 484.
12. KETY, S. S.; SHENKIN, H. A.; and SCHMIDT, C. F.   *Journal of Clinical Investi-
    gation*, 1948, 27, p. 493.
13. KETY, S. S.; WOODFORD, R. B.; HARMEL, M. H.; FREYHAN, F. A.; APPEL, K.
    E.; and SCHMIDT, C. F.   *American Journal of Psychiatry*, 1948, 104, p. 765.
14. LENNOX, W. G., and GIBBS, E. L.   *Journal of Clinical Investigation*, 1932, 11,
    p. 1155.
15. SHENKIN, H. A.; HARMEL, M. H.; and KETY, S. S.   *Archives of Neurology
    and Psychiatry*, 1948, 60, p. 240.
16. SOKOLOFF, L.; WECHSLER, R. L.; BALLS, K.; and KETY, S. S.   *Journal of
    Clinical Investigation*, 1950, 29, p. 847.
17. WECHSLER, R. L.; DRIPPS, R. D.; and KETY, S. S.   *Anesthesiology*, 1951,
    12, p. 308.
18. WECHSLER, R. L.; KLEISS, L. M.; and KETY, S. S.   *Journal of Clinical Investi-
    gation*, 1950, 29, p. 28.

Discussion

HAROLD G. WOLFF, M.D.

I propose to comment upon the general direction of studies in cerebral circulation over twenty-five years.

A quarter of a century ago it was generally held that the brain circulation
was not a modifiable feature of the animal adjustment. Because of the
rigidity of the skull it was inferred that there could be but little variation
in the amount of blood flow through the brain owing to its own vasomotor
function, and that such changes as did occur were merely the reflection of
the systemic arterial pressure.

The first important change in this point of view came with the realization
that there is an extraordinary amount of variation in the over-all cerebral
circulation quite independent of the mean blood pressure. This developed
from blood flow studies made by direct observation of pial vessels through
trephined skull holes in animals.

This earlier work, because of the method, was limited to animal studies
chiefly on cats and dogs and, to some extent, on rhesus monkeys. It is

interesting to note how extensively these observations in animals have been supported and confirmed by the subsequent studies on man's cerebral circulation made possible by Dr. Kety's technic.

The dramatic vasodilator effect of agents such as carbon dioxide upon the cerebral circulation has led to the inference that humoral factors are probably more important than neurogenic factors in modifying cerebral blood flow. Indeed, although there is a nerve supply to the blood vessels which exerts a vasoconstrictor and in all likelihood a vasodilator influence also, it has not been exactly defined under what circumstances and just how much this neurogenic factor operates.

However, on the basis of what Dr. Kety points out about the cerebral circulation in hypertensives and that which we have observed in the renal circulation in hypertensives, there are indications that the brain and the kidney may have similar neurogenic regulating mechanisms. For example, the peripheral resistance in the kidneys is raised in the patient with hypertension, as is the peripheral resistance in the brain of the patient with hypertension. Thus, in spite of elevated systemic blood pressure, the blood flow in the kidney of the hypertensive remains about the same as the normotensive, or slightly less. If the kidney be denervated, the blood flow isn't changed under ordinary circumstances, and if the major sympathetic supply to the brain be removed, there doesn't seem to be much change in cerebral blood flow. However, when the blood pressure becomes elevated under circumstances of stress with intact nerve supply to the kidney, the renal circulation is shut down appreciably. In the case of the denervated kidney, the renal blood vessels do not constrict so effectively and the renal blood flow is temporarily increased. Sustained elevation of systemic blood pressure brings with it compensatory constriction of cerebral blood vessels so as to maintain a steady and almost constant flow, but a sudden increase in systemic pressure may significantly dilate the cerebral blood vessels. This is noticed when the bladder is disturbed in paraplegics or in patients with pheochromocytomas and hypertensive crises. These observations would indicate that the nerve supply for these important organs has a protective purpose—perhaps to help the brain and kidney to withstand stresses and to make adaptations that are effected more slowly by other means.

Dr. Kety suggested that the changes in cerebral blood flow in those with brain tumor are accomplished by means of a pressor response. This is compensatory and improves the brain circulation when the peripheral resistance is increased owing to the presence of a foreign body in the head. For the most part, however, patients in the early stages of increased intracranial pressure associated with tumor do not have elevated blood pressure, yet their blood flow remains adequate, and the patient's mentation is good. In experimental animals the total blood flow likewise remains adequate under these circumstances, owing to a compensatory vasodilatation very much like that which occurs during other periods of cerebral circulatory embarrassment, such as during diabetic acidosis or a sudden fall in blood pressure.

Now, what is the direction from here? Having established that, for man, many of the predictions of the behavior of cerebral circulation made from animals hold and, having shown in addition that in diseases peculiar to man—hypertension, cerebral arteriosclerosis, diabetic coma—a special regulation of cerebral blood flow occurs, what can be said to be the direction that will be the most profitable for our future explorations of cerebral circulation?

If one takes what hints are available, it seems probable that there are local changes in cerebral circulation—local changes which are not to be detected by over-all studies such as have been made by Dr. Kety. For example, Dr. Gerard, many years ago, showed that if the retina of a cat is exposed to bright light the circulation in the occipital cortex increases. There are evidences that such local increases occur in other animals and circumstances—that certain parts of the brain at moments of use get more blood. Also, it is to be remembered that the brain is not a homogeneous organ in regard to blood supply. Areas rich in synapses are more richly supplied with blood vessels than those that are poor in synapses. There seems to be a close relationship between the total surface area of the neurons per unit of brain tissue and the amount of blood received.

It is possible that during disease states there are disturbances in supply not recognizable from total blood flow studies. Could a schizophrenic who has an adequate and normal blood flow as determined by these over-all studies still have local disturbances? Is it not possible that the bad thinking and feeling may be associated with local alterations in blood flow? It has been established that vasoconstrictor phenomena can participate in protecting other parts of the body, such as the kidney, during circumstances of stress, but that such a protective reaction, if inappropriately used and prolonged, may lead to ischemia of renal tissue and perhaps irreversible injury. Since it has been repeatedly demonstrated that even transient general cerebral ischemia may seriously impair, if not irreversibly damage, brain tissue, may it not be that during protective reactions induced by stress, blood supply to some specific part or parts of the brain is impeded? May not such adjustments during periods of stress damage the brain and impair its function? A need exists for methods to study the possibilities of such local alterations in cerebral blood supply.

DR. SOLOMON KATZENELBOGEN: Since no one else has taken the floor, I shall express my reactions to the very enlightening paper by Dr. Kety.

He made the remark, the gist of which, as I understood it, is that normal and abnormal mental functioning do not necessarily require different physiologic-biochemical reactions. It is mainly the reaction of the audience to this remark which makes me feel that it may be appropriate to quote Sherrington's statement regarding brain and mind: "As for me, what little I know of the one does not even begin to help me toward the how of the other. The two, for all I can do, seem to remain disparate and disconnected."*

* Sherrington, C.: The Brain and Its Mechanism. New York, The Macmillan Company, 1933.

CHAPTER 4

Blood-Brain Barrier*

ROBERT D. TSCHIRGI, M.D.

In 1885 PAUL EHRLICH[8] casually described a series of experiments on the staining properties of subcutaneously injected aniline dyes. The fat-soluble dyes, whether acidic or basic, readily imparted their color to most tissues, but these dyes, and especially the acidic ones, left the central nervous system relatively unstained. From these observations both the concept and the problem of the blood-brain barrier were developed. Relatively little has since been added to clarify this phenomenon.

In 1900, Lewandowsky[24] noticed that sodium ferricyanide given intravenously produced almost no symptoms even in fairly high concentrations; nor could the salt be identified in brain parenchyma although it had thoroughly penetrated all other tissues. However, when he introduced into the cerebrospinal fluid even one tenth the amount found innocuous by the intravenous route, the animal developed pronounced symptoms and usually died in convulsions.

The classic experiments of this genre were conducted by Goldmann[13] from 1909 to 1913, using the acid, semicolloidal dye Trypan Blue. This dye has since been regarded as the prototype of stains which, in general, color the central nervous system only after intrathecal injection or following excessively high intravenous doses.

Goldmann noticed an interesting exception to this generalization, namely, that the choroid plexus does stain following small intravenous injections. But this observation, while a tribute to his acuity, led him to the erroneous conclusion that the seat of blood-brain barrier activity is the choroid plexus. It was his further misfortune to expand this concept into the generalization that all substances must pass from the blood through the choroid plexus in order to enter the brain.

In 1933, Spatz[33] brought some order out of chaos with a review of the subject, and the subsequent work of King,[20] Broman,[3] Friedemann,[10] and

* The original work referred to herein was aided in part through a contract between the Office of Naval Research and the University of Chicago, and in part by a research grant from the National Institutes of Health, Public Health Service.

others has added many details to our knowledge of the blood-brain barrier.

Despite the mass of data which has accumulated, the only generalizations which can safely be made remain phenomenological: that the blood-brain barrier is a mechanism for producing a peculiarity in the exchange of most substances between the plasma and the intercellular fluid of the central nervous system; that this peculiarity manifests itself as a decreased rather than an increased rate of exchange; and that this phenomenon is not localized to the choroid plexus, but is associated with the entire cerebral vasculature. I shall limit my discussion to this pan-vascular barrier without considering the blood-cerebrospinal fluid barrier, which apparently resides for the most part in the choroid plexus, the cerebrospinal fluid-brain barrier, or the inter-intracellular fluid barrier. I shall further confine myself to a question not generally considered, i.e., what possible significance this unusual exchange mechanism may have for the normal function of the central nervous system. The dictates of time necessitate the neglect of most bacteriologic, pharmacologic, and clinical aspects, but these have been recently reviewed by Friedemann[10] and Broman.[3] I will close with an hypothesis which, though tenuous and incomplete, is consistent with the meager facts, and stimulating to imaginative research.

Difficulties in Interpretation of Intravital Staining Characteristics of Brain

Most of the conclusions regarding the site and mechanism of the blood-brain barrier have been derived from studies of the intravital staining characteristics of brain as compared with other tissues. It is therefore worthwhile to consider the difficulties of interpretation attending this type of experimentation.

One can make the general statement that, although large variations exist from dye to dye, the majority of intravenously injected dyes do not color the brain to nearly the extent that they color most other organs. It is then necessary to ask: What properties of these dye molecules are responsible for this phenomenon and where do they produce their effect? At various times, the answer to the first portion of the question has been sought in the soluble state of the dye (simple solution, semicolloidal or colloidal suspension), the molecular size and related mobility of the dye ion, the electrical charge, the lipoid solubility, the protein-binding characteristics of the molecule, and the toxicity of the dye to the barrier. By choosing the proper experimental conditions, and the proper dyes, it is possible to magnify any one of these factors to the exclusion of the rest. There follows all too easily, then, the development of a unitary hypothesis for blood-brain barrier action based on one or another of these properties.

Frequently the experimenter has neglected the fact that he is dealing essentially with a rate phenomenon, and not with an "all-or-none" reaction. The penetration of dyes, and, as we shall see, of many other substances, from plasma to the intercellular fluid of the central nervous system is seldom, if ever, zero. Therefore comparisons are only valid when the temporal dimension is carefully evaluated. Furthermore, since diffusion is involved, plasma levels must be carefully controlled on a molar basis, and not, as is frequently done, by injecting equal gram per cent solutions intravenously, without subsequent determinations of blood concentration. And one hardly needs to comment that the stainability of excised brain fragments in distilled water dye solutions, as used by one investigator, can have little, if any significance for the *in vivo* situation.

Even if these considerations are strictly adhered to, it is still virtually impossible to conclude from visual observation alone, that more or less dye has penetrated to the intercellular fluid of the central nervous system simply because the central nervous system is grossly or microscopically of a different color intensity than other organs, or more or less colored than with equimolar concentrations of other dyes. The final coloration will depend not only on the amount of dye present in the intercellular fluid, but upon the color intensity of the dye, the oxidation-reduction reactions which markedly affect the color of many dyes, methods of sample preparation for observation, and upon the penetration and accumulation of the dye within the cells, e.g., the specific tissue affinity or "stainability."

It would seem safe to conclude that only a modest insight into the blood-brain barrier as a normal physiologic mechanism can be gained by even a minute scrutiny of the many dye studies, and, in fact, without the supporting evidence cited below, one could hardly prove that the whole barrier phenomenon is more than a staining artifact.

Ion Penetration

With respect to inorganic ions, the functional significance becomes much more exciting. Here again, we may make the generalization that all ions studied, either cationic or anionic, show a markedly decreased rate of penetration from plasma to the intercellular fluid of the central nervous system when compared to other tissues; and in addition, the final steady-state ratio of plasma concentration to intercellular fluid concentration for some ions cannot be explained by either the Donnan membrane equilibrium or by plasma protein binding.

Early observations of marked and prolonged dehydration of the central nervous system following intravenous hypertonic salt solutions—a reaction not occurring in other tissues—gave the first clue that the central nervous system was penetrated only with difficulty by these ions. More recent studies using radioactive tracer technics[16, 32] have corroborated and extended this conclusion with respect to many ions. As yet, no extensive use has been made of radio tracer methods for studying the blood-brain barrier per se, and the widely scattered bits of data which pertain to the problem do not justify a strictly quantitative conclusion. Nevertheless there can be no doubt about the observation that following intravenous administration of tracer doses, bromide, iodide, thiocyanate, phosphate, and chloride equilibrate throughout the body's extracellular water within five to ten minutes, except in the central nervous system. They are not even approximately in equilibrium with the intercellular fluid of the central nervous system after three hours.[16] Likewise, intravenous sodium equilibrates outside the central nervous system in about eleven minutes, but requires sixty-two hours for equilibration with the sodium space (presumably largely extracellular) of the central nervous system. Potassium behaves similarly, but its rate of penetration into the central nervous system is somewhat more rapid. For many of these ions there is a similar relation between blood and cerebrospinal fluid.[14]

As Krogh[22] has pointed out, this ionic behavior is very reminiscent of cell membrane permeability, and, as suggested below, may indeed actually be a special case of cellular penetration.

The ingenious experiments of Wallace and Brodie[36] have further elaborated this already complex picture. These authors administered sodium or potassium salts of iodide, thiocyanate, and bromide to dogs, and determined the final ratio of these ions to the chloride normally present in the plasma and in the tissues. In all organs examined except the brain, the three anions were distributed in the same ratio to chloride as in the plasma, indicating a true equilibrium. In the central nervous system, however, the ratio of anion to chloride was the same as in the cerebrospinal fluid, and this ratio was considerably less than that found in plasma. From these results it was concluded that iodide, thiocyanate, bromide, and chloride are distributed in the intercellular water of the central nervous system in ionic equilibrium, not with plasma, but with cerebrospinal fluid. If we may conclude from these data that the central nervous system intercellular fluid is similar to cerebrospinal fluid, then the problems of cerebrospinal fluid production also pertain to central nervous system intercellular fluid production. Since a secretory mechanism, probably localized in the choroid plexus, seems necessary to provide the ionic composition of cerebrospinal fluid from plasma,[9] and since the weight of evidence favors the view that central nervous system intercellular fluid is not derived from cerebrospinal fluid,[37] it is necessary to hypothesize a similar secretory mechanism which accompanies the central nervous system vasculature, and manufactures the intercellular fluid.

Penetration of Organic Crystalloids, Protein, and Other Substances

With respect to organic crystalloids, the blood-brain barrier has usually been invoked by the experimenter to explain awkward discrepancies, especially between *in vivo* and *in vitro* results of metabolic substrate utilization. Although in the *in vivo* situation, only glucose, and to a lesser extent glutamic acid, mannose, and maltose plus a few others have been found capable of restoring normal electroencephalographic patterns or consciousness following insulin shock or hepatectomy hypoglycemia,[26, 28] brain brei or slices are much less discriminate in their dietary regimen. Not only can they oxidize the above compounds, but also lactate, α-ketoglutarate, succinate, fumarate, pyruvate, and other intermediates.[7, 25, 38] It is facile to say that those compounds metabolized *in vitro*, but found ineffective *in vivo*, cannot penetrate the blood-brain barrier. However, at least two other possibilities exist: (1) that the substance both penetrates and is metabolized by neurones, but is somehow not geared to the metabolic machinery necessary for impulse conduction, or (2) that the substance is metabolized by neuroglia, and not by neurones. We have obtained evidence that some such explanation is apparently the case for succinate.[35]

There is, nevertheless, direct evidence for a relatively slow penetration of glucose from the plasma to the intercellular fluid of the central nervous system. The clinical use of intravenous hypertonic glucose solutions for cerebral dehydration is dramatic evidence of delayed glucose penetration, since other tissues are not nearly so dehydrated by this procedure. Furthermore, the concentration of glucose in the intercellular fluid of the brain is only about one half its concentration in the plasma,[22] and, finally, Geiger and Magnes[12] have demonstrated with the isolated, perfused cat brain that glucose penetration is capricious, at best, and seems to be related to some factor found in liver extracts.

Evidence also exists for relative impermeability of the blood-brain barrier to other sugars and urea.[22]

Chloroform, ethyl alcohol, and ethyl urethane penetrate rapidly and in that order—which, interestingly enough, is also their order of lipoid solubility.[22]

Of particular interest is the extreme impermeability of the blood-brain barrier to protein. The evidence is no longer controversial that capillaries outside the central nervous system leak significant quantities of protein, a major exception being those of the kidney glomeruli. However, the cerebrospinal fluid, and apparently the intercellular fluid of the central nervous system contain only negligible amounts.[18] The many antibody and bacteriologic investigations of blood-brain protein impermeability[10] as well as our own studies with protein-bound dyes[34] are quite convincing on this point.

The use of labeled water and gases (other than oxygen and carbon dioxide, for which no data exist) has demonstrated that these substances exchange with the central nervous system as rapidly as with any other organ.[22]

Anatomic Location of Blood-Brain Barrier

Although one can no longer doubt the existence of a blood-brain barrier, its anatomic location has remained elusive and obscure. The early choroid plexus hypothesis of Goldmann has been referred to and discarded. Of the many subsequent theories which involved, among other structures, meninges and the reticuloendothelial system, only two remain as distinct and logical possibilities. The first of these, proposed by Gärtner,[11] attributes the barrier action to the perivascular glial membrane of Held. Spatz[33] acknowledges this possibility as theoretically sound, but on the basis of three lines of evidence excludes the glial membrane, and assigns the barrier to the vascular endothelium. This theory, which has had wide acceptance, rests on the following evidence:

1. Following intravenous injections of Trypan Blue the walls of the cerebral blood vessels were said not to stain, as they do in other organs, especially in the liver. (Certain notable exceptions are in the choroid plexus, the pineal body, the pituitary, and the area postrema, where not only do the vessel walls stain, but the dye is found in the surrounding tissue.) From this he concluded that the Trypan Blue was stopped by the endothelial lining before reaching the connective tissue of the vessel walls.

2. Intrathecal saline solutions of Trypan Blue will stain the brain, the dye penetrating the tissue uniformly and in much the same fashion as it diffuses into a block of gelatin. He concluded that the superficial pia-glial membrane—anatomically continuous with, and similar to, the perivascular glial sheath—is easily penetrated by the dye.

3. Histologic sections subsequent to intravenous injections of Trypan Blue fail to reveal the dye in the perivascular Virchow-Robin spaces which separate the outer wall of the blood vessel from the surrounding glial sheath.

Impressive though this evidence may be, our recent experiments concerning this problem, coupled with other observations from the literature, have led us to believe that the perivascular glial membrane is still the more likely candidate for the blood-brain barrier. In essence, we have found that the blood vessel walls throughout the central nervous system do stain with Trypan Blue following intravenous injection, provided one does not perfuse the brain post mortem with clear saline, as was done by Broman.[2] Under these conditions the dye penetrates to, but stops sharply at, the outer border of the vessel wall. From vessels of comparable size in the liver, the dye continues to diffuse outwards into the surrounding parenchyma. Apparently perfusion for even a few seconds with clear saline is sufficient to remove the small amount of dye which has diffused into the vessel walls of the central nervous system; but in those tissues where the dye has diffused on out into the parenchyma, a "reservoir" of stain is available which diffuses back into the vessel wall as rapidly as it is withdrawn into the colorless perfusate. Thus in the latter cases a great deal more perfusion is necessary before the dye will have been completely removed from the tissue, and the vessel walls left colorless.

From these results, we conclude that Trypan Blue is not prevented from diffusing outwards by the endothelial lining of the vessels of the central nervous system, but rather is rigidly stopped by some layer immediately surrounding the outer wall of each vessel.

With respect to the intrathecal administration of Trypan Blue, the injection of saline-dye solutions into the cerebrospinal fluid, which contains almost no protein, is hardly comparable to the intravenously injected dye which combines to a large extent with the plasma proteins.[29] When we placed Trypan Blue in plasma on the cortex of anesthetized animals, no staining of the brain occurred, even when the dye was applied for several hours, although the surrounding dura, fascia, and muscle which came in contact with the dye-plasma solution were deeply colored. When the superficial pia-glial membrane was damaged by a slight tear, however, the plasma-dye solution readily stained the underlying brain tissue in the area of the defect. Using Bennhold's[1] gelatin diffusion technic for determining the relative amounts of protein-bound and unbound dye present in the solution, we were able to show that the amount of stain which diffused into the uninjured brain, following topical application of purified plasma albumin-dye solutions, was directly related to the amount of unbound dye present and to the duration of application. Furthermore, the phenomenon could be quite accurately duplicated by a physical system consisting of white opaque gelatin (to represent brain tissue) separated from the various protein-dye solutions by a protein-impermeable "viskin" membrane.

However, it must also be stated that, while qualitatively similar, quantitatively the protein-free dye can penetrate the brain through the superficial pia-glial membrane more readily than from the vasculature. Thus the superficial pia-glial membrane—which probably represents a cerebrospinal fluid-brain barrier—is by no means identical to the blood-brain barrier, except with respect to its protein impermeability. This is further indicated by the more rapid rate of radioactive phosphorous penetration into the brain from the cerebrospinal fluid than from the blood stream.[30]

Spatz's final argument for the endothelial hypothesis, that no dye was observed in the Virchow-Robin spaces, is, we believe, explained by the fact that normally no Virchow-Robin spaces exist. These potential spaces seem to appear only under certain pathologic conditions or as the result of shrinkage artefacts in inadequately fixed preparations. Rapid perfusion immediately after death with isotonic fixative prevents their formation. While this view represents the consensus among the pathologists and anatomists at the University of Chicago, as well as my own, I hasten to add that the Virchow-Robin "camp" is still very much divided.

An illuminating series of experiments was performed in 1923 by Schaltenbrand and Bailey[31] which I have not previously seen alluded to in this regard. These workers perfused hypertonic sodium chloride through one carotid artery of a dog, and distilled water through the other. The hydrodynamics of the cerebral circulation is such that the two perfusates remained essentially unmixed, and consequently one half of the brain was perfused with a hypertonic solution, and the other half with a hypotonic solution. The animal shortly succumbed, with convulsions limited to the side of the body opposite the hemisphere receiving the hypertonic saline. Gross examination of the brain revealed the side perfused with hypertonic solution to be shrunken and dehydrated, whereas the side perfused with hypotonic solution was swollen and edematous. Obviously profound osmotic changes had occurred. Microscopic examination of the side which had received the hypertonic saline showed large, distended Virchow-Robin spaces separating the vessel walls from the glial membrane, and on the parenchymal side of this membrane the intercellular spaces were markedly reduced and in many cases almost obliterated, so that the cells were packed tightly together. On the side perfused with hypotonic solution there were no Virchow-Robin spaces, and the intercellular spaces were greatly enlarged. The authors' conclusion is, I believe, the only explanation consistent with the facts: that the perivascular glial membrane is relatively impermeable to sodium and chloride. I would add, further, that to obtain the picture they describe, the vascular endothelium must present almost no barrier to the free diffusion of these ions.

The capricious and artifactitious nature of the central nervous system histologic stains makes any observational conclusions concerning the continuity of the glial membrane tenuous indeed. However, the evidence presented by the Schaltenbrand and Bailey experiments is very convincing for the existence of a continuous protoplasmic sheet, either syncytial in nature or composed of relatively leakproof intercellular junctions, which completely invests the cerebral vasculature. This sheath is thought to be composed largely of astrocytic processes and glial fibers.

It is interesting to note that in those few exceptional areas alluded to above where intravascular dye readily penetrates to the parenchyma of the central nervous system, the usual glial pattern does not exist, and the areas themselves are suspected of a primary secretory rather than neuronal function.

Mechanism of Action of Blood-Brain Barrier

The mechanism of barrier action has received as many answers as the question of planetary motion. I am afraid we still await the appropriate Kepler. Only a few of the more tenable hypotheses will be mentioned here. Friedemann[10] has championed the theory that the zeta potential is the factor which determines the penetrability of a substance. His major evidence is derived from experiments using negatively charged versus positively charged dyes, as well as various infectious agents, and he concludes that only positively charged particles can readily pass the barrier. These experiments are subject to all of the difficulties of interpretation outlined earlier, plus the evidence of his own data, that the conclusion does not hold true for all dyes. Furthermore, the recent work with radioactive ions clearly indicates that positively charged ions, particularly sodium, are remarkably slow to exchange. We have attempted to shed some light on the incontrovertible observation that, generally speaking, intravenous basic dyes do stain the central nervous system more readily than acidic ones. Our experiments indicate that at least part of the explanation lies in the greater propensity for protein conjugation, at blood pH, by the acidic dyes, as shown by Bennhold[1] some years ago. Two dyes as similar in molecular weight, color intensity, and other properties as possible, but differing in charge, were perfused in equimolar concentrations in oxygenated Tyrode's solution through rat brains. (Reflexes could be elicited throughout this procedure.) When perfused for equivalent times, the two dyes showed about equal penetration. When, however, plasma albumin was added to the two perfusates in place of gum acacia, the amount of acidic dye which penetrated the central nervous system in a given time was considerably less than the amount of basic dye. Using the penetrability of the free dye radical as a base line, it could be shown by manipulating the protein concentration, that penetration of the acidic dye was inversely related to protein concentration and directly related to duration of perfusion. We have concluded that although charge probably plays some role in determining blood-brain penetration, it is neither a simple nor a unique factor in this regard.

In an exhaustive review of Trypan Blue studies, King[20] advanced the theory of "tissue affinity," or the lack of it, as an explanation of the blood-brain barrier phenomenon, at least with respect to Trypan Blue. "Tissue affinity," which I assume to mean cellular permeability to the dye and the formation of dye-protein complexes within the cell, is no doubt quite significant in determining the ultimate color intensity of the tissue. This whole problem has been further obscured, as King points out, by the failure of many workers to distinguish between chronic dye experiments, with subsequent phagocytosis and accumulation of dye in reticuloendothelial elements, and acute experiments, where the dye may penetrate easily to the intercellular fluid, but be unable to penetrate the cell membranes. In the latter case, of course, a relative lack of color in the central nervous system would have nothing to do with the true blood-brain barrier, but rather would be a measure of the inter-intracellular barrier. Here, again, is an example of the Gordian knot complexity of interpretation of dye study. Suffice it to say that although "tissue affinity" is an important, though aggravating, factor in dye experiments, it cannot be the explanation where tracer isotopes and chemical determinations have been used.

There can be little doubt that particle size has some influence on blood-brain transfer. Differences in penetration of a few otherwise similar dyes can be fairly well correlated with their molecular size. Further data are necessary to establish the possibility that size and mobility of inorganic ions is a controlling factor in their exchange rates, but preliminary results seem to exclude this as the selective mechanism.

Krogh[22] has recently reintroduced the concept of lipoid solubility as a predominant factor in determining barrier permeability. This hypothesis, while quite satisfactory for some series of compounds, is, for example, unable to account for the rapid penetration of barbiturates.[17] Thus it seems quite unlikely that lipoid solubility is the universal answer.

Again, the striking parallelism between blood-brain permeability and the problem of cellular permeability is manifest. We believe it is safe, therefore, to conclude tentatively that for solutes to pass from the plasma to the intercellular fluid of the central nervous system (with the exceptions noted) they must, for the most part, pass through, not between, cells; that this cellular barrier is not the vascular endothelium, but the perivascular glial membrane; and that this membrane does not represent a simple sievelike impediment to otherwise free diffusion, but rather is a distinct, polarized, secretory mechanism which governs the concentration of certain solutes in the intercellular fluid. This does not, of course, imply the exclusion of diffusion forces, which are no doubt involved to a significant extent.

Functional Significance of Blood-Brain Barrier

From this meager array of facts and tentative conclusions, we are faced with the problem of inferring the functional significance of the blood-brain barrier, i.e., the role of this peculiar permeability in the normal neuronal activity of the central nervous system. It is obvious that no complete answer can be given, but with your indulgence I should like to present the following hypothesis as one possibility.

Let us first consider the purpose of a central nervous system. This organ has seemingly developed to coordinate and integrate the activity of the organism with respect to its external environment. This environment includes not only the outside world, but also the rest of the organism external to the central nervous system. The nervous system must, therefore, be acutely aware of both the kind and magnitude of environmental changes within and without the body, and must, furthermore, be able to set in motion the proper responses to cope with them.

In order to accomplish this, the neuronal mechanisms, which are profoundly affected by slight fluctuations in the composition of their bathing fluid, require a highly stable local environment which will keep them relatively immune from otherwise disastrous shifts in blood solutes. From this standpoint, the blood-brain barrier may be thought of as a second-order homeostatic mechanism for maintaining a central neuronal milieu more constant than is possible by the blood alone. Such a possibility may be traced phylogenetically as the central nervous system develops increasing sensitivity and selectivity. In the coelenterate, the internal and external environments are essentially alike, and the simple nerve net is relatively nonselective, and indiscriminate in response. As one ascends the phylogenetic scale, the organism achieves greater freedom from external vicissitudes by the development of circulating blood which provides an environmental constancy sufficient for most tissues, but not for the increasingly delicate nervous system. The problem is solved by leaving the central nervous system unvascularized and providing secretory cells (probably ependymal in nature) to manufacture a specially fabricated liquor—the cerebrospinal fluid—which is both highly constant in composition and optimum for neuronal activity. Thus, in amphioxus, the central nervous system contains no blood vessels but is bathed in a separate fluid. However, this solution to the problem imposed a serious limitation on the organism. Since the neurones must receive all of their necessary metabolites, and discharge their wastes, through this enveloping fluid, the rapidly metabolizing neurone perikarya must remain near the periphery, and the total size of the central nervous system is limited by relatively short diffusion distances. To bring the metabolites into intimate relation with the cells and allow an essentially unlimited increase in the size of the central nervous system, vascularization was the obvious answer; but how to solve the necessity for environmental constancy? It is noteworthy in this regard that with the advent of simple capillary loops in the brains of cyclostomes, the first true neuroglia appear.[4] Arising from the ependyma—the original secretory cells—these specialized versions applied themselves in an unbroken sheath around the invading vasculature and manufactured locally the fluid environment that had previously been available to the neurones only by circuitous flow and diffusion. As the sensitivity and complexity of neuronal mechanisms increased, the local environmental control became ever more precise with the development of increased vascularization and greater numbers of neuroglia.

Although this may seem to provide a sufficient rationale for the blood-brain barrier, the concept may be carried one step further. There is some evidence that the barrier does not merely maintain a constant homogeneous intercellular fluid throughout the central nervous system, but may actually vary the quality of its "secretion" under different circumstances. For example, Grieg and Holland[15] found that eserine and acetylcholine markedly increased the penetration of acid fuchsin into the brain. Furthermore, both tumor analyses[39] and histochemical studies[21] have indicated that the highest concentration of cholinesterase in the central nervous system is in the astrocytes. Cholinesterase and astrocytes also appear simultaneously during embryologic development, and increase proportionately.[19] Finally, there is convincing evidence from the studies of Marui[27] on the Mauthner's cell of fish, and of Kuntz[23] on peripheral autonomic ganglia, that behavior of neuroglia can be markedly influenced by functional activity of neurones. Here, then, is the possibility that the ionic and metabolic environment of neurones can be controlled locally in response to neuronal activity within a small region. The stimulus affecting the glial barrier might be acetylcholine released at the synapse in proportion to the number of arriving impulses, and the cholinesterase in the target cells (the astrocytes) would serve to keep the effect localized to the area involved. Thus the threshold of neurones might be, in part, determined by the admission or exclusion of, say, calcium or potassium ions to their environment. Some such phenomenon might explain the slow electrical potential, pH, and threshold changes seen following regional activity in the cortex.[5, 6]

If this picture is in any way correct, the consequences of malfunction of the blood-brain barrier would be quite significant. Changes in neuronal threshold caused by improper maintenance of intercellular ionic concentrations could readily result in such profound syndromes as epileptiform attacks, as well as much subtler forms of mental disturbance. It would seem not at all impossible that the unique activity of the blood-brain barrier, and the more conjectural role of the neuroglia, may indicate new parameters of central nervous system lability which might provide an insight into several heretofore obscure phenomena.

REFERENCES

1. BENNHOLD, H. *Ergebnisse der inneren Medizin und Kinderheilkunde*, 1932, 42, p. 273.
2. BROMAN, T. *Acto Physiologica Scandinavica*, 1941, 2, p. 83.
3. BROMAN, T. The Permeability of the Cerebrospinal Vessels in Normal and Pathological Conditions. Copenhagen, E. Munksgaard, 1949.
4. CRAIGIE, E. H. *Proceedings of the Association for Research in Nervous and Mental Disease*, 1938, 18, p. 3.
5. DUSSER DE BARENNE, J. G.; MARSHALL, C. S.; McCULLOCH, W. S.; and NIMS, L. S. *American Journal of Physiology*, 1938, 124, p. 631.
6. DUSSER DE BARENNE, J. G., and McCULLOCH, W. S. *Journal of Neurophysiology*, 1939, 2, p. 319.
7. ELLIOTT, K. A. C.; SCOTT, D. B. M.; and LIBET, B. *Journal of Biological Chemistry*, 1942, 146, p. 251.
8. ERLICH, P. Das Sauerstoffbedürfnis des Organismus. Eine farbenanalytische Studie. Berlin, 1885.
9. FLEXNER, L. B. *Physiological Review*, 1934, 14, p. 161.
10. FRIEDEMANN, U. *Physiological Review*, 1942, 22, p. 125.
11. GARTNER, W. *Zeitschrift für Neurologie*, 1932, 140, p. 572.
12. GEIGER, A., and MAGNES, J. *Federation Proceedings*, 1949, 8, p. 54.
13. GOLDMANN, E. E. Vitalfärbung am Zentralnervensystem. Berlin, G. Reimer, 1913.
14. GREENBERG, D. M.; AIRD, R. B.; BOELTER, M. D. D.; CAMPBELL, W. W.; COHN, W. E.; and MURAYAMA, M. M. *American Journal of Physiology*, 1943, 140, p. 47.
15. GRIEG, M. E.; and HOLLAND, W. C. *Science*, 1949, 110, p. 237.
16. HEVESEY, G. Radioactive Indicators. Their Application in Biochemistry, Animal Physiology, and Pathology. New York, Interscience Publishers, Inc., 1948.
17. KAHN, J. B. *Current Researches in Anesthesia and Analgesia*, 1950, 29, p. 273.

18. KATZENELBOGEN, Z.   The Cerebrospinal Fluid and Its Relation to the Blood: A Physiological and Clinical Study. Baltimore, Md., The Johns Hopkins Press, 1935.
19. KERSHMAN, J.   Archives of Neurology and Psychiatry, 1938, 40, p. 937.
20. KING, L. S.   Proceedings of the Association for Research in Nervous and Mental Disease. 1938, 18, p. 150.
21. KOELLE, G. B., and FRIEDENWALD, J. S.   Proceedings of the Society for Experimental Biology and Medicine, 1949, 70, p. 617.
22. KROGH, A.   Proceedings of the Royal Society of London, 1946, 133, p. 140.
23. KUNTZ, A., and SULKIN, N. M.   Journal of Comparative Neurology, 1947, 86, p. 467.
24. LEWANDOWSKY, M.   Zeitschrift für klinisch Medizin, 1900, 40, p. 480.
25. LONG, C.; OCHOA, S.; and PETERS, R. A.   Journal of Physiology, 1939, 96, p. 5.
26. MADDOCK, S; HAWKINS, J. E.; and HOLMES, E. G.   American Journal of Physiology, 1939, 125, p. 551.
27. MARUI, K. J.   Comparative Neurology, 1919, 30, p. 253.
28. MAYER-GROSS, W. E., and WALKER, J. W.   Biochemical Journal, 1949, 44, p. 92.
29. RAWSON, R. A.   American Journal of Physiology, 1943, 138, p. 708.
30. SACKS, J., and CULBRETH, G. G.   American Journal of Physiology, 1950, 163, p. 746.
31. SCHALTENBRAND, G., and BAILEY, P.   Zeitschrift für Psychologie und Neurologie, 1928, 35, p. 199.
32. SIRI, W. E.   Isotopic Tracers and Nuclear Radiations. New York, McGraw-Hill Book Co., Inc., 1949.
33. SPATZ, H.   Archiv für Psychiatrie und Nervenkrankheit, 1933, 101, p. 267.
34. TSCHIRGI, R. D.   American Journal of Physiology, 1950, 163, p. 756.
35. TSCHIRGI, R. D.; GERARD, R. W.; JENERICK, H.; BOYARSKY, L. L.; and HEARON, J. Z.   Federation Proceedings, 1949, 8, p. 166.
36. WALLACE, G. B., and BRODIE, B. B.   Journal of Pharmacology and Experimental Therapeutics, 1939, 65, p. 220.
37. WEED, L. M.   Physiological Reviews, 1934, 141, p. 161.
38. WEIL-MALHERBE, H.   Biochemical Journal, 1936, 30, p. 665.
39. YOUNGSTROM, K. A.; WOODHALL, B.; and GRAVES, R. W.   Proceedings of the Society for Experimental Biology and Medicine, 1941, 48, p. 555.

Discussion

SOLOMON KATZENELBOGEN, M.D.

Dr. Tschirgi deserves credit for reviving the subject, at least in this country, of the blood-brain barrier. To my knowledge, very few studies have been reported in the last ten or fifteen years.

I shall avail myself of the privilege to discuss a topic which is pertinent to the subject matter of Dr. Tschirgi's comprehensive and effectively presented paper. My remarks will be concerned with the clinical aspect of the so-called hematoencephalic barrier, the barrier between blood and cerebrospinal fluid.

I shall take the liberty to question the justification of certain therapeutic procedures which are derived from our present-day knowledge of the function of the barrier, namely, intraspinal treatment with drugs and other procedures the aim of which is either to assure the presence of the injected drug or to increase its concentration or the concentration of a blood substance in the cerebrospinal fluid. Such procedures include spinal puncture combined with parenteral administration of a drug; spinal drainage associated with intravenous injection of hypotonic solutions or with the administration of large amounts of water orally; intravenous injection of hypertonic solutions prior to intravenous administrations of a drug; oral administration of certain substances, such as urotropin, sodium salicylate, and caronamide; and such procedures as fever therapy or aseptic meningitis therapy combined with oral or parenteral administration of drugs. They are designed to increase the barrier permeability and thereby assure or augment the penetration of substances from the blood into the cerebrospinal fluid.

The assumption that an increased barrier permeability is therapeutically beneficial is derived from the following concepts of the function of the barrier and of the cerebrospinal fluid:

1. For a substance to have an effect on the nerve tissues it must be present in the cerebrospinal fluid.

2. There is a definite parallelism between the effect of a substance on the nerve tissues and the degree of the passage of that substance from the general circulation into the cerebrospinal fluid.

3. The barrier between blood and cerebrospinal fluid offers resistance to the passage of substances from the blood into the cerebrospinal fluid.

4. The barrier permeability can be increased.

These concepts have led to the therapeutic procedures just mentioned, the object of which, to reiterate, is to increase the barrier permeability.

From the therapeutic standpoint the question arises: Is it really necessary to employ these measures in an attempt to assure the presence of a drug or a blood substance in the cerebrospinal fluid? Formerly, therapy with mercury, salvarsan, and bismuth was considered quite effective against syphilis. Yet, one knows that these substances, under ordinary conditions and even when the barrier permeability is increased, do not at all pass into the cerebrospinal fluid, or pass there in extremely small amounts.

I should like to add another point. Not only from the therapeutic standpoint is one not justified in being concerned about the presence or absence of a certain drug in the cerebrospinal fluid, but also from facts known concerning the function of the barrier itself, namely, although the barrier offers a resistance to the passage of substances from blood into cerebrospinal fluid, it offers no resistance at all in the reverse direction, i.e., to the passage of substances from the cerebrospinal fluid into the general circulation. Therefore, drugs administered through the cerebrospinal cavity easily pass into the general circulation.

REFERENCES

1. KATZENELBOGEN, SOLOMON.   The Cerebrospinal Fluid and Its Relation to the
   Blood. A Physiological and Clinical Study. Baltimore, Md., The Johns Hopkins Press, 1935.
2. BOGER, W. P.; WILSON, W. W.; and BAKER, R. B.   *Transactions of the American Neurological Association.* Annual Meeting, 1948.

Technic for Perfusion of the Completely Isolated Brain in the Living Cat

REGINALD M. TAYLOR, M.D.

I am not going to discuss the preceding paper, in spite of what the chairman has told you, except to say that I find it and the "dreamlike" theory
of Dr. Tschirgi exceedingly interesting. I cannot help wondering, however, if, in part, Dr. Tschirgi has not conceived of the brain as being too
well insulated against changes in the blood. It is true that the brain must
be relatively stable so that it is not at the mercy of every slight whim of
the blood; but I think that it is also highly desirable and necessary that
certain blood changes must, within a very short time, affect the brain.

I am not discussing Dr. Tschirgi's paper because, while his theory certainly bears upon the work undertaken by my colleagues and myself, there
is nothing I think in our work which would have any direct bearing either
to support or refute any of his very interesting suggestions and conclusions.

Dr. Kruse has thought that you would be interested in hearing of some
of the work that Dr. Geiger, Dr. Magnes, and I have been doing on the
perfusion of the completely isolated brain in a living cat. I shall discuss,
very briefly, the technic and the idea behind it, and shall mention just a few
of the salient and what I think are the most useful results we have obtained
to date.

Doctors Geiger and Magnes[1] have been working on this problem since
1940. For the past three years they worked in the New York State Psychiatric
Institute.

The problem as they see it—of brain perfusion—is to obtain sufficient
isolation of the circulation so that it is assured that all of the perfusion
fluid used reaches the brain and that all the fluid flowing from the brain is
collected for analysis or other purposes.

Since we have been using cats entirely in this work, I should like briefly
to review the main blood supply of the brain of the cat, which differs
somewhat from that of the monkey. The arterial supply is, of course, from
the vertebrals, the internal maxillary division of the carotid, the anterior
spinal which, in the cat, is very small, and the internal carotid, the lumen
of which is not patent—in fact, according to some authorities, there is
no lumen at all. The venous return is by the vertebral veins, the paravertebral venous sinuses, and the internal jugulars. If the latter are very small,

as they are in most cats, they are disregarded; if they are appreciably large, they are tied. Occasionally one finds a cat with a very large internal jugular, and when this occurs the external jugular is relatively very small.

The paravertebral venous sinuses are made up of a dorsal and ventral branch, leaving the brain through the foramen magnum, and uniting in the atlas to form the sinuses. These sinuses are located inside the spinal column and are enclosed by layers of dura; at each interspace they communicate by short branches with the vertebral veins which run through foramina in the transverse processes. Finally, the vertebral vein, at the atlanto-occipital articulation, connects by a lateral loop, running around the outer border of the bulla tympani to the posterior or anterior facial branch of the external jugular vein.

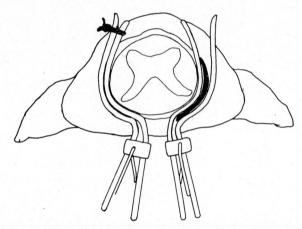

Fig. 1.   Clips used to occlude paravertebral venous sinuses. Clip on right shown open with dilated sinus between jaws. Clip on left is closed and jaws pulled firmly together by tie across open end thus compressing sinus between jaws.

From this description it may be appreciated that the venous outflow is particularly difficult to control. If one merely ties the veins, the venous sinuses, for example, at one level and the vertebral veins at another, then, owing to the cross connections, the blood flows down through the venous sinus to the point of ligation and, being stopped there, promptly is diverted to one or more of the lateral branches anterior to the point of ligation, thence it flows into the vertebral vein and thus shunts or bypasses around the points of ligation and reaches the body circulation. Also this lateral loop, passing from the vertebral veins to the external jugular vein, acts as a bypass so that it is necessary to clamp at the same level all the venous outflow from the vertebral veins and vertebral sinuses. This is accomplished by using a set of clips.

Therefore the technic in general consists first of all in ligating the vertebral arteries at the point of their entry into the spinal column, which is at the sixth cervical interspace; ligating the superior thyroid and the dorsomuscular branches of the common carotid; ligating the lingual, the external maxillary, and the submaxillary branches of the external carotid; and ligating finally the terminal branch of the internal maxillary artery rostral to its short communicating branches supplying the brain via the circle of Willis. This terminal branch we ligate through a small cut in the roof of the mouth, near the junction of the maxilla and palatine bones.

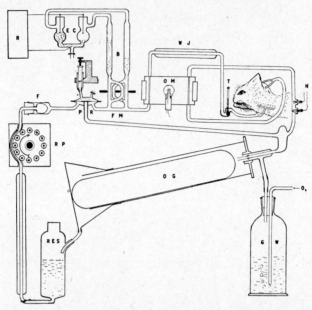

FIG. 2. Diagram of apparatus. RES=blood reservoir. RP=roller pump. PR= pressure regulator (upper chamber and syringe saline-filled; pressure placed on rubber diaphragm by adjusting thumbscrew on syringe barrel). FM=flow meter with electromagnetic valve controlling alternate rise and fall of blood in burettes B, which displaces a measured volume of Ringer's solution in electrolytic contactor EC which, through relay R, actuates electromagnetic valve, the number of actuations per unit time being recorded. OM=photoelectric oximeter with photocells at ends connected in compensation to an indicating galvanometer. WJ=warming water jacket. T=thermometer for blood temperature. H=pH electrodes. GW= gas wash bottle for O_2. OG=rotary oxygenator with internal rolling closed glass cylinder.

The venous outflow is obtained by drilling two holes, one in each side of the occiput lateral and dorsal to the occipital condyles to penetrate the transverse sinuses. After heparin is injected into the circulation, two small cannulae are driven in, and these are joined and returned to a branch of the external jugular. At present we are using one of the large brachial veins, which drains the blood tapped from the transverse sinuses and thus aids in preventing clotting.

The perfusion is made through two cannulae inserted into both common carotids. The common carotids can then be clamped posteriorly to the insertion of these perfusing cannulae.

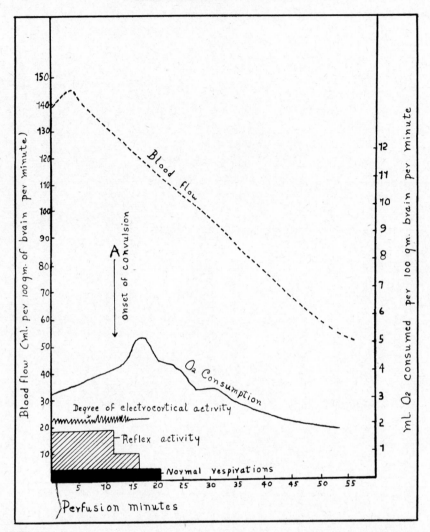

FIG. 3.   Perfusion with glucose-free suspension of bovine red blood cells in Ringer's solution and albumin. Note failure of electrocortical activity, reflex activity, and respiration shortly after hypoglycemic convulsions; also the marked fall in blood flow and the steady fall in oxidative metabolism after a peak value (brought about by the convulsive process.)

The final procedure is to apply clips which compress the venous sinuses at a level between the atlas and occiput; and also, at that level, the vertebral veins and the lateral communicating loops are ligatured.

Figure 1 shows the two clips inserted and passing between the inner and outer layers of the dura. When tied on the dorsal side they clamp the venous sinuses between them thus thoroughly shutting off the outflow from these sinuses.

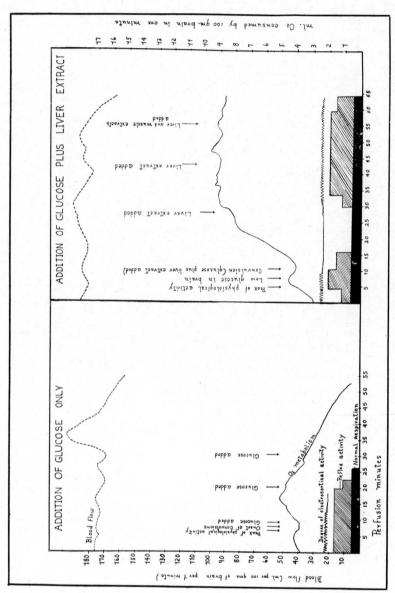

Fig. 4. The effect of liver extracts on uptake of glucose by brain. In left-hand graph, addition of glucose alone to glucose-free blood has no effect on failing metabolism, electrocortical activity, reflexes, and respiration (cf. Fig. 3). In right-hand graph, addition of liver extract together with the glucose increases and maintains metabolism and restores electrocortical activity, reflexes, and respiration.

Figure 2 presents a diagram of the apparatus. This consists of a blood reservoir; a pressure regulator; a rubber roller type of perfusion pump; a simple flow-meter; an oximeter using an excitor lamp and two photocells which give the arterial-venous oxygen difference directly on a galvanometer, the latter being connected in compensation across the two photocells; and a warming water jacket which keeps the perfusion fluid at a temperature of 37.5° C.

Very briefly, I wish to indicate one or two of the results. Figure 3 shows the normal result of perfusion with glucose-free blood, that is, a bovine red blood cell suspension in Ringer's solution and albumin to which no glucose has been added. The electrical activity ceases shortly after a hypoglycemic convulsion begins. Following this convulsion, the oxygen consumption rises slightly and then falls steadily to a lower value. The blood flow falls steadily to a much lower value.

The effects of the muscle extracts, mentioned by Dr. Tschirgi, are presented in Figure 4. There are two sets of experiments. On the left, is one similar to that shown in Figure 3. The blood flow, the oxidative metabolism, and the point at which hypoglycemic convulsions occur are all indicated. Immediately following the convulsion, glucose is added. Figure 4, left, shows a rise in metabolism due to the convulsion similar to that seen in Figure 3; but in spite of the additions of glucose at two points, the metabolism steadily falls; the blood flow stays up but falls rapidly later; electrocortical activity ceases shortly after the convulsion. The reflex activity then ceases, and, finally, respiration ceases.

But if in the same circumstances after the convulsion has occurred, an aqueous extract of cat liver is added together with the glucose, a very different phenomenon may be seen (Fig. 4, right). The metabolism rises and, after liver extract is again added, it remains high. After the electrocortical activity has ceased it returns again and continues on in the normal fashion. Similarly, the reflex activity, the corneal reflexes and twitching of lips and ears which had disappeared entirely, have now returned.

We interpret these experiments as indicating that there is some substance in fresh aqueous extracts of liver and also of cat muscle which is responsible for and necessary for the permeability of the brain cells to glucose. We have other data of similar glucose-free perfusions in which the brain tissue was studied for its glucose content; we find that the glucose content is very low and that it returns to its normal or higher values only with the addition of the liver extract. Merely adding an abundance of glucose alone to the blood does not increase brain glucose.

REFERENCE

1. GEIGER, A., and MAGNES, J. *American Journal of Physiology*, 1947, 149, p. 517.

CHAPTER 5

Brain Tissue Respiration and Glycolysis

K. A. C. ELLIOTT, SC.D.

I PROPOSE TO summarize some of our present information concerning mammalian brain tissue "respiration" (i.e., oxygen uptake) and glycolysis (i.e., lactic acid formation), and to attempt to bring the results of some *in vitro* studies into relation with observations made *in vivo*. The purpose of the type of study to be outlined has been to discover aspects of the behavior and potentialities of the integrated tissue in order to predict or interpret physiologic events. The intermediate reactions and enzymic mechanisms underlying the metabolism of the tissue will be discussed by others taking part in this symposium.

Methods

Most of the work on this subject has consisted of measurements of oxygen consumption, carbon dioxide evolution, and acid change by means of the well-known Barcroft or Warburg apparatus and modifications of both of these. Chemical determinations of lactic acid and other substances have supplemented the measurements.

For much of the work, thin slices of the tissue have been used for study. This type of preparation is probably the best compromise between the practical problems of *in vitro* study and the ideal of maintaining the physiologic structure of the tissue. There is considerable variability, however, between individual slices. Since slices lack a capillary circulation, all exchanges between the inner layers of the slice and the surrounding medium depend upon diffusion through an appreciable thickness of tissue.[31, 105] Consequently slices are unsuitable for some types of study.

These difficulties are overcome at the expense of more extensive loss of tissue structure, with some loss of metabolic activity, by the use of suspensions prepared by light homogenization in isotonic medium.[35, 36]

Homogenates in which structures are more drastically altered, as by preparation in water, require for maximum activity the addition of various co-factors. When appropriately supplemented they may show higher activity than slices. These preparations, as well as tissue extracts, are extremely useful for enzymologic studies. Results obtained with them, however, are to be discussed by others and will not be considered further in this outline.

The slice is usually bathed, or the suspension prepared, in a solution isotonic with and similar in inorganic composition to serum or cerebrospinal fluid. This solution is maintained at approximately physiologic pH by buffering either with phosphate or bicarbonate. The latter buffer requires the presence of 5 per cent carbon dioxide in the gas phase which complicates the measurement of respiration, but, since bicarbonate-carbon dioxide is the physiologic buffer, it is preferable. Unless otherwise indicated, all results to be summarized have been obtained in glucose-containing medium.

The following diagram shows the units most commonly used to express rates measured *in vitro* and *in vivo* and indicates how they may be interconverted, taking the dry weight of tissue as about 20 per cent of the fresh weight.

Units used in gas exchange measurements

Q values
μl (mm³) per mg. dried tissue per hour

+5 ↗   ↖ +3

ml. per Gm. fresh wt.   ×0.6   ml. per 100 Gm. fresh wt.
per hour   ⟵   per minute

Rates for substances like lactic acid are usually expressed in terms of equivalent gas. In fact, glycolysis is often measured gasometrically in terms of the carbon dioxide liberated by lactic acid from bicarbonate. Conventionally, gas evolution is considered positive, gas uptake negative.

Oxygen Uptake

There is much variability in the average rates of oxygen uptake reported by various workers. This is partly due to variations in conditions and technic. But even under standard conditions, variability up to 40 or 50 per cent is encountered from animal to animal and smaller but considerable variability between slices from the same animal. In Table 4 two sets of average results, obtained under standardized conditions with cerebral cortex from various animals, are summarized. The results procured by me[33] were obtained in a bicarbonate buffered medium having the inorganic salt composition of cerebrospinal fluid. The results of Krebs[70] were obtained in a newly developed medium containing glucose and also pyruvate, fumarate, and glutamate, representative of metabolically active substances present in serum but added here in much higher concentrations. The rates in the supplemented medium of Krebs are much higher than what have thus far been regarded as normal *in vitro* values. It is at present difficult to decide which medium represents the most physiologic environment.

TABLE 4. AVERAGE RESPIRATION RATES $(-Q_{o_2})$ OF CEREBRAL CORTEX
SLICES FROM VARIOUS ANIMALS

Animal	Elliott[33] Complete Saline*	Krebs[70] Supplemented Saline†	Animal	Elliott[33] Complete Saline*	Krebs[70] Supplemented Saline†
Mouse	14.2	22.9	Dog	7.0	14.8
Rat	11.2	19.2	Sheep		11.3
Guinea pig	8.7	17.4	Man	6.1	
Cat	8.4	15.5	Beef	5.3	12.1
Rabbit	7.4	15.1	Horse		10.5

Both media contained glucose.
* Medium contained 1.3 mM calcium, other salts, and 25 mM bicarbonate in the presence of 5 per cent CO_2, 95 per cent oxygen. The fresh weight of tissue was determined and figures are based on dry weight taken as one-fifth of fresh weight.
† Medium contained 2.5 mM calcium, other salts, 5 mM each of pyruvate, glutamate, and fumarate, and low, 3.6 mM bicarbonate in presence of 100 per cent oxygen. Figures based on dry weight found after experiment.

The respiration rate per unit weight of tissue decreases, somewhat irregularly, with increasing size of animal. This is shown more clearly in Figure 5. Results in the presence and absence of calcium ion are shown. In the absence of calcium the initial rates are higher. The graph shows average oxygen uptake rates plotted against the average body weights of the animals used, on logarithmic scales. The rates are roughly inversely proportional to the tenth root of the body weight. Brain cortex respiration thus is partly dependent on the body weight of the species but not so greatly as total metabolism which is approximately inversely proportional to the fourth root of body weight.[67] Neither Krebs nor I found any relation of the respiration rate to the body weight of individual adult animals within a species.

The rates thus far mentioned are for cortex from mixed areas. Slices from the dorsal aspect of the hemisphere respire 10 to 20 per cent more actively than do slices from the lateral aspect in all animals studied. Surface slices tend to respire a little less actively than second slices but this is variable.[33]

Average figures[27, 54] for the activity of various parts of the brain are shown in Table 5. Cerebellar tissue seems to be the most active tissue *in*

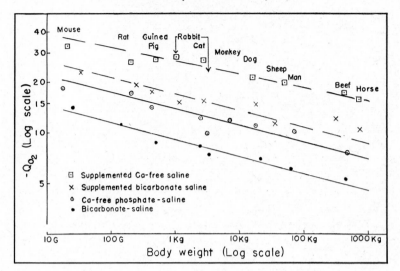

Fig. 5. Relation of average oxygen uptake rate of cerebral cortex to average body weight of different species. The points for supplemented (with pyruvate, fumarate, and glutamate) media are from Krebs,[70] the others are from Elliott and Henderson.[33]

vitro and there is much variability between brain regions. White matter respires at half or less the rate of cortex. [27, 36, 72]

The respiration rate of brain tissue *in vitro* is not, as often stated, exceptionally high. In Table 6 rates obtained with various rat tissues are compared. Retina and kidney cortex respire more actively than does cerebral cortex, and several other tissues are nearly as active.

It is not possible to compare directly rates obtained *in vivo* and *in vitro*. Slices constitute only local samples of the brain while quantitative measurements *in vivo* are made on the whole brain. Suspensions of whole brain, corrected for loss of activity consequent to disintegration, might give a

TABLE 5. AVERAGE OXYGEN UPTAKE RATES BY VARIOUS PARTS
OF THE BRAIN (*ml. per gram per hour*)

Beef Brain Slices (Dixon and Meyer[27])		Dog Brain* Mince (Himwich and Fazekas[54])	
Cerebral cortex	1.7	Cerebral cortex	1.16
Cerebellar cortex	2.55	Cerebellar cortex	1.4
Corpus striatum	1.95	Caudate nucleus	1.36
Thalamus	1.17	Thalamus	1.01
Cornu ammonis	1.26	Midbrain	0.92
Globus pallidus	0.36	Medulla	0.69

Both in saline-phosphate-glucose medium.
* Efforts made to eliminate white matter.

TABLE 6.　RESPIRATION RATES OF VARIOUS RAT TISSUES

Tissue	$-Q_{O_2}$	Tissue	$-Q_{O_2}$
Cerebral cortex slices	10–16	Intestinal mucosa, intact	12
Retina, intact	22–33	Diaphragm, intact	7–8
Kidney cortex slices	21–24	Lung slices	8
Liver slices	8–17	Pancreas slices	4
Spleen slices	11–12	Tumors, various, slices	6–14
Testis, teased out	11–12	Whole resting animal	4.8–6.0

Figures from Krebs and Johnson.[71] In bicarbonate-saline-glucose medium.

better comparison, but whole brain suspensions have been studied only from small animals. However, by making some assumptions, an approximate estimate for "whole brain slices" can be obtained from figures of Elliott and Henderson.[33] Rates obtained with suspensions of *whole* brain are corrected for the 30 per cent loss of activity which occurs when cortex slices are reduced to a suspension, and for 10 per cent loss during the time between excision and measurement. The estimates thus obtained for "slices of whole brain" average 80 per cent of the rates found for *cortex* slices of small animals. This fraction of the values for cortex slices of other animals should represent roughly the figure for whole brain in these animals.

As shown in Table 7, estimates thus obtained, using a conventional medium, correspond to rates obtained *in vivo* in conditions of depressed functional activity. The rates obtained by Krebs with his medium, containing glutamate, fumarate, and pyruvate, are about twice as great and, if a similar correction were applicable, would correspond to "conscious," "resting," or "normal" rates *in vivo*.

When the concentration of potassium in the medium bathing brain slices is raised to a high level, a very variable and temporary but often large increase in oxygen uptake rate occurs.[3, 23, 25] A considerable though tem-

TABLE 7.　OXYGEN UPTAKE BY WHOLE BRAIN IN VITRO AND IN VIVO
$-Q_{O_2}$ (*microliters per mg. dry weight per hour*)

	In vitro (Estimated)	In vivo			Reference
Cat	6.8	No reflexes 6.9	Conscious? 12–15	Convulsing 15–21	Geiger and Magnes[44]
Monkey	5.9	Depressed (Hemorrhage) 5.6	"Normal" 11.1 (Mean)	Convulsing 19.5	Schmidt, Kety, and Pennes[97]
Man	4.8	Coma diabetic, insulin 5.1　5.7	Resting 9.9		Kety Schmidt, and others[63,64,66]

porary increase in respiration rate also occurs when calcium, especially, and magnesium ions are omitted from the medium.[23, 36] It is well known that potassium is released during nervous activity. The potassium so released into the cell environment may be part of the mechanism which stimulates the extra respiration associated with activity. Changes in the state of ionization of calcium may also be concerned in this function.

Substrates of Respiration

The brain *in situ* under normal conditions respires almost exclusively at the expense of glucose (see, e.g., Gibbs and associates[45]). If glucose and oxygen are provided in a suitable medium, brain slices and suspensions will respire at a nearly constant rate for hours. Analytic studies have shown that the respiration can be 80 to 90 per cent accounted for by glucose consumption.[38]

In the absence of added substrate, small amounts of lactate, originally present in the tissue or formed from endogenous glucose, are consumed, and then oxidation of non-carbohydrate material sets in.[38] Kety and co-workers have shown that the oxygen consumption by human brain during insulin hypoglycemia cannot be accounted for by the glucose utilized.[62] *In vitro* the rate of respiration in the absence of substrate falls off steadily and largely irreversibly, indicating that deficiency of energy-yielding processes or consumption of the non-carbohydrate material involves destruction of metabolic ability. In this connection it is of interest to note that, in the presence of iron and ascorbic acid which cause rapid oxidation of lipid material, the metabolic activity of brain tissue is rapidly destroyed.[37]

Although brain tissue *in vitro* will respire at its full rate in the presence of extremely low glucose concentrations, 2 mg. per cent,[34] symptoms of hypoglycemia can occur when the blood glucose is still appreciable. This emphasizes the fact that the concentrations of metabolites at tissue cells *in vivo* are not necessarily the same as in the blood since such materials have to diffuse out of capillaries and through some distance to tissue cells.

The consumption of non-carbohydrate material by brain, when deprived of normal substrate, suggests a possible basis for the insulin shock treatment in psychoses. The material consumed is probably at least partly derived from structural materials the consumption of which would be expected to alter the functional condition of the tissue.

Very rapid irreversible destruction of the metabolic capacity of brain tissue occurs if it is incubated in the absence of both oxygen and substrate —about 88 per cent inactivation in 20 minutes.[21, 35] This fits in with the rapid electrographic silence and death which occur on occlusion of the cerebral circulation *in vivo*.

The breakdown of glucose involves the intermediate production of pyruvic acid. Pyruvic acid is readily reduced to lactic acid, especially under anaerobic conditions, and lactic acid is readily oxidized to pyruvic acid. Therefore, as might be expected, pyruvate and lactate can take the place of glucose as substrate for oxidation *in vitro*. Succinate causes a marked increase in oxygen uptake with little or no increase, however, in carbon dioxide production. It is oxidized rapidly through only one step, to fumarate and malate; further oxidization takes place only slowly.[32, 90] Fructose, mannose, and, to a lesser extent, galactose can replace glucose as substrate *in vitro*, but other saccharides tested are almost inert.[22, 73, 90] The small amounts of glycogen in brain decrease in insulin-treated animals,[60] but glycogen is probably first hydrolyzed to glucose before it is burnt.[38] Lipoid material does not seem to be oxidized by brain under normal conditions. Acetic acid is produced to some extent *in vitro*,[38, 74] but free acetate is not oxidizable[32, 38] and its production may be an artefact of *in vitro* conditions.

Glutamic acid appears to be the most important of non-carbohydrate materials oxidizable by brain. It is the only amino acid which has been found to be oxidizable in this tissue[90, 108] and it is of great interest from several points of view. It does not seem to be as readily oxidizable as glucose.

The effect of the new medium of Krebs[70] in greatly increasing the respiration rate of brain and other tissue slices is still difficult to explain. None of the extra additions to the medium—pyruvate, fumarate, or glutamate—individually increase the respiration rate of brain when added to glucose-containing medium.

Fructose, lactate, pyruvate, succinate, and glutamate can all support oxygen uptake by brain *in vitro*. Injected lactate, however, does not prevent or alleviate hypoglycemic convulsions in hepatectomized dogs nor rouse patients from insulin coma.[76, 111] Fructose, pyruvate, glutamate, and succinate do not restore normal cortical electrical potentials when injected into hepatectomized, eviscerated dogs.[75] Injection of large amounts of glutamic acid has sometimes roused patients from insulin coma, but this effect does not seem to be connected with specific oxidizability of this amino acid.[80]

There are possible explanations for the failure of these substances to replace glucose *in vivo*. The rate of transfer of fructose, lactate, glutamate, and succinate from blood to brain is much lower than that of glucose and may not be sufficient to support adequate respiration.[68] Pyruvate does seem to penetrate to the brain tissue rapidly where it is converted to lactate, but *in vitro* studies[38] show that a higher concentration of lactate than of glucose is required for the full rate of respiration to occur. The affinity of fructose for hexokinase—the first enzyme concerned in monosaccharide metabolism—is much lower than that of glucose.[82] Since added succinate is oxidized by brain rapidly only through one step, it is unlikely that it could support function effectively. Glutamate, *in vitro*, is not as actively used as glucose and can scarcely compete with it. It may also be of significance that none of these substances, including fructose, which seem inactive *in vivo*, are subject to glycolysis by brain slices.

Other Factors Affecting Respiration

Brain tissue respiration can be affected by a great many other factors, only a few of which can be mentioned here.

Pure oxygen at atmospheric pressure causes a slowly developing inhibition of respiration; higher pressures of oxygen inhibit more rapidly.[20, 36, 78, 98] Tissue from animals killed by high oxygen pressure, however, respires normally and, though many enzyme systems are inhibited by oxygen, the rapidity with which high oxygen pressure induces convulsions and other toxic symptoms has not yet been accounted for by *in vitro* studies.

The temperature coefficient, Q_{10}, for rat brain respiration between 10° and 40° C. is 2.13—a normal value for chemical reactions. At 40° C. the rate falls off with time, and at higher temperatures the loss of activity is more rapid and largely irreversible.[42] The effect of elevated temperature in raising the tissue respiration rate fits in with the observation that cerebral oxygen consumption is increased in patients undergoing fever therapy.[53] The irreversible loss of respiratory activity at temperatures over 40° C. may be a factor in the loss of reflexes and death of animals at such temperatures.[42]

Variations in pH and bicarbonate or CO_2 concentration do affect brain respiration somewhat, but, within the physiologic or pathologic range of variation of these factors, the effects are probably not very significant.[9, 31]

Although various vitamins of the B group are concerned, as parts of coenzymes, in brain and other tissue metabolism, it is only in thiamine deficiency that an obvious defect in brain tissue metabolism has been detected. The work of Peters and his school (e.g., Peters[87]) has shown that brain from pigeons suffering from avitaminosis B_1 respires at a lower rate than is normal in the presence of glucose, lactate, or pyruvate, and, with glucose or lactate, pyruvate accumulates. Addition of thiamine to the medium raises the respiration rate to normal and causes the pyruvate to disappear. Although thiamine pyrophosphate, cocarboxylase, is not immediately effective with brain mince (this is apparently due to failure to penetrate to active sites), it is now established that thiamine pyrophosphate is an essential coenzyme of pyruvate metabolism. Similar effects of the vitamin deficiency and the addition of thiamine have been obtained with rat brain.[84]

Insulin, added *in vitro* or administered to the animal, does not appear to exert any obvious direct action on brain tissue metabolism. The respiration of tissue removed from an insulinized animal falls off more rapidly than it does normally in the absence of added substrate, but this is due to the fact that tissue removed from a hypoglycemic animal contains less than the usual amount of glucose and lactate.[36, 38]

No change of respiration rate of cortex slices from hyperthyroid rats has been observed[11] although an increase has been reported with brain mince.[14]

Adrenalectomy does not appear to affect the respiration of cortex slices.[15] Desoxycorticosterone, progesterone, testosterone, and stilbestrol inhibit oxygen uptake by brain suspensions.[46] The respiration rate of suspensions from castrated rats has been reported[39] to be 32 per cent above normal, but it can be brought nearly to normal by treating the animals with testosterone or various derivatives, with progesterone, or with desoxycorticosterone acetate. Respiration of brain from animals treated with estradiol propionate was elevated.

Considerable stimulation of the respiration of cortex slices, but not of suspensions, has been observed in the presence of extremely low concentrations of certain other steroid derivatives, namely, protoveratrine, veratridine, and cardiac glycosides.[110] This effect, and others mentioned later, seems to be specific for brain. Cortex from animals poisoned with protoveratrine shows the same effect.

As may be discussed more fully by Dr. Quastel, narcotics of various types in concentrations which are likely to be present in the tissue fluids of narcotized animals, cause a definite, reversible inhibition of brain tissue respiration at the expense of glucose, lactate, pyruvate, or glutamate.[57, 59, 91, 93] Other tissues besides brain are similarly affected. In higher concentrations, irreversible damage to the metabolic system rapidly sets in as a result of great inhibition of respiration and glycolysis.[106] The inhibitory effect of narcotics on brain respiration is paralleled by observations *in vivo*. Cerebral oxygen consumption is decreased in pentothal or ether anesthesia in man[55, 61] and by various barbiturates in the cat brain perfused *in situ*.[44] Local oxygen uptake in the cortex is strongly inhibited by local perfusion with pentobarbital.[48]

The addition to the medium of certain toxic amines—particularly tyramine, phenylethylamine derivatives including mescaline, and also indole and skatole—causes marked inhibitory effects on brain respiration, while these substances are themselves oxidized to the aldehydes.[88, 92] It appears that the aldehydes formed, rather than the amines themselves, are responsible for the inhibition of respiration. Some amines are not oxidized and inhibit the oxidation of the others. Benzedrine (phenyl methyl ethylamine) is one of these and, in very low concentration, it prevents the inhibition which ordinarily follows the addition of the toxic amines.[77]

Of the many other substances of biochemical and pharmacologic interest which affect brain tissue respiration to various extents I will merely enumerate a few. Accelerations of glucose oxidation are observed with pyocyanine[113] and with various oxidation-reduction indicator dyes[17, 30] and dinitrophenols[28, 30, 86, 103] in low concentration. Inhibitions are obtained with higher concentrations of these and with cyanide[2, 26, 104] and azide,[56] iodoacetate,[6] fluoride[24] and glyceraldehyde,[4] malonate,[49, 102] hydroxymalonate,[58] nicotine and nicotinic acid,[5] triodobenzoate,[7] para-aminophenol,[8] oxazolidenediones,[43] atabrine,[112] and trivalent arsenicals.[47] Substances which are chiefly known as cholinesterase inhibitors have been found to inhibit frog brain respiration.[10] Various convulsive agents including sodium fluoroacetate have little or no effect on brain respiration.[10, 107, 106]

Glycolysis

Under anaerobic conditions brain, like a number of other tissues, carries on active glycolysis or, more precisely, glucolysis—the splitting of glucose to lactic acid. The actual rate of glucose utilization under anaerobic conditions is often several times the rate under aerobic conditions. Glycolysis makes some energy available for biologic processes, but the energy yield per molecule of glucose consumed is far less than in complete oxidation. In glycolysis, 54 kilocalories are released and 2 units of high energy phosphate are produced, while in complete oxidation about 690 kilocalories are released and 32 or more units of high energy phosphate are produced per molecule of glucose.

TABLE 8.   ANAEROBIC GLYCOLYSIS RATES OF CEREBRAL
CORTEX SLICES

Animal	$Q \dfrac{N_2}{G}$	
	On dry wt. at end of experiment	
Rat	9.0–25.2	Dickens and Greville[21]
Rat	3.5–10.5	Bumm, Appel and Couciero[12]
Rat	5.7–21.4	Elliott and Henry[35]
	On dry wt. taken as ⅕ of fresh wt.	
	Averages from Elliott and Henderson[33]	
	Plain	With pyruvate
Mouse	2.8	7.0
Rat	4.4	7.7
Guinea pig	6.8	10.1
Rabbit	7.0	8.0
Cat	6.8	11.0
Dog	10.5	13.3
Man	10.4	11.7

Bicarbonate-saline-glucose medium.

Examples of results by different workers, shown in Table 8, illustrate the extreme variability of measurements of glycolysis. The average rate per unit weight increases with increasing size of animal. Since the rate of respiration decreases with size, the ratio of glycolytic to respiratory activity increases considerably with size.

Glycolysis is markedly increased by the presence of a trace of pyruvate in the medium. During aerobic metabolism a small amount of pyruvate is always present.[38] Consequently glycolysis is increased by the presence of a little oxygen[35] or by a period of aerobiosis preceding the establishment of anaerobiosis.[96]

The anaerobic glycolytic activity of gray matter from different parts of adult cat and dog brain has been found[13] to decrease in the order: caudate nucleus, cortex, thalamus, corpus quadrigemina, cerebellum, medulla, cord. In the infant brain the relative activities are different and Chesler and Himwich[13] conclude from determinations at various ages that "the part of the brain exhibiting the highest glycolytic rate advances in a rostral direction as growth proceeds."

Suppression of glycolysis under aerobic conditions occurs to varying extents with almost all tissues capable of anaerobic glycolysis. This suppression of glycolysis is commonly referred to as the Pasteur effect (Pasteur reaction) since Pasteur drew attention to the similar situation in which production of alcohol by yeast is depressed under aerobic conditions.

The suppression of glycolysis in brain slices takes time, and fairly active aerobic glycolysis has been observed during the first few minutes of anaerobiosis[32] or for longer periods,[33] depending on the handling of the slices. In all cases, however, glycolysis by brain under aerobic conditions finally decreases to a low value while the respiration rate continues high.

Functions of Glycolysis

It is commonly believed that, in muscle and perhaps in other tissues, glycolysis serves as a method for producing energy-rich phosphate bonds when these are used up during functional activity faster than they can be provided by oxygen supply and respiration. This seems to be true for brain since lactic acid accumulates in the brain under conditions of hyperactivity[69, 100] as well as in hypoxia [41, 50] and cyanide poisoning.[1, 85] Himwich and his co-workers believe that anaerobic glycolysis is an important source of energy especially in the brains of newborn animals. The survival time of both adult[41] and infant[52] animals subjected to anoxia is lowered by poisoning with the glycolysis inhibitors iodoacetate or fluoride. Newborn animals survive much longer periods of anoxia than do adults.[40] Their survival time is increased by increase in blood sugar level, and considerable amounts of lactic acid are found in their brains after anoxia.[52] Although the glycolytic activity of the infant brain is lower than that of the adult, the respiratory activity is relatively still lower. It seems that glycolytic activity is nearly adequate for the lower energy demands in the newborn.[51, 54]

It seems likely, however, that besides the provision of energy, glycolysis may be concerned in other functions which may be even more continuously essential. With normal resting human subjects, lactic acid is added to the blood stream by the brain in an amount equivalent, on the average, to 16 per cent of the glucose consumed.[45] The lactic acid content of rat brain is decreased, but is still considerable, during sleep and anesthesia, and is increased during excitement.[95]

It is possible that glycolysis is concerned in the regulation of pH since glycolytic acid formation, aerobic or anaerobic, decreases when the pH falls.[9] It is probably also concerned in regulation of circulation in the brain as a whole or in local regions. The extra production of acid during hypoxia, local or general, would tend to counteract the hypoxic condition since the glycolytically produced acid, or increased carbon dioxide released from bicarbonate by the acid, would tend to dilate cerebral blood vessels (see e.g., Nims and associates[83] and Kety and Schmidt[65]). Further, it is to be expected that the production of acid within nerve cells would strongly affect their functional activity.

While some glycolysis probably occurs under fully aerobic conditions, it seems likely that in local regions it is often increased to the anaerobic level. The oxygen tension measured at the cortex surface varies, and at points distant from visible vessels it is very low.[94] Tissue can respire at its full rate at very low oxygen tensions,[34] but very brief decrease in the blood supply near such a region, or an increase in the demand as a result of increased activity, could produce oxygen lack and the onset of a high rate of glycolysis.

Factors Affecting Glycolysis

The glycolytic activity of brain tissue is remarkably sensitive to various influences. A slight change in technic of handling slices seems to cause glycolysis to continue under aerobic conditions longer than was previously observed.[33] High potassium concentrations, besides increasing oxygen uptake rate, markedly increase aerobic glycolysis but inhibit anaerobic glycolysis.[3, 23, 25] The effects are immediate but rather short-lived. Glutamic acid also causes an increase in aerobic glycolysis and a decrease in anaerobic glycolysis.[109] Its effects develop gradually. Maleic acid also causes a gradual increase in aerobic glycolysis.[109] The veratrum alkaloids and cardiac glycosides, besides stimulating respiration, also increase aerobic glycolysis to the anaerobic level and completely inhibit anaerobic glycolysis.[110] In extremely low concentrations, a number of nitrogenous compounds—including especially guanidine and derivatives—raise the aerobic glycolysis to the anaerobic level or higher, usually with some increase in the oxygen uptake rate.[16, 18, 19, 30] Unlike high potassium and other substances just mentioned, these compounds do not inhibit anaerobic glycolysis.

It seems possible that marked effects on glycolysis may occur *in vivo* under the influence of substances of physiologic or pathologic origin, like guanidines, and might provide a mechanism for increasing energy production or controlling pH, or might affect function in useful or pathologic ways. Dickens, who made most of these observations, suggests that the tetanic convulsive effect of guanidine may be connected with its effect on aerobic glycolysis.[19]

Glycolysis may be stimulated to the anaerobic level in the presence of oxygen if oxygen usage is inhibited, for instance, by cyanide. As might be expected then, a large increase in aerobic glycolysis occurs in the presence of narcotics of various types. The maximum is reached when about 50 per cent of the respiration is inhibited. With higher concentrations of narcotic the glycolysis falls again and inhibition becomes irreversible.[106] The concentration at which any narcotic causes maximal glycolysis correlates fairly well with narcotic potency, and the effect on glycolysis is possibly of equal significance to that on oxygen uptake.

Other Activities

Certain other activities of brain tissue which are probably fundamentally concerned in physiologic function have been found to be closely associated with respiration and glycolysis.

The synthesis of acetylcholine by brain slices is dependent upon the presence of oxygen and glucose or other oxidizable substrate.[79, 89] It is markedly increased by a relatively high concentration of potassium[79, 89] which also, as mentioned, affects respiration and glycolysis. Brain slices, and retina, lose potassium to the medium on incubation unless the medium contains glucose and l-glutamate. When both glutamate and glucose are present, glutamate and potassium are concentrated in the tissue in considerably greater concentration than in the medium. The combustion of glucose seems necessary to provide energy for the maintenance of tissue potassium against diffusion, and glutamate seems to be the anion corresponding to the potassium since glutamate and potassium are taken up in approximately equivalent concentrations.[101]

A rapid fall in phosphocreatine and an increase in organic phosphate occurs post mortem, but this is reversed in brain cortex slices when they are incubated in the presence of oxygen and glucose or glutamate.[81] Since the function of respiration is largely to produce high-energy phosphate compounds, this observation is in accord with current concepts.

Brain cortex slices, suspended in saline medium, swell appreciably unless protein osmotic pressure is provided as in serum.[29] The swelling is considerably more marked under anaerobic conditions[99] which is in accordance with the belief that the energy-yielding processes of respiration are required to maintain normal permeability. Such observations are relevant to the problem of cerebral edema.

Work *in vitro* and *in vivo* in the field discussed has in general provided mutually confirmatory or interlocking information. We may feel that final conclusions concerning many biologic phenomena can only be reached on the basis of studies on the living animal, but there is no doubt that *in vitro* studies, which are so much more easily controlled, can fairly reliably serve as pathfinders.

REFERENCES

1. ALBAUM, H. G.; TEPPERMAN, J.; and BODANSKY, O.: *Journal of Biological Chemistry,* 1946, 164, p. 45.
2. ALT, H. L.: *Biochemische Zeitschrift,* 1930, 221, p. 498.
3. ASHFORD, C. A., and DIXON, K. C.: *Biochemical Journal,* 1935, 29, p. 157.
4. BAKER, Z.: *Biochemical Journal,* 1938, 32, p. 332.
5. BAKER, Z.; FAZEKAS, J. F.; and HIMWICH, H. E.: *Journal of Biological Chemistry,* 1938, 125, p. 545.
6. BARKER, S. B.; SHORR, E.; and MALAM, M.: *Journal of Biological Chemistry,* 1939, 129, p. 33.
7. BERNHEIM, F., and BERNHEIM, M. L. C.: *Journal of Biological Chemistry,* 1941, 138, p. 501; 140, p. 441.
8. BERNHEIM, F.; BERNHEIM, M. L. C.; and MICHEL, H. O.: *Journal of Pharmacology and Experimental Therapeutics,* 1937, 61, p. 311.
9. BIRMINGHAM, M. K., and ELLIOTT, K. A. C.: *Journal of Biological Chemistry,* in press.
10. BROOKS, V. B.; RANSMEIER, R. E.; and GERARD, R. W.: *American Journal of Physiology,* 1949, 157, p. 299.
11. BROPHY, D., and McEACHERN, D.: *Proceedings of the Society for Experimental Biology and Medicine,* 1949, 70, p. 120.
12. BUMM, E.; APPEL, H.; and COUCIERO, P.: *Zeitschrift Physiologische Chemie.* 1933, 220, p. 186.
13. CHESLER, A., and HIMWICH, H. E.: *American Journal of Physiology,* 1944, 142, p. 541.
14. COHEN, R. A., and GERARD, R. W.: *Journal of Cellular and Comparative Physiology,* 1937, 10, p. 223.
15. CRISMON, J. M., and FIELD, J., 2nd: *American Journal of Physiology,* 1940. 130, p. 231.
16. DICKENS, F.: *Biochemical Journal,* 1934, 28, p. 537.
17. DICKENS, F.: *Biochemical Journal,* 1936, 30, p. 1064.
18. DICKENS, F.: *Biochemical Journal,* 1936, 30, p. 1233.
19. DICKENS, F.: *Biochemical Journal,* 1939, 33, p. 2017.
20. DICKENS, F.: *Biochemical Journal,* 1946, 40, p. 145.
21. DICKENS, F., and GREVILLE, G. D.: *Biochemical Journal,* 1933, 27, p. 1134.
22. DICKENS, F., and GREVILLE, G. D.: *Biochemical Journal,* 1933, 27, p. 832.
23. DICKENS, F., and GREVILLE, G. D.: *Biochemical Journal,* 1935, 29, p. 1468.
24. DICKENS, F., and SIMER, F.: *Biochemical Journal,* 1929, 23, p. 936.
25. DIXON, K. C.: *Journal of Physiology,* 1949, 110, p. 87.
26. DIXON, M., and ELLIOTT, K. A. C.: *Biochemical Journal,* 1929, 23, p. 812.
27. DIXON, T. F., and MAYER, A.: *Biochemical Journal,* 1936, 30, p. 1577.
28. DODDS, E. C., and GREVILLE, G. D.: *Nature,* 1933, 132, p. 966.
29. ELLIOTT, K. A. C.: *Proceedings of the Society for Experimental Biology and Medicine,* 1946, 63, p. 234.
30. ELLIOTT, K. A. C., and BAKER, Z.: *Biochemical Journal,* 1935, 29, p. 2396.
31. ELLIOTT, K. A. C., and BIRMINGHAM, M. K.: *Journal of Biological Chemistry,* 1949, 177, p. 51.
32. ELLIOTT, K. A. C.; GRIEG, M. E.; and BENOY, M. P.: *Biochemical Journal,* 1937, 31, p. 1003.
33. ELLIOTT, K. A. C., and HENDERSON, N.: *Journal of Neurophysiology,* 1945, 11, p. 473.

34. ELLIOTT, K. A. C., and HENRY, M.: *Journal of Biological Chemistry*, 1946, 163, p. 351.
35. ELLIOTT, K. A. C., and HENRY, M.: *Journal of Biological Chemistry*, 1946, 163, p. 361.
36. ELLIOTT, K. A. C., and LIBET, B.: *Journal of Biological Chemistry*, 1942, 143, p. 227.
37. ELLIOTT, K. A. C., and LIBET, B.: *Journal of Biological Chemistry*, 1944, 152, p. 617.
38. ELLIOTT, K. A. C.; SCOTT, D. B. M.; and LIBET, B.: *Journal of Biological Chemistry*, 1942, 146, p. 251.
39. EISENBERG, E.; GORDON, G. S.; and ELLIOTT, H. W.: *Science*, 1949, 109, p. 337; *Federation Proceedings*, 1950, 9, p. 269.
40. FAZEKAS, J. F.; ALEXANDER, F. A. D.; and HIMWICH, H. E.: *American Journal of Physiology*, 1941, 134, p. 281.
41. FAZEKAS, J. F., and HIMWICH, H. E.: *American Journal of Physiology*, 1943, 139, p. 366.
42. FIELD, J., 2nd; FUHRMAN, F. A.; and MARTIN, A. W.: *Journal of Neurophysiology*, 1944, 7, p. 117.
43. FUHRMAN, F. A., and FIELD, J., 2nd: *Journal of Cellular and Comparative Physiology*, 1942, 19, p. 351; *Journal of Pharmacology*, 1943, 77, p. 229.
44. GEIGER, A., and MAGNES, J.: *American Journal of Physiology*, 1947, 149, p. 517.
45. GIBBS, E. L.; LENNOX, W. G.; NIMS, L. F.; and GIBBS, F. A.: *Journal of Biological Chemistry*, 1942, 144, p. 325.
46. GORDON, G. S., and ELLIOTT, H. W.: *Endocrinology*, 1947, 41, p. 517.
47. GORDON, J. J., and QUASTEL, J. H.: *Biochemical Journal*, 1948, 42, p. 337.
48. GRENELL, R. G., and DAVIES, P. W.: *Federation Proceedings*, 1950, 9, p. 52.
49. GREVILLE, G. D.: *Biochemical Journal*, 1936, 30, p. 877.
50. GURDJIAN, E. S.; STONE, W. E.; and WEBSTER, J. E.: *Archives Neurology and Psychiatry*, 1944, 51, p. 472.
51. HIMWICH, H. E.; BAKER, Z.; and FAZEKAS, J. F.: *American Journal of Physiology*, 1939, 125, p. 601.
52. HIMWICH, H. E.; BERNSTEIN, A. O.; HERRLICH, H.; CHESLER, A.; and FAZEKAS, J. F.: *American Journal of Physiology*, 1942, 135, p. 387.
53. HIMWICH, H. E.; BOWMAN, K. M.; GOLDFARB, W.; and FAZEKAS, J. F.: *Science*, 1939, 90, p. 398.
54. HIMWICH, H. E., and FAZEKAS, J. F.: *American Journal of Physiology*, 1941, 132, p. 454.
55. HIMWICH, W. A.; HOMBERGER, E.; MARESCA, R.; and HIMWICH, H. E.: *American Journal of Psychiatry*, 1947, 103, p. 685.
56. HOLLINGER, N.; FUHRMAN, F. A.; LEWIS, J. J.; and FIELD, J.: *Journal of Cellular and Comparative Physiology*, 1949, 33, p. 223.
57. JOWETT, M.: *Journal of Physiology*, 1938, 92, p. 322.
58. JOWETT, M., and QUASTEL, J. H.: *Biochemical Journal*, 1937, 31, p. 275.
59. JOWETT, M., and QUASTEL, J. H.: *Biochemical Journal*, 1937, 31, p. 565.
60. KERR, S. E., and GHANTUS, M.: *Journal of Biological Chemistry*, 1936, 116, p. 9.
61. KETY, S. S.: *American Journal of Medicine*, 1950, 8, p. 205.
62. KETY, S. S.; LUKENS, F. D.; WOODFORD, R. B.; HARMEL, M. H.; FREYHAN, F. A.; and SCHMIDT, C. F.: *Federation Proceedings*, 1948, 7, p. 64.

63. KETY, S. S.; POLIS, B. D.; NALDER, C. S.; and SCHMIDT, C. F.: *Journal of Clinical Investigation*, 1948, 27, p. 500.

64. KETY, S. S., and SCHMIDT, C. F.: *Journal of Clinical Investigation*, 1948, 27, p. 476.

65. KETY, S. S., and SCHMIDT, C. F.: *Journal of Clinical Investigation*, 1948, 27, p. 484.

66. KETY, S. S.; WOODFORD, R. B.; HARMEL, M. H.; FREYHAN, F. A.; APPEL, K. E.; and SCHMIDT, C. F.: *The American Journal of Psychiatry*, 1948, 104, p. 765.

67. KLEIBER, J.: *Physiological Review*, 1947, 27, p. 511.

68. KLEIN, J. R.; HURVITZ, R.; and OLSEN, N. S.: *Journal of Biological Chemistry*, 1946, 164, p. 509; 1947, 167, p. 1.

69. KLEIN, J. R., and OLSEN, N. S.: *Journal of Biological Chemistry*, 1947. 167, p. 747.

70. KREBS, H. A.: *Biochimica Biophysica Acta*, 1950, 4, p. 249.

71. KREBS, H. A., and JOHNSON, W. A.: *Tabulae Biologicae*, 1948, 19 Part 3, p. 100.

72. KREBS, H. A., and ROSENHAGEN, H.: *Zeitschrift Gesamte Neurologie*, 1931, 134, p. 643.

73. LOEBEL, R. O.: *Biochemische Zeitschrift*, 1925, 161, p. 219.

74. LONG, C.: *Biochemical Journal*, 1938, 32, p. 1711.

75. MADDOCK, S.; HAWKINS, J., JR.; and HOLMES, E.: *American Journal of Physiology*, 1939, 125, p. 551.

76. MANN, F. C., and MAGATH, T. B.: *Archives of Internal Medicine*, 1922, 30, p. 171.

77. MANN, P. J. G., and QUASTEL, J. H.: *Nature*, 1939, 144, p. 943.

78. MANN, P. J. G., and QUASTEL, J. H.: *Biochemical Journal*, 1946, 40, p. 139.

79. MANN, P. J. G.; TENNENBAUM, M.; and QUASTEL, J. H.: *Biochemical Journal*, 1939, 33, p. 822.

80. MAYER-GROSS, W., and WALKER, J. W.: *Biochemical Journal*, 1949, 44, p. 92.

81. McILWAIN, H., and CHESHIRE, J. D.: *Biochemical Journal*, 1950, 47, xviii.

82. MEYERHOF, O.: *Archives of Biochemistry*, 1947, 13, p. 485.

83. NIMS, L. F.; GIBBS, E. L.; and LENNOX, W. G.: *Journal of Biological Chemistry*, 1942, 145, p. 189.

84. O'BRIEN, J. R., and PETERS, R. A.: *Journal of Physiology*, 1935, 85, p. 454.

85. OLSEN, N. S., and KLEIN, J. R.: *Journal of Biological Chemistry*, 1947, 167, p. 739.

86. PEISS, C. N., and FIELD, J.: *Journal of Biological Chemistry*, 1948, 175, p. 49.

87. PETERS, R. A.: *The Lancet*, 1936, 1161; *Chemistry and Industry*, 1940, 59, p. 373.

88. PUGH, C. E. M., and QUASTEL, J. H.: *Biochemical Journal*, 1937, 31, p. 286 and p. 2306.

89. QUASTEL, J. H.; TENNENBAUM, M.; and WHEATLEY, A. H. M.: *Biochemical Journal*, 1936, 30, p. 1668.

90. QUASTEL, J. H., and WHEATLEY, A. H. M.: *Biochemical Journal*, 1932, 26, p. 725.

91. QUASTEL, J. H., and WHEATLEY, A. H. M.: *Proceedings of the Royal Society, London*, B, 1932, 112, p. 60.

92. QUASTEL, J. H., and WHEATLEY, A. H. M.: *Biochemical Journal*, 1933, 27, p. 1609; 1934, 28, p. 1521.

93. QUASTEL, J. H., and WHEATLEY, A. H. M.: *Biochemical Journal*, 1934, 28, p. 1521.

94. REMOND, A.; DAVIES, P. W.; and BRONK, D. W.: *Federation Proceedings*, 1946, 5, p. 86.

95. RICHTER, D., and DAWSON, R. M. C.: *American Journal of Physiology*, 1948, 154, p. 73.

96. ROSENTHAL, O.: *Biochemie Zeitschrift*, 1929, 207, p. 263; 1929, 211, p. 295; 1930, 227, p. 354; 1931, 233, p. 62; 1932, 244, p. 133.

97. SCHMIDT, C. F.; KETY, S. S.; and PENNES, H. H.: *American Journal of Physiology*, 1945, 143, p. 33.

98. STADIE, W. C.; RIGGS, B. C.; and HAUGAARD, N.: *Journal of Biological Chemistry*, 1945, 160, p. 191.

99. STERN, J. R.; EGGLESTON, L. V.; HEMS, R.; and KREBS, H. A.: *Biochemical Journal*, 1949, 44, p. 410.

100. STONE, W. E.; WEBSTER, J. E.; and GURDJIAN, E. S.: *Journal of Neurophysiology*, 1945, 8, p. 233.

101. TERNER, C.; EGGLESTON, L. V.; and KREBS, H. A.: *Biochemical Journal*, 1950, 47, p. 139.

102. TYLER, D. B.: *Proceedings of the Society for Experimental Biology and Medicine*, 1942, 49, p. 537.

103. TYLER, D. B.: *Journal of Biological Chemistry*, 1950, 184, p. 711.

104. VAN HEYNINGEN, W. E.: *Biochemical Journal*, 1935, 29, p. 2036.

105. WARBURG, O.: *Biochemische Zeitschrift*, 1923, 142, p. 317.

106. WEBB, J. L., and ELLIOTT, K. A. C.: *Journal of Pharmacology and Experimental Therapeutics*, 1951, 103, p. 24.

107. WEBB, J. L., and ELLIOTT, K. A. C.: *Canadian Journal of Research E*, 1948, 26, p. 239.

108. WEIL-MALHERBE, H.: *Biochemical Journal*, 1936, 30, p. 665.

109. WEIL-MALHERBE, H.: *Biochemical Journal*, 1938, 32, p. 2257.

110. WOLLENBERGER, A.: *Federation Proceedings*, 1950, 9, p. 326; *Journal of Pharmacology and Experimental Therapeutics*, 1949, 97 Part 2, p. 311, and personal communication.

111. WORTIS, J.; BOWMAN, K. M.; GOLDFARB, W.; FAZEKAS, J. F.; and HIMWICH, H. E.: *Journal of Neurophysiology*, 1941, 4, p. 243.

112. WRIGHT, C. I., and SABINE, J. C.: *Journal of Biological Chemistry*, 1944, 155, p. 315.

113. YOUNG, L.: *Journal of Biological Chemistry*, 1937, 120, p. 659.

Metabolism of Cell-free Brain Preparations

EFRAIM RACKER, M.D.

Dr. Elliott has given us a broad survey of the metabolic properties of brain cells *in vitro*. In most of these studies the structure of the cells has been preserved as much as possible. In our laboratory we have been concerned with changes in brain metabolism which occur when the brain cell structure is disrupted by treatment with distilled water. We have only one excuse for such a barbaric procedure: we wanted to study the metabolism of certain phosphorylated intermediates in the brain. Some of these compounds which are produced as normal metabolites within the cell are not utilized when added to a brain slice *in vitro* because they do not readily penetrate the cell membrane. In our studies on water homogenates of brain, we have made a number of observations of which I have chosen two for this discussion. I feel they may be of interest not only to brain biochemists but also to those who are interested in brain perfusion and, perhaps, even to those who are interested in brain confusion.

If we take a brain, e.g., from a mouse, and grind it up in distilled water, glucose utilization completely ceases. This is not due to loss of enzymes but rather to liberation of enzymes which are capable of destroying coenzymes.

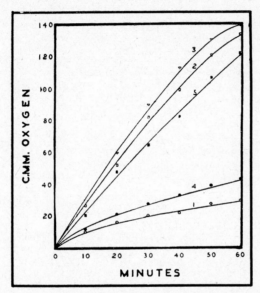

Fig. 6. Effect of sodium and phosphocreatine on oxygen uptake by brain homogenates. Curve 1, no glucose; Curve 2, 0.024 M glucose; Curve 3, 0.024 M glucose plus 0.0055 M phosphocreatine; Curve 4, 0.024 M glucose plus 0.08 M NaCl; Curve 5, 0.024 M glucose, 0.08 M NaCl plus 0.0055 M phosphocreatine. (This figure was published in the *Journal of Biological Chemistry*, 1945, 161. p. 459.)

In addition, there occurs a striking change with respect to the effect of certain ions on glycolysis. While the intact cells are very well able to metabolize glucose in the presence of sodium ions, which do not permeate too readily into the cells, the disrupted brain cells show a remarkable sensitivity to sodium ions. In order to obtain actively glycolyzing homogenates, we must replace the sodium salts by potassium salts and we have to add the coenzymes diphosphopyridine nucleotide and adenosine triphosphate in excess. In fact, in such a system, glycolysis proceeds ten to twenty times as rapidly as in brain slices.[3] However, on addition of only 0.08 M sodium chloride to the brain homogenate, glucose utilization is inhibited 80 to 90 per cent. As shown in Figure 6 the sodium inhibition can be reversed by the addition of phosphocreatine, indicating that the sodium ions inhibit the phosphorylation mechanism. A similar inhibitory effect of sodium ions had been observed a number of years previously by Ohlmeyer and Ochoa[2] in studies on fermenting yeast extracts. The brain system appears to be particularly sensitive to sodium ions and I wonder whether I might propose in speculation that in certain pathologic conditions or, even, in the state of narcosis, an altered permeability of the brain cells to sodium ions might be found which might increase their entrance into the cells and lead to a marked disturbance of the phosphorylation process.

The second observation which I would like to discuss concerns another ion, namely, the ferrous ion. Our work originally started with a study of the effect of certain neurotropic viruses on brain glycolysis. We found that mice infected with the Lansing strain of poliomyelitis and particularly those infected with the Theiler FA strain of mouse encephalomyelitis show an impairment of brain glycolysis. In analyzing this phenomenon we found that one particular glycolytic enzyme, triose phosphate dehydrogenase, was affected. Then we found that we could imitate the behavior of an infected brain by incubating a normal brain homogenate at 38° C. with a few micrograms of ferrous sulfate for about 20 minutes prior to the addition of the coenzymes.

TABLE 9.   RESTORATION OF BRAIN GLYCOLYSIS BY
TRIOSE PHOSPHATE DEHYDROGENASE

Experiment No.	Brain Preparation	Addition	Lactic Acid Produced (Micrograms)
1	Normal mouse brain homogenate	—	2100
2	Normal mouse brain homogenate + ferrous sulfate	—	350
3	Normal mouse brain homogenate + ferrous sulfate	Triose phosphate dehydrogenase	2100
4	Theiler FA infected brain homogenate	—	600
5	Theiler FA infected brain homogenate	Triose phosphate dehydrogenase	2600

What is responsible for the effect of the virus or the effect of the iron salt? Our studies have shown that ferrous sulfate activates a "proteolytic" enzyme present in normal brain which, in turn, inactivates triose phosphate dehydrogenase. As shown in Table 9, we can fully restore glycolytic activity to an infected brain homogenate or an iron inactivated homogenate by adding crystalline triose phosphate dehydrogenase—the enzyme which is inactivated.[4] We have recently found that a small molecular substance, namely, glutathione, can act as a substrate for the iron activated "proteolytic" enzyme.

We have speculated on the significance of these findings. We feel that these observations, although obtained with disrupted brain cells, may shed light on the infectious process. We may be wrong, of course, but we are going to test the hypothesis. As shown in Table 10, we have found several small molecular peptides and amino acid derivatives which inhibit *in vitro*

TABLE 10. PROTECTIVE EFFECT OF PHENYL GLYCINE ETHYL ESTER
ON BRAIN GLYCOLYSIS

Tissue Preparation	Addition	Lactic Acid Produced (Micrograms)
Brain homogenate	—	2000
Brain homogenate	Phenyl glycine* ethyl ester	2000
Brain homogenate + ferrous sulfate	—	700
Brain homogenate + ferrous sulfate	Phenyl glycine ethyl ester	1800

* Other compounds such as leucine amide, leucine ethyl ester, cysteine ethyl ester, phenylglycine, amide, and glutathione similarly protect the glycolytic activity in the presence of ferrous sulfate.

the "proteolytic" enzyme in brain.[1] However, so far, none of them readily pass the blood-brain barrier. If we can find one which is a good inhibitor of the "proteolytic" enzyme and, at the same time is nontoxic for mice and can penetrate the blood-brain barrier, we shall proceed with *in vivo* experiments. We hope, incidentally, besides finding support for our hypothesis, to find a protective effect of these peptides against the neuron destruction which occurs during this virus infection.

REFERENCES

1. KRIMSKY, I., and RACKER, E.: *Journal of Biological Chemistry*, 1949, 179, p. 903.
2. OHLMEYER, P., and OCHOA, S.: *Biochemische Zeitschrift*, 1937, 293, p. 338.
3. RACKER, E., and KRIMSKY, I.: *Journal of Biological Chemistry*, 1945, 161, p. 453.
4. RACKER, E., and KRIMSKY, I.: *Journal of Biological Chemistry*, 1948, 173, p. 519.

CHAPTER 6

Oxidation and Reduction in Brain Tissue

ERIC G. BALL, PH.D.

AT THE OUTSET it should be made clear that the title assigned to my address is somewhat misleading. What I shall present to you is an outline of the underlying pattern or theme that seems to run through nearly all biological oxidations. Most of this information has been obtained on tissues other than brain. We have no reason to believe that brain deviates in any significant way from the general pattern of biological oxidations.

We may conveniently divide all biological oxidations into three fundamental types of reactions: (1) dehydrogenations, (2) decarboxylations, and (3) conversions or condensations. To illustrate, let us follow the oxidation pathway of lactic acid. The over-all reaction for the oxidation of lactic acid may be written:

$$C_3H_6O_3 + 3O_2 \rightarrow 3CO_2 + 3H_2O \tag{1}.$$

Now, biologically the first step in its oxidation is a dehydrogenation, thus:

$$CH_3 \cdot CHOH \cdot COOH + A \rightarrow CH_3CO \cdot COOH + AH_2 \tag{2}.$$

Two hydrogens are removed and transferred to a compound which we may call for the moment an acceptor (A). These two hydrogens eventually are handed over to oxygen to form the water of equation (1). We will return to this aspect of biological oxidations later. Our attention now is focused on the product formed from lactic acid, namely, pyruvic acid. This product now undergoes the second type of reaction on our list, decarboxylation, which we may write here as follows:

$$CH_3CO \cdot COOH \rightarrow CH_3CHO + CO_2 \tag{3}.$$

This type of reaction is responsible for the production of all the CO_2 that originates from oxidative processes in the body. Oxygen is not involved directly in its production as equation (1) might imply.

The other product of decarboxylation of pyruvate is acetaldehyde. It in turn is now due to be dehydrogenated. This, however, cannot occur in the living cell before it undergoes the third of our fundamental types of reaction,

74

a conversion. In the case of acetaldehyde it may be represented as the addition of water, thus:

$$CH_3CHO + H_2O \rightarrow CH_3 \cdot \overset{\displaystyle OH}{\underset{\displaystyle OH}{\overset{|}{\underset{|}{C}}}}-H \qquad (4).$$

or of phosphate

$$CH_3CHO + H\overset{=}{PO_4} \rightarrow CH_3 \cdot \overset{\displaystyle OH}{\underset{\displaystyle O\overset{=}{PO_3}}{\overset{|}{\underset{|}{C}}}}-H \qquad (5).$$

Now the removal of two hydrogens becomes possible biologically and dehydrogenation may be represented as occurring as follows:

$$CH_3 \cdot \overset{\displaystyle OH}{\underset{\displaystyle OH}{\overset{|}{\underset{|}{C}}}}-H + A \rightarrow CH_3 \cdot \overset{\displaystyle O}{\overset{||}{C}}-OH + H_2A \qquad (6).$$

We have now gone full circle and have begun the second cycle of these three basic reactions.

How fundamental this basic pattern is to biological oxidations is perhaps best seen by the fate of a molecule like acetic acid, the product of equation (6). The living cell has apparently devised no way to degrade a two-carbon compound directly to CO_2 and water by the steps just outlined. The fate of all two-carbon residues, whether they come from sugar, fat, or protein appears to be the same. They are fed into a metabolic cycle, often called the Krebs citric acid cycle, in which the first step is the condensation of the two-carbon particle with a four-carbon compound, oxalacetate, to form citrate. The citrate undergoes the changes shown in outline in Figure 7. In essence what occurs is a series of reactions of the three basic types just discussed which lead to the complete breakdown of the two-carbon particles with regeneration of the oxalacetate. The conversion reactions are represented as occurring with water though phosphate may be involved. The dehydrogenation reactions are represented as yielding H_2 though this is symbolic only and an acceptor is, of course, involved. Thus the citric acid cycle may be said to consist of four dehydrogenation reactions, two decarboxylations, and at least four reactions of the conversion type. The oxalacetate which is regenerated serves as a cyclic chain reactor, though it is of interest to note that pyruvate and CO_2 may condense to furnish a supply of this compound.

This then is the basic pattern of reactions which centers around the breakdown of all foodstuffs to water and carbon dioxide. Involved in these reactions are a multitude of enzymes and coenzymes. Yet the net energy to be gained by the cell from these reactions is small. These reactions serve principally to furnish the fuel for energy production, namely, the hydrogen removed by the acceptor in equation (2).

Let us therefore now turn our attention to the fate of this hydogen removed from the foodstuffs by the process of dehydrogenation. The chief acceptor A of equation (2) in the living cell is one of the two pyridine nucleotides, diphosphopyridine nucleotide or triphosphopyridine nucleotide. By accepting hydrogen these compounds become reduced and there thus starts a cycle of oxidation-reduction reactions involving a series of

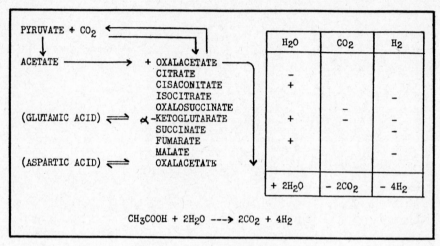

Fig. 7.   The citric acid cycle.

compounds, each in turn becoming reduced until the last one, which reacts directly with O_2, produces H_2O. This series of oxidation and reduction reactions yields the cell most of its energy. Unfortunately we are not too certain about the number or nature of the compounds involved in this series of reactions. Our latest views may be summarized by the diagram in Figure 8. In this diagram, for the purposes of simplification, a flow of hydrogen from foodstuff to oxygen is represented. What actually happens is a flow of electrons with hydrogen ions accompanying them only in certain instances. This group of compounds then may be labeled as an electron transmitter system, and with the passage of electrons from compound to compound a voltage drop may be said to occur at each step. This voltage drop may be calculated in certain cases where the oxidation-reduction potentials of the participating systems are known and the energy release estimated. This aspect of the subject has been treated elsewhere[1] and need not be elaborated upon here.

It should be noted that in this diagram the pathway of hydrogen from succinate, a component of the citric acid cycle (Fig. 7), is different from that of most of the foodstuffs. This is a new finding made by Slater[5] and confirmed in our laboratories. Previously cytochrome b has been included in both pathways for lack of more specific information to the contrary. It now begins to appear more clearly that cytochrome b is specifically involved in the oxidation of succinate to fumarate and that the succinate-fumarate system with its relatively high oxidation-reduction potential requires a pathway initially different from those more negative systems which react through the pyridine nucleotides.

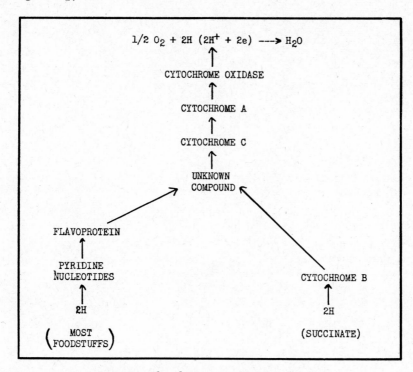

FIG. 8.   The electron transmitter system.

Some unknown compound appears to lie at the crossroads gearing both branches to cytochrome c and the remainder of the iron-containing cyto-chrome compounds. Evidence for the existence of such a compound stems largely from inhibition studies made in a variety of laboratories.[2, 4, 6]

At this point several questions probably arise in your minds. One could be: Why is such a large series of compounds needed to pass along electrons from foodstuff to oxygen? Would not one suffice? A possible answer is that by a scheme of this sort the cell obtains its energy in more convenient units, a little at each step instead of in one large parcel as might occur if only one compound were involved. It is known that the energy released in this electron transmitter system can appear in the form of high energy phosphate bonds whose formation requires 12,000 to 14,000 calories and that some 25,000 calories can be released for each electron passing through the system.[1]

One might also ask why so much uncertainty exists concerning the identity of the components of this system and their participation in various electron transfers. The answer lies in the physical nature of this electron transmitter system. With the exception of the pyridine nucleotides, all the components of this system are bound together into a complex which cannot be obtained in true solution. It is localized in the mitochondria of the cell. One can obtain what may be called dispersions of this complex which can be subjected to some purification as we have done with heart muscle.[3] Such purified dispersions are turbid and the complex can be thrown down by high speed centrifugation (25,000 g.). Analysis of the dark brown precipitates of the complex so obtained from heart muscle preparations show that some 38 per cent of the dry weight is lipid material. An analysis of the lipid material obtained by extraction of this complex has been made with the aid of Dr. Gerhard Schmidt. The results indicate that this electron transmitter system is composed of about 12 per cent lecithin, 15 to 17 per cent cephalin, and 2 per cent cholesterol. Several analyses performed by Dr. Folch-Pi indicate that inositol is present and also a lipid protein of the type described by him as occurring in brain. If we assume that the proteins in the complex have a molecular weight of around 100,000 and the lipids 800, then we may calculate that we are dealing largely with a complex of enzymes and phospholipids in which there are 75 to 100 molecules of lipid for each enzyme molecule.

The function of the lipids in this complex is unknown. Whether they play any part in the transfer of electrons or generation of high energy phosphate bonds remains to be determined. One may speculate that their only function is to cement together a group of enzymes which must react with one another and whose spatial fixations in juxtaposition results in a more efficient role for each of them. I prefer to imagine that these phospholipids play a more active role and that the elucidation of this role may help us to a better understanding of their function in brain tissue where they are so abundant.

A marked change in the physical state of this electron transmitter complex may be obtained by its treatment with 2 per cent solutions of desoxycholate. Turbid dispersions are transformed into transparent reddish solutions from which the complex can no longer be precipitated by high-speed centrifugation. It would appear that this result is achieved by a reaction of the bile salt with the phospholipids. Enzymatic activity can still be demonstrated in preparations so treated. Moreover, quantitative spectroscopic observations may now be made on the changes occurring in the components of the complex as they are subjected to reductions. Figures 9 and 10 contain such data. Figure 9 shows absorption spectra obtained in the visible region. The

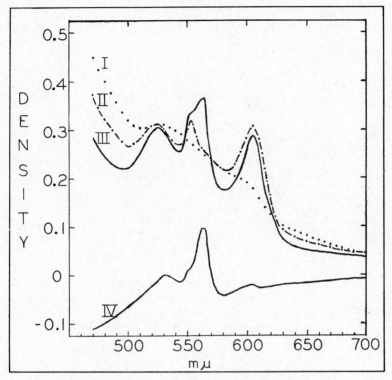

Fig. 9.   Absorption spectra of the electron transmitter system in the
visible region.

The heart muscle preparation described by Ball and Cooper[3] was centrifuged
at 25,000 g. for 1 hour at 4° C., the precipitate homogenized in a 2 per cent
solution of desoxycholate in 0.05 M glycylglycine buffer, pH 7.4, and recentri-
fuged. The supernatant fluid was employed for these studies. Spectra were determined with a Beckman Quartz Spectrophotometer, Model DU, slit width 0.02 mm.,
light path 1 cm. A special cell consisting of a Thunberg tube sealed to an optical
cell was employed. All spectra of the reduced forms were carried out in an atmosphere of purified nitrogen. Curve I—Oxidized form in the presence of air. Curve
II—Reduced by the addition of sodium ascorbate. Curve III—Reduced by the
addition of $Na_2S_2O_4$. Curve IV—Curve III minus Curve II.

effect of the addition of ascorbic acid to the preparation is shown by Curve
II of this figure. Ascorbic acid causes the appearance of the reduced band
of cytochrome a at 605 mμ and of cytochrome c at about 551 and 520 mμ.
The addition of a strong reducing agent, $Na_2S_2O_4$, brings out not only the
reduced bands of cytochromes a and c, but also that of cytochrome b at 563
mμ (Curve III). Subtraction of Curve II from Curve III yields Curve IV,
the reduced band of cytochrome b. It should also be noted that Curve IV
indicates that $Na_2S_2O_4$ has caused a diminution of absorption in the region
of 470 to 530 mμ. This is suggestive that a flavo-protein with a maximum

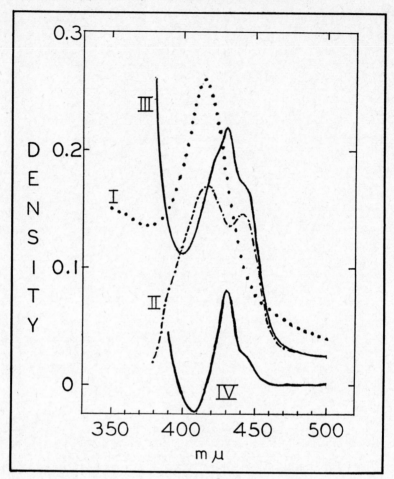

FIG. 10.   Absorption spectra of the electron transmitter system in the ultraviolet region.

The same preparation was employed as described for Figure 9 except that it was diluted 1:10. Curve I—Oxidized form in the presence of air. Curve II—Reduced by the addition of sodium ascorbate. Curve III—Reduced by the addition of $Na_2S_2O_4$. Curve IV—Curve III minus Curve II.

absorption at 450 mμ in the oxidized state has been converted to the leuco form.

The spectra observed in the ultraviolet are shown in Figure 10. The reduced bands of cytochromes a, b, and c in this region are located at 441, 430, and 415 mμ respectively.

If other reducing agents are employed, one obtains variations of these basic spectra. For example, ferrocyanide causes the appearance of only a portion of the cytochrome a band. Succinate reduces cytochromes a and c completely, but causes only about half of the cytochrome b band to appear. Reduced diphosphopyridine nucleotide will produce spectra similar to those given by the addition of ascorbic acid. It is from studies such as these that the pathway of interactions given in Figure 8 has been deduced, and we shall probably not be entirely certain of the sequence of reactions of this pathway until the various components involved in it can be isolated from this enzyme-lipid complex.

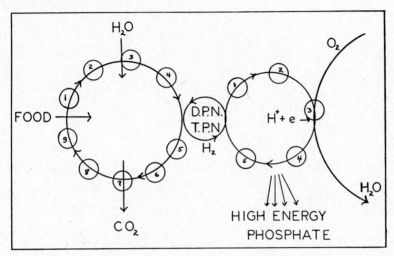

FIG. 11.   Schematic representation of biologic oxidation and energy production.

To summarize our present concept of the pattern of biological oxidations we may represent the chain of events diagrammatically as shown in Figure 11. The series of reactions involving dehydrogenation, decarboxylation, and conversion may be represented by the large circle on the left of this figure. The foodstuffs enter this cycle and by a series of reactions which may involve the addition of water or phosphate they yield hydrogen to the pyridine nucleotides and produce CO_2. The pyridine nucleotides act as water-soluble conveyers of the hydrogen atom and are geared into the electron transmitter system represented by the circle on the right. This cycle is the power plant of the cell. It converts the hydrogen removed from the foodstuffs to water and furnishes energy in the form of phosphate compounds. These compounds may be looked upon as the transmission lines of the power plant which serve to carry energy to all parts of the cell.

REFERENCES

1. BALL, E. G.: Annals of the New York Academy of Sciences, 1944, p. 363.
2. BALL, E. G.; ANFINSEN, C. B.; and COOPER, O.: Journal of Biological Chemistry, 1947, 168, p. 257.

3. BALL, E. G., and COOPER, O.: *Journal of Biological Chemistry*, 1949, 180, p. 113.
4. SLATER, E. C.: *Biochemical Journal*, 1949, 45, p. 14.
5. SLATER, E. C.: *Biochemical Journal*, 1950, 46, p. 484.
6. STRAUB, F. B.: *Zeitschrift für physiologische Chemie*, 1942, 272, p. 219.

Analgesics and the Adrenal Cortex

FREDERICK BERNHEIM, PH.D.

Dr. Ball and Dr. Elliott have mentioned phospholipids and I would like to take that subject a little further and describe some reactions we have been interested in.

In the brain, and to a lesser extent in other tissues, there is a non-enzymic oxidation of linolenic acid which is combined in the phospholipid molecule. This oxidation, as Dr. Elliott pointed out, is catalyzed by ascorbic acid. In the brains of scorbutic guinea pigs the oxidation is greatly depressed. The oxidation involves peroxide formation on the double bond furthest from the carboxyl group, and this peroxide reacts with thiobarbituric acid to produce a stable red color which can be estimated. Since the reagent gives a color with a few gamma of the peroxide, the formation of the latter in the brain would not be detected in over-all measurements of respiratory quotients.

If an animal is injected for a few days with either ACTH or cortisone the peroxide formation in brain is increased two to three times. This indicates that the peroxide formation is regulated by adrenal cortical hormones and gives a possible reason why when they are released from the adrenal cortex ascorbic acid is released at the same time. Injections of ascorbic acid alone are without effect.

If morphine, meperidine, or methadone is injected into the animal for a few days the peroxide formation in the brain is also increased. This does not, however, occur in hypophysectomized animals. This observation suggests that these three drugs cause a release of ACTH from the hypophysis.

Other analgesic drugs such as codeine, acetanilide, and acetylsalicylic acid as well as barbiturates are without effect. These drugs, unlike the first group, produce no euphoria. The general clinical impression is that cortisone-treated patients become euphoric with the exception of certain psychotics whose psychoses may become exacerbated. It may be, therefore, that the euphoria produced by morphine and its substitutes is the result of cortisone release by these drugs through stimulation of the hypophysis.

The peroxide formation occurs in mitochondria and nuclei. Since these structures contain a number of important enzymes, their activity may in some way be affected by the number of peroxide linkages present and thus come under the influence of the adrenal cortical hormones.

DR. EFRAIM RACKER: Dr. Ball, have you investigated the effect of lipases on these tissue particle preparations?

DR. ERIC G. BALL: I am glad you asked that question, because I meant to mention the fact that Dr. McFarlane has recently published in the *Biochemical Journal*, 1950, 47, p. xxix, an abstract in which it is reported that the succinate oxidase activity of rabbit liver mitochondria is inhibited by *Clostridium welchii* lecithinase. Similar studies with lipase and lecithinase are planned on the heart muscle preparation whose lipid composition I have described here.

CHAPTER 7

Carbohydrate Metabolism in Brain Tissue

OTTO MEYERHOF, M.D.

IF WE APPLY our study of tissue preparations, be it tissue slices, tissue pulp, homogenates, or enzyme extracts, to the metabolism of the living cell, we must be aware of the limitations of these methods. Even in tissue slices the milieu plays an important role, and the influence of hormones can be demonstrated only in a few cases. In the homogenates, if they are made according to the technic of Potter and Elvehjem,[18] the single enzymes and coenzymes are released, and without proper adjustments, the steady state of the reaction sequence in the living cell is lost. Finally, in the enzyme extract, we deal exclusively with the extractable or water-soluble enzymes. In spite of these limitations much is to be learned from such studies about the turnover of the living cell.

From the studies of tissue slices, introduced by Otto Warburg,[23] three types of tissues were found which had a high anaerobic glycolysis—that is, lactic acid formation from sugar in the absence of air: first, growing tissue; secondly, cells and tissues able to move or do mechanical work, like muscle, spermatozoa, and leukocytes; thirdly, nervous tissue, like brain or retina.

In the meantime we have learned much about the intimate mechanism of these glycolytic reactions by disentangling the intermediary steps, the various enzyme and coenzyme systems of these steps, and the energy relationships. From these data, we know, for instance, that in the case of oxygen want, the anaerobic reactions can temporarily substitute for oxidation in supplying energy. This is established for growing cells, for the work in muscle, and for nerves in the conduction of nerve impulses.

Abbreviations used in this chapter: ATP=adenosine triphosphate; ADP=adenosine diphosphate; AMP=adenosine monophosphate; HDP=hexose diphosphate; DPN= diphosphopyridine nucleotide or cozymase.

The work on which this chapter was based was supported by the American Cancer Society; recommended by the Committee on Growth of the National Research Council; the Division of Research Grants and Fellowships of the National Institutes of Health; United States Public Health Service; the David, Josephine and Winfield Baird Foundation; and the Rockefeller Foundation.

We know also that in the anaerobic as well as in aerobic conditions, the energy of the oxidative steps, or more accurately of the "oxidation-reduction steps," is collected in the high energy phosphate bond of adenosinetriphosphate (ATP). In the case that this energy is not immediately used, it can be stored in other high energy bonds, especially phosphocreatine.[9] This is present in large amounts in muscle, in the electric organs of fishes, and also in brain and nerve. Especially the investigations of Nachmansohn and Machado have shown that the choline acetylase which synthesizes acetylcholine needs ATP which is replenished from the store of phosphocreatine.[16, 17] Undoubtedly, phosphocreatine has a similar role in all these cases.

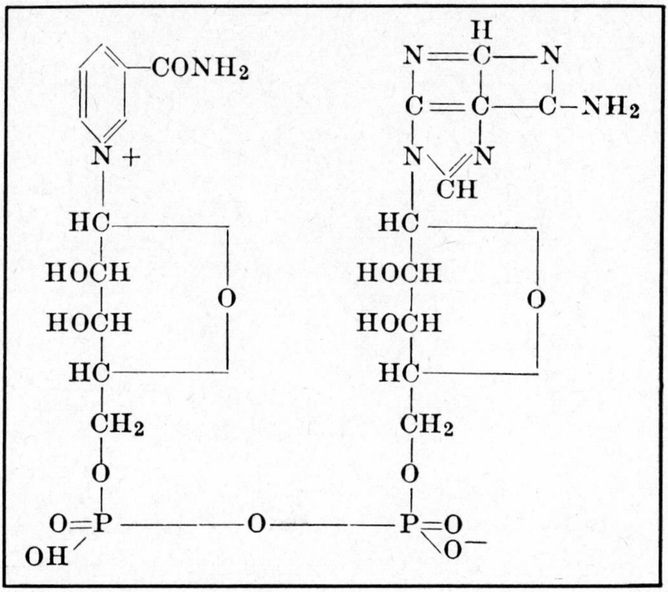

FIG. 12.   Diphosphopyridine nucleotide or cozymase. The nucleosidase of brain splits between the N^+ of the nicotinamide and ribose. The DPN pyrophosphatase of Kornberg present in most organs splits the oxygen bridge connecting the two phosphate groups.

For analyzing the metabolic reactions in detail we have to disintegrate the tissue, and from these tissue preparations we can obtain the enzymes, the coenzymes, or the intermediaries of metabolism if we use suitable methods of separation, or inhibition, or interception by means of special interfering substances. In this way the three organic coenzyme systems were isolated: the oxidation-reduction coenzyme, DPN or cozymase; the phosphorylating coenzyme system, or adenylic system; and the decarboxylating coenzyme, cocarboxylase or thiamine diphosphate. The first one was cleared up chemically by Otto Warburg;[24] the latter two were discovered in my former laboratory in Heidelberg by Lohmann.[5, 7] The importance of these coenzyme systems for the metabolism of brain need not be stressed. All three contain vitamins or vitamin-like substances: nicotinamide, adenylic acid, and thiamine.

I will restrict myself here to the description of one single line of attack, that is, to find out the conditions for a steady rate of glycolysis in brain homogenates and extracts, and the relation of this glycolysis to that of the living brain tissue. To achieve this the intactness of the two coenzyme systems, the pyridine nucleotide and the adenylic systems, play overwhelmingly important roles.

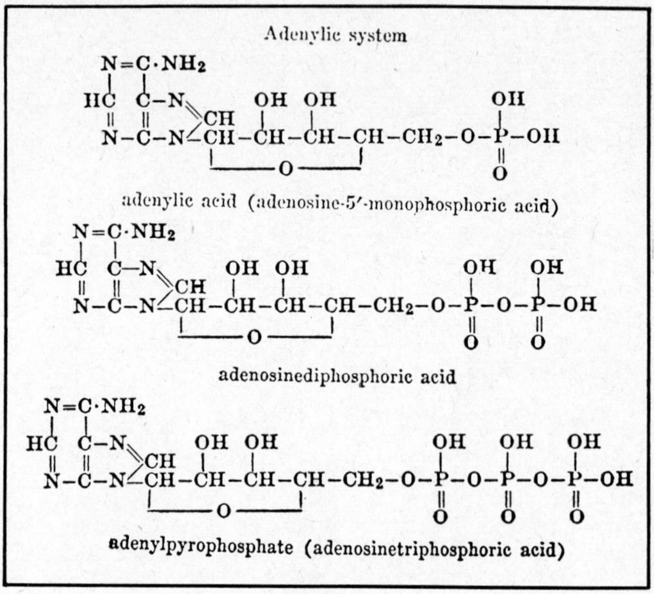

FIG. 13.   Adenylic system.

Not long ago some of our colleagues still spoke of so-called "nonphosphorylating glycolysis" which should go on in various organs including the brain. This idea was purely one of imagination, not demonstrated in a single case. This term, for a nonexisting type of reaction, was based exclusively on negative evidence, that is, the inability of these workers to obtain the same enzymatic reactions in brain extracts as were known and demonstrated in muscle extracts. Besides some other reasons, the apparent inactivity of these extracts stems from the rapid decomposition of the two named coenzyme systems. With regard to DPN, it was first shown by Mann and Quastel[8] and later by Handler and Klein[2] that the brain contained a powerful DPN nucleosidase by which nicotinamide is split off from cozymase (Fig. 12).

For preventing the splitting, one has to add relatively high concentrations of nicotinamide, about 1/30 to 1/50 M, to a brain extract. Some years later

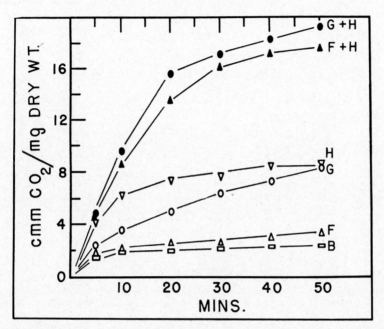

Fig. 14. Glycolysis in complete homogenate with glucose and fructose, with and without HDP addition. Three-tenths cc. homogenate (15 mg. dry weight) in 1.2 cc. total volume in each sample. △ H=HDP with 450 γ hexose (112 mm. 3CO₂), which can give in maximo 7.5 mm.3/mg. dry weight. ○G=glucose (4 mg.), △F=fructose (4 mg.), □B=blank, ●G+H and ▼F+H=mixtures of 4 mg. glucose or fructose with 450 γ hexose of HDP. (*Archives of Biochemistry*, 1948, 17, p. 153, Fig. 3, p. 159.)

```
        (ATP-ase)
1.   ATP ——————→ ADP + phosphate

        (Myokinase)
2.   2 ADP ————→ATP + AMP (adenylic acid)

        (ADP-ase)
3.   ADP ——————→  AMP + phosphate

4.   AMP ——————→ adenosine + phosphate

        (Deaminase)
5.   AMP ——————→ inosinic acid + NH₂
```

Fig. 15.   Enzymatic breakdown of ATP.

Dr. Kornberg[4] discovered a DPN pyrophosphatase by which the splitting occurs between the two phosphates; here nicotinamide mononucleotide is obtained. However, in the brain the other reaction prevails, while in the kidney Kornberg's enzyme is more important.

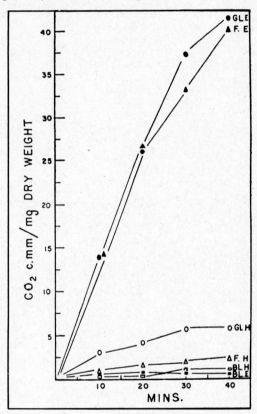

FIG. 16.   Glycolysis in complete homogenate (H) and, after centrifuging, in extract (E). Homogenate frozen and thawed. Volume 0.75 cc. containing 0.2 cc. homogenate or extract (1:3) with Ca-free Ringer, bicarbonate and MgSO₄, nicotinamide to 0.6 per cent final concentration. Five one-hundredths cc. hexo-sediphosphate (20 γ P); 2 minutes before start 0.05 coz. (0.3 mg. DPN), 0.05 cc. ATP (30 γ 7-min.P) 0.05 cc. isoton. bicarbonate tipped in. ■Bl. E and □Bl. H. Blank of extract and homogenate. ●Gl. E. and ○Gl. H. 3 mg. glucose in extract and in homogenate. ▲F. E. and △F. H. 3 mg. fructose in extract and in homogenate. (*Archives of Biochemistry*, 1947, 12, p. 405, Fig. 2, p. 411.)

Preservation of DPN is only half of the picture. The other half is the necessity to keep the phosphorylating and the dephosphorylating reactions in step so that the various components of the adenylic system are simultaneously present (Fig. 13).

Before I studied in 1946 the dependence of glycolysis on the activity of the phosphorylating and dephosphorylating enzymes[11] on brain extract and homogenate, Utter, Wood, and Reiner[22] had already the year before obtained a relatively steady glycolysis with water homogenate of brain. However, they did not start with glucose alone but with a mixture of glucose and hexose diphosphate. The latter not only contributed itself to the lactic acid formation but it increased the yield from glucose. Figure 14 shows an experiment from brain homogenate from my own series.[13]

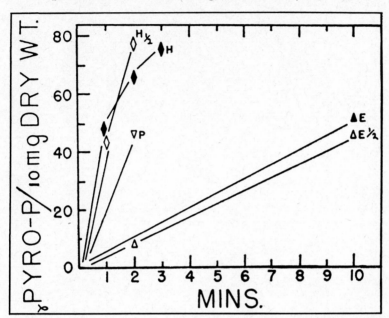

Fig. 17. Activity of apyrase in homogenate (H), centrifuged extract (E), and washed particles (P). Three-tenths cc. or 0.15 cc. Ringer-homogenate or extract or 0.3 cc. particles washed in Ringer solution are used. Two tenths cc. ATP with 90 γ pyro-P added in the beginning. Total volume 0.8 cc. Ordinate pyro-P split off, determined as difference between 7-min. P and direct P. The dry weight refers to the amount of tissue taken, not to the amount in solution 38° C. H ♦ 0.3 cc. homogenate; H½ ◊0.15 cc. homogenate. E ▲ 0.3 cc. extract from this homogenate; E½ △0.15 cc. extract. P ▽0.3 cc. particles filled, after washing, to the original volume of the homogenate. (*Archives of Biochemistry,* 1947, 14, p. 71, Fig. 1, p. 73.)

In it may be seen the results with the blank, glucose, and fructose alone; to the difference of both, I shall return later. Addition of HDP to glucose or fructose produces higher values than the sum of each single substance. This fact is easily explained by a sparing action of HDP on the adenylic system: HDP can react further without ATP while glucose needs two mols of ATP to attain the phosphorylated stage of HDP.

For preserving the adenylic system, phosphocreatine still is much more effective than HDP. With addition of phosphocreatine one can indeed increase the rate of glycolysis in brain homogenates about eight times. We must remember that the living brain contains phosphocreatine in about double to fourfold the amount of ATP on a molecular basis, and that this phosphocreatine is always completely broken down in homogenates and extracts of brain. The reason for such strong effects of phosphate donors on the glycolytic rates in homogenates is the great excess of dephosphorylating enzymes, and principally ATP-ase in the homogenate. The various reactions which occur here are shown in Figure 15.

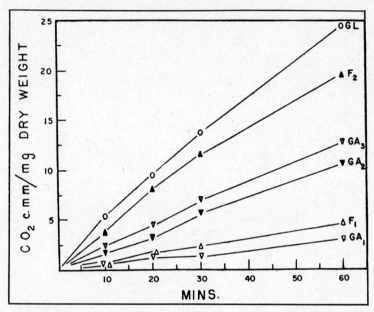

Fig. 18.   Glycolysis in slices of transplanted sarcoma (Gl. 32). Volume 2 cc.; dry weight 3 to 6 mg.; 5 per cent CO_2 in N_2. ○Gl. 4 mg. glucose, △F_1 4 mg. fructose, ▲F_2 190 mg. fructose. ▽Ga_1 4 mg. galactose, ▲Ga_2 48 mg. galactose, ▽ Ga_3 96 mg. galactose. (*Archives of Biochemistry*, 1947, 12, p. 405, Fig. 1, p. 409.)

The last two of the enzymes presented in the figure are of a special importance because they irreversibly destroy the adenylic system as phosphorylating coenzyme. On the other hand, the first three reactions can be reversed by phosphorylating steps of glycolysis by which the ATP is brought back into circulation.

Figure 16 shows what happens when one uses not a mixture of sugar and phosphate donor but sugar alone either in homogenate or extract.

The astounding difference one obtains by centrifuging out the particulate matter and using an enzymatic extract stems from the removal of ATP-ase. Nine-tenths of the ATP-ase is firmly bound to the particles as shown in Figure 17.[12] By removal of this excess ATP-ase the adenylic system is preserved, and the glycolysis obtained is several times higher than that of living brain tissue. Utter has recently confirmed this result and has also investigated the influence of ions. In my laboratory we use mostly a calcium-free Ringer solution to which magnesium is added in place of calcium, besides some NH_4 ions. If sodium is completely left out and only potassium and magnesium used as cations then the result is quantitatively changed. According to Utter, the ATP-ase is less active in potassium than in sodium, and, on the other hand, the transphosphorylating enzymes are activated.[21] In this way the very great difference between the homogenate and extract would become somewhat smaller but the general outcome still would be the same.

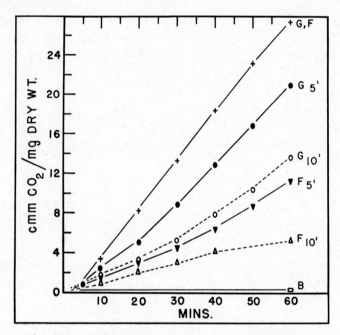

Fig. 19. Glycolysis of glucose and fructose in centrifuged extract with different times of centrifugation (4500 r.p.m.). +G,F=glucose and fructose with optimal amount of ATP (50 γ pyro-P/cc.). ●G₅, and ▼F₅,=glucose and fructose with 5 min. centrifuged extract, 5 γ pyro-P/cc. ○G₁₀, and △F₁₀,=glucose and fructose with 10 min. centrifuged extract, 5 γ pyro-P/cc. □B=blank. Ordinate: mg. dry weight, referring to the tissue from which the extract is made, not to the actual dry weight in the extract. (*Archives of Biochemistry*, 1948, 17, p. 153, Fig. 1, p. 157.)

Now I come to another aspect of these experiments which clearly shows that from the study of these enzyme systems we learn much about the processes going on in the living tissues. This is the problem of the different reactivity of the various sugars. It has already been known for a long time that in most animal tissues, especially in brain and malignant tumor, the rate of glycolysis of glucose is practically independent of concentration but that the rate for fructose in normal concentration, 0.2 per cent, is only about one-tenth of that of glucose. If, however, this concentration is raised, one obtains values which can approach the glucose values.[1] These results shown in Figure 18 were obtained from my own experiments.[11]

These data are from a malignant tumor but the results with brain although less regular would be similar. From the studies with enzyme extracts of brain it can be shown that this difference between fructose and

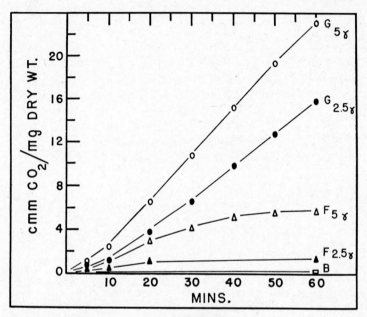

Fig. 20.   Glycolysis of glucose and fructose with very low ATP concentrations. All samples contain 0.95 cc. total volume, 0.3 cc. extract (1 part tissue to 3.3 parts modified Ringer solution), 1×10^{-2} M glutathione, 0.3×10^{-2} M NaHCO₃, 5×10^{-3} M phosphate, 0.3 mg. DPN, HDP with 7 γ P and 2 mg. sugar.

B $\qquad$ □ Blank
$G_{5\gamma}$ $\qquad$ O———O 1 mg. glucose 5γ pyro-P of ATP.
$F_{5\gamma}$ $\qquad$ △———△ 1 mg. fructose 5γ pyro-P of ATP.
$G_{2.5\gamma}$ $\qquad$ ●———● 1 mg. glucose 2.5γ pyro-P of ATP.
$F_{2.5\gamma}$ $\qquad$ ▼———▼ 1 mg. fructose 2.5γ pyro-P of ATP.
(*Archives of Biochemistry*, 1947, 13, p. 485, Fig. 1, p. 486.)

glucose stems from the low affinity of fructose for ATP in the presence of the enzyme hexokinase. If the concentration of ATP and sugar is high enough there is no difference in rate. If one of them, either ATP or sugar, is considerably lowered, the rate of glucose phosphorylation remains nearly the same, but the rate of fructose phosphorylation is appreciably less. In the homogenate, the ATP concentration decreases very much on account of ATP-ase. As a result of this glucose reacts, although not maximally, but several times faster than does fructose. If, however, ATP is pre-

TABLE 11. HEXOKINASE IN BRAIN
μmoles per 1.3 cc: 2.2 ATP, 12 min. 3.8° C.

ADDED SUGAR		P-transfer (7' P decrease)	Sugar (decrease)
Glucose	22.2	1.62	
Fructose	22.2	1.88	
Glucose	1.7	1.78	1.30
Fructose	1.7	0.85	0.66

served either by adding it continuously or by using phosphocreatine as P donor, the difference between both sugars nearly disappears. On the other hand, in the centrifuged extract of brain with an optimal amount of ATP, about 10^{-3} M, the difference disappears. If in such an extract we lower the added ATP ten times of that which is normally used, that is to 10^{-4} M, then the difference reappears again. This is shown in Figures 19 and 20, the former presenting the results from different times of centrifugation,[13] and the latter, from different amounts of ATP (γ pyro P per 1 cc.).[10]

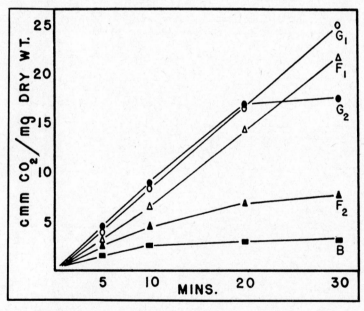

FIG. 21. Glycolysis in centrifuged extract. Three tenths cc. extract, 1:4.6 in 1.5 cc. total volume containing the sugar as well as a trace of HDP (17 γ P) as primer. (For G_2 and F_2 0.3 cc. and 0.2 cc. extract gave nearly identical points.) One-tenth cc. cozymase (0.3 mg. DPN), 0.1 cc. ATP (35 γ pyro-P), 0.05 cc. isotonic sodium bicarbonate is tipped in from the side arm at the start. B=blank, G_1 and F_1=3 mg. glucose and 3 mg. fructose, respectively. G_2 and F_2=0.6 mg. glucose and 0.6 mg. fructose, respectively. (*Archives of Biochemistry* 1948, 19, p. 502, Fig. 1, p. 504.)

The same can also be demonstrated if the ATP concentration remains at 10^{-3} M but the sugar concentration is much lower. This is shown in Table 11 from an experiment published in 1948.[14] With 0.3 per cent glucose and fructose the phosphate transfer, that is, the formation of hexose monophosphate, is the same. If, however, the concentration of the sugar is lowered twelve times to 0.020 per cent then a difference appears in

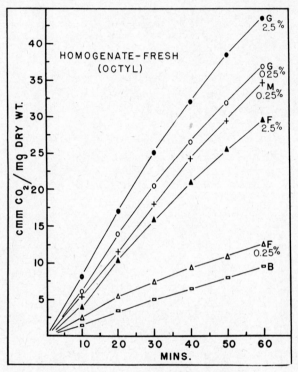

FIG. 22. Glycolysis of various sugars in the homogenate of fresh tumor in the presence of octyl alcohol. B=blank; G=glucose; M=mannose; F=fructose; GA= galactose. The curve for 2.5 per cent mannose, not drawn, nearly coincides with that of 2.5 per cent glucose. (*Archives of Biochemistry*, 1949, 21, p. 1, Fig. 7, p. 16.)

which phosphate is transferred to glucose at the same speed as at high concentration, but to fructose only half as much. The same can be seen by the sugar decrease.

Results from a quite similar experiment, in which the corresponding rates of glycolysis are measured, are shown in Figure 21. With normal glucose and fructose concentration (0.2 per cent) in brain extract, there is practically no difference in speed. If the concentration is, however, lowered to 0.04 per cent, glucose is glycolyzed until exhaustion with the same speed as with the five times higher concentration. Fructose, however, is glycolyzed with less than a third of this speed. Finally, I may say that mannose behaves like glucose (Figure 22). Although homogenate of malignant tumor was used instead of brain, the relative rates of sugar and the effect of concentrations are quite similar.[15] However, a new device was used to inhibit the excess of ATP-ase by octylalcohol which has no effect on all other glycolytic enzymes. Twenty-five one-hundredths per cent glucose and 0.25 per cent mannose give practically the same value, but 0.25 per cent fructose gives a very low value, very little more than the blank. If we increase the concentration of fructose ten times, it approaches the speed of the other sugars. Increase of the concentration of glucose has also in this instance some effect but a very small one.

```
          (Hexokinase (yeast, brain))
1. glucose + ATP ──→ glucose-6-phosphate + ADP
2. fructose + ATP ──→ fructose-6-phosphate + ADP

          (Fructokinase (muscle, liver))
3. fructose + ATP ──→ fructose-1-phosphate + ADP

          (Phosphohexoisomerase)
4. glucose-6-phosphate ⇌ fructose-6-phosphate

          (Phosphohexokinase (=phosphofructokinase))
5. fructose-1-phosphate + ATP ──→ HDP + ADP
   fructose-6-phosphate + ATP ──→ HDP + ADP
```

FIG. 23.   Diagram of evidence indicating existence of only one brain hexokinase.

These experiments show definitely that the affinity of fructose for ATP in the presence of hexokinase is much smaller than that of glucose but the experiments do not answer directly the question whether there are two different kinases concerned, glucokinase and fructokinase, as described by Cori and Slein for liver and muscle. From my experiments the question of their existence in brain remained open although I had never found an additive effect of simultaneous addition of glucose and fructose.

Recent experiments by Quastel and Harpur[3] and more detailed ones by Slein and Cori[20] have given a definite answer to this question. Quastel and co-worker have found that glucosamine, glucose, and fructose compete with each other in the presence of brain hexokinase which speaks in favor of only one brain hexokinase. Quite recently Cori and co-workers have conclusively shown that in contrast to liver and muscle, brain has only one hexokinase. This enzyme, as was already discussed by me, has a much lower affinity to fructose than glucose in the presence of ATP. Moreover, the first product of phosphorylation is fructose-6-phosphate, while with fructokinase it is fructose-1-phosphate. The whole situation is summed up in Figure 23: In yeast and brain we have the same hexokinase, which forms the hexose-6-phosphates, and in muscle and liver there is a special fructokinase forming fructose-1-phosphate.

The next step for the further reaction of the hexose monophosphates is the isomerization by an enzyme demonstrated by Lohmann[6] (phosphohexose isomerase), and finally the phosphorylation of fructose-6-phosphate or fructose-1-phosphate by a phosphohexokinase to the same HDP. According to Slein and Cori there are two different enzymes concerned: one which reacts with fructose-6-phosphate and the other which reacts with fructose-1-phosphate.[20] The same would also hold if the initial sugar would be mannose which Slein[19] has shown would first form mannose-6-phosphate and, by a phosphomannoisomerase, come into an equilibrium with glucose-6-phosphate from where the normal HDP would arise.

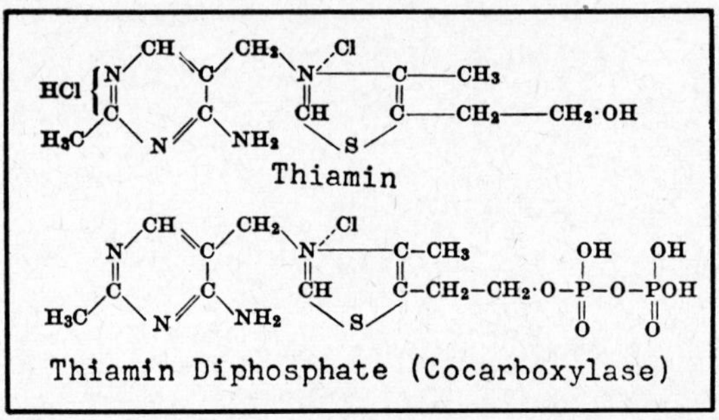

Fig. 24.   Formulae for thiamine and thiamine diphosphate.

Now we can see that with some precautions we may very well apply these findings to the living cell. The fact that fructose has a much lower affinity to ATP with the hexokinase of brain than does glucose allows us to conclude that the low reactivity of the fructose in the living brain must be caused by a low-acting concentration of ATP. As Cori and co-worker have mentioned in their paper, it is quite apparent that the inability of fructose to relieve the hypoglycemic shock, while mannose can accomplish this, is caused by the same mechanism. It seems also to follow that phosphocreatine, which *in vitro* can abolish the difference between glucose and fructose by raising the ATP concentration, has *in vivo* no detectable influence on the relative rates of both sugars. This could be explained in various ways.

I have restricted myself to this one point: that we can learn something about the rate of sugar utilization in brain by studying the reaction rate of the sugars in the presence of ATP and hexokinase. If there would have been more time, other enzymatic studies could be quoted for the same purpose. Indeed, ATP was discovered in muscle extract as phosphorylating coenzyme. The reactive form of vitamin B_1 in the living nervous tissue was discovered by Lohmann and Schuster[7] in studies with washed out yeast where it was shown that cocarboxylase was thiamine diphosphate (Figure 24).

REFERENCES

1. BOYLAND, E., and BOYLAND, M. E.: *Biochemical Journal,* 1938, 32, p. 321.
2. HANDLER, P., and KLEIN, T. R.: *Journal of Biological Chemistry,* 1942, 143, p. 49.
3. HARPUR, R. P., and QUASTEL, J. H.: *Nature,* 1949, 164, p. 693.
4. KORNBERG, A.: *Journal of Biological Chemistry,* 1950, 182, p. 779.
5. LOHMANN, K.: *Naturwiss,* 1929, 17, p. 624.
6. LOHMANN, K.: *Biochemische Zeitschrift,* 1933, 262, p. 137.
7. LOHMANN, K., and SCHUSTER, PH.: *Naturwiss,* 1937, 28, p. 26.
8. MANN, P. J. G., and QUASTEL, J. H.: *Biochemical Journal,* 1941, 35, p. 502.
9. MEYERHOF, O.: *Biological Symposia* III, 1941, p. 239, Jacques Cattell Press.
10. MEYERHOF, O.: *Archives of Biochemistry,* 1947, 13, p. 485.
11. MEYERHOF, O., and GELIAZKOWA, N.: *Archives of Biochemistry,* 1947, 12, p. 405.
12. MEYERHOF, O., and WILSON, J. R.: *Archives of Biochemistry,* 1947, 14, p. 73.
13. MEYERHOF, O., and WILSON, J. R.: *Archives of Biochemistry,* 1947, 17, p. 153.
14. MEYERHOF, O., and WILSON, J. R.: *Archives of Biochemistry,* 1948, 19, p. 502.
15. MEYERHOF, O., and WILSON, J. R.: *Archives of Biochemistry,* 1949, 21, p. 1.
16. NACHMANSOHN, D.; COX, R. T.; COATES, C. W.; and MACHADO, A. L.: *Journal of Neurophysiology,* 1943, 6, p. 383.
17. NACHMANSOHN, D., and MACHADO, A. L.: *Journal of Neurophysiology,* 1943, 6, p. 397.
18. POTTER, V. R., and ELVEHJEM, C. A.: *Journal of Biological Chemistry,* 1936, 114, p. 495.
19. SLEIN, M. W.: *Journal of Biological Chemistry,* 1950, 186, p. 753.
20. SLEIN, M. W.; CORI, G. T.; and CORI, C. F.: *Journal of Biological Chemistry,* 1950, 186, p. 763.
21. UTTER, M. F.: *Journal of Biological Chemistry,* 1950, 185, p. 499.
22. UTTER, M. F.; WOOD, H. G.; and REINER, J. M.: *Journal of Biological Chemistry,* 1945, 161, p. 197.
23. WARBURG, O.: Stoffwechsel der Tumoren. Berlin, Springer, 1926.
24. WARBURG, O., and CHRISTIAN, W.: *Biochemische Zeitschrift,* 1936, 287, p. 391.

Pyruvate Oxidation in Brain

SEVERO OCHOA, M.D.

The points which I want to discuss refer mainly to the oxidative metabolism of the brain. I feel I should offer an apology for the fact that most of the work I am going to outline was performed over ten years ago when I was in Professor R. A. Peters' laboratory in Oxford.

At the outset I must emphasize the fact that the energy metabolism of the brain does not differ significantly from that of any other tissue. However, it so happens that some of the characteristics of the pyruvate oxidation system in animal tissues were first studied in Oxford using brain as the experimental tissue.[9]

When pyruvate is added to homogenates of pigeon brain, prepared by grinding with ice-cold isotonic potassium chloride or phosphate buffer, a large uptake of oxygen is obtained. Under these conditions some of the

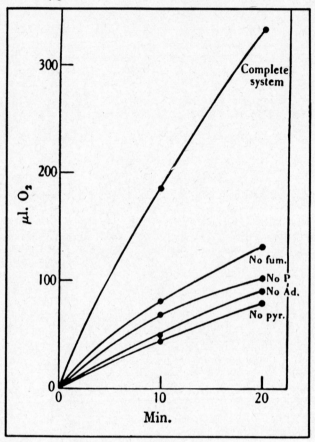

FIG. 25.   Effect of phosphate (0.05 M), fumarate (0.005 M), and adenylic acid (0.00014 M) on the oxidation of pyruvate by dialyzed homogenates of normal pigeon brain. One and five tenths cc. of enzyme (dialyzed 2 hours) to 2.0 cc. with additions including 0.1 mg. of $MgCl_2$. The complete system contained enzyme+$MgCl_2$+phosphate (P)+fumarate (fum.)+adenylic acid (Ad.)+pyruvate (pyr.). The brain homogenate contained optimal amounts of diphospho-thiamine. Incubation in air at 38° C. (From Ochoa, S.: Cocarboxylase. The Biological Action of the Vitamins. Chicago, University of Chicago Press, 1942.)

pyruvate disappears by oxidation to carbon dioxide and water according to the equation $CH_3—CO—COOH+2.5\ O_2=3\ CO_2+2\ H_2O$. If the homogenates are dialyzed for a few hours against a large volume of isotonic KCl, their capacity to oxidize pyruvate disappears almost completely but it can be restored by the addition of the following substances: inorganic phosphate, a magnesium salt, small amounts of a dicarboxylic acid such as fumaric, malic, or oxalacetic acid, and small amounts of an adenine nucleotide such as muscle adenylic acid or adenosine triphosphate (ATP). These facts[1] are illustrated in Fig 25. The blank oxygen uptake, i.e., the uptake in the absence of added pyruvate, is due to the fact that the homogenates contain some glycogen which gives rise to pyruvate by glycolysis.

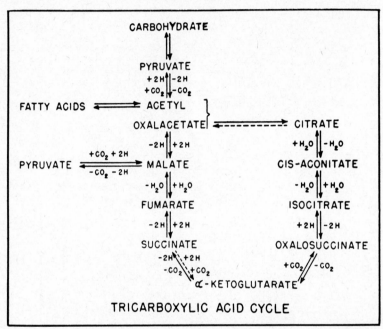

FIG. 26. Tricarboxylic acid cycle. (From Ochoa, S.: *Physiological Reviews,* 1951, 31, p. 56.)

There is good evidence[7] that oxidation of pyruvate in brain, as well as in many other tissues, proceeds by way of the tricarboxylic acid cycle of Krebs illustrated in Figure 26. Oxidation via the tricarboxylic acid cycle explains why a dicarboxylic acid is needed for oxidation of pyruvate in brain. The condensing enzyme, which is responsible for the catalysis of the key reaction of the cycle, i.e., the condensation of an active acetate derivative (referred to as acetyl in Fig. 26) with oxalacetate to form citrate, has recently been isolated and crystallized in our laboratory.[10] This enzyme is present in high concentrations in brain by comparison with other tissues. The reactions below illustrate the way in which the condensing enzyme was assayed.

(1) Acetate + ATP $\longrightarrow$ "active acetate" + ADP + phosphate (*E. coli* extracts)
(2) "Active acetate" + oxalacetate $\longrightarrow$ citrate (condensing enzyme)

Sum: Acetate + ATP + oxalacetate $\longrightarrow$ citrate + ADP + phosphate

TABLE 12.   CONDENSING ENZYME ACTIVITY IN OX BRAIN AND
KIDNEY EXTRACTS

Additions		Citrate Synthesis
E. coli Extract	Tissue Extract	
+	None	0.0
None	Brain	0.0
+	Brain	64.0
None	Kidney	1.8
+	Kidney	16.0

Incubation, 1 hour at 25° C. Citrate synthesis expressed in
micrograms per milligram of protein in tissue extracts.

An enzyme system present in extracts of *Escherichia coli* forms what may
be referred to as "active acetate" by a reaction between acetate and ATP
(reaction 1). These bacterial preparations form no citrate by themselves
because they contain little or no condensing enzyme, but if supplemented
with tissue extracts containing condensing enzyme, citrate is formed by
reaction between "active acetate" and oxalacetate (reaction 2). Data on the
condensing enzyme content of brain and kidney extracts, obtained as outlined above, are given in Table 12. The data show that, per milligram of

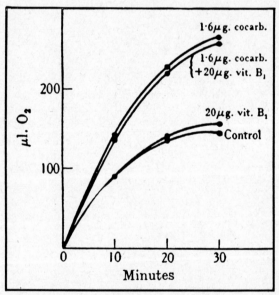

FIG. 27.   Comparison of the effects of thiamine (vitamin B_1) and diphosphothiamine (cocarboxylase) on the oxidation of pyruvate in homogenates of brain
from thiamine-deficient pigeons. Incubation in air at 38° C. (From Ochoa, S.:
Cocarboxylase. The Biological Action of the Vitamins. Chicago, University of
Chicago Press, 1942.)

protein, brain contains about four times more condensing enzyme than does kidney. Most other tissues, with the exception of heart muscle and pigeon breast muscle, contain less condensing enzyme than does brain.

The role of thiamine in biologic oxidations was first established for brain by the pioneering work of Peters and his associates at Oxford.[9] In 1936 the Oxford investigators observed that certain preparations of brain from thia-

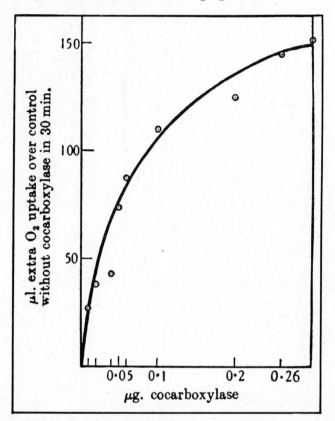

Fig. 28. Effect of increasing concentrations of diphosphothiamine (cocarboxylase) on the rate of pyruvate oxidation in homogenates of brain from thiamine-deficient pigeons. Incubation in oxygen at 38° C. (From Ochoa, S.: Cocarboxylase. The Biological Action of the Vitamins. Chicago, University of Chicago Press, 1942.)

mine-deficient pigeons were almost unable to oxidize pyruvate, but this compound was oxidized as rapidly as by normal brain when a few micrograms of thiamine were added. In 1937, cocarboxylase, the coenzyme needed for the decarboxylation of pyruvate by yeast carboxylase, was isolated by Lohmann in Meyerhof's laboratory[4] and proved to be a pyrophosphoric ester of thiamine. Cocarboxylase will be referred to in this paper as diphosphothiamine. By means of a specific enzymatic method for the separate determination of thiamine and diphosphothiamine Peters and I[8] found that brain, as most other tissues, contained diphosphothiamine but little or no thiamine. This was a strong indication that diphosphothiamine, and not thiamine, was the coenzyme required for the oxidation of pyruvate by animal tissues, an indication which was amply confirmed by subsequent experiments.

With homogenates of brain from thiamine-deficient pigeons we found that the oxidation of pyruvate was markedly stimulated by diphosphothiamine while there was little or no stimulation by thiamine. Typical results[2] are illustrated in Figure 27. Figure 28 shows the dependence of the rate of oxygen uptake, due to pyruvate oxidation in brain homogenates of thiamine-deficient pigeons, on the concentration of added diphosphothiamine.[2] In further experiments it was found that the stimulation of pyruvate oxidation by thiamine, observed with certain brain preparations, was really the result of phosphorylation of thiamine to diphosphothiamine.[2] This is illustrated by the results of the experiment reproduced in Table 13. The pigeon brain homogenate used for this experiment showed some stimulation of pyruvate oxidation by thiamine and marked stimulation by diphosphothiamine. This homogenate was analyzed for diphosphothiamine after incubation with pyruvate and fumarate and either without or with 10 micrograms of thiamine in an atmosphere of oxygen (Table 13, A). The sample incubated without thiamine contained 0.16 micrograms and that incubated with thiamine contained 0.21 micrograms of diphosphothiamine. The difference of

TABLE 13.   PHOSPHORYLATION AND ACTIVITY OF THIAMINE ON PYRUVATE
OXIDATION IN HOMOGENATES FROM BRAIN OF
THIAMINE-DEFICIENT PIGEONS

A	
	Micrograms of Diphosphothiamine
Sample incubated 40 minutes without thiamine	0.16
Sample incubated 40 minutes with 10 micrograms of thiamine	0.21
Diphosphothiamine synthesis	0.05

B		
	Rate of Oxygen Uptake (Cubic Millimeters per Hour Over Control Without Coenzyme)	
Time Period in Minutes	In Sample with 10 μg. of Thiamine	In Sample with 0.05 μg. of Diphosphothiamine
0–10	60	190
10–20	186	130
20–30	100	114

1.5 cc. of undialyzed homogenate (equivalent to 320 mg. of brain) brought to 2.0 cc. with additions including phosphate buffer pH 7.3, pyruvate, and fumarate. Oxygen in the gas phase; temperature, 38° C.

0.05 micrograms corresponds to the amount of diphosphothiamine synthesized by phosphorylation of thiamine during the incubation period. The effect of 10 micrograms of thiamine on the oxidation of pyruvate by another portion of the same brain homogenate was then compared with that of 0.05 micrograms of diphosphothiamine. It may be seen (Table 13, B) that during the first ten minutes the small amount of diphosphothiamine was much more effective than the large amount of thiamine while, owing to the relatively slow phosphorylation of thiamine, the effects became the same as time went on.

In thiamine deficiency the quantity of diphosphothiamine in the tissues is markedly decreased. Administration of thiamine to thiamine-deficient animals leads to a large accumulation of thiamine and a marked increase of diphosphothiamine in the liver within thirty minutes; little increase of either compound occurs in brain, muscle, and heart in this time. However, when polyneuritic pigeons received small daily doses of thiamine for three days, the content of diphosphothiamine of these tissues approached the normal values; whereas, it was well below normal in the liver, as if the other tissues had replenished their diphosphothiamine stores at the expense of the diphosphothiamine previously stored by the liver.[8] The lowest level of diphosphothiamine in pigeon brain (average 0.4 micrograms per gram of tissue) was found in animals with symptoms of acute beriberi; whereas the brain of birds maintained on a diet of polished rice for twenty-five days, but not yet showing symptoms of thiamine deficiency, contained an average of 1.2 micrograms of diphosphothiamine (as against 3.0 micrograms for normal brain). Only the brain of the acutely polyneuritic pigeons shows a decreased capacity to oxidize pyruvate *in vitro*, which is obviously correlated with a decrease of the brain diphosphothiamine below a critical level.[6]

Goodhart and Sinclair[3] showed that diphosphothiamine is present in nucleated blood cells, including nucleated red cells, but is absent from blood plasma, which contains only small amounts of unphosphorylated thiamine. The evidence discussed above indicates that thiamine reaching the blood stream from the intestine is taken up mainly by the liver (and also by the kidney[11]), where it is phosphorylated and stored as diphosphothiamine.[8, 11] All tissues, but mainly the liver and kidney, can dephosphorylate diphosphothiamine and supply free thiamine to the blood; this is transported in the plasma to other tissues, which rephosphorylate it more slowly.[5]

REFERENCES

1. BANGA, I.; OCHOA, S.; and PETERS, R. A.: *Biochemical Journal,* 1939, 33, p. 1980.
2. BANGA, I.; OCHOA, S.; and PETERS, R. A.: *Biochemical Journal,* 1939, 33, p. 1109.

3. GOODHART, R. S., and SINCLAIR, H. M.: *Biochemical Journal*, 1939, 33, p. 1099.
4. LOHMANN, K., and SCHUSTER, P.: *Biochemische Zeitschrift*, 1937, 294, p. 188.
5. OCHOA, S.: *Biochemical Journal*, 1939, 33, p. 1262.
6. OCHOA, S.: COCARBOXYLASE. In: The Biological Action of The Vitamins, edited by E. A. Evans, Jr., Chicago, University of Chicago Press, 1942.
7. OCHOA, S.: *Physiological Reviews*, 1951, 31, p. 56.
8. OCHOA, S., and PETERS, R. A.: *Biochemical Journal*, 1938, 32, 1501.
9. PETERS, R. A.: *Lancet*, 1936, 230, p. 1161.
10. STERN, J. R.; SHAPIRO, B.; and OCHOA, S.: *Nature*, London, 1950, 166, p. 403.
11. WESTENBRINK, H. G. K., and GOUDSMIT: *Enzymologia*, 1938, 5, p. 307.

Discussion

CHAIRMAN CARL F. CORI: Thank you, Dr. Ochoa, for calling our attention once more to the importance of thiamine and diphosphothiamine for brain metabolism.

I think we have a few minutes' time before we leave carbohydrate metabolism —one or two minutes for a few questions that anybody might want to ask.

I myself would like to bring up one point, if I may, that seems important: the well-known fact that pyruvate does not relieve hypoglycemia. If pyruvate does get in, and we have heard that it does, what is there between glucose and pyruvate that keeps the brain in an active state? I wonder whether anyone wishes to talk on this point or has considered the question: Why is glucose essential when pyruvate could, from an energy standpoint, be just as effective as glucose, although it is not equivalent to glucose. We know, of course, all the steps that occur between glucose and pyruvate. Their function is one of the mysteries, I believe.

DR. K. A. C. ELLIOTT: I have a suggestion. Part of the pyruvate which gets in acts as a hydrogen acceptor, and that means that hydrogen atoms or electrons are not passing to quite so large an extent through the cytochrome system. A lot of hydrogen is being accepted by the pyruvate. It was shown that a lot of the pyruvate is reduced to lactate.

CHAIRMAN CARL F. CORI: Isn't it well oxidized?

DR. K. A. C. ELLIOTT: Yes, but you are having simultaneously the pyruvate acting as an acceptor and so competing with the energy-yielding process of electrons passing through cytochrome.

DR. SEVERO OCHOA: Where does the hydrogen come from?

DR. K. A. C. ELLIOTT: Other molecules of pyruvate which are being oxidized.

My point is that quite a lot of the energy that is ordinarily produced in the oxidation of pyruvate is in the passage of the electrons beyond the flavoprotein stage through the cytochrome. When pyruvate, instead of glucose, is the initial substrate, some of the hydrogen is not going that way. It is going to other molecules of pyruvate. Some pyruvate molecules are being oxidized but some are acting as hydrogen acceptors. Further, pyruvate is so rapidly metabolized by other parts of the body that I do not think a concentration sufficient to allow the full rate of brain respiration could be maintained for more than a very short time.

DR. SEVERO OCHOA: I wonder if the explanation of Dr. Cori's question might not be that when pyruvate is given alone it is not well oxidized because of the unavailability of enough dicarboxylic acids. It might be that, when glucose is administered, formation of dicarboxylic acids (which are needed for oxidation of pyruvate via the tricarboxylic acid cycle) is facilitated.

DR. RALPH W. GERARD: Maybe I can settle the discussion and resolve your difficulties by reminding the group that, at least in the perfused spinal cord, pyruvate can restore function in the aglycemic state.

CHAPTER 8

Nitrogen Metabolism in the Brain

HEINRICH B. WAELSCH, M.D.

EVEN BEFORE biochemists had made a serious effort to investigate the nitrogen metabolism of the brain, ammonia and amines played a considerable role in the thinking of psychiatrists interested in the etiology of diseases of the nervous system. The "toxic amine hypothesis" was drawn upon to explain not only convulsive disorders but also a variety of mental disorders. This postulation has served to only a limited degree the main purpose of such hypotheses, namely, to stimulate inquiries into the basic metabolism of nitrogenous compounds of the brain. Such studies started with the development of our general knowledge of intermediary metabolism.

Ammonia in the nervous system, as in any other tissue, will be derived essentially from the following sources: amino acids and proteins, purines and pyrimidines, and their derivatives, and particularly in lipid-rich organs such as the brain, the amino alcohols, ethanolamine, choline, and sphingosine. We have only limited information on the deamination of nucleosides or nucleotides by brain tissue and no information on the degradation of the amino alcohols. Our knowledge of the amino acid metabolism in the central nervous system, though rudimentary, affords a qualitative outline of the role which these compounds may play in transport and utilization of ammonia. The amino acids which occur in the nonprotein fraction are presumably the pool from which the building stones for protein synthesis are drawn and to which they are returned during protein degradation. The free amino acid fraction, which comprises somewhat less than 0.5 per cent of the brain weight, shows an interesting composition. The concentration of free glutamic acid[16] in brain is higher than in any other organ analyzed (Table 14). Glutamic acid comprises about 35 per cent of the α-amino nitrogen of the nonprotein fraction of the brain, and together with glutamine close to 50 per cent. This is true for all animal brains analyzed. In rat brain the nine essential amino acids, together with arginine, proline, and tyrosine, comprise only 7 per cent of the total α-amino nitrogen.[12] Therefore glycine, alanine, serine, oxyproline, cystine, aspartic acid, and peptides must account for about 40 to 45 per cent of this fraction.

106

TABLE 14. GLUTAMIC ACID AND GLUTAMINE CONTENT OF BRAIN, LIVER AND KIDNEY
(*values expressed in mg. per 100 Gm.*)

Tissue	Animal	Glutamic Acid		Glutamine		References
		Mean	Range	Mean	Range	
Brain	Rat (18)	153	133–170	58	48–70	(13)
	Mouse (11)	168	145–180	69	53–82	(13)
	Rabbit (1)	152		45		(18)
	Pigeon (2)	151	138, 165	63	52, 75	(18)
	Pigeon (4)	142	90–205	84	66–103	(8)
	Cat (1)	146		77		(8)
	Sheep g(2)	154	146, 163	55	62, 49	(8)
	Sheep w(2)	90	103, 78	48	48, 49	(8)
	Calf g(1)	128		68		(18)
	Calf w(1)	90		55		(18)
	Dog (1)			64	52–78	(6)
Liver	Rat (15)	49	33–66	55	49–58	(13)
	Mouse (3)	19		35		(13)
	Sheep (3)	85	80–96	24	0–39	(8)
	Cat (1)	42		54		(8)
	Pigeon (3)	88	84–95	55	0–87	(8)
	Pigeon (2)	59	37, 81	31	43, 20	(18)
	Dog			45	47, 43	(6)
Kidney	Rat (18)	96	88–112	22	8–42	(13)
	Mouse (3)	78		10		(13)
	Sheep c(3)	91	71–116	10	0–18	(8)
	Cat c(1)	138		16		(8)
	Sheep m(3)	93	62–104	19	0–31	(8)
	Cat m(1)	78		54		(8)
	Dog			11.3	6.2–11.5	(6)

g, gray matter of brain; w, white matter of brain; c, kidney cortex; m, kidney medulla.
From Waelsch, H.: Advances in Protein Chemistry, Vol. VI, 1951.

The high concentration of glutamic acid and glutamine in the central nervous system is a characteristic of the unmyelinated brain as well as of the fully functioning, myelinated organ. In the rat, myelination of the brain starts between the tenth to twelfth day after birth and approaches completion around the fortieth day of life. The glutamic acid and glutamine concentration of the rat brain stays constant when calculated on dry weight basis from birth through the period of myelination. It appears on the basis of the scanty data on protein content of rat brain during development[16] that the concentration of the two amino acids parallels that of the proteins of the brain (Table 15).

In view of the high concentration of free glutamic acid and glutamine in the brain it is of interest to inquire as to the origin of the two amino acids in this organ. They may be able to penetrate the blood-brain barrier and therefore be supplied by the circulating blood, or one may be derived from the blood and be the source of the other after having been taken up by the brain. There exists also the possibility that the carbon skeleton—ketoglutaric acid—is produced in the main through the citric acid cycle and the ammonia furnished from sources other than the dicarboxylic acid or its amide. In order to contribute to the elucidation of the origin of brain glutamic acid and glutamine, large amounts of the two compounds were injected intravenously into rats and mice, and the brain and other organs analyzed[13] at different time intervals after the administration (Table 16).

TABLE 15.   GLUTAMIC ACID AND GLUTAMINE CONTENT OF PROTEIN-FREE FILTRATES OF RAT BRAIN DURING THE FIRST THIRTY DAYS OF LIFE ON THE BASIS OF WET (W) AND DRY (D) WEIGHT

Age (Days)	Number of Animals	Glutamic Acid		Glutamine		Total Amino Nitrogen	Glutamic Acid and Glutamine NH₂-N of Total
		W (Mg. Per Cent)	D (Mg. Per Cent)	W (Mg. Per Cent)	D (Mg. Per Cent)	W (Mg. Per Cent)	(Per Cent)
0.5–1	7	89	884	55	510	28	50
0.5–1	9	74	612	54	460	32	38
2	8	84	720	61	530	33	42
6	4	125	925	54	400	36	47
8	5	94	730	53	410	35	40
13	2	158	930	66	390	40	53
22	2	165	880	75	400	54	43
29	2	171	925	78	420	44	54

From Waelsch, H.: Advances in Protein Chemistry, Vol. VI, 1951.

In none of the experiments in which glutamic acid was administered did the concentration of the amino acid in the brain rise beyond the range of the values found in the control animals, whereas after the administration of glutamine significantly higher values were found in a number of experiments. In these experiments liver behaved as did brain by taking up large amounts of glutamine and only insignificant amounts of the dicarboxylic acid. Whereas only the direct determination of glutamic acid and glutamine in an organ can give an unequivocal answer to the question of uptake of these compounds by the organ, it should be mentioned that it had been shown previously that the intravenous administration of protein hydrolysate, glycine, histidine, lysine, alanine, and glutamic acid did not result in an increase in the total amino nitrogen of the nonprotein fraction of the rat brain.[4] The present experiments do not rule out the exchange of glutamic acid between blood and brain nor do they show whether small amounts of

TABLE 16. GLUTAMIC ACID (ACID) AND GLUTAMINE (AMIDE) CONCENTRATION
IN RAT ORGANS AFTER INTRAVENOUS INJECTION OF
GLUTAMIC ACID OR GLUTAMINE
(*values expressed as mg. per 100 Gm.*)

Min.	Brain		Liver		Muscle		Kidney		Blood	
	Acid	Amide	Acid	Amide	Acid	Amide	Acid	Amide	Acid	Amide
0*	152	57	49	55	18	40	96	22	3	6.1
†	±16	±8.1	±14	±3.7	±2.6	±12	±4.5	±11	±0.7	±1.4
Glutamic Acid Administered										
10	120	65	**94**	38	40	35				
10	144	52	**99**	31	**86**	58	**400**	29	**109**	5.4
15	122	58	63	69	18	42	**490**	38	**63**	7.5
15	111	34	**111**	65	**54**	55	**520**	43	**90**	7.1
20	140	56	72	45						
20	158	62	**114**	44			**424**	39	**85**	6.6
30	116	37					**510**	47	**68**	6.2
60	131	67					**260**	40	4.6	4.3
Glutamine Administered										
10	120	68	**210**	**210**	18	68				
15	161	78	**370**	92			219	**99**	5.1	**32**
15	165	**85**					146	**239**	6.7	**86**
20	140	**84**	**200**	73	13	53				
30	136	36	**157**	128			180	**185**	4.4	**34**
30	155	**88**					274	**174**	6.1	**36**
60	147	78					94	21	3.6	7.5

* Each average in this row represents six groups of three animals each, except for liver and muscle for which five and three groups were used, respectively.

† Standard deviation. The bold faced values differ from the control values significantly (*P* < 0.05).

From Schwerin, P.; Bessman, S. P.; and Waelsch, H.: *Journal of Biological Chemistry,* 1950, 184, p. 37.

glutamic acid normally present in blood enter the nervous system. This question may be decided by measurement of the arterio-venous difference for glutamic acid. Our experiments show only that glutamine enters the brain and the liver with greater ease under conditions of elevated blood concentration of the two compounds.

The ability of glutamine to penetrate the blood-brain barrier and its easy uptake by the liver center our interest on the role of the amide in nitrogen metabolism. Specific function of the amide configuration—to which we shall return—has come up only recently, but up to this time glutamine has been considered to be a transport and storage form of ammonia. Since glutamine is able to enter the brain it may furnish the amino group for amino acids such as alanine, aspartic acid, and glutamic acid whose carbon structure is generated through the citric acid cycle.

There is in nervous tissue an array of enzymatic activities which are involved in the metabolism of glutamic acid and its amide and, thereby, in the last analysis, in that of ammonia. After Thunberg[15] had shown that glutamic acid can serve as a substrate for oxidative processes in mammalian peripheral nerve tissue, Quastel and Wheatley[9] demonstrated that the amino acid may be oxidized by brain tissue homogenates in lieu of glucose. Glutamic acid appears to be oxidized in brain at a considerably more rapid rate than any other amino acid since it was the only amino acid of thirteen tested which was oxidized by brain cortex slices.[19] Not only the oxidative deamination of glutamic acid but also the reductive amination of ketoglutaric acid to glutamic acid was demonstrated with aid of brain cortex slices. These findings and the direct demonstration of the occurrence of glutamic acid dehydrogenase in nervous tissue show that as in other tissues glutamic acid is the main entrance of inorganic ammonia into the pool of α-amino groups of amino acids. In brain tissue, as in other tissues, glutamic acid is a primary member of transamination reactions.[1]

The central position of glutamic acid in ammonia metabolism is further indicated by the susceptibility of the amino acid to enzymatic amidation to glutamine. The synthesis of the amide from glutamic acid and ammonia was first demonstrated by Krebs[7] in brain cortex slices fifteen years ago. Recent work with cell-free extracts of brain and liver[3, 14] showed that the enzymatic amidation of glutamic acid involves the participation of adenosine triphosphate probably through the intermediate formation of an acyl phosphate. In addition to the enzyme system which synthesizes glutamine the brain contains a powerful glutaminase which splits the amide into its two components.

Since ammonia in unphysiological concentrations is considered a toxic and convulsive agent, the role of glutamine formation as a detoxifying mechanism for ammonia has been investigated. Convulsive agents and anoxia lead to a marked increase of the concentration of free ammonia in the brain of animals, but without a concomitant rise in the glutamine concentration.[10] In insulin convulsion the glutamic acid concentration of the brain of rats decreases considerably without the change in the glutamine concentration[2] which would be expected if glutamine formation serves as a detoxifying mechanism of the liberated ammonia. The possibility that increased amounts of glutamine are removed by the circulating blood can, of course, not be excluded.

The studies summarized up to now show a function of glutamine as a carrier of glutamic acid and ammonia through the blood-brain barrier and as a store of the two components which may be easily liberated from or recombined to the amide by enzymatic action. A further specific role for the amide is suggested by the recent discovery of an enzyme system which

catalyzes the exchange of the amide group with other amines, e.g., hydroxylamine or ammonia (isotopic).[5, 17] This enzyme system was first found in
cell-free bacterial extracts. With glutamine or asparagine and hydroxylamine
as substrates the corresponding hydroxamic acid was formed. At present
we see the significance of these enzymatic activities in the possibility that
amino acids may substitute as the biologic substrates for hydroxylamine and
that the exchange of the amide group with amino acids would lead to the
formation of γ-glutamyl or β-aspartyl peptides. These peptides which do
not contain true α-peptide linkages may then by rearrangement form α-
peptides.

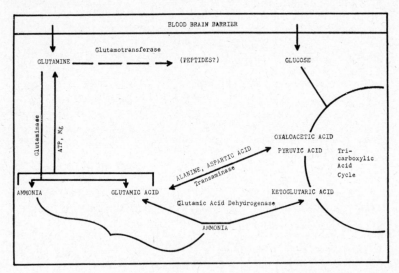

FIG. 29.   Metabolism of glutamic acid, glutamine, and ammonia in the brain.

Recently the enzyme system which catalyzes the exchange of the amide
group of glutamine has been found in mammalian tissues.[11] A particularly
potent source is the brain cortex. Aqueous extracts of acetone dried powder
of brain cortex are inactive but manganous salts restore the enzymatic activity, which is greatly enhanced by the addition of phosphate.

In Figure 29 the main features of the metabolism of glutamic acid,
glutamine, and ammonia in brain are summarized according to our present
knowledge based on the fact, apparently characteristic for the central
nervous system, that glucose and glutamine are able to enter the organ.
This scheme gives only the qualitative aspects of the metabolism of the
three nitrogenous constituents of the brain since we do not know anything
about the rates of the metabolic reactions.

The same is true for the proteins of the brain for which the amino acids
serve as building stones. There are indications in the literature, from studies

carried out with the aid of isotopes, that the brain proteins have a very slow turnover, but cytochemical studies suggest that the turnover may be rather fast. The question of the turnover of brain protein is particularly intriguing since the brain, owing to the selective action of the blood-brain barrier, may represent a unit which to a larger degree than any other organ reuses amino acids liberated in protein breakdown for synthetic purposes before they have left the central nervous system.

REFERENCES

1. COHEN, P. P., and HEKHUIS, G. L.: *Journal of Biological Chemistry*, 1941, 140, p. 711.
2. DAWSON, R. M. C.: *Nature*, 1949, 164, p. 1096.
3. ELLIOT, W. H.: *Nature*, 1948, 161, p. 129.
4. FRIEDBERG, F., and GREENBERG, D. M.: *Journal of Biological Chemistry*, 1947, 168, p. 411.
5. GROSSOWICZ, N.; WAINFAN, E.; BOREK, E.; and WAELSCH, H.: *Journal of Biological Chemistry*, 1950, 187, p. 111.
6. HAMILTON, P. B.: *Journal of Biological Chemistry*, 1945, 158, p. 375.
7. KREBS, H. A.: *Biochemical Journal*, 1935, 29, p. 1951.
8. KREBS, H. A.; EGGLESTON, L. V.; and HEMS, R.: *Biochemical Journal*, 1949, 44, p. 159.
9. QUASTEL, T. H., and WHEATLEY, A. H. M.: *Biochemical Journal*, 1932, 26 p. 725.
10. RICHTER, D.: *Journal of Biological Chemistry*, 1948, 176, p. 1199.
11. SCHOU, M.; GROSSOWICZ, N.; LAJTHA, A.; and WAELSCH, H.: Nature, 1951, 167, p. 818.
12. SCHURR, P. E.; THOMPSON, H. T.; HENDERSON, L. M.; WILLIAMS, J. N.; and ELVEHJEM, C. H.: *Journal of Biological Chemistry*, 1950, 182, p. 39.
13. SCHWERIN, P.; BESSMAN, S. P.; and WAELSCH, H.: *Journal of Biological Chemistry*, 1950, 184, p. 37.
14. SPECK, J. F.: *Journal of Biological Chemistry*, 1949, 179, p. 1405.
15. THUNBERG, T.: *Skandinavica Archives für Physiologica*, 1923, 43, p. 275.
16. WAELSCH, H.: Advances in Protein Chemistry, Vol. VI, 1951.
17. WAELSCH, H.; OWADES, P.; BOREK, E.; GROSSOWICZ, N.; and SCHOU, M.: *Archives of Biochemistry*, 1950, 27, p. 237.
18. WAELSCH, H., and SCHWERIN, P.: Unpublished.
19. WEIL-MALHERBE, H.: *Biochemical Journal*, 1936, 30, p. 665.

Discussion

DAVID RITTENBERG, PH.D.

Dr. Waelsch has very clearly presented some of the fundamental questions of protein synthesis. This problem has several aspects. Among these are the problems of rate and of mechanism.

Dr. Waelsch has pointed out that there are at the present time practically no data on the rate of protein synthesis. This aspect of protein synthesis has interested me for many years, and the more I have worked on it the more

I have realized that it was a most subtle problem, for, as Dr. Waelsch has just pointed out, neither the brain nor any other system synthesizing protein is a homogenous chemical entity. It is almost certain that there are wide differences in the rate of protein synthesis within the individual parts of any particular cell.

As far as the question of mechanism is concerned, even less is known of it than about the problem of rate, but some of the concepts that Dr. Waelsch has told us about are extraordinarily stimulating.

Quite by accident, a number of years ago, we investigated the rate of utilization of the amide nitrogen of glutamine. This was done by one of my former collaborators, Dr. Hirs.

If one administers to rats small doses of an amino acid labeled by an appropriate isotope, in this case a heavy isotope of nitrogen, and follows the rate of excretion of the N^{15}, it is possible to trace the pathway taken by the substance and to estimate the rate of utilization for protein synthesis. In general, about 40 per cent of the amino acid nitrogen is excreted after two days. The remaining 60 per cent of the nitrogen has been utilized in the organism, principally for protein synthesis.

If one feeds ammonia, about 85 to 90 per cent is excreted in two days. Ammonia is less efficiently utilized for protein synthesis than are the amino acids and so is more rapidly excreted.

When amide-labeled glutamine is administered the excretion pattern closely follows that of the amino acids, suggesting that the amide group is utilized in some way quite different from ammonia. It is probably directly utilized for amino acid synthesis, a concept which Dr. Waelsch has just presented. This occurs despite the fact that the amide nitrogen is chemically rather easily split off to yield ammonia and glutamic acid and one would therefore expect glutamine-amide N to be treated as is ammonia.

The concept which Dr. Waelsch presents concerning the utilization of glutamine for peptide synthesis is extraordinarily attractive, and from the chemical standpoint one can even begin to write mechanisms by which this reaction could occur. I should like to present one. A process by which the glutamine attaches itself to the enzyme through the γ-amide and possibly the α-carboxyl and α-amino groups can be visualized. The enzyme functions by polarizing the amide group by drawing away the bonding electrons of the carbonyl group from the carbon atom in the direction of the oxygen atom as follows:

$$
\begin{array}{ccc}
\text{C} & & \text{C} \\
\text{O::C:N:H} & \rightleftarrows & \text{O::C:N:H} \\
\text{H} & & \text{H}
\end{array}
$$

The bond between the carbon and oxygen atoms partakes of the properties of an ionic bond. The carbon atom, deficient in electrons, is formally positive and the oxygen atom is formally negative. It is known that normally this ionic structure makes quite an appreciable contribution to the structure of the carbonyl group and I merely suggest that the enzyme produces more of what already exists. Under these conditions, another amino group, of an α-amino acid, or a hydroxyl ion, both of which have a free pair of electrons, can now approach this positive carbon atom. As it approaches, the amide group is expelled and the new group enters. This is, I believe, what the organic chemists call an over-the-barrel mechanism. An exchange of one group for another has occurred. If it is a hydroxyl that enters, the glutamine has been hydrolyzed. With a peptide bond, if one may continue along the line of thought which Dr. Waelsch suggested, it is now necessary merely to bring up a carboxyl group to this bond; the same reaction occurs and a new peptide bond is now obtained.

This mechanism provides not only the energy necessary for a peptide bond formation which resides in the amide group, but also the structure required for the preparation of the particular peptide bond. The particular protein, of course, would be determined by the particular enzyme which holds the whole structure together.

This mechanism for peptide synthesis has as yet but little experimental backing at the present time. In glutathione, however, the glutamic acid is coupled in the γ-position, and it is known from the work of Waelsch and Rittenberg that glutathione is a substance which is regenerated very rapidly.

I shall conclude by leaving with you the thought that this general notion which Dr. Waelsch has presented so eloquently for brain metabolism may be a very general metabolic pathway for the synthesis of the large complex structure of the protoplasm.

DR. HEINRICH B. WAELSCH: The preferential entry of glutamine when compared with glutamic acid into brain and liver, which we have found, has recently been confirmed by Handler and associates (*Federation Proceedings*, 1950, 9, p. 396). These authors infused glutamic acid or glutamine at a constant rate into dogs. Urea formation was taken as a measure of the entry of the compounds into the liver. The urea production from glutamine was about twenty-eight times that from glutamic acid, a finding which indicates clearly that the amide enters the liver with much greater ease than does the dicarboxylic acid.

The concept which we have presented as to the role of glutamine in peptide synthesis has found support recently in experiments reported by Hanes and associates (*Nature*, August 18, 1950). Extracts from kidney catalyzed the transfer of the glutamyl radical from glutathione to other amino acids thereby forming γ-glutamyl peptides.

DR. DAVID RITTENBERG: It seems to me that you have clearly proved that you can't find glutamic acid in the liver when you introduce it in the blood stream, but have you proved that it doesn't go into the liver, because the question arises, is it immediately metabolized once having entered?

DR. HEINRICH B. WAELSCH: Our findings do not exclude the exchange of blood glutamic acid with the glutamic acid of brain or liver. There is no direct evidence in support of the suggestion that glutamic acid may be metabolized at such a rapid rate in these organs that one would not find any increase after the intravenous administration of large amounts of the amino acid. There are powerful enzymes in brain as well as in liver which could split glutamine and remove the liberated glutamic acid, but still an increase of the amide is found after its administration. Furthermore, after the entrance of glutamine into the liver, glutamic acid is liberated (Table 16). We had no difficulties finding the increase in glutamic acid content in the liver after the administration of glutamine. These results together with those of Handler to which I have referred make it unlikely that under our experimental conditions large amounts of the dicarboxylic acid entered the liver or the brain.

CHAIRMAN CARL F. CORI: I wonder, Dr. Waelsch, if it would not be worth while to point out what a large concentration difference there is between the glutamic acid and glutamine inside and outside the brain, and isn't there the concept that active work is necessary to maintain such a concentration difference?

DR. HEINRICH B. WAELSCH: The maintenance of the great difference in concentration of glutamic acid in brain and blood plasma could be explained by the fact that active work may be required to get the amino acid into the organ. In a remarkable series of experiments Stern and associates (*Biochemical Journal*, 1949, 44, p. 410) showed that brain cortex slices accumulate glutamic acid from the medium against the concentration gradient only when the slices oxidized glucose simultaneously. This situation apparently applied only to slices and may give a picture of the conditions under which glutamic acid is taken up by slices or cells, but it seems not to apply to the brain as an organ which is protected from the indiscriminate uptake of body constituents by the selective activity of the blood-brain barrier. Furthermore, I do not think that one can decide with certainty whether the energy derived from respiration is not utilized to synthesize glutamine which enters the slice and is then again split into glutamic acid and ammonia.

DR. K. A. C. ELLIOTT: May I help a little bit on that point? I think Krebs' picture is that the respiration is somehow or other concerned with maintaining the cell membrane in the right shape so that potassium is absorbed selectively. The glutamic acid merely follows it in, and the main energy is in concentrating the potassium, glutamic acid being the corresponding anion.

CHAPTER 9

Lipid Metabolism of the Brain

WARREN M. SPERRY, PH.D.

I COULD SAVE some of the time of this conference by first saying that too little is known about the metabolism of lipids in the brain to justify discussion of that subject, and then sit down. I am not going to do this because I understand that it is the purpose of this conference to stimulate discussion, even of subjects concerning which there is not much concrete, tangible information. The fact that the lipids comprise over half of the non-aqueous constituents of nervous tissue, and must have some important function there, provides a sufficient excuse for the presentation of the little information we have concerning their metabolism.

Such evidence as is available may be taken, and has been taken, to indicate that the function of the brain lipids is more structural or physical than metabolic. If I were to ask any of you, or at least any of you who are not biochemists, what you know about the metabolism of lipids in the brain, you would probably reply that there is no metabolism, that the brain is unable to oxidize fat. This is the only so-called fact that is widely known and taught concerning brain lipid metabolism. I say "so-called" fact because, as far as I am aware, the only evidence for it is the finding by several investigators of an R. Q. of 1 both in the living animal by the A-V difference method, and in brain tissue. Admittedly this is strong evidence, but in a recent investigation Geyer, Matthews, and Stare[9] found with the isotope-labeling technic that brain slices were able to oxidize fatty acids. When octanoic acid was supplied in low concentration, brain tissue actually surpassed liver slices in ability to oxidize this fatty acid, and, even more striking, a substantial oxidation of the triglyceride, trilaurin, was observed.

The investigators were interested in other aspects of their study and made no comment on the significance of this particular finding, but it seems to me that the demonstration of what appears from their results to be a well-developed mechanism for the oxidation of fatty acids in brain tissue is of considerable importance. At the least it is of theoretic interest even though it does not prove at all that fatty acids are oxidized in the intact brain under normal conditions. One cannot assume that a biochemical mechanism, an

116

enzyme system, shown beyond question to be present in isolated tissue, is necessarily active in the intact organ from which the tissue came. On the other hand, since nature usually does things with a purpose, this finding opens up the possibility that oxidation of fatty acids may occur, under some conditions at least, in the brain.

In any event, since the evidence against fat oxidation in the brain is indirect, it seemed to us worth while to subject the hypothesis to a more direct test, and even before the publication by Stare and his colleagues appeared we had been planning to find out whether the brain can oxidize fatty acids, or their metabolites, under the conditions of the Geiger-Magnes brain perfusion technic.[8] We now have a greater incentive from the results of Geyer, Matthews, and Stare to undertake the study, and my colleagues, Dr. Taylor and Dr. Meltzer, are busily engaged in preparing for it. The compounds to be tested will be labeled with C^{14} and added to the perfusing fluid. Any oxidation should manifest itself by the appearance of the isotope in the carbonate of the perfusate.

Being naturally a pessimist, I am predicting that the outcome will be negative. I hope I am wrong; positive proof that the intact brain can burn fat would be of considerable importance. But other evidence, which I shall discuss in a moment, makes the odds rather high against such an outcome. Nevertheless, we think the experiment is worth trying.

Labeling Technic in Tests of Lipid Metabolism

The few studies which have been carried out on the intermediate metabolism of lipids in the brain have, as far as I know, without exception employed the labeling technic. Elaidic acid, deuterium, and radioactive phosphorus have been used.

Results with Elaidic Acid as Indicator: Elaidic acid is an unnatural isomer of oleic acid. Its approximate concentration can be determined in the presence of natural fatty acids by a simple procedure. Sinclair used this compound as a label in several investigations of lipid metabolism, and he showed that it is readily absorbed and apparently utilized like natural fatty acids. McConnell and Sinclair[13] administered elaidic acid to rats during the period from birth to the third month of life. Up to the third week none, or at the most a trace, of the compound was found in the phosphatides of the brain, whereas in the same rats high concentrations were present in the phosphatides of liver and muscle. This result is of particular interest because it is during this period of life that large amounts of lipids are deposited in the brain. By the third month of life a small but apparently significant concentration of elaidic acid could be detected in the brain phosphatides, but the amount was almost negligible in comparison with that found in liver and muscle.

There are three possible interpretations of these results. First, the selection of fatty acids for the building up of phosphatides may be more rigorous in the brain than in other tissues; the brain with its specialized needs can utilize the unnatural elaidic acid to only a very small extent, if at all. This is the explanation which was advanced by McConnell and Sinclair. It cannot be entirely ruled out, but in view of other evidence, which I shall discuss in a moment, I doubt that it is correct.

Secondly, elaidic acid may have been rejected, not because of its particular chemical composition, but because the turnover rate of all fatty acids in the brain is exceedingly slow. In other words, according to this interpretation, elaidic acid was serving as a good indicator. It was rejected, as any other fatty acid would have been, because the brain has no need, or little need, for fatty acids to replace those broken down in metabolism. This explanation can be ruled out with considerable certainty because there is conclusive evidence, which I shall discuss later, that there is a very rapid metabolism of fatty acids in the rat brain during the period of life which was studied.

Thirdly, elaidic acid may have functioned as a good indicator in reflecting an inability, or a small ability, of fatty acids to penetrate into the brain. This is, I believe, the most likely interpretation of McConnell and Sinclair's findings.

Results with Deuterium as Indicator: A similar result was obtained by Waelsch, Stoyanoff, and me[15] with a different type of label, and a somewhat different experimental approach. We administered a single dose of fat, labeled with deuterium, to adult rats. At intervals up to forty-eight hours thereafter the rats were killed, and the amount of the labeled fatty acids present in the brain and other tissues was determined. Large quantities were found in liver and kidney, and significant amounts in the remaining carcass, but at the most a trace was present in the brain.

This result can hardly be explained on the basis of a rigorous selection of fatty acids by the brain since the labeled fat, deuteriumated linseed oil, must have contained natural fatty acids such as are normally present in brain lipids. It is unlikely, also, that the brain rejected these fatty acids because the rate of lipid metabolism was so slow that it did not need them. As I shall show you in a moment, there is an appreciable turnover of fatty acids in the adult rat brain. This leaves only the third possibility, namely, an inability, or very low ability, of fatty acids to penetrate into the brain cells, as the most likely explanation of our results.

In experiments which were carried out before ours, but which were unknown to us, Cavanagh and Raper[2] with a procedure almost the same as that we used, except for a different method of fractionating the lipids, obtained the same result we did at six and twenty-four hours after the labeled fat was administered: A trace, at the most, of deuterium was found in the brain lipids. But at ten hours the concentration of the label, though small in comparison with that found in other tissues, was well above the experimental error of the determination. These results of the English workers appear to show that a small fraction of the administered fat did penetrate into the brain and was quite rapidly metabolized, having disappeared at the end of twenty-four hours. Such an assumption can hardly be accepted on the basis of the two experimental values given by Cavanagh and Raper, but the finding does introduce a factor of doubt, which must be resolved by further study.

Waelsch, Stoyanoff, and I[16] have used deuterium in another way in the study of brain lipid metabolism. We maintained the atom per cent deuterium of the body water of rats at an elevated and fairly constant level for various periods of time, after which the deuterium content of the fatty acids and unsaponifiable fractions of the brain and other tissues was determined. The principal findings can be summarized briefly. In the fatty acids from the brains of adult rats a small, but significant, increase in deuterium concentration was found. From the values obtained we calculated that approximately 20 per cent of the brain fatty acids had been replaced in one week, whereas in the livers of the same animals there was a turnover of about 50 per cent of the fatty acids in one day. Thus there appears to be a definite metabolism of fatty acids in the adult brain. By contrast, only a questionable trace of the label was found in the brain unsaponifiable fraction, which is largely composed of cholesterol.

During the period of early development from birth to the fortieth day of life the picture was quite different.[17, 18] The percentage of deuterium derived from body water in the unsaponifiable and fatty acid fractions of brain and spinal cord was higher than in the corresponding fractions from liver and carcass during the first few days of life. These results show that the lipids which are deposited in large quantity in nervous tissue during early development are synthesized within the central nervous system itself and not transported there from some other organ.

Results with Radioactive Phosphorus as Indicator: Radioactive phosphorus has been employed as an indicator of brain phosphatide metabolism by Hevesy,[11] Artom,[1] Chaikoff,[3, 6] Chargaff,[4, 5] Hunter,[12] and their colleagues. In most of these studies a dose of P^{32} in the form of inorganic phosphate was administered to a rat, a rabbit, or a cat, and at various times thereafter the amount of the label in the lipids of the brain and of other tissues was determined. This procedure does not permit the determination of turnover rate since there is no base line from which such a calculation can be made. Most of the investigators have related the findings to dose administered, and have reported their results as percentages of the total P^{32} given found in the tissue lipids per milligram of lipid phosphorus or per gram of tissue. Such data have been assumed to have comparative value. The finding, in which all agree, that the values obtained in this way are smaller for the adult brain than for any other organ or tissue—though not much smaller, I may say in passing, than those found in skeletal muscles—has been taken as evidence that the rate of phosphatide metabolism in the adult brain is less than that of any other tissue. This result appears to agree with the deuterium and elaidic acid findings in showing a low rate of metabolism of lipids in the adult brain.

Chargaff[4] and Hevesy and Hahn[11] pointed out, however, that this is not necessarily true. The amount of the label found in the phosphatides of an organ is the resultant of two processes, namely, the rate at which the overall synthesis from inorganic phosphorus takes place in the tissue cell, and the rate at which inorganic phosphorus penetrates into the cell. This statement is an oversimplification. It omits the possibility that phosphatides, synthesized in one organ, such as the liver, are transported to the brain. This omission is probably justified; Chaikoff and his colleagues have recently presented evidence that phosphatides are not transported from one organ to another by way of the blood stream.[10] The statement also ignores the fact that the incorporation of inorganic phosphorus into phosphatide must involve several steps, about which nothing is known. The rate of the slowest of these reactions will govern the over-all rate. The true turnover rate of the phosphatides is the rate at which they are formed from their immediate precursor, or precursors. There is no way to get at that at present, but there is some value in knowing the over-all rate, just as the information concerning the over-all rate at which hydrogen atoms from water are incorporated into fatty acids has been found valuable.

Hevesy and Hahn[11] devised a procedure for determining the rate at which phosphorus is incorporated into tissue phosphatides. They administered labeled phosphate frequently in small amounts, or continuously, over relatively long periods of time in order to bring the concentration of inorganic P^{32} in the cells to a constant level and maintain it there. They measured the activity of the labeled phosphate in the cells and thus had a base line from which to calculate the significance, in terms of turnover rate, of the P^{32} activity they found in the tissue phosphatides. This procedure also has its uncertainties. For one thing there is the possibility that a precursor might be synthesized elsewhere and brought to the organ under investigation. This is rather unlikely, but there is also the possibility that the synthesis takes place at the external surface of the cell, and that it is the concentration of the label in the extracellular instead of the intracellular fluid which governs the activity found in the synthesized compound. Actually, Hevesy and Hahn calculated their results on most of the tissues they studied in both ways.

These calculations could not be applied with confidence to the data obtained on the brain. Whereas in other tissues the equilibration of inorganic phosphorus between plasma and extracellular fluid is considered to be practically instantaneous, in the brain that is not true. Hevesy and Hahn found that after four hours the total amount of P^{32} in the brain was only one-third of the quantity which should have been in the extracellular fluid alone if equilibration with the plasma had occurred. Furthermore, the impossibility of avoiding the decomposition of creatine phosphate prior to the extraction of inorganic phosphorus may have affected the results. Nevertheless, the data of Hevesy and Hahn indicate that the penetration of phosphate into the brain cells is very slow, slower than into the cells of any other organ, and that the actual rate of phosphatide turnover is, therefore, considerably faster in the adult brain than the measurements which have been reported by several investigators appear to show. In experiments on rabbits the ratios of specific activities of brain phosphatides to brain inorganic phosphorus were 0.11 at twelve hours, 0.29 at nine days, and 0.77 at fifty days, or, in other words, the apparent rates of turnover were 11, 29, and 77 per cent, respectively. These are by no means small, and even if they were divided by two to correct for the effect of phosphorus from creatine phosphate, they would still be much larger than the rate of metabolism indicated by the specific activities of the phosphatides alone, as reported by several investigators.

As you can see from what I have said, this is a complicated subject, and it is still more complicated. Up to this point I have discussed the phosphatides as if they were a single entity. Actually, as you all know, they comprise a group of compounds which are probably synthesized by different routes and at different speeds. Chargaff, Olson, and Partington,[5] and Hevesy and Hahn[11] have shown that the "cephalin" fraction of brain takes up considerably more P^{32} than lecithin in short-time experiments. In experiments extending over several days the difference was small, though in the same direction. A few data on the phosphosphingosides were reported by these investigators and also by Hunter.[12]

The subject is also complicated by the fact that the brain has many different structures. Chaikoff and his colleagues[3, 6] used P^{32} in the conventional manner to study phosphatide metabolism in the forebrain, cerebellum, medulla, and cord of rats. They found considerable differences which were related to age. Time does not permit a detailed discussion of this study, but it should be noted that very high activities were found during early development with a rapid decrease up to a body weight of about 50 Gm. and a slower decline thereafter. The P^{32} of the inorganic phosphorus was not determined so the findings cannot be interpreted in terms of turnover rate, but there can be no doubt that the metabolism was far faster in young than in old rats.

Summary

In summary, the available evidence on the intermediate metabolism of brain lipids supports the following interpretations:

1. The metabolism of all lipids which have been studied is a great deal faster during early development of the brain than it is in later life.

2. There is a small, but definite, turnover of fatty acids in the adult brain.

3. The metabolism of unsaponifiable lipids is exceedingly slow in the adult brain.

4. The metabolism of the phosphatides, as measured by radioactive phosphorus, may be quite rapid; considerably faster than most of the data which have been presented would appear to indicate. The "cephalin" fraction is metabolized faster than lecithin.

5. Fatty acids penetrate into the brain, if at all, at a very slow rate.

6. Lipids, present in the brain, are synthesized there and not transported to the brain from other sources. This important deduction is supported by the direct evidence which Waelsch, Stoyanoff, and I obtained with deuterium as an indicator, and in addition there is indirect evidence for it. It follows automatically as a corollary of the assumption that fatty acids do not penetrate into the brain cells. Furthermore, Chaikoff and his colleagues have shown with P^{32} as an indicator that phosphatides are synthesized and also degraded in brain tissue and sciatic nerve *in vitro*.[7] The uptake of P^{32} in the tissue phosphatides was increased markedly, as much as tenfold, by the addition of glucose or other hexoses, but not of pentoses, to the medium.[14] For reasons which were discussed before such evidence does not prove that synthesis takes place in the intact brain or nerves under normal conditions, but it certainly adds strong support to other evidence for this assumption.

Finally, the fact that the lipids of nervous tissue are unique quantitatively, and perhaps in some respects qualitatively, may be cited as evidence, indirect of course, for synthesis in the nervous tissue itself. As far as I am aware the 24-carbon fatty acids, which are important constituents of the brain lipids, have not been demonstrated to be present elsewhere in the body.

The only positive conclusion which I can draw without reservation from this survey is that further study of the metabolism of brain lipids is much needed.

REFERENCES

1. ARTOM, C.; SARZANA, G.; and SEGRÉ, E.: *Archives Internationales de Physiologie*, 1938, 47, p. 245.
2. CAVANAGH, B., and RAPER, H. S.: *Biochemical Journal*, 1939, 33, p. 17.
3. CHANGUS, G. W.; CHAIKOFF, I. L.; and RUBEN, S.: *Journal of Biological Chemistry*, 1938, 126, 493.
4. CHARGAFF, E.: *Journal of Biological Chemistry*, 1939, 128, p. 587.
5. CHARGAFF, E.; OLSON, K. B.; and PARTINGTON, P. F.: *Journal of Biological Chemistry*, 1940, 134, p. 505.
6. FRIES, B. A.; CHANGUS, G. W.; and CHAIKOFF, I. L.: *Journal of Biological Chemistry*, 1940, 132, p. 23.
7. FRIES, B. A.; SCHACHNER, H.; and CHAIKOFF, I. L.: *Journal of Biological Chemistry*, 1942, 144, p. 59.
8. GEIGER, A., and MAGNES, J.: *American Journal of Physiology*, 1947, 149, p. 517.

9. GEYER, R. P.; MATTHEWS, L. W.; and STARE, F. J.: *Journal of Biological Chemistry*, 1949, 180, p. 1037.
10. GOLDMAN, D. S.: CHAIKOFF, I. L.; REINHARDT, W. O.; ENTENMAN, C.; and DAUBEN, W. G.: *Journal of Biological Chemistry*, 1950, 184, p. 727.
11. HEVESY, G., and HAHN, L.: *Kongelige Danske Videnskabernes Selskab, det, Biologiske Meddelelser*, 1940, 15, 5, 60 pp.
12. HUNTER, F. E.: *Proceedings of the Society for Experimental Biology and Medicine*, 1941, 46, p. 281.
13. MCCONNELL, K. P., and SINCLAIR, R. G.: *Journal of Biological Chemistry*, 1937, 118, p. 131.
14. SCHACHNER, H.; FRIES, B. A.; and CHAIKOFF, I. L.: *Journal of Biological Chemistry*, 1942, 146, p. 95.
15. SPERRY, W. M.; WAELSCH, H.; and STOYANOFF, V. A.: *Journal of Biological Chemistry*, 1940, 135, p. 281.
16. WAELSCH, H.; SPERRY, W. M.; and STOYANOFF, V. A.: *Journal of Biological Chemistry*, 1940, 135, p. 291.
17. WAELSCH, H.; SPERRY, W. M.; and STOYANOFF, V. A.: *Journal of Biological Chemistry*, 1940, 135, p. 297.
18. WAELSCH, H.; SPERRY, W. M.; and STOYANOFF, V. A.: *Journal of Biological Chemistry*, 1941, 140, p. 885.

Discussion

DR. K. A. C. ELLIOTT: Mr. Chairman, what I have to say isn't really very important. It is just this: that it has been pointed out to us that at least in the adult animal the complex lipids of the brain do not seem to undergo much change, but the point is generally brought out as if metabolism is necessarily anabolism and catabolism. It seems to me that though you might not necessarily be building these things up at a great rate and breaking them right down, nevertheless they could be undergoing changes during function, reversible changes, so that the same molecules break or change and rebuild themselves, that these changes are part of the function of a tissue but do not necessarily involve exchange with the rest of the body.

I do not know how one would work experiments and test that sort of thing.

DR. WARREN M. SPERRY: Of course, the indicators should show that. That is the whole point; they should show such changes unless one is not getting at the part of the molecule which is changing. For example, radioactive phosphorus shows changes only in phosphorus. Fatty acids could be split off and put on the phosphatide molecule at a rapid rate, and phosphorus would not necessarily change at all. The same might apply to ethanolamine or choline, though that is rather unlikely. It seems to me, however, that in the deuterium work, if there were any rapid building up or tearing down of fatty acids, it should have shown up. It is possible that in some of the little known compounds of which Dr. Folch-Pi told us changes might be occurring that would not be picked up by indicators.

DR. HEINRICH B. WAELSCH: What little we know about the blood-brain barrier relates to the direction from the blood to brain. We know next to nothing about the activity of the blood-brain barrier in the direction from the brain to the blood. The turnover of fatty acids in the brain may look quite different if there should be a rebuilding of the lipids from the same fatty acids which were liberated from the brain lipids, retained in the cell, and reused for synthetic purposes.

CHAPTER 10

Inorganic Metabolism of the Brain

JEANNE F. MANERY, PH.D.

THE SUBJECT "inorganic metabolism of the brain" is, I feel, a particularly difficult one to present in a short time, traversing as it does so many fields of brain biology. Rather than discuss one aspect of the subject in detail to the exclusion of all others I have chosen, perhaps unwisely, to allude to several properties of brain which are influenced by electrolytes. This, I regret to say, must be done by a brief citation of the findings without reference to author. In general, electrolytes influence the osmotic pressure, function, and metabolism of the brain.

Histochemistry of Brain

It has long been my contention that an important prerequisite to the study of the role played by any chemical constituent in heterogeneous systems such as tissues, is a knowledge of the morphologic distribution of the constituent in question. As a prelude to the main theme of this presentation, I feel compelled to allude briefly to the histochemistry of brain; by this I refer to the identification of each electrolyte with the anatomic structures of which the tissue is composed.

Tissues are both functionally and morphologically divisible into at least two phases. The first is the cellular phase which performs the specific function characteristic of each tissue (for example, contraction in muscle and conduction in nerve) and which is called the intracellular phase. In brain this phase consists of the neuron with its nucleated cell body, its axone and dendrites. The second, the extracellular phase, contains those anatomic elements and associated fluids essential for the physical support and nutritive maintenance of the cellular phase. In the extracellular phase are the blood vessels, interstitial fluids, and non-nervous connective tissue: the ependyma which lines ventricles, the neuroglia cells, and fibers. Both phases are inexorably interwoven, making mechanical separation impossible. In muscle a chemical separation of the extra- and intracellular phases has been effected which has proved most fruitful in the advance of muscle research. It has shown that the volumes of the extra- and intracellular phases can be altered

124

in a variety of ways; both phases may swell or both may shrink; each may change independently of the other; one may even increase or decrease at the expense of the other. When investigating the participation of any constituent in a metabolic process we can, in muscle from analyses of the tissue as a whole, follow the concentration changes of this constituent within the muscle cells themselves.

Although the information regarding brain is meager I shall endeavor to outline the procedure followed in attempting to partition the total water of this tissue. In addition to analyzing brain or nerve as a whole, two facts must first be established: (1) that some constituent is confined to one of the phases, and (2) that its concentration there can be estimated. In muscle, chloride fulfills these requirements and—in a manner described in detail in a footnote*—makes possible a calculation of the volume of extracellular water, intracellular water and thence the intracellular concentration of any ion.

If the chloride of brain can be shown to be similarly disposed the water of brain can likewise be partitioned. Brain contains about 35 mEq. of chloride per kilogram. Much of this must be extracellularly situated because the chloride concentration is high in both the cerebrospinal fluid (124 mEq. per liter), which is in intimate contact with the external surfaces of brain, and the plasma (109 mEq. per liter) of the deep cerebral capillaries. Moreover connective tissue in general,[37] and dura matter (unpublished) and nerve sheath[54] in particular, are known to possess a relatively high chloride concentration. The chloride of vertebrate nerves both *in vivo*[1] and *in vitro*[22] behaves as though most of it were extracellularly situated. Brain slices appear to be relatively impermeable to both sodium and chloride.[17] Even the sodium and chloride of brain *in vivo* respond as extracellular ions to plasma changes, when a sufficiently long period of time is allowed for these changes to be reflected in the central nervous system.[34, 57]

For purposes of this presentation let us assume that the first fact has been established, namely, that all of the chloride in brain is extracellularly situated being, however, fully cognizant of the fact that direct and unequivocal proof is not yet available. In order to calculate the volume of extracellular water we must know the concentration of chloride there and, hence, are confronted with the choice of brain extracellular fluid.

* Assuming that all of the chloride of brain is confined to the extracellular phase, and that it exists there in the same concentration as in brain extracellular fluid, a calculation can be made of the volume of extracellular water, $(H_2O)_E$, as follows:

$$(H_2O)_E \text{ (Gm. per Kg. of brain)} = \frac{(Cl)_T}{(Cl)_E} \times 1000,$$

where $(Cl)_T$ and $(Cl)_E$ represent the chloride concentration in brain (T) and its extracellular fluid (E) in milliequivalents per kilogram and liter respectively. $(H_2O)_C = (H_2O)_T - (H_2O)_E$, where $(H_2O)_C$ and $(H_2O)_T$ represent the water content (in Gm. per Kg.) of original tissue of the intracellular phase (C) and the whole brain (T), respectively.

The choice lies between plasma ultrafiltrate, which must pervade the pericapillary and perineuronal spaces deep in brain tissue, and cerebrospinal fluid to which all brain surfaces are obviously exposed. When equilibrium has been established between the blood and cerebrospinal fluid the latter resembles plasma ultrafiltrate so closely in composition that the choice becomes one of academic interest only. But if equilibrium is slowly established, marked differences in composition can occur, and it is essential to know which fluid—plasma or cerebrospinal fluid—best represents that which intimately bathes brain cells at the time of sampling the brain for analysis.

In general, several hours must elapse before the cerebrospinal fluid concentration of substances injected intravenously begins to approximate the concentration in plasma. This applies not only to large organic molecules, to bromide, iodide, and thiocyanate,[51, 52] but also to the more physiologic ions, chloride, sodium, potassium, and phosphate.[25, 53] The choroid plexus obviously affords a real barrier to diffusion. If plasma ultrafiltrate traversed the capillary walls of brain as freely as it does those of other tissues, the brain tissue itself might equilibrate with blood more rapidly than the cerebrospinal fluid. But such is not the case. Radioactive chloride,[39] sodium,[36] and potassium,[42] after intravenous injection, enter the chloride, sodium, and potassium-containing phases much more slowly in brain than in other tissues. Furthermore, bromide from the blood replaces chloride in brain and in cerebrospinal fluid to the same extent[51, 52, 55] and to a much less degree than in other tissues where the replacement is the same as that in plasma. We are forced to the conclusion that the same type of barrier is interposed between cerebrospinal fluid and blood as between brain and blood and that the cerebrospinal fluid must resemble closely the true interstitial fluid in the deep brain substance. The implications of such a decision are important because if this is so, then, in studying the effect on brain metabolism of many substances, particularly electrolytes, cerebrospinal fluid and not plasma must be sampled and analyzed to ascertain the concentration to which the brain has been exposed.

Wallace and Brodie[52] have proceeded a step further by suggesting that the deep cerebral capillaries actually comprised the major site of formation of cerebrospinal fluid rather than the plexuses, because the distribution of bromide is much more uniform in brain if the bromide is injected intravenously than if injected into the fluid of the cisterna magna. This poses a problem which I hope will stimulate the histologists to a discussion, because obviously some barrier to diffusion must reside in the region of the brain capillaries. Like Dr. Tschirgi I have long wondered if a peculiar disposition of the glial cell processes about the vessel walls might act as membrane. I should not like to ascribe to this membrane any secretory function at this time but to think of it as a second layer of cells which act as a brake on the rate of diffusion.

If brain chloride is extracellular and if the cerebrospinal fluid of the cavities can be considered to best represent the fluid bathing nerve cells at the time of sampling, then the volume of extracellular water is about 30 per cent of the wet weight; it is similar to that of liver and about twice that in muscle.

Sodium, for the most part, like chloride, seems to be typically an extracellular ion in resting nerve and in brain as it is in many other tissues, whereas potassium behaves like an intracellular ion.[22] Squid axons, for example, will concentrate potassium from sea water very rapidly but will only absorb a constant small amount of sodium.[28] The swelling of nerves known to occur in solutions in which some of the sodium has been replaced by potassium, can be prevented if the potassium is added to the solution without removal of sodium.[45] This demonstrates relative impermeability to sodium as does the prevention of swelling by brain slices when sodium or chloride salts are added to sugar solutions.[17]

TABLE 17.   CONCENTRATIONS OF WATER AND INORGANIC ELEMENTS IN BRAIN

Tissue	H_2O	Na^+	K^+	Ca^{++}	Mg^{++}	Cl^-
	(Gm. per Kg.)		(mEq. per Kg.)			
Serum	924	141.4	4.7	4.9	1.9	108.8
Brain	761	57.0	95.6	2.1	11.3	36.7
Muscle	774	30.0	98.5	1.9	16.2	20.0

Utilizing the above method of partitioning water and salts we find that an "excess" sodium occurs in brain, i.e., more sodium than can exist in the extracellular fluid. The disposition of this extra sodium is entirely a matter of conjecture. Moreover, the calculated intracellular potassium is 25 per cent higher than it is in liver and muscle. In short, we have in brain excess total base; brain contains 210 mEq. of total base per liter of water compared to 189 in muscle and 164 in serum. (For chemical analyses of brain see Table 17 and Manery and Hastings,[40] Yannet,[56, 57] Tupikova and Gerard,[50] and Eichelberger and Richter.[16]) Little is known about intracellular anions except the phosphate esters[11] which must bind one-third to one-half of the total base. Peripheral nerve has very little bicarbonate,[22] and not much protein nitrogen. Hence an inorganic anion deficit occurs in vertebrate[22] and invertebrate nerve[46] which, however, may be partly made up by amino acids[46] particularly glutamic and aspartic. I am curious to know the base-binding power of the lipids which Dr. Folch-Pi discussed because some years ago it was shown that at neutrality cephalin can bind appreciable quantities of base.[6] If cephalin is a myelin constituent, in white matter[30] it alone would be capable of binding 25 mEq. per kilogram of brain. It may be merely fortuitous, nevertheless it is interesting to note, that the "excess" sodium begins to appear in the developing brain of the embryo guinea pig at the same time as the cell processes greatly increase in number and size.[23] Possibly cephalin or like compounds in neural tissue bind base in considerable quantities.

From all of this a tentative histochemical picture of brain emerges. Brain is a tissue with intra- and extracellular phases. The intracellular phase contains cellular solids, high potassium and magnesium concentrations, and may have little or no sodium or chloride. The extracellular phase has an unusually high concentration of extracellular solids in the form of myelin, a certain fraction of the total base perhaps associated with the myelin, and the remaining sodium and chloride in solution in the extracellular water. It is interesting that when this type of reasoning is applied to some analyses which we have of embryo chick brain it, like embryo chick muscle, has much more water than the brain of the adult. During growth the extracellular water volume (as measured by chloride) decreases and the calculated intracellular potassium concentration increases as you would expect if chloride were typically extracellular and potassium intracellular.

Metabolism of Electrolytes of Brain

It is with some humility that I now embark upon a discussion of the metabolism of the electrolytes in brain. The subject is difficult to present briefly because, whereas the literature is rife with reports of the relation of electrolytes to the function of peripheral nerve, a paucity of research dealing directly with brain exists. Hence much of our information regarding neuron function in brain is derived as an extension from peripheral nerve investigations.

Experiments which demonstrate the influence of electrolytes on nerve function are myriad.[5] High external potassium and low external calcium decrease the resting potential of peripheral nerve thereby presumably increasing its excitability.[10, 21, 24] Electrical activity of brain increases with increased potassium.[15, 35] Nerves are known to lose calcium in low calcium solutions[49] and to gain potassium when the external potassium is high,[22, 44] indicating the dependence of function on the intracellular concentration of these ions. The depressant effect of magnesium on the central nervous system is well known but only the serum magnesium levels (6 to 14 mEq. per liter)[29] at which magnesium block occurs have been reported. No analyses of the central nervous system under these conditions are available. Sodium ions, too, alter the electrical activity of squid axons.[28] Not only do inorganic ions alter nerve function but the reverse is true, that is, the process of conduction produces electrolyte changes. The loss of potassium due to activity, although demonstrable in ganglia, has been difficult to establish in peripheral nerve[2] because of the obstacle to diffusion afforded by the myelin sheath. [20, 26] The loss is more apparent in unmyelinated nerves.[9, 58] Recently a more satisfactory demonstration of potassium loss due to activity has been shown firstly[31] by using K^{42}, and secondly by catching the liberated potassium in a thin layer of saline around an oil-immersed nerve.[27]

According to the membrane theory of nervous action the surface of a nerve is permeable to potassium but relatively impermeable to sodium; excitation leads to a loss of the selective nature of this permeability and sodium and perhaps other ions are permitted to enter. With slight modifications, such as permeability to chloride in resting nerve[45] and a greater permeability to sodium than to potassium as a result of excitation,[28] this theory still receives wide acceptance. It should be possible, therefore, to demonstrate the uptake of sodium during activity. This has been attempted using Na^{24} with cat sciatic nerves[19] but not too successfully. A few investigators have employed analytic procedures to find sodium and potassium alterations in brain due to activity. We know from some unpublished experiments on shock that brain tissue will absorb potassium from the incoming blood. Yannet[56] showed that prolonged insulin hypoglycemia produced a marked rise in sodium, chloride, and water and a fall of potassium in brain as a whole. The reciprocal relation between sodium and potassium suggested that an exchange had occurred. Potassium loss via cerebral venous blood during convulsions has been reported[7] and also a displacement of potassium ash by sodium in microincinerated brain sections after experimental convulsions had been induced.[8] It is interesting in this connection to note that convulsive activity is accompanied by decreased concentrations of brain glucose, phosphocreatine, and adenosine triphosphate.[32]

The relation of electrolytes to metabolic processes as demonstrated in isolated systems is much too detailed to discuss here. Only brief allusion to a few of these can be made. Magnesium ions have, for a long time, been known to be essential for some, and accelerators of other, important reactions associated with carbohydrate degradation. In general the concentrations of magnesium required by these enzyme systems is much lower than the concentrations which actually occur in brain. Brain contains 11 mEq. of magnesium per kilogram or about 30 mEq. per kilogram of cell water. But, in concentrations of 5 to 10 mEq. per liter, magnesium induces maximal activation of a highly purified brain phosphatase which specifically hydrolyses ATP.[4] The idea of high local concentrations is brought to mind and it is interesting to note that isolated nuclei from cells of the cerebral cortex have been reported to contain an active alkaline phosphatase.[43] Sodium has been found to be a strong inhibitor of anaerobic glycolysis in brain, inhibiting the transfer of phosphate from phosphopyruvate to adenylic acid and stimulating the dephosphorylation to ATP.[50a]

And now we turn to potassium—the key ion in brain activity—and its relation to metabolic processes. Many aspects must be neglected including the important relation which potassium bears to acetylcholine. This relationship has been illustrated again by the fact that potassium is required in high concentrations for the functioning of the enzyme choline acetylase; this enzyme forms acetylcholine under anaerobic conditions and in the presence of adenosine triphosphate. On dialysis the enzyme loses its activity, but this can partly be restored by the addition of potassium and glutamic acid (see Nachmansohn[41] for references).

Of all the vagaries of the potassium ion, none demands so much attention at the present time as its connection with carbohydrate metabolism. Potassium ions in concentrations of 30 to 50 mEq. per liter cause intense aerobic stimulation and anaerobic inhibition of the glycolytic metabolism of cerebral cortex.[3, 12, 14] High oxygen consumptions by brain slices are reported if the external potassium concentration is raised to values (O.1 M) approaching intracellular concentrations rather than those in extracellular fluids.[18] The reverse relation is also apparent because the metabolism of glucose seems to be necessary for the maintenance of the high intracellular potassium concentration in brain.[13] Findings of a similar nature have recently been reported for leukocytes and frog muscle.[38]

This research illustrates again the fact that the maintenance of the permeability relations in cells in general, and in neurons in particular, is not a physical property of a membrane, but is dependent on a supply of energy. Krebs and his colleagues during their years of interest in glutamic acid observed that brain possessed an appreciable concentration of this substance.[33] They also observed that slices of brain when suspended in a saline medium absorbed glutamic acid against a concentration gradient. Aerobic conditions and glucose were essential for this accumulation.[47] Finally it was demonstrated by Terner, Eggleston, and Krebs in this same laboratory[48] that slices of brain cortex lost potassium to a saline medium. This loss could be prevented by two substrates, glucose and L-glutamate in the presence of oxygen. Neither glucose nor glutamate alone prevented the loss. The authors suggest, although they by no means proved it, that glutamate provides the anion essential for potassium transport and that the energy necessary to move both ions against a concentration gradient is supplied by processes involving glucose (or its equivalent) metabolism.

It is tempting, although unwise at this time, to permit mental excursions into unknown realms. In due time the pieces of the puzzle will fall together and I predict that the central theme will revolve about potassium, glutamic acid, glucose, and acetylcholine.

Finally, I should like to persuade Dr. Kety to hitch another needle to his human subjects and thereby obtain samples of cerebrospinal fluid. I should like to see him procure a flame photometer and an unemotional technician who can bear the frustrations caused by this unfortunate instrument long enough to obtain highly accurate potassium analyses of cerebrospinal fluid.

REFERENCES

1. AMBERSON, W. R.; NASH, T. P.; MULDER, A. G.; and BINNS, D.: *American Journal of Physiology*, 1938, 122, p. 224.
2. ARNETT, V., and WILDE, W. S.: *Journal of Neurophysiology,* 1941, 4, p. 572.
3. ASHFORD, C. A., and DIXON, K. C.: *Biochemical Journal*, 1935, 29, p. 157.
4. BINKLEY, F., and OLSON, C. K.: *Journal of Biological Chemistry*, 1950, 186, p. 725.
5. BRINK, F., JR.; BRONK, D. W.; and LARRABEE, M. G.: *Annals of the New York Academy of Sciences*, 1946, XLVII, p. 457.
6. CHRISTENSEN, H. N., and HASTINGS, A. B.: *Journal of Biological Chemistry*, 1940, 136, p. 387.
7. CICARDO, V. H.: *Journal of Nervous and Mental Disease*, 1945, 101, p. 527.
8. COLFER, H. F., and ESSEX, H. E.: *American Journal of Physiology*, 1947, 150. p. 27.
9. COWAN, S. L.: *Proceedings of the Royal Society of London*, series B, 1934, 115, p. 216.
10. CURTIS, H. J., and COLE, K. S.: *Journal of Cellular and Comparative Physiology*, 1942, 19, p. 135.
11. DAWSON, R. M. C., and RICHTER, D.: *American Journal of Physiology*, 1950, 160, p. 203.
12. DICKENS, F., and GREVILLE, G. D.: *Biochemical Journal*, 1935, 29, p. 1468.
13. DIXON, K. C.: *Biochemical Journal*, 1949, 44, p. 187.
14. DIXON, K. C.: *Journal of Physiology*, 1949, 110, p. 87.
15. DUBNER, H. H., and GERARD, R. W.: *Journal of Neurophysiology*, 1939, 2, p 142.
16. EICHELBERGER, L., and RICHTER, R. B.: *Journal of Biological Chemistry*, 1944, 154, p. 21.
17. ELLIOTT, K. A. C.: *Proceedings of the Society of Experimental Biology and Medicine*, 1946, 63, p. 234.
18. ELLIOTT, K. A. C.: *Journal of Neurophysiology*, 1948, 11, p. 473.
19. EULER, H. V.; EULER, U. S. V.; and HEVESY, G.: *Acta Physiologica Scandinavica*, 1946, 12, p. 261.
20. FENG, T. P., and LIU, Y. M.: *Journal of Cellular and Comparative Physiology*, 1949, 34, p. 1.
21. FENG, T. P., and LIU, Y. M.: *Journal of Cellular and Comparative Physiology*, 1949, 34, p. 33.
22. FENN, W. O.; COBB, D. M.; HEGNAUER, A. H.; and MARSH, B. S.: *American Journal of Physiology*, 1934, 110, p. 74.
23. FLEXNER, L. B., and FLEXNER, J. B.: *Journal of Cellular and Comparative Physiology*, 1949, 34, p. 115.
24. GRAHAM, H. T., and BLAIR, H. A.: *Journal of General Physiology*, 1947, 30, p. 493.
25. GREENBERG, D. M.; AIRD, R. B.; BOELTER, M. D. D.; CAMPBELL, W. W.; COHN, W. E.; and MURAYAMA, M. M.: *American Journal of Physiology*, 1943, 140, p. 47.
26. HARREVELD, A., VAN: *Journal of Cellular and Comparative Physiology*, 1950, 35, p. 331.
27. HODGKIN, A. L., and HUXLEY, A. F.: *Journal of Physiology*, 1947, 106, p. 341.
28. HODGKIN, A. L., and KATZ, B.: *Journal of Physiology*, 1949, 108, p. 37.

29. HOFF, H. E.; SMITH, P. K.; and WINKLER, A. W.: *American Journal of Physiology*, 1940, 130, p. 292.
30. JOHNSON, A. C.; McNABB, A. R.; and ROSSITER, R. J.: *Biochemical Journal*, 1949, 44, p. 494.
31. KEYNES, R. D.: *Journal of Physiology*, 1951, 113, p. 99.
32. KLEIN, J. R., and OLSEN, N. S.: *Journal of Biological Chemistry*, 1947, 167, p. 747.
33. KREBS, H. A.; EGGLESTON, L. V.; and HEMS, R.: *Biochemical Journal*, 1949, 44, p. 159.
34. LEÖVEY, F., and KERPEL-FRONIUS, E.: *Archiv für Experimentelle Pathologie und Pharmakologie*, 1928, 138, p. 372.
35. LIBET, B., and GERARD, R. W.: *Journal of Neurophysiology*, 1939, 2, p. 153.
36. MANERY, J. F., and BALE, W. F.: *American Journal of Physiology*, 1941, 132, p. 215.
37. MANERY, J. F.; DANIELSON, I. S.; and HASTINGS, A. B.: *Journal of Biological Chemistry*, 1938, 124, p. 359.
38. MANERY, J. F.; FISHER, K. C.; GOURLEY, D. R. H.; TAYLOR, M. F. J.; and WILSON, D. L.: *The Biological Bulletin*, 1950, 99, p. 312.
39. MANERY, J. F., and HAEGE, L. F.: *American Journal of Physiology*, 1941, 134, p. 83.
40. MANERY, J. F., and HASTINGS, A. B.: *Journal of Biological Chemistry*, 1939, 127, p. 657.
41. NACHMANSOHN, D.: *Annals of the New York Academy of Sciences*, 1946, XLVII, p. 395.
42. NOONAN, T. R.; FENN, W. O.; and HAEGE, L.: *American Journal of Physiology*, 1941, 132, p. 474.
43. RICHTER, D., and HULLIN, R. P.: *Biochemical Journal*, 1949, 44, p. lv.
44. ROTHENBERG, M. A., and FELD, E. A.: *Journal of Biological Chemistry*, 1948, 172, p. 345.
45. SHANES, A. M.: *Journal of Cellular and Comparative Physiology*, 1946, 27, p. 115.
46. SILBER, R. H., and SCHMITT, F. O.: *Journal of Cellular and Comparative Physiology*, 1940, 16, p. 247.
47. STERN, J. R.; EGGLESTON, L. V.; HEMS, R.; and KREBS, H. A.: *Biochemical Journal*, 1949, 44, p. 410.
48. TERNER, C.; EGGLESTON, L. V.; and KREBS, H. A.: *Biochemical Journal*, 1950, 47, p. 139.
49. TIPTON, S. R.: *American Journal of Physiology*, 1934, 109, p. 457.
50. TUPIKOVA, N., and GERARD, R. W.: *American Journal of Physiology*, 1937, 119, p. 414.
50a. UTTER, M. F.: *Journal of Biological Chemistry*, 1950, 185, p. 499.
51. WALLACE, G. B., and BRODIE, B. B.: *Journal of Pharmacology and Experimental Therapeutics*, 1939, 65, p. 220.
52. WALLACE, G. B., and BRODIE, B. B.: *Journal of Pharmacology and Experimental Therapeutics*, 1940, 68, p. 50.
53. WANG, J. C.: *Journal of General Physiology*, 1948, 31, p. 259.
54. WEBB, D. A., and YOUNG, J. Z.: *Journal of Physiology*, 1940, 98, p. 299.
55. WEIR, E. G., and HASTINGS, A. B.: *Journal of Biological Chemistry*, 1939, 129, p. 547.
56. YANNET, H.: *Archives of Neurology and Psychiatry*, 1939, 42, p. 237.
57. YANNET, H.: *American Journal of Physiology*, 1940, 128, p. 683.
58. YOUNG, A. C.: *Journal of Neurophysiology*, 1938, 1, p. 4.

Discussion

DR. ROBERT A. CLEGHORN: Mr. Chairman, having known Dr. Manery in her and my adrenal insufficiency days, I want to say how much I have appreciated hearing this extension of her studies, which has been such a magnificent presentation. She has been singularly cautious, and I want to do what I can to stimulate her to abandon a bit of this caution. Could she give us some indication of what she knows, or thinks might, occur in the brain in adrenal insufficiency?

I want to add a rider to that, and ask her what happens, or what she thinks happens, in the brain following the administration of cortisone or ACTH.

DR. JEANNE F. MANERY: Dr. Cleghorn knows much more about this aspect of the subject than I do. I might mention Davenport's paper in the *American Journal of Physiology*, 1949, 156, p. 322. It was reported that there was no difference between adrenalectomized and normal rats in the concentration of brain electrolytes (sodium, potassium, and chloride) and water although the adrenalectomized rats had lower electroshock seizure thresholds and lower plasma sodium concentrations.

We have again the problem of the blood-brain barrier. As Yannet's experiments have shown, considerable time must elapse before small plasma electrolyte changes are reflected in the cerebrospinal fluid or brain. I should not like to predict what variation in brain electrolytes might occur following the administration of cortisone, or ACTH, or, indeed, that any would be apparent. Changes in the plasma concentrations, however, might be expected to eventually influence the cerebrospinal fluid.

DR. J. FOLCH-PI: The question of brain electrolytes is full of implications, and I think it illustrates why there is so much difficulty in working with brain. In the masterful presentation of Dr. Manery of a field to which she has contributed so much, she has pointed out most of the difficulties, but I think there are a couple of points that bear emphasis. In a way, I think she would like me to say what I am going to say now.

She mentioned what has been called the anion deficit—the brain anion deficit. That means that there are not in brain enough anions of the types usually found in tissues, such as chlorions, phosphations, sulfations, bicarbonate ions, and acidic groups in proteins, exactly to counterbalance the amount of cations present. We know now that this anion deficit is made up by lipids and by phosphoric acid esters, such as ATP. The lipids that contribute the necessary negative charges are the acidic phosphatides and the sulfatides. Our results on this point, which check with results obtained in Dr. Hoagland's laboratory, show that some 40 mEq. of base can be bound by lipids in the human brain.

These 40 mEq. just about make up for all the so-called anion deficit. The interesting point is that lipid-bound bases are not exactly comparable to free ions, but exhibit a lesser degree of spatial freedom than free ions have. For instance, Drs. Christiansen and Hastings have shown that sodium in sodium cephalinate is un-ionized. What exact implications this has in terms of the manifold functions assigned to ions in the central nervous system I am certainly not competent to say, but I think that the basic fact that a significant amount of cations and anions in brain are not present as free ions must be taken into account in any consideration of function of ions in brain. It is very likely that in the case of cations, cations bound to lipids constitute a reservoir which is interchangeable with free ions.

That was one point I wanted to make. The other point is the concept of extra-

and intracellular fluid in brain. As Dr. Manery said, the proof of what the state of things is in brain is, so far, unobtainable. I want to insist upon that. Technically it is practically impossible to have a measurement of brain extracellular fluid. Is myelin extra- or intracellular? How are myelin and water related? Is the water in myelin bound water or free water? Is myelin to be considered a space in which ions can diffuse freely, or is it a space in which water and ions have a lesser degree of freedom than they have in the usual sort of extracellular fluid?

Then there is the question of edema, which has not been mentioned here yet, and I certainly should be the last person to talk about it since I have done no work on it. There is an abundance of literature on brain edema, both under experimental conditions and as a consequence of disease; but in reading most of the papers I have been horrified by the loose criteria used by the authors. For instance, often authors write about brain edema in patients who exhibit a rich pathologic picture which conclusively proves that their brain vascular system has been shot to pieces. In other cases, studies on brain edema have been carried out after perfusion of brain with distilled water.

Should not the distinction be made between edema in cases such as those in which brain capillaries are physiologically, or even anatomically, altered, and what might be called physiologic edema, that is to say, a condition in which the amount of water in the extracellular space is increased but still remains essentially an ultrafiltrate of blood plasma? In the case of the latter, the interesting question arises that, while water diffuses freely across the wall of the brain capillaries, most ions are affected by the blood-brain barrier and diffuse from the capillaries into the extracellular fluid at a very slow rate. Thus, it might be possible that the extracellular fluid in brain physiologic edema would have a lower electrolyte concentration than plasma.

CHAPTER 11

Electrical Manifestations of Action in Neurons

DAVID P. C. LLOYD, D.PHIL.

FUNDAMENTAL to the pursuit of knowledge concerning the electrical manifestations of action in the nervous system is a thoroughgoing appreciation of the fact that the tissues of the body constitute a volume conductor, and that records obtained by the use of electrodes applied to structures within the body must be interpreted according to the laws governing the distribution of currents in conducting media. The use of monophasic recording in the study of exsected nerves placed in an insulating medium, or, when feasible, in the study of responses discharged into spinal roots and nerves, insulated but still associated with the central nervous system, calls for no apology whatever, but some parts of the nervous system cannot so conveniently be torn from their conducting surround. Those most interesting parts of a neuron, its soma and the terminal regions of its axon, lie enmeshed inextricably within the confines of the central nervous volume. Since, therefore, the study of the more interesting parts of neurons demands acceptance of the conditions imposed by the fact of volume conduction it is well to have an elementary understanding of those conditions.

Form of Electrical Response in Volume

The monophasic lead is made by placing one electrode of a recording pair upon an intact region of insulated nerve, the other electrode being located at a killed region of that nerve. As a volley of impulses passes the first of those electrodes a deflection such as that illustrated in Figure 30,A is recorded measuring in effect the course of change in membrane voltage. A lead in volume is made by placing one electrode close to (ideally upon) the active nerve and the other at a great distance. As an impulse volley traverses the volume a fluctuating field of current flow exists throughout that volume during the whole time that any part of the nerve in volume is occupied by the impulse volley. The strength of the field attenuates sharply with distance so that in approximation the distant electrode records nothing. Configuration of the external current field is determined by the spatial ar-

135

rangement of the sources and sinks of current flow. Reference to Figure 30,B shows that during the course of the spike potential current first flows out through the membrane, then in through the membrane, and finally out through the membrane. There is, therefore, a sequence of source-sink-source. It is change in membrane current that is recorded by an electrode placed upon a nerve in volume. A positive potential is recorded when the electrode is located near a source of current flow, a negative potential when near a sink of current flow. In consequence the volley as recorded yields a potential sequence like that represented in Figure 30,C.

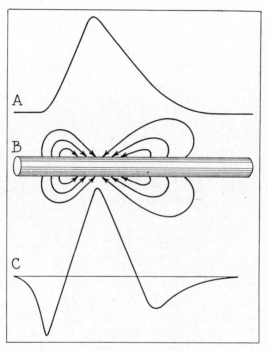

Fig. 30.   Diagrammatic representations of electrical events associated with impulse conduction in nerve. *A*, monophasic spike potential recorded from an insulated nerve; *B*, field of current flow established in an external conducting medium; *C*, triphasic response recorded from a nerve in volume.

The impulse proper is confined to the sink of current flow. With respect to the impulse negativity the positive deflections that precede and follow may be termed the prodromal and metadromal phases respectively. Until now the changes discussed have been considered as occurring in space. It is obvious, since nerve impulses travel, that the changes depicted in Figure 30 will take place in time at a given point in the stretch of nerve lying within the volume. Thus the following statement can be made: as an impulse approaches a point that point acts as a source of current flow; as the impulse reaches that point it acts as a sink; as the impulse recedes from that point it again acts as a source.

When a neuron lies wholly within a volume conductor obviously an impulse in that neuron is not merely conducted along its length, but must arise at some point and conduct to some other point at which it dies. The types of potential changes to be anticipated in recordings from the several parts of a neuron can be described, with the aid of a nerve model, by means of records made at the point of entry of the nerve into a volume conductor (Fig. 31,A), in its mid-course through the conductor (Fig. 31,B), and at the point of its exit therefrom (Fig. 31,C). At the point of entry, or of impulse origin, the deflection is diphasic in negative-positive sequence, in mid-course it is triphasic in accord with the principles already discussed, and at the point of exit, or of impulse death, it again is diphasic, but in positive-negative sequence. Emphasis must be placed upon the fact that the nerve model

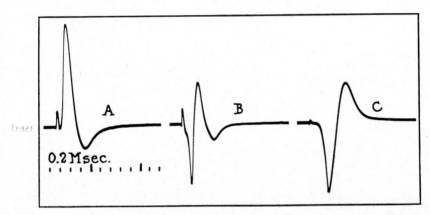

Fɪɢ. 31.   Recordings of an impulse volley in a cat peroneal nerve obtained by means of electrodes placed at the point of entry of the nerve into a volume (A), at a point near mid-volume (B), and at the point of exit from the volume (C). Another electrode at a distance in the volume completes the recording circuit.

reveals events in an ideally uniform structure, whereas neurons are strikingly non-uniform in their terminal regions where impulses normally arise and die. The demonstrated principle is not modified in any way thereby, for the influence of non-uniformity finds its expression not in variation from the fundamental pattern, but in terms of relative magnitudes and durations of the phases, in the exact configuration of various rising and descending limbs, and in the complexities introduced by potentials relating to the flow of after-currents. So it is, by reference to the forms recorded in the nerve model, that spikelike deflections encountered by a probing microelectrode in the central nervous system can be judged to represent action beginning at the electrode locus and retreating therefrom, action that begins elsewhere and passes the electrode on its way to another place, or action that, having originated elsewhere, stops at the region of recording. Injury of neurons, by one means or another, unfortunately adds to the variety of spikelike forms that confront the observer.

Significance of Changes in Response Amplitude

In volume, change in recorded amplitude of response may indicate change in either direction, or no change in the number of responding units. The explorer of the nervous system, sometimes accustomed to the shape of things as they are in monophasic recording, may encounter in the observation of responses in volume certain changes in form that predispose to misinterpretation. Let us consider two such instances. In general, increase in the negative phase of a spike potential has been taken as evidence of an increased

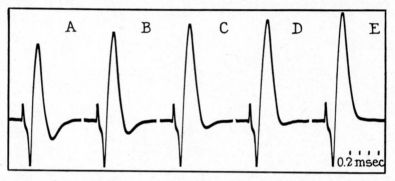

Fig. 32.   Change in form of the response of a cat peroneal nerve in volume during the development of a cocaine block located at a point just below the recording site. A, Normal triphasic response; B, C, and D, intermediate stages; E, full block established so that all the impulses constituting the volley die at the region of recording. (From Lloyd: In press.)

response whether that be due to increase in spike per unit or increase in the number of active units, as by facilitation, or by the relief of a block. Conversely, refractoriness and inhibition have associations with decrease in recorded spike potential. Of these situations, block and refractoriness are amenable to study in the nerve model.

It is common knowledge and predictable from first principles that the triphasic response of normal nerve in volume becomes diphasic, positive-negative in sequence, at the upper margin of a block, whereas below the block it becomes or at least approaches a monophasic positive deflection. Of particular interest, however, is to observe not so much the response of normal and blocked nerve as the change that takes place during development of a block. It is sufficient to the present purpose to record, as in Figure 32, change in form of response at the upper margin of a developing block due in this instance to the application of cocaine. Record A presents the normal response. In subsequent records the metadromal positive phase is lost progressively as increasing numbers of fibers fail to conduct impulses through the treated region. Prodromal positivity in accord with expectancy is unaffected throughout. What strikes the eye is that the negative phase increases in amplitude with increasing severity of the block. The principle is this: that the sink of current flow at a point that subsequently, and in the normal course of conduction, would become a source for sinks developing beyond that point increases in intensity if that point subsequently for some reason (i.e., block) does not become a source. Knowledge of this effect invites caution, for instance, in the interpretation of asphyxial changes in responses of the spinal cord wherein transient increase in response might be considered to indicate relief of a normally occurring block rather than the beginning imposition of an asphyxial block.

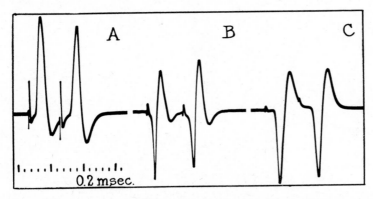

FIG. 33.   Change in form of the response of a cat peroneal nerve occasioned by partial refractoriness. The nerve was stimulated twice at an interval of 1 msec. A, response recorded at the entry into volume; B, at mid-volume; C, at the exit from volume. (From Lloyd: *Journal of General Physiology*, 1951, 35, pp. 255-288.)

A peripheral nerve stimulated twice within a millisecond or two will conduct two impulse volleys. The monophasic action potential of the second volley, by comparison with that of the first, is reduced in amplitude and delayed in time. Transferring the nerve to volume does not alter its physiological properties, but the change in physical conditions of recording introduces changes in form that prove deceiving in an unexplored situation. Figure 33 contains recordings made at the point of entry into (A), at mid-stretch (B), and at the point of exit from (C) a volume conductor. Each recording contains the result of a double stimulation by shocks arranged so that the second impulse volley travels in partially refractory nerve. At each position of recording, the initial phase, negative or positive as the case may be, of the response to the second stimulus is reduced from normal amplitude in accordance with the partially refractory state of the nerve at the time of the second response. Subsequent phases of the second response, however, appear with amplitudes increased from normal despite the fact that a monophasic lead proves the response diminished. Situations are encountered in the study of the central nervous system in which the effect might be construed as evidence for a relief by prior stimulation of a block, or indeed for some other form of increased response, but the nerve model permits no such equivocation.

Factors that Determine Response Amplitude

Other things being equal, amplitude of a recorded response is a function of the amount of active tissue. In volume, however, this relation need not imply that amplitude forms a measure of the number of neurons active. Stated otherwise, the amount of active tissue need bear no relation to the

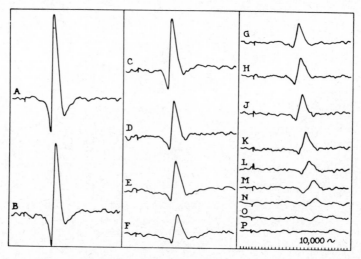

FIG. 34. Appearance of an afferent impulse volley close to the region of its entry into the dorsal column of the spinal cord (A) and at successive 5-mm. steps in the course of its ascent of the dorsal column to reach Clarke's nucleus. The afferent fibers yielding the recorded responses take origin in the stretch receptors of the knee flexors of the cat. In all the impulses are traced over a distance of 7 cm. (After Lloyd and McIntyre: *Journal of Neurophysiology*, 1950, 13, pp. 39-54.)

number of active neurons. This not unimportant rule is demonstrated by experiment in one of the very few situations that permit study of activity in a spinal tract by means not only of volume recording, but also of monophasic recording. This unique opportunity is provided by the dorsal column which contains a remarkably uniform bundle of fibers arising peripherally among the tension receptors of hindlimb muscles and terminating centrally in Clarke's column. Stimulating these fibers in a muscle nerve gives rise to an impulse volley that ascends the dorsal column in a manner illustrated in Figure 34, by recordings made by means of a surface electrode placed at a succession of levels. Monophasicity is achieved by stimulating the dorsal column at various levels whilst recording the resulting volleys after they have conducted back into the peripheral nerve. Figure 35, in which amplitude of response is plotted against total conduction distance, presents the results obtained by the two methods, curve A being the result by monophasic recording, curve B that by volume recording from the dorsal column.

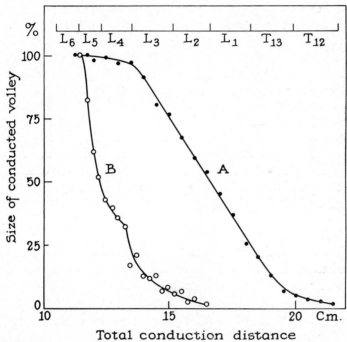

FIG. 35. Contrast between amplitude change with distance of a volley in quadriceps afferent fibers when recorded monophasically (A) and in the volume of the spinal cord (B). Curve A was obtained by stimulating the dorsal column at the segmental levels indicated at the top of the figure and by recording from the quadriceps nerve. Curve B was obtained by stimulating the quadriceps and recording activity at various segmental levels in the manner illustrated in Figure 34. Total conduction distance in centimeters is indicated at the bottom, and measured amplitude of the response, in per cent of maximum, at the side. (Modified from Lloyd and McIntyre: *Journal of Neurophysiology*, 1950, 13, pp. 39-54.)

Since one is dealing with the nearly synchronous response of a uniform group of neurons, amplitude of the monophasic response approximates a measure of the number of neurons active. Thus curve A yields an expression of the numbers of neurons that extend from the muscle nerve to any given level within the dorsal column; it shows that substantially all the neurons extend to the lower limit of Clarke's column in the third lumbar segment, and that substantially all those neurons terminate within the upper lumbar and lower thoracic segments. Obviously then in curve B the first step in amplitude decrease cannot be related to decrease in the number of active neurons. Nevertheless there is a sharp decrease in the amount of active tissue, for an impulse that enters the dorsal column by any one of the afferent neurons under discussion immediately occupies not only the parent fiber, but also the ascending and descending members of the initial dichotomy and a heavy local concentration of reflex collaterals. At this region an electrode records the maximal response for here there is a large number of active fibers per active neuron. As the electrode is shifted forward it leaves behind all save the ascending branch, hence the decrease in amplitude of dorsal column response in the absence of appreciable change in the nerve response. According to the evidence of curve A, loss of fibers from the dorsal column is one factor in the second state of amplitude decrease in curve B, but there is another.

The afferent fibers destined to end in Clarke's nucleus in ascending the dorsal column come to occupy a deep position adjacent to the gray substance and the nucleus of termination. In so doing they shift away from a surface-applied electrode. Magnitude of the recorded response of a given impulse volley in volume is a function of proximity between electrode and active tissue.

Conditions for Production of "Slow Waves"

It has been noted that the monophasic lead records change in membrane voltage whereas the lead in volume records change in membrane current. It follows that the faithful monophasic lead will reveal such differing deflections as spikes and after-potentials according to their relative magnitudes regardless of their wave lengths. Magnitude of response in volume depends upon membrane current density which varies not only as the voltage difference, but also as the inverse of wave length. With the foregoing in mind it is instructive to contrast the recorded response of a nerve in volume with its response as it appears in the monophasic lead, other conditions being held as constant as possible. This is done in Figure 36 which contains in a series of amplifications on the left the response in volume and to the right the response in monophasic form. It is obvious that a given volley of impulses creates a much smaller recordable electrical disturbance when traveling in volume. Equally striking is the fact that the after-potential, so prominent in monophasic recording, makes no contribution to the electrical sign of conduction in volume. Admittedly the potential value of the after-potential is low by comparison with that of the spike, but this is not sufficient reason for its non-appearance at high amplification. The important reason is the relatively enormous wave length of the after-potential deflection by reason of which the density of membrane current during the after-potential process approaches zero. To facilitate comparisons it may be noted that wave length of the spike in a ventral root axon of high velocity is about 6 cm., that of its negative after-potential is about 3.6 M., and that of its positive after-potential approaches 11 M.

Now it just so happens that the central nervous system has attracted considerable investigative attention for the reason that "slow waves" are recordable therefrom. It is obvious that similar orientation of similarly acting structures, a degree of synchronization of action, and the existence of a relatively durable membrane change provide conditions favorable for the production of recordable slow waves, but these are insufficient since the nerve model, which exhibits them ideally, in volume yields no slow waves. It follows that relatively uniform structures such as tracts or "pathways" in the central nervous system virtually can be eliminated as producers of slow waves

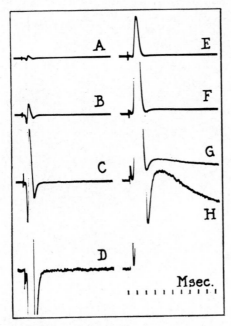

Fig. 36. Responses of bullfrog sciatic nerve in volume (left column) and in insulating medium (right column). Each pair of recordings (A-E, B-F, etc.) was made at constant amplification. Between each such pair from above down amplification was increased approximately fivefold.

either by summation of dispersed discharges, for these having similar area above and below the base line would neutralize rather than sum, or through the medium of more durable changes.

Having brought the argument to this point, it is not difficult to surmise that the only means available to a neuron in volume for generating a slow wave by means of its membrane potential mechanism is for that neuron to behave in a dissimilar manner in its different parts. This in fact it does towards its natural ends, although the intervening stretch of axon may be the paradigm of uniformity.

How Motoneurons Produce Slow Waves

Motoneurons of the spinal cord provide a useful system in which to study some of the factors involved in the production of slow waves. The study is facilitated by the fact that leads placed upon the surface of the spinal cord at certain loci record action at the dendritic pole of the intramedullary motoneurons and at certain other loci record action at the axonal pole. In conjunction, recordings from the two poles of the intramedullary motoneurons yield information as to the exchange of current flow between somata and axons. Figure 37 illustrates in the upper record from the dendritic pole, and in the lower record from the axonal pole, the slow potential changes realized following the conduction of an antidromic volley of impulses. The

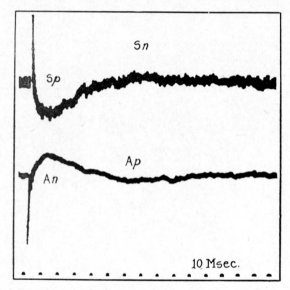

Fig. 37. After-current cycles of spinal motoneurons (cat) recorded at the dendritic pole (above) and at the axonal pole (below) of the intramedullary portion of the motoneurons. Activity caused by "antidromic" stimulation. The designations indicate positivity or negativity (source or sink) of the somata (S) and axons (A) respectively.

Sp-An phase, lasting 45 msec., indicates current flow in the direction from dendrites to axons. Subsequently, and for 75 msec., the direction of current flow reverses as indicated by the Sn-Ap deflections. It is proposed to name the currents *after-currents*; they arise as the result of non-uniformity in the generation of after-polarization by different parts of the intramedullary motoneurons.

Flow of after-currents can be manifested in other ways. For instance, one may test by suitable means the average excitability of a small group of motoneurons while a larger number of their neighbor motoneurons are

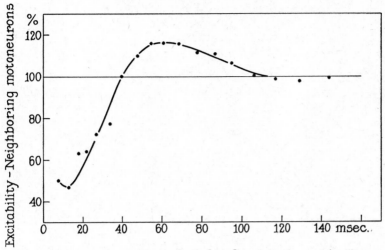

FIG. 38. Influence of antidromically induced activity in certain motoneurons upon excitability of neighboring motoneurons tested by their response to monosynaptic reflex stimulation. (From Lloyd: *Journal of General Physiology*, 1951, 35, pp. 289-321.)

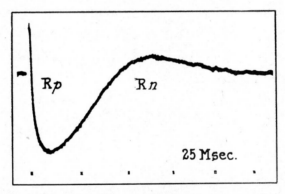

FIG. 39. Ventral root electrotonic potential following antidromic stimulation. The recording is made by means of two electrodes placed upon intact ventral root, one close to the spinal cord, the other more than 12 mm. from the spinal cord and more than 30 mm. from the distal severed end of the ventral root. Stimulation applied near that cut end.

passing through the after-current cycle. Excitability of the one group is affected by after-current flow about the other group. Figure 38 illustrates the effect; excitability is depressed throughout the Sp-An phase of after-current flow and is enhanced during the ensuing Sn-Ap phase of after-current flow. The resulting excitability curve reflects the somatic after-currents faithfully and with greater sensitivity than in practice is attainable by direct recording.

Yet another means of measuring the flow of after-currents is to record them in the form given by electrotonic extension into the extramedullary stretch of ventral root. It is current flow through the intramedullary axons that spreads to the ventral root. Hence it is the axonal after-currents that are reflected by ventral root electrotonus. Inwardly directed current gives rise to a negativity in volume (*cf.* Fig. 30) and, by electrotonic extension, to a positive deflection in a ventral root. In Figure 39 it may be noted that the anelectrotonic deflection Rp is the counterpart of deflection An, the catelectrotonic deflection Rn that of deflection Ap.

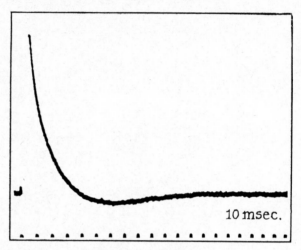

10 msec.

Fig. 40.   After-potentials of ventral root fibers consisting initially of a negative after-potential succeeded by a positive after-potential. While there exists a general similarity between the after-potential cycles of various kinds of fibers, it is noteworthy that the cycle of ventral root motor fibers has about twice the duration of that characteristic of afferent fibers and the negative after-potential relatively is much greater.

Since the appearance in volume of slow waves depends upon non-uniform behavior of parts of the neurons, it is a fair question to ask how each of the non-uniformly behaving parts behaves. A direct answer is not forthcoming for we cannot remove the motoneuron from volume to measure the after-potentials of its several parts. But one may achieve an answer by indirection. The method depends upon measurements of excitability.

Motor axons emerge from the spinal volume to form ventral roots and in so doing make possible the study of their responses not only in volume, but also in the monophasic lead. Response in volume during the recovery cycle was depicted in Figure 37. Figure 40 shows the form of a ventral root after-potential in monophasic recording. It is negative during some 30 to 40 msec. following impulse conduction and positive for some 80 msec. thereafter. In agreement with well-established principles, excitability change during the after-potential cycles reflects the course of potential change. We may think of the process underlying the after-potential and recovery cycles as the intrinsic change. Let us now compare in similar circumstances excitability change of the intramedullary axon segment, subjected as it is to current flow, with that of extramedullary axon segment isolated from current flow, bearing in mind that current flow modifies excitability even when the neuron in a manner of speaking applies the current to itself. The result of one such comparison is presented in Figure 41. Recovery of intramedullary axons

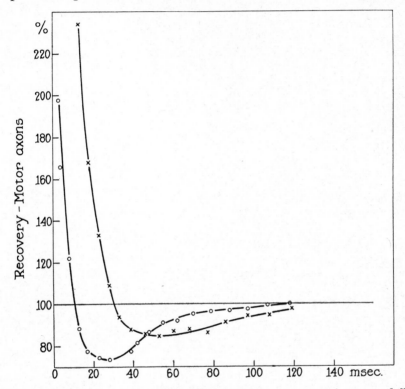

FIG. 41.   Contrast between excitability during recovery of intramedullary motor axons (circles) and extramedullary motor axons (crosses). The latter closely resembles the after-potential cycle of extramedullary axons (Fig. 40). Difference between the two curves is that to be expected on the basis of the known current flows through the intramedullary axons.

should differ from that of extramedullary axons not because of fundamental difference in properties but by reason of the current flow. When current is outwardly directed excitability will be greater, and when current is inwardly directed excitability will be less than it would be if the intrinsic change took place unaccompanied by current flow. Thus during the initial 45 msec. of the recovery cycle excitability of the intramedullary axons is less than that of the extramedullary axons owing to the inward current flow denoted by deflection An (Fig. 37). Otherwise stated, the somata by extrinsic action superimpose an anodal polarization upon the intrinsic status of the axons. Finally when current reverses, as signaled by deflection Ap, (Fig. 37), excitability comes to be less depressed among intramedullary axons than it is in a ventral root; that is, the intrinsic depression of the intramedullary axons is relieved in part by cathodal polarization of extrinsic origin.

Since the after-currents flow between axons and somata, the somata cannot escape the influences of current flow any more than do the axons, but the somatic effect will be complementary to the axonal effect, which is to say: when excitability of the axons is depressed by after-current flow, excitability of the somata will be enhanced. An often repeated experiment is the measurement of somatic recovery to reflex stimulation following the conduction

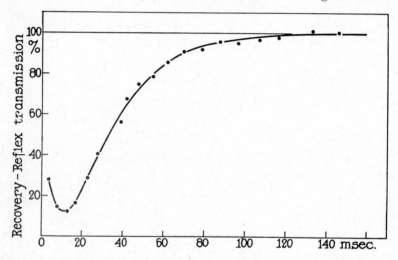

FIG. 42.　Recovery of motoneurons to synaptic excitation following conduction of an antidromic volley.

of an antidromic volley: a typical result is plotted in Figure 42. In the circumstance of after-current flow it is clear that the measured recovery course (Fig. 42) of motoneurons can bear no direct and simple relation to the course of the intrinsic somatic recovery process. Since no direct method is capable of measuring the latter one may be permitted to construct a fictitious recovery curve based upon measured recovery and a suitable allowance for threshold changes relating to after-current flow.

Curve A of Figure 43 recapitulates the recovery curve of Figure 42. Curve B introduces the allowance to be made for the influence of after-current flow. Curve C is the curve of difference. Now, although still other factors must be accommodated, curve C at least may be considered as representing a first step in approximation to the true course of intrinsic change in the motoneuron somata.

A second step in approximation incorporates the influence of certain intrasomatic current flows superimposed upon the after-currents and results in

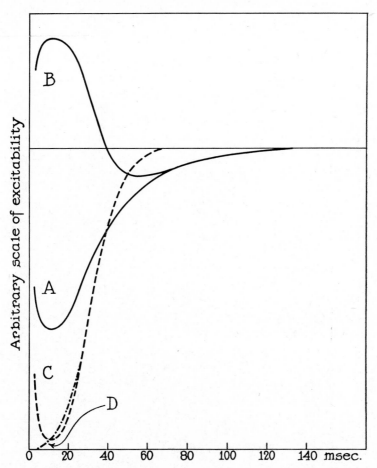

FIG. 43. Analysis of motoneuron recovery to illustrate the presumed course of the intrinsic recovery process of the somata. (From Lloyd: *Journal of General Physiology*, 1951, 35, pp. 289-321.)

the further change in configuration indicated by D. At the present time the simplest assumption capable of accommodating the known facts would provide for somatic recovery from refractoriness through a single phase of subnormality, some 60 msec. in duration. Finally, by taking cognizance of the relation between after-potential cycle and excitability cycle one may suggest that the after-potential of the motoneuron soma, could it be measured, would have the form of a simple positive deflection enduring for approximately 60 msec.

How Root Electrotonus Reveals Central Activity

One of the most important practical results of the inquiry into the properties of motoneurons is the demonstration that electrotonic changes recorded in a ventral root (Fig. 39) reproduce with high fidelity the direction and

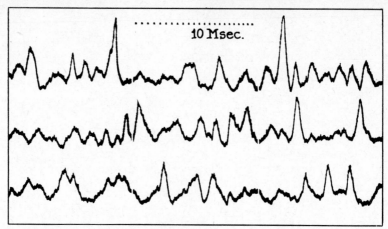

FIG. 44. Ventral root waves recorded, in the absence of any specific stimulation, by means of electrodes disposed upon a ventral root in the manner suitable for the recording of electrotonus (cf., Fig. 39).

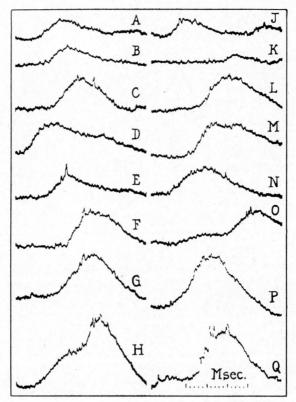

FIG. 45. Ventral root waves similar to those recorded in Figure 44. A much-expanded time base, however, is used to enable the direct comparison of these "spontaneous" waves with the electrotonic potentials, to be found in Figure 46, that result from reflex excitation in a monosynaptic reflex pathway.

time course of current flow changes in the intramedullary motoneurons (Figs. 37 and 38). By the one fact all manner of hypotheses that involve considerations of root electrotonus and that assume electrotonic slowing of major dimensions at once become suspect. The recording of electrotonic change in a ventral root rather than current flow about the intramedullary neuron possesses one outstanding advantage, for a current flow of a given density yields a much larger deflection by electrotonic extension into an insulated ventral root than it does in the volume.

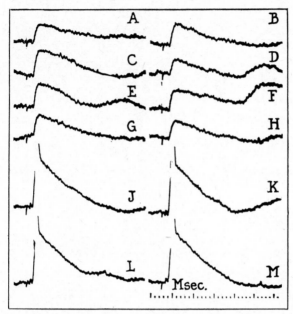

FIG. 46.   Ventral root electrotonus associated with action in the monosynaptic reflex pathway of gastrocnemius muscle. *A-H*, strength of stimulus to afferent fibers below that required to secure reflex discharge; *J-M*, stimulation strength above reflex threshold. Monosynaptic reflex discharge is responsible for the early break in the tracings.

Fluctuations of electrotonic origin constantly occur in a ventral root of the decapitate unanaesthetized preparation (Fig. 44). These have interest for they bear witness to the constant more or less random fluctuation of the somatic membrane potential and so too of excitability. In general these electrotonic waves are negative in sign and may exhibit near their peaks a few spike potentials indicative of motor discharge (Fig. 45). Very small doses of barbiturates are sufficient to remove this form of activity. Somewhat similar deflections result from specific afferent stimulation, but these latter are more resistant to the action of barbiturate. However, their form seemingly is modified by drugs, and it is well to eschew narcosis if one's interest is concerned with time relations.

Of particular concern are the electrotonic potentials that appear in a ventral root in association with transmission through the monosynaptic reflex pathway of the myotatic unit. Such are seen in Figure 46, in which records A to H illustrate the form of the potential when evoked by afferent stimulation at a strength below reflex threshold, and records J to M illustrate the

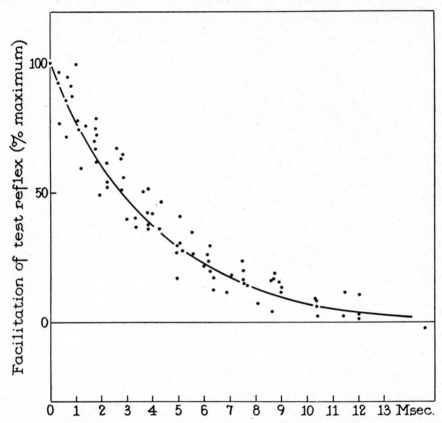

Fig. 47.   Facilitation at the synaptic junctions of monosynaptic reflex pathways. Each muscle such as semitendinosus or gastrocnemius possesses a monosynaptic reflex pathway through which a reflex discharge is returned to the muscle from which it arose, but not elsewhere. An impulse volley in the monosynaptic reflex afferent fibers of one muscle will, however, facilitate the monosynaptic reflex discharge pertaining to an immediate synergist. It is the time course of this facilitating action that is here represented. (From Lloyd: *Journal of Neurophysiology*, 1946, 9, pp. 421-438.)

potential evoked by stimuli increased to the extent that a monosynaptic reflex discharge results. A fluctuating base line is the price one pays for absence of narcosis. The potentials are negative in sign, the rising phase is completed within the time span of the monosynaptic reflex discharge, and the descending phase lasts some 15 msec. Potential sign of these electrotonic deflections indicates that the intramedullary axons are sources of current flow to sinks

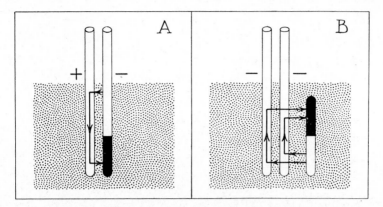

FIG. 48. Diagram to show how the polarizing action upon intramedullary projections of a given dorsal root of current flow about neighboring dorsal root projections (A), and about secondary neurons (B), can be differentiated. Stippling represents the volume of the spinal cord, the solid black regions the sinks of current flow, and the arrows the direction of current flow. The afferent fibers and neurons are represented as single units. When action in afferent fibers is the polarizing agent, current flow through the membranes of the active and neighboring fibers will have opposite direction, so the resulting electrotonic potentials recordable from the two dorsal roots will have opposite sign. Conversely, when action of secondary neurons is the agent, membrane current and electrotonus in the two dorsal roots will have like direction and sign. (After Lloyd and McIntyre: *Journal of General Physiology*, 1949, 32, pp. 409-443.)

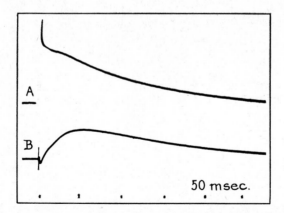

FIG. 49. Dorsal root potentials following single shock stimulation of a dorsal root and recorded by electrodes placed upon the stimulated root (A) and upon a neighboring root (B). The prolonged negative deflections, being similar in both roots are of secondary origin. Bullfrog preparation. (From Lloyd and McIntyre: *Journal of General Physiology*, 1949, 32, pp. 409-443.)

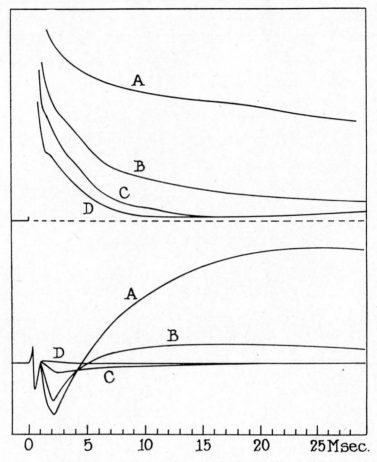

FIG. 50. Early course of dorsal root potentials in a cat preparation. Above, potentials in the stimulated root; below, potentials in a neighboring root. In each case curve A represents the normal potential; B, C, and D the potential in successive stages of asphyxia. The last fraction of dorsal root potential to disappear in asphyxia (the change from C to D) has negative sign in the stimulated root and positive sign in the neighboring root. This fraction could have arisen only as the result of an enduring sink of current flow (i.e., residual negativity) in the terminal regions of the active afferent fibers as indicated in Figure 48, A. (From Lloyd and McIntyre: *Journal of General Physiology*, 1949, 32, pp. 409-443.)

located more centrally, presumably in the somata. That current flow is associated with a threshold change measurable by responsiveness of the motoneuron pool to suitable test volleys of afferent impulses and having the direction and time course depicted in Figure 47. It is notable that the course of facilitation in the monosynaptic system is not unlike that of the electrotonic deflection recordable in a ventral root when the two events are examined in carefully controlled circumstances.

Having studied the response of motoneurons that are the postsynaptic elements of the monosynaptic reflex path, it is natural to inquire what manner of presynaptic activity impinges upon the motoneurons to evoke that response. To word the question differently: what are the properties of the terminal regions of axons? We could wish for much more information than we now possess. But two facts stand out: conduction velocity in the reflex collaterals is much less than in the parent axons, and the time course of action is greatly protracted.

Some idea of the form and duration of action in afferent axon terminals can be gained from a study of the so-called dorsal root potentials. A fundamental article in the theory of dorsal root potentials is presented in Figure 48. Following stimulation of a given dorsal root, potentials of electrotonic

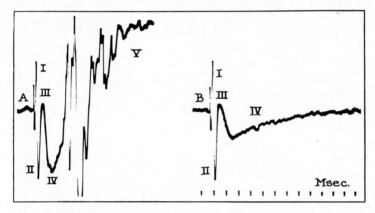

FIG. 51. To show the time course in a neighboring root of dorsal root potential (*IV*) due to residual negativity in the active primary afferent fibers. *A*, recorded in the normal preparation; *B*, recorded at a critical stage of asphyxia. *I*, *II*, and *III*, dorsal root potentials due to polarization by the entering afferent impulses; *IV*, dorsal root potential due to residual negativity; *V*, dorsal root potential due to activity of secondary neurons. The blaze of spikes on the rising phase of *V* in record *A* is the so-called dorsal root reflex. (From Lloyd and McIntyre: *Journal of General Physiology*, 1949, 32, pp. 409-443.)

origin appear in that root and in its neighbors. Since the collaterals of neighboring roots are splayed out through the gray substance in parallel array, it follows, as shown by the current flow diagrams of Figure 48, that dorsal root potentials resulting from current flow generated by the primary fibers themselves must appear with opposite electrical sign in the active and neighboring roots (Fig. 48,A), whereas those resulting from current flow generated by secondary neurons must appear with like sign in the active and neighboring roots (Fig. 48,B).

At first sight the most striking change in dorsal root potential following stimulation of a dorsal root is a prolonged negative wave that appears alike in stimulated (Fig. 49,A) and neighboring (Fig. 49,B) roots. Actually the origin of dorsal root potentials is rather complex, but to some extent the fractions can be segregated by means of asphyxia. If the potentials in stimulated and neighboring roots be examined concurrently during development of the asphyxial state (Fig. 50) the negative deflections decrease progressively and in parallel (the change from A to B to C in each part of Fig. 50), but at a certain stage there remains a fraction that is negative in the stimulated root and positive in the neighboring root. This fraction is represented by the difference between C and D in Figure 50, and must have origin in the central projection of the primary afferent fibers. It is seen to best advantage in the neighboring root, for there it is unencumbered by

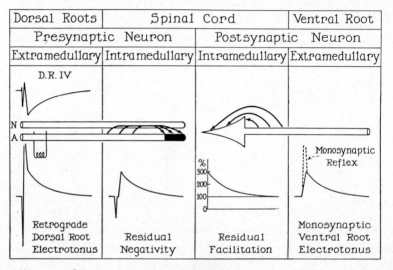

Dorsal Roots	Spinal Cord		Ventral Root
Presynaptic Neuron		Postsynaptic Neuron	
Extramedullary	Intramedullary	Intramedullary	Extramedullary
Retrograde Dorsal Root Electrotonus	Residual Negativity	Residual Facilitation	Monosynaptic Ventral Root Electrotonus

Fig. 52.   A schema to summarize discussion of electrical events associated with synaptic transmission. Active (A) and neighboring (N) presynaptic neurons and a postsynaptic neuron are represented. Arrows describe the current flows. Arranged about the neurons are representations of the various phenomena that have been described.

root fiber after-potentials. Labeled deflection IV in Figure 51, it is found to have a rising phase of 1 msec. or less and to decay to half value in about 3 msec.: in electrical sign the change calls for the existence in the terminal regions of the primary afferent fibers of a current flow in the direction toward the termini. Action in the presynaptic termini has an enduring quality quite unlike that of spikes in peripheral axons.

Perhaps this all too brief and superficial treatment of events accompanying reflex transmission can be integrated by reference to the schema illustrated in Figure 52.

A dorsal root A is stimulated and the resulting impulse volley generates an enduring current flow about the intramedullary collaterals which is recordable as a negative deflection in a motor nucleus. Outward current flow in the active axons causes the appearance of a retrograde negative dorsal root electrotonus in the stimulated root while the inwardly directed current in neighboring axons results in a positive electrotonus in a neighboring root (D.R. IV). These electrotonic deflections are depicted as they appear when freed from the dorsal root potentials of secondary origin.

Under the influence of activity in monosynaptic reflex collaterals, change takes place in the motoneurons. This change is measurable in terms of threshold to monosynaptic reflex test stimuli, and is known as residual facilitation. Motoneuron change also involves a flow of current from axons to somata, independently measurable in a ventral root by virtue of electrotonic extension thereinto.

Summary and Concluding Remarks

The study of electrical activity in the nervous system is the study of current flows in volume conductors. One records therein changes in membrane current rather than changes in membrane potential. Magnitude of a response depends therefore not only upon change of membrane potential but also upon wave length of the change. Other factors determining magnitude are the degree of proximity between electrode and active tissue, and the amount of active tissue, also the degree to which active elements are similarly orientated and act in synchrony. Increase in amplitude of a deflection in volume may as well represent a decrease in response as an increase.

After-potentials are not recorded in volume of the central nervous system; differences between after-potentials in adjacent parts of neurons may be; those differences denote the flow of after-currents. After-potentials are signs of processes. In giving rise by differences to current flow the after-potentials come to act as agents, and events in one part of a neuron help to determine excitability in another part. Thus only in the absence of current flow could a measured excitability cycle approach in form the course of intrinsic change at a given region of a neuron.

Ventral root electrotonus reflects with high fidelity the direction and time course of current flow change in the intramedullary motoneurons. That fact established, the relatively large ventral root electrotonic potentials become a useful indicator of relatively small intramedullary current flows. Dorsal root electrotonus likewise reflects faithfully current flow change in the terminal regions of the primary afferent fibers, but the pattern is overlaid by and must be extricated from deflections due to secondary activity.

Certain events that occur in the presynaptic and postsynaptic elements of the monosynaptic reflex pathway have been depicted in the schema of Figure 52, but we know so little of the manner in which the presynaptic neurons exert their action upon the postsynaptic neurons, at the points of contact, that the problem seems hardly ripe for discussion. The next advance well may come from histological study of the monosynaptic reflex articulation. Certainly the diagrams of that articulation which one draws frequently, and as frequently should discard, are much too unsubtle to serve as basis for useful hypothesis.

Electrical Activity of Dendrites

H.-T. CHANG, PH.D.

Probably one of the most important points brought forward by Dr. Lloyd is the electric activity of dendrites. I like to emphasize the importance of this point for the understanding of cortical potentials. From anatomic studies we know that the great mass of tissue of the cerebral cortex is made up of dendritic processes. This is especially true for the superficial layer of the isocortex which is filled with a dense pile of apical dendrites of pyramidal cells from the underlying layers. Therefore much of the potential change recordable from the cortical surface is a manifestation of the activity of dendrites.

Recently we have undertaken to stimulate the apical dendrites directly with a single shock and to record the electrical response from a region a few millimeters away from the point of stimulation. We have been able to identify and differentiate the cortical dendritic potential from the potentials produced by the activity of intracortical neurons. Although the electrical activity of dendrites follows the same principles as applied to peripheral nerves and axons, there are definitely some characteristics unique to dendrites, such as: (1) its low threshold; (2) its susceptibility to the effect of anoxia; (3) its specific reaction to different drugs; (4) its comparatively short wave length of impulse; and (5) above all, its extremely slow conduction velocity.

The conduction velocity of impulses passing along apical dendrites of cortical pyramids, as we have determined, is about 1 M. per second in cats and 0.6 to 0.7 M. per second in monkeys.

Neurophysiologists used to estimate the number of synapses involved in a given neuronal circuit by dividing the latency by a constant value of 0.6 to 0.9 msec.—the minimal synaptic delay. The method as applied to the cerebral cortex is obviously erroneous, in view of the slow conduction velocity of dendrites and the special orientation of the cortical neurons. The pyramidal cells of the cortex may be taken as an example. The large pyramidal cells in the motor cortex of monkeys have a vertical dendritic shaft extending from the surface to the cell body about 3 mm. long. Suppose an impulse is initiated by a presynaptic volley at the apical dendrites and recorded from the axon in the white matter, it would take about 5 msec. for the impulses to reach the cell body, and consequently the latency would be more than 5 msec., even though there is only a single neuron involved. However, it is probably less important in the brain stem and spinal cord where the neurons have comparatively short dendrites without definite orientations.

From a clinical point of view the identification of cortical dendritic potential seems to point to a possibility of utilizing the dendritic potential as a means to diagnose certain kinds of nervous disease, such as schizophrenia, in which the impairment of cortical dendrites might be specifically involved but cannot be demonstrated by ordinary pathologic technics.

Neurophysiology and Behavior

GEORGE H. BISHOP, PH.D.

Having listened to the preceding chemical papers, and anticipating the psychiatric papers to come, the question is forced upon me: What is an electrophysiologist doing at this conference? I am forced to wonder how many of his hearers will understand what the electrophysiologist is talking about. I would rather discuss this than add any further information of the kind that Dr. Lloyd has so excellently presented.

In this spectrum of nervous activity, from the chemistry of the comminuted and well-stirred macerate of dead nerve cells on the one hand, to the behavior of millions of functioning nerve cells on the other, the latter acting in groups so complexly that their malfunction is not detectable by any means short of observation of total behavior, what role does the electrophysiologist fill in our attempts to understand the activity of nervous tissue?

The electrophysiologist has been placed in the middle in this program, between the students of the chemical bases of metabolism, which produce and modify the potential he observes, and the psychiatrists who might hope to correlate mental behavior of nervous tissue with the functioning of nerve cells in terms of the electrical activity of the cells. He belongs in the middle technically, in that he works with a possible means of correlating metabolic and mental behavior. He is in the middle in more senses than the literal one, in that he has so far found little that he can accomplish in this correlation.

Like other investigators, the electrophysiologist has a technic. This is one, as Dr. Lloyd has shown so elegantly, that is particularly designed to record changes in electrical potentials of living nerve cells. The technic can be a very precise one, and can record the pattern of relations between cells as well as their individual activity. We neurophysiologists are so preoccupied at present with the elaboration of that technic, and with the solving of those intricate problems of space conduction and cell relation in terms of the activity of specific neurons, that we have not as yet more than started the study of patterned behavior of large neuron groups.

In relation to this conference the electrophysiologist has two possible functions. One is to study a most intricate mechanism for itself, because this is something of interest—many of us are engaged in taking the clock works apart, and we are chiefly intrigued by the parts we find. The other is to determine the behavior of the human animal in relation to the functioning of his nerve cells, i.e., reassembling the works and finding how the parts function in terms of human behavior, the most fascinating of all phenomena. Dr. Lloyd has presented the first function to which I have referred. That is in fact the necessary preliminary to the second. My aim is to anticipate what extension toward the second is liable to be accomplished by neurophysiologists.

These technics indicate the state of the resting neuron as well as its activity. Every chemical process in a nerve cell is presumably represented by an electrical change, and every electrical phenomenon presumably correlates with mental function. However precisely measured, at present these potentials are in a sense nonspecific; an electrical change does not tell what chemical change produced it nor what mental phenomenon results from it. But we recognize that all electrical changes in tissues are electrochemical, and no physiologist would hesitate to presume a fairly inclusive correlation between the pattern of electrical activity in groups of neurons and the mental behavior that accompanies it. Between the oxidative metabolism of nerve cells and the mental behavior of the nervous system, the electrical record of activity is the natural bridge, the common medium in which both of these can be evaluated. How shall we use this intermediary?

One approach is by experimental modification of function. For instance, the same electrical forces which nerve cells exhibit can be applied to them to change their functioning. A large amount of work on polarization of peripheral nerve can now be applied to the central nervous system. The same effects of polarizing currents are induced in brain tissues as in peripheral nervous tissues, and the records of these changes properly interpreted, in accordance with such principles as Dr. Lloyd has laid down, may permit us to correlate cell potentials with nervous tissue function. The externally applied currents seem to do practically the same thing to this function as do the currents generated by the nerve cells' metabolism, and electroshock therapy, experimental induction of paroxysm and depression, changes in amplitude of potential, and excitability of synapses can best be understood in terms of electrical influences, whether metabolically or externally originating. The electrical record becomes the appropriate as well as the most revealing of technics for following the pattern of behavior of nervous complexes. It may require a recording apparatus as complex as the tissue which it records, but the construction of mechanical brains is already in the works.

Dr. Lilly, whom you will hear from later, is applying twenty-five amplifiers to a square centimeter of recording surface of the brain, and he does not figuratively even scratch the surface. In the spinal cord we can trace many of the correlates of motor behavior. It may be a long time before we can record from the whole brain a large enough complex to represent even the simplest type of mental behavior. The next generation may accomplish it; I do not expect to see it in my day. But perhaps some of the patterns at present detectable in neuronal activity may be expanded in a logical manner to indicate of what the more complex activities must consist.

Two notable attempts have been made by psychologists to specifically correlate neurophysiologic and mental behavior. One by Harrington, "A Biological Approach to the Problem of Abnormal Behavior," attempted to correlate mental functions with the physiologic activities detectable at lower functional levels—inhibition, facilitation, summation, and the like. The attempt, I think, was not particularly successful chiefly because the physiologic mechanisms available at the time were quite inadequate to serve as correlates of the mental functions with which he dealt. Dr. Hebb has recently employed a similar approach in the "Organization of Behavior," and has made use of the more elaborate neurophysiologic concepts available today with considerably more success. I know of no comparable work correlating the chemistry of nervous tissues with the physiologic functioning of neurons, but material is becoming available for such a treatment. When we can deal with the chemistry of the neuron in terms of its physiologic activity, and mental behavior in terms of the patterned activity of neuron groups, the electrical response may serve both in the measurement of chemical activity of the neuron and in the analysis of the patterned activity of mental behavior.

Two developments are necessary however before the electrophysiologist can function successfully as the middleman. Both involve giving specific meaning to what is still largely a nonspecific electrical potential. On the one hand we must have the chemical information in terms of observable neural functions. It is not enough to know, for instance, that certain enzymes accomplish substrate oxidation in nerve; we must know how these chemical reactions result in electrochemical excitability and response. On the other hand we should have mental behavior broken down into components capable of corresponding to practicably recordable patterns of neural behavior. That such a breakdown should be possible follows from the premise that mental behavior is a function of nervous tissue. It is difficult to conceive of a neural pattern corresponding to anxiety, or to a dissociation from reality; if there is one, it must be too hopelessly complex to be recorded by any current apparatus. There must be simpler mental components conceivable, as there will certainly be more complex electrical recordings possible, in terms of which the neurophysiologist and the psychologist can find a common ground; but this common ground must be approached from both directions.

This present conference will not accomplish any such coordination. But even to emphasize its present impossibility is to serve a current purpose.

CHAPTER 12

Role of Quaternary Compounds in Neural Activity

JOSEPH L. LILIENTHAL, JR., M.D.

THE BIOLOGIST frequently envies the physicist his opportunity to describe a phenomenal system by synthesizing a general expression. Similarly, the biologist admires the chemist's capacity to define within a complex system that single factor which determines the direction or velocity of a reaction. A strong conviction exists among biologists that an analysis of living systems will lead in time to formulations as satisfying in their general applicability as those constructed by physicists and chemists. But sometimes this same conviction evokes attempts to make the simple formulation before the system has been described fully. There can be no reasonable cavil at these stimulating attempts when their fragmentary state is emphasized and their hypothetical state is acknowledged.

A general example of this type of biologic thought is to be found in the strivings by biochemists, pharmacologists, and physiologists to discover reliable relationships between chemical structure and biologic activity. A more specific example is the continued interest in a series of compounds which vary in chemical structure and in biologic effect but share in common the possession of a quaternary ammonium component.

By definition, a quaternary ammonium or tetra-alkylamine is a nitrogen atom coordinated by four bonds with carbon atoms; and the compound carries a positive cationic charge. The simplest prototype is tetramethylammonium (TMA); $(CH_3)_4N^+$.

This kind of compound, an "onium" salt, occurs with other central elements, such as phosphorus, sulfur, arsenic, antimony, and iodine. Certain of these related non-nitrogenous onium compounds are biologically active, but there is no present evidence that any of them occurs in mammalian tissue, and their existence is noted here but is not discussed further.

There are several derivative representatives of the quaternary ammonium group which are present in tissues and appear to enter as essential links

The work on which this lecture was based was supported in part by a contract between the Office of Naval Research, Department of the Navy, and The Johns Hopkins University (NR 113-241).

into certain energy-transforming cellular mechanisms. Prime examples of quaternary ammonium compounds whose structure has been established and whose function has been described, at least partially, are the diphosphopyridine and triphosphopyridine nucleotides, coenzymes I and II, which are concerned so intimately with the transport of electrons in several related dehydrogenase systems. Cocarboxylase, the pyrophosphate of thiamine, is another quaternary ammonium compound and is required for dissimilation of pyruvic acid. Because substances like these are requisite components of the systems that transform energy in cells, they are essential likewise to the specialized activity of highly excitable structures—the neural activity with which we are especially concerned here. Although there are observations which suggest a specific neural function of thiamine,[65] the general distribution makes it appear that these compounds probably play a supporting role, albeit an important one, rather than a specialized function in subserving that peculiar explosive excitability which distinguishes neural activity. We shall consider here rather those onium compounds, both naturally occurring and exogenous, which in minute amounts appear to effect intense changes in the function of specific excitable tissues.

Development of the Concept of Chemical Transmission

It is now more than eighty years since Crum Brown and Fraser[21] first described the curariform properties of certain quaternary ammonium bases. Burn and Dale[16] in an extensive survey of the effects of tetramethylammonium first pointed out that this simple ion, in addition to blocking transmission of stimulation from nerve ending to striated muscle (curare action), also mimicked the varied effects of activity in the peripheral parasympathetic nerves (muscarine action) as well as stimulating sympathetic ganglia (nicotine action). In this same study they demonstrated that a closely related congener, tetraethylammonium (TEA), did not exhibit the same effects as tetramethylammonium despite the similarity of their structures. But tetraethylammonium was discovered to block transmission across ganglionic synapses, as do larger doses of nicotine. In this early study Burn and Dale posed the central problem which is unanswered still: what "specific constitution of an excitable structure" makes it respond so differently to such simple organic cations which are so similar structurally. It would be important at this point to emphasize that the engaging theories which have been proposed to answer this puzzle and which are based, for example, on patterns of molecular structure[46, 47, 70, 76, 77] or differences in solubility of these compounds in lipids,[66] are often hypotheses which exceed to an appreciable degree the experimental evidence available to support them. The same reservations may be entered in acceptance of theories which are based conversely on Langley's fruitful hypothesis of a "receptive substance" in the excitable structure and its presumed structural relationship to the exciting agent.[55, 76] Theories of this nature are valuable, nonetheless, for their provocative nature; emphasis is laid here on the gap which exists between the theory and experimental test.

There has grown steadily, nevertheless, an orderly accumulation of evidence which leads inescapably to the conclusion that certain characteristic functions of excitable tissues, such as synaptic transmission, are linked inextricably with distinctive chemical events. Our story, in skeleton form, begins with the suggestion by Elliott[33] in 1905 that since epinephrine mimicked the effects of activity of peripheral sympathetic nerves, it might be the chemical mediator between sympathetic nerves and their effector cells. A somewhat neglected suggestion by Dixon and Hamill[27] in 1909 proposed that the similar actions of muscarine and of electrical excitation of the vagus nerve warranted the assumption that "excitation of nerve induces the local liberation of a hormone which causes specific activity by combination with some constituent of the end organ, muscle or gland."

The conspicuous vasodepressor activity of very small amounts of acetylcholine (ACh) had been noted by Hunt and Taveau[45] when Dale[22] examined several choline derivatives and discovered that they exhibited in varying degree both muscarine- and nicotine-like actions. Of the group examined, ACh was especially prominent for the resemblance which existed between its effect and the effects of activity in certain divisions of the autonomic nervous system.

And there the matter rested. There was a wealth of information to indicate that several chemical agents, prominent among them certain simple quaternary ammonium compounds, possessed the capacity to evoke peripheral responses which resembled the effects of activity in the autonomic nervous system. Whether any of these substances played a role in normal function was a matter for speculation alone, and the ensuing war years brought experimentation to a close.

Then in 1921 Loewi[59] reported his simple, cunning, and convincing observation that, when its vagus nerve was stimulated, the isolated frog heart would pour into its perfusing fluid a substance which would reproduce the effects of vagal excitation when transferred to another isolated heart.* This discovery established the fact that a chemical substance was involved in the excitation of effectors by the vagus, but its identity was unknown. The similarity between the actions of this *Vagusstoff* of Loewi's and the effects of ACh described by Dale in 1914 was noted immediately, but, in actual fact, the natural occurrence of ACh in tissue was not established by chemical isolation until 1929.[25] There still existed certain pharmacologic obstacles to the complete acceptance of acetylcholine as Loewi's transmitter, but their

---

* The restrictions imposed by space and emphasis preclude consideration of the classic contributions of Walter B. Cannon, his colleagues, and his scientific descendants to the development of our concepts of chemical mediation by means of epinephrine. These elegant experiments were reported first in the same year that Loewi observed parasympathetic chemical mediation[18] and later were woven into an embracing hypothesis.[17, 72]

correspondence seemed almost sure; and there was, and for that matter still is, general agreement that the relatively slow effect of activity in certain autonomic nerves was mediated by the appearance of ACh at the endings of those nerves which have been classified as cholinergic according to Dale's definition.[23]

Although transmission of excitation from any one cellular unit to another probably must follow some general pattern or employ some common mechanisms, nevertheless, excitation of smooth muscle and glands by autonomic nerves has parameters which make it difficult to relate immediately to similar activity in the central nervous system. Sherrington has expressed the view that "the transmission of excitation from a motor nerve ending to a voluntary muscle fibre probably furnishes a pattern, or paradigm, of what happens at a central synapse,"[24] and Eccles[28, 29] has considered the sympathetic ganglion as providing a peripheral example of synaptic phenomena occurring deep within the neuraxis. But in addition to these arguments for viewing these peripheral structures as models of central function, there were the older observations of Dale that ACh produced nicotine-like effects on both striated muscle and ganglion cells. If the muscarine-like effects of ACh on parasympathetic effectors reflected a physiologic mechanism, was not a similar role to be expected in those areas where nicotine effects were evoked? Whether or not these peripheral junctions will be proved eventually to share common mechanisms with central synapses, it has been agreed generally that the awful complexity of central phenomena made necessary some clarification of the relatively simple and isolable events occurring at the neuromuscular junction and in the peripheral sympathetic ganglion.

Feldberg and his colleagues[36, 37] demonstrated a release of ACh by the ganglion during transfer of excitation across its synapses, and an excitation of the ganglion cells by ACh. Thus, at last evidence was forthcoming to strengthen the suspicion that ACh might play an intimate part in transmission of excitation in the ganglion. The evidence that ACh was involved also in neuromuscular transmission rested on a similar set of observations of the release of ACh during activity[26] and the evocation of a twitch in a striated muscle when it was perfused suddenly with minute amounts of ACh via a local artery.[11]

At this point in the yet unfinished story of the development of concepts of the role of chemical mediation in transmission of nervous excitation there arose a storm of critical opposition which has never died away completely. Much of the criticism was based on valid reservations arising from the obvious paucity of information regarding the intimate characteristics of the release of ACh at its supposed site of action. This critical evaluation was responsible for continuing refinement in experimental technic; and with each refinement the case for chemical transmission became more difficult to ignore. Some of the criticism then and now appears to arise from that common tendency to exclusive preoccupation with the particular tool of measurement or symbolic currency with which the analyst is most familiar. Lewis Carroll described the syndrome in *Through the Looking Glass:*

"'What is it you want to buy?' the Sheep said. at last.

"'I don't *quite* know yet,' Alice said very gently, 'I should like to look all round me first, if I might.'

"'You may look in front of you, and on both sides, if you like,' said the Sheep, 'but you can't look *all* round you—unless you've got eyes at the back of your head.'

"But these, as it happened, Alice had *not* got."

There has been a welcome decline in the dichotomizing approach which once considered phenomena in excitable tissues to be explicable in either electrical or chemical terms, while the importance of a pluralistic view has been stressed.[8, 9] It seems trite now to re-emphasize that electrical activity accompanies chemical events and that chemical changes cannot be dissected from their physical aspects. An engaging demonstration of these inextricable relationships has been provided by Beutner and Barnes.[4, 5, 6] They showed that in an aqueous-nonaqueous system the positive potential existing at the phase boundary could be converted rapidly by minute amounts of ACh into an impressive negative potential, of the order occurring at the membrane in excitable tissues. This effect could be produced by other agents but none of those observed was active in as small a molar concentration as ACh. The behavior of this artificial system reflects the intense depolarizing action of ACh on such special structures as, for example, the end-plate.[51]

The arrangement of this essay has been planned to present in the general order of development those observations and hypotheses which point to acetylcholine as a special quaternary ammonium cation which plays an extraordinarily immediate role in the transmission of excitation during neural activity. In order to avoid neglect of collateral evidence, it appears appropriate at this juncture to note the warning signs that acetylcholine may well have a much broader cellular function than the one restricted to neural activity. For example, one would have some difficulty selecting two organs more "non-neural" in their function than placenta and spleen; yet, these two tissues contain enormous quantities of acetylcholine; there are suggestions that acetylcholine is related intimately to the integrity of the surface membrane of the erythrocyte;[74] and the concentration of ACh in various structures in the nervous system is related more closely to resistance to hypoxia than to the apparent functional pattern.[75] There is reawakened interest in the real probability that acetylcholine cannot be identified with neural activity alone, but that, in addition to certain derivative functions in nervous tissues, it acts more generally as, for example, a trophic substance or coenzyme in the regulation of cell membranes,[75] or as a local hormone which regulates rhythmic activity in such structures as auricle or gut.[15] These considerations inevitably will broaden our views of the over-all function of ACh, but in no sense do they make frivolous the continuing efforts to define the special roles played by the quaternary ammonium cations in nervous activity. A comparable case may be made for the potassium ion: its ubiquity bespeaks the part it plays in so many processes, and yet it has peculiarly specific tasks in nervous function.

With a frank acknowledgment that to focus on neural activity may neglect other important phases of ACh function, we may return to our more restricted story. The evidence that ACh appears at cholinergic nerve-endings has been adduced in so many different circumstances that there is little doubt of the fact. Although ACh stimulates in small amounts, an accumulation of ACh in concentration greater than a critical level paralyzes synapses at neuromuscular and ganglionic junctions. It was this property which led Dale,[22] in his first speculations regarding the physiologic significance of choline esters, to point out the probability that some mechanism must exist to inactivate ACh rapidly when it was released. And then later, Loewi and Navratil[60] discovered that the heart did contain an esterase which would inactivate both ACh and their *Vagusstoff*. This finding was the first in a torrent of observations which have made the family of cholinesterases (ChE) one of the most exhaustively described enzyme systems.[2, 7] The demonstration that ChE existed in body tissues did not, however, establish that a sufficient concentration resided at the junction to insure the almost instantaneous hydrolysis of ACh. Nachmansohn[67] and his colleagues undertook a series of investigations which took advantage of such specialized organs as the electroplaxes of *Torpedo* and *Electrophorus*, as well as muscle and ganglia and brain, and, in experiments of increasing precision, were able to show that indeed there did exist at the proper site amounts of ChE adequate to hydrolyze ACh in the brief instant that was required. In point of fact, the familiar prodigality of nature is displayed so strikingly in this case, that Gerard[39] calculated that if the ChE in frog nerve "were fully active, the ACh hydrolysis heat alone would account for more than the full extra heat production of active nerve." Thus, there is much evidence to support the view that there is ample ChE available at strategic locations to inactivate ACh. As with ACh, there are other indications that ChE is involved in tissue mechanisms not related primarily to neural activity: ChE occurs in high concentration in non-neural structures such as serum and erythrocyte, and there are distinctions to be made between ChE's derived from various sources on the basis of their capacity to hydrolyze specific substrates.[2, 7] Nonetheless, the answer to Dale's requirement has been furnished, and the means are available to prevent accumulation of paralyzing concentrations of ACh at synaptic areas. And, furthermore, considerable assurance can be gained from the realization that there is intense local concentration of a necessary and specific enzyme precisely where the theory demands it should be.[49] However, there remains the open question as to whether these enzymes perform functions of quite different a nature; e.g., destroy ACh before it can excite. Possibilities of this sort exist but lack any experimental support.

We have indicated the primary evidence that there is involved in nervous function a peculiarly potent quaternary ammonium cation, ACh, and an esterase to check its activity, ChE. Another and important link in the chain was provided by Nachmansohn[67] and his colleagues when they discovered a specific enzyme responsible for ACh synthesis, choline acetylase (ChA); they have defined also several features of this choline-acetylating system which relate it intimately to the other familiar cellular mechanisms for the provision and transformation of energy.

What began as astute intuitive deductions by Elliott and Dixon and Dale and Loewi now looms as a complex system in which there has been described and defined the agent, ACh, as well as its synthetic (ChA) and hydrolytic (ChE) enzymes. There is fairly general agreement regarding the intimate part played by this ACh system in transmitting excitation from several autonomic nerves to their effectors.[72] The exact mode of participation of the ACh system in transmission at the neuromuscular junction, across the peripheral ganglionic synapse, and within the central nervous system is under continued analysis. Before examining the evidence it is worthwhile pointing out that these three sites have been listed above in a rank order proportional to the increasing degree of controversy which surrounds them.

Neuromuscular Transmission

In an analysis of synaptic transmission we may begin with the neuromuscular junction. With each succeeding year the reported studies have added more and more evidence to support the current view that ACh is the sole agent responsible for transmission of excitation at this site. The reviews of Acheson,[1] Eccles,[31] and Kuffler[53, 54] provide documentation of the very considerable evidence which makes the original scheme suggested by Dale, Feldberg, and Vogt still the best available. Furthermore, Kuffler's evidence renders it unlikely indeed that neuromuscular transmission can result at all from current flow impinging on excitable resting end-plate from the neighboring nerve-ending. An abbreviated selection of the particularly telling experiments and relationships might include the following: juxta-terminal anodal block of the nerve prevents the normal action potential from producing any effect on the end-plate anticipated on the basis of the current flow hypothesis; the neuromuscular delay of about 1 msec. is a period of complete electrical quiet, a finding incompatible with electrotonic spread; the duration of the end-plate potential (e.p.p.) exceeds by some five times the period of action potential in the nerve ending; veratrine, in amounts which prolong the after-potential of nerve without induction of repetitive firing, fails to alter the e.p.p.;[52] and, finally, distortion of normal neurohumoral relationships by a variety of anticholinesterases produces proportional changes in the e.p.p., a demonstration of the dependence of the e.p.p. on the activity of ACh.[32] Concordant results are to be found in the effect of curare which is to be discussed below. And, finally, Burgen, Dickens, and Zatman have taken telling advantage of that experiment of nature provided by botulinus toxin; they showed that when botulinus toxin had created a neuromuscular block, the nerve still conducted and the end-plate was excitable but the local release of ACh had declined to ineffective amounts.[14] We may conclude, therefore, that the overwhelming weight of evidence today supports with considerable decisiveness the hypothesis that transmission of excitation across the neuromuscular junction results from the release of ACh at the nerve ending and the consequent depolarization of the end-plate. The observations which prevent acceptance without any reservation have been marshalled and weighed by Gerard.[40] Emphasis is laid on the conclusion that neuromuscular transmission is best explained today by the ACh hypothesis because as we consider more centrally disposed synapses no such satisfying judgment can be reached.

Ganglionic Transmission

If one concludes from present evidence that ACh is the transmitter at the neuromuscular junction, then one is obliged to entertain the possibility that ACh performs, perhaps in part, a similar duty at other sites in the nervous system. The sympathetic ganglion has proved to be particularly susceptible to observation in which a degree of experimental isolation is feasible. The original demonstration of release of ACh during neural activity established the fact that ACh plays some part in ganglionic activity, and ganglionic stimulation by minute quantities of ACh was in accord with this finding. Degeneration of preganglionic fibers is followed by disappearance of the ACh system in the ganglion whose cells retain their sensitivity to ACh;[12] and this occurrence suggests that the ACh system is not simply an accompaniment of ganglion cell metabolism, but is related to activity in the preganglionic terminals. And, furthermore, the persistent discharge of ganglion cells following bursts of preganglionic stimulation, as described by Larrabee and Bronk[56, 57] is compatible with local persistence of a chemical mediator because the one-to-one arrangement of the ganglion precludes the operation of internuncial, reverberatory systems. Their description of prolonged facilitation after activity cannot be explained so simply.[58] It is because of evidence of this sort that there has persisted the reasonable suspicion that ACh plays an immediate part in ganglionic synaptic transmission. However, the experimental support of this hypothesis is by no means as firm as that which applies to the neuromuscular junction. Eccles[29] has expressed and put to certain experimental tests an hypothesis of ganglionic transmission which describes a synaptic potential composed of (1) an initial, very brief potential which is not affected by anti-ChE compounds and, therefore, is attributed to the action current of the preganglionic impulses; and (2) a later, slower, and prolonged potential which is enhanced after repetitive activity or inhibition of ChE activity. This latter potential is attributed to the effect of ACh. Eccles' elegant theoretic analyses and investigations have clarified a number of aspects of transmission in the ganglion; but more important still, he himself has emphasized certain phenomena which make it difficult to assign a totally subsidiary role to ACh. These difficulties arise especially from those effects of curare and of anti-ChE compounds which are better explained in terms of their interference with the known properties of the ACh mechanism. An escape from the dilemma might appear if a single nerve-to-ganglion cell synapse were susceptible to the analysis provided by Kuffler for a single nerve-muscle junction; but until some such approach, direct or indirect, has been perfected, any judgment must remain tentative.

Central Transmission

It was noted earlier that as our serial consideration of the role of ACh in neural activity followed a centripetal route the difficulties, both experimental and analytic, would increase.[30] Indeed, the difficulties are so great that even the most tentative judgments must be based on speculation rather than any balance of evidence. Until recently the reasons for suspecting that ACh might enter into transmission of excitation in the central nervous system were essentially two in kind. The first was a reasonable central extension of mechanisms which were gaining support from experimental analysis of peripheral synapses. The validity of this reason continues to be as solid as ever on philosophic, phylogenetic, and analytic grounds, despite the fact that it may prove eventually to be only partially or not-at-all true. The second reason might be either a fruitful lead or a treacherous pharmacologic trap; for it might be the familiar illusion that an agent which produces a physiologic effect must represent a natural process. Feldberg[34] has accumulated the bewildering array of reported observations on the central effects of ACh. These effects are so varying, so susceptible to misinterpretation, and, in several cases, so contradictory that no one has dared to integrate them all into a unitary plan. And at this point there would seem little more to be concluded than that ACh exerts effects when introduced into a number of loci in the neuraxis, and the significance of these effects is not clear.

However, the case for a role played by ACh in central neural function cannot be rejected for reasons to be noted here. There are scattered observations which indicate a release of ACh during intense activity of large central neural masses.[13] And recent experiments with improved technics suggest that significant fluctuations in concentration of free ACh occur in the brain during activity and rest.[71]

Then, too, several anti-ChE agents produce striking effects in central nervous system function.[43, 50] It was suggested guardedly that the extraordinary symptoms produced by DFP in man were explicable in terms of inhibition of ChE, because at the time these observations were made no other action of DFP had been defined.[42] Since then DFP and other anti-ChE agents have been reported to reduce oxygen metabolism of the isolated frog brain and nerve and their capacity to suppress spontaneous electrical activity or conduction has been correlated with a reduction in respiration rather than with the inhibition of ChE activity.[10, 40] These constitute valuable extensions of our knowledge concerning the possible scope of action of anti-ChE compounds but the extraordinary differences in the experiments make it difficult to compare them. DFP in minute amounts invoked epileptic-like changes in the electrical activity of the brain of normal man and these synchronized bursts of overactivity were erased by atropine; in the frog, DFP first reduced spontaneous electrical waves at a concentration of 10 mM, and atropine had no blocking effect. All these varying observations which cannot be fitted into a satisfying pattern require that utmost caution be exercised in attempting either to exclude or to establish ACh as a central transmitter on the basis of actions of anti-ChE compounds.

Feldberg and his colleagues[35, 38] are responsible lately for devising a fresh and promising approach to the problem. By refinements in the Nachmansohn-Machado technic for *in vitro* measurement of choline acetylase, they have examined local nuclear masses and tracts of the central nervous system to assess the contribution of ACh in terms of its synthesizing enzyme rather than in terms of evanescent ACh itself. Their preliminary findings are extraordinary: there are functional units which are cholinergic (anterior horn cells, cranial motor nuclei, second sensory neurones, retina) and others which are so low in content of ChA that they are unlikely to employ the ACh system in function (posterior roots and spinal columns, eighth nerve nuclei, optic tract). These findings suggest to Feldberg that there may be alternating cholinergic and non-cholinergic neurons in both efferent and afferent pathways. This bold and engaging hypothesis does no violence to the pattern which has been established for peripheral mechanisms; there are autonomic nerves which are adrenergic in chemical mediation, and yet their cell bodies in the ganglion are stimulated by cholinergic preganglionic fibers. If Feldberg's theory stands under the scrutiny of continuing investigations it will provide a basis for still further search for the specific role of ACh in central neural function; and at this time it assuages the discomfiture caused by the many inexplicable observations which have dealt with the central nervous system as a unit instead of a fabric whose threads may vary qualitatively in their chemical mode of performance. No fact described to date establishes ACh as a central chemical mediator with the same probability that exists for the neuromuscular junction. This lack of proof requires strident emphasis; but, on the other hand, there are many indications which make it a most attractive possibility.

Block of Transmission

The principle of metabolic antagonism by structurally related compounds as an experimental tool for assessing the role of a specific substance has found general application. There are a number of quaternary ammonium compounds which possess the capacity to block transmission, especially at neuromuscular and sympathetic ganglionic synapses, and this faculty has been employed experimentally to explore the role of the naturally occurring chemical mediator, ACh.[44] Perhaps the simplest of these compounds is the tetraethylammonium cation which has been recognized for so long as a blocking agent.[64] By far the greatest mass of investigation has been devoted to curare and its active constituent, d-tubocurarine.[19, 63, 68] Aside from their usefulness as analytic tools, curare, and the other quaternary ammonium compounds which display blocking activity, are of especial interest because of their peculiar property of rendering certain effectors insensitive to ACh despite continuation of ACh release at the synapse, and the maintenance of effector excitability to other modes of stimulation. What is known about these blocking agents fits well with the general view that they compete with the chemical mediator for an hypothetic "receptor substance" in the effector.[55] There are, however, a sufficient number of inexplicable anomalies to render this form of analysis subject to limitation in its general application. For example, the possession of a quaternary ammonium component *per se* cannot be requisite because atropine blocks powerfully at several peripheral cholinergic nerve endings. Then, too, in the light of what is known it would be necessary to envisage a somewhat different sort of receptive substance at several effector sites: for TEA blocks at the ganglion but only very slightly at the neuromuscular junction; curare blocks at the neuromuscular junction but less effectively at the ganglion; and atropine blocks slightly only in very high concentration at the neuromuscular and ganglionic junctions. Just when inconsistencies like these make it seem advisable to hold the hypothesis in temporary abeyance, a new set of observations occurs to reopen the question. These appear as descriptions of new blocking agents composed of two terminal trimethylammonium groups separated by simple hydrocarbon chains varying in length.[3, 69] When the chain consists of ten carbon atoms the substance, C_{10}, is curariform; when the chain contains only five carbon atoms, C_5, the agent blocks at autonomic ganglia. And to add to the neatness of the story, C_5 blocks C_{10} at the neuromuscular junction. Further observations have shown that C_{10} possesses the unique quality of blocking the propagated action potential in denervated muscle and this action is in turn blocked by d-tubocurarine.[48] Thus, despite the unexplained variations, the case remains good for continued belief that some special stereochemical properties of both active agents and the effectors on which they act are responsible for the relationships which have been exemplified above. The action of quaternary ammonium blocking agents on central neural function is sufficiently controversial to justify omission of discussion here, other than to indicate that evidence adduced to conclude that no central action occurs[73] may be compared with other observations which suggest direct central blocking actions.[62]

Conduction and Excitability in Nerve

Sharp disagreement exists among the views held regarding the precise part played by the ACh system in the propagation of the conducted action potential in nerve. Nachmansohn[67] has argued forcibly that the kinetics of the ACh system, the distribution of its component parts along the axon, and the permeability of the myelin sheath all support the hypothesis that the release and removal of ACh during neural activity are essential events in nervous conduction as well as in transmission. It is unwarranted at this stage in the growth of knowledge to attempt to tally the score and arrive at a final decision. I believe it reasonable to assume the following temporary position: the demonstration that many nervous structures contain the complete ChA-ACh-ChE system makes inescapable the conclusion that this system enters importantly into certain aspects of neural function; nevertheless, only a few of the objections leveled against the theory are sufficient to warrant the utmost circumspection in embracing it. For example, despite disagreements regarding technical validity, it appears likely at this date that nerves will conduct when all their ChE has been inactivated;[20, 41] and there are neuronal systems which appear to be virtually lacking in an ACh system.[35] For these and other related observations we are not justified now in assuming more than that the ACh system functions in some as yet undefined manner in some nerves, and that its presence is not essential to all forms of neural activity.

The final consideration here of the role played by quaternary ammonium compounds in neural activity has to do with the extensive investigations of great interest which have been reported by Lorente de Nó.[61] It needs saying at the outset that the experimental basis for the far-reaching hypothesis is confined to observations of isolated frog nerve; transfer of the findings to other neural functions must await further study. Lorente de Nó has discovered that in frog nerve maintenance of excitability is dependent solely on the availability of oxgyen and sodium in the immediate environment. The fading of excitability which accompanies deprivation of sodium may be reversed by provision of a number of related quaternary ammonium ions, but not, for example, by ACh, TMA, or thiamine. From the many observations inadequately indicated here, Lorente de Nó suggests that intracellular conversion of tricovalent to tetracovalent nitrogen, with its strong ionic charge, participates in the establishment of electric double layers, or polarization, in the nerve membrane. He has extracted, further-more, from ox brain certain bases, which may be quaternary ammonium ions, and which restore excitability to frog nerve deprived of sodium. From these investigations and theories is derived the reasonable suspicion that one or several unidentified quaternary ammonium ions may be essential elements in the control of polarization across membranes in neural struc-tures.

Summary

By deliberate selection of reported investigations, balanced by reference to more extensive reviews, we have considered the widespread and complex participation in neural activity of a series of compounds which share the possession of quaternary ammonium components. Whether or not this is an illusory common denominator is not clear; but at least it can be said that if an agent contains a quaternary ammonium structure, it or a structural congener is very likely to produce in small amounts one or both of the following phenomena in neural structures: stimulation of effectors innervated by cholinergic fibers (glands, smooth muscle, striated muscle, sympathetic ganglia, and some central structures), or block of transmission of excita-tion at a variety of synaptic junctions which contain cholinergic members.

Acetylcholine, its synthesizing enzyme choline acetylase, and its hydro-lyzing enzyme acetylcholine esterase appear together in many, but not all, neural structures in a relationship which suggests reasonably that the synthesis, release, and destruction of ACh enters into neural activity as an immediate and essential cycle. The evidence that ACh is a natural chemical mediator for transmission of excitation from cholinergic autonomic nerves to their effectors and from motor nerves to striated muscle is satisfyingly good; the evidence for such participation at sympathetic ganglia and in central structures is less decisive, but the possibility remains real, attractive, and increasingly probable. There is much evidence that the ACh system plays a much wider part in general cellular economy than the special role assigned to it here in a consideration of neural activity.

REFERENCES

1. ACHESON, G. H.: *Federation Proceedings*, 1948, 7, pp. 447-51.
2. AUGUSTINSSON, K-B.: *Acta Physiologica Scandinavica*, 1948, 15, Suppl. 15.
3. BARLOW, R. B., and ING, H. R.: *British Journal of Pharmacology and Chemo-therapy*, 1948, 3, pp. 298-304.
4. BARNES, T. C.: *Anatomical Review*, 1947, 99, p. 618.
5. BARNES, T. C.: *Anatomical Review*, 1947, 99, p. 618.
6. BEUTNER, R.: Bioelectricity (in Glasser's "Medical Physics"). Year Book Publishers, Chicago, 1944.
7. BODANSKY, O.: *Annals of the New York Academy of Science*, 1946, 47, pp. 521-547.

8. BRINK, F., JR.; BRONK, D. W.; and LARRABEE, M. G.: *Annals of the New York Academy of Science*, 1946, 47, pp. 457-485.

9. BRONK, D. W.: *Journal of Neurophysiology*, 1939, 2, pp. 380-401.

10. BROOKS, V. B.; RANSMEIER, R. E.; and GERARD, R. W.: *American Journal of Physiology*, 1949, 157, pp. 299-316.

11. BROWN, G. L.; DALE, H. H.; and FELDBERG, W.: *Journal of Physiology*, 1936, 87, pp. 394-424.

12. BROWN, G. L., and FELDBERG, W.: *Journal of Physiology*, 1936, 88, pp. 265-283.

13. BÜLBRING, E., and BURN, J. H.: *Journal of Physiology*, 1941, 100, pp. 337-368.

14. BURGEN, A. S. V.; DICKENS, F.; and ZATMAN, L. J.: *Journal of Physiology*, 1949, 109, pp. 10-24.

15. BURN, J. H.: *Physiological Reviews*, 1950, 30, pp. 177-193.

16. BURN, J. H., and DALE, H. H.: *Journal of Pharmacology*, 1915, 6, pp. 417-438.

17. CANNON, W. B., and ROSENBLUETH, A.: Autonomic Neuro-effector Systems. The Macmillan Co., New York, 1937.

18. CANNON, W. B., and URIDIL, J. E.: *American Journal of Physiology*, 1921, 58, pp. 353-364.

19. CRAIG, L. E.: *Chemical Reviews*, 1948, 42, pp. 285-410.

20. CRESCITELLI, F. N.; KOELLE, G. B.; and GILMAN, A.: *Journal of Neurophysiology*, 1946, 9, pp. 241-252.

21. CRUM BROWN, A., and FRASER, T.: *Proceedings of the Royal Society of Edinburgh*, 1869, 6, p. 556. Quoted by Burn and Dale.[16]

22. DALE, H. H.: *Journal of Pharmacology*, 1914, 6, pp. 147-190.

23. DALE, H. H.: *Journal of Physiology*, 1933, 80, pp. 10-11P.

24. DALE, H. H.: *The Harvey Lectures*, 1937, 32, pp. 229-245.

25. DALE, H. H., and DUDLEY, H. W.: *Journal of Physiology*, 1929, 68, pp. 97-123.

26. DALE, H. H.; FELDBERG, W.; and VOGT, M.: *Journal of Physiology*, 1936, 86, pp. 353-380.

27. DIXON, W. E., and HAMILL, P.: *Journal of Physiology*, 1909, 38, pp. 314-336.

28. ECCLES, J. C.: *Journal of Physiology*, 1944, 103, pp. 27-54.

29. ECCLES, J. C.: *Annals of the New York Academy of Science*, 1946, 47, pp. 429-455.

30. ECCLES, J. C.: *Journal of Neurophysiology*, 1947, 10, pp. 197-204.

31. ECCLES, J. C.: *Annual Review of Physiology*, 1948, 10, pp. 93-116.

32. ECCLES, J. C., and MACFARLANE, W. V.: *Journal of Neurophysiology*, 1949, 12, pp. 59-80.

33. ELLIOTT, T. R.: *Journal of Physiology*, 1905, 32, pp. 401-467.

34. FELDBERG, W.: *Physiological Reviews*, 1945, 25, pp. 596-642.

35. FELDBERG, W.: *British Medical Bulletin*, 1950, 6, pp. 312-321.

36. FELDBERG, W., and GADDUM, J. H.: *Journal of Physiology*, 1934, 81, pp. 305-319.

37. FELDBERG, W., and VARTIAINEN, A.: *Journal of Physiology*, 1934, 83, pp. 103-128.

38. FELDBERG, W., and VOGT, M.: *Journal of Physiology*, 1948, 107, pp. 372-381.

39. GERARD, R. W.: *Annals of the New York Academy of Science*, 1946, 47, pp. 575-600.

40. GERARD, R. W.: *Recent Progress in Hormone Research*, 1950, 5, pp. 37-61.

41. GERARD, R. W.; LIBET, B.; and CAVANAUGH, D.: *Federation Proceedings*, 1949, 8, pp. 55-56.

42. GROB, D.; HARVEY, A. M.; LANGWORTHY, O. R.; and LILIENTHAL, J. L., JR.: *Bulletin of the Johns Hopkins Hospital*, 1947, 81, pp. 257-266.

43. GROB, D.; LILIENTHAL, J. L., JR.; HARVEY, A. M.; and JONES, B. F.: *Bulletin of the Johns Hopkins Hospital*, 1947, 81, pp. 217-244.

44. HUNT, C. C., and KUFFLER, S. W.: *Journal of Pharmacology*, 1950, 98 (Part II), pp. 96-120.

45. HUNT, R., and TAVEAU, R. DEM.: *British Medical Journal*, 1906, 2, pp. 1788-1791.

46. ING, H. R.: *Physiological Reviews*, 1936, 16, pp. 527-544.

47. ING, H. R.: *Science*, 1949, 109, pp. 204-266.

48. JARCHO, L. W.; EYZAGUIRRE, C.; TALBOT, S. A.; and LILIENTHAL, J. L., JR.: *American Journal of Physiology*, 1950, 162, pp. 475-488.

49. KOELLE, G. B., and FRIEDENWALD, J. S.: *Proceedings of the Society for Experimental Biology and Medicine*, 1949, 70, pp. 617-622.

50. KOELLE, G. B., and GILMAN, A.: *Journal of Pharmacology and Experimental Therapeutics*, 1949 (Part II), 95, pp. 166-216.

51. KUFFLER, S. W.: *Journal of Neurophysiology*, 1943, 6, pp. 99-110.

52. KUFFLER, S. W.: *Journal of Neurophysiology*, 1945, 8, pp. 113-122.

53. KUFFLER, S. W.: *Federation Proceedings*, 1948, 7, pp. 437-466.

54. KUFFLER, S. W.: Transmission Processes at Nerve-Muscle Junctions. Michaelis Memorial Volume, to be published.

55. LANGLEY, J. N.: *Journal of Physiology*, 1909, 39, pp. 235-295.

56. LARRABEE, M. G., and BRONK, D. W.: *Proceedings of the Society for Experimental Biology and Medicine*, 1938, 38, pp. 921-922.

57. LARRABEE, M. G., and BRONK, D. W.: *Federation Proceedings*, 1946, 5, p. 60.

58. LARRABEE, M. G., and BRONK, D. W.: *Journal of Neurophysiology*, 1947, 10, pp. 139-154.

59. LOEWI, O.: *Archiv für die gesamte Physiologie*, 1921, 189, pp. 239-242.

60. LOEWI, O., and NAVRATH, E.: *Archiv für die gesamte Physiologie*, 1926, 214, pp. 678-688.

61. LORENTE DE NÓ, R.: *Journal of Cellular and Comparative Physiology*, 1949, 33, supplement.

62. MARRAZI, A. S.; HART, E. R.; and KING, E. E.: Cerebral Curarization. In press.

63. McINTYRE, A. R.: Curare. Its History, Nature and Clinical Use. Chicago, University of Chicago Press, 1947.

64. MOE, G. K., and FREYBURGER, W. A.: *Journal of Pharmacology and Experimental Therapeutics*, 1950, 98 (Part II), pp. 61-95.

65. V. MURALT, A.: *Experientia*, 1945, 1, pp. 136-147.

66. NACHMANSOHN, D.: Metabolism and Function. Studies on Permeability in Relation to Nerve Function. I. Axonal Conduction and Synaptic Transmission. New York, Elsevier Publishing Co., 1950.

67. NACHMANSOHN, D.: The Hormones (Edit. Pincus, G., and Thimann, K. L.), vol. 2, pp. 515-599, 1950.

68. PATON, W. D. M.: *Journal of Pharmacy and Pharmacology*, 1949, 1, pp. 273-286.

69. PATON, W. D. M., and ZAIMIS, E. J.: *British Journal of Pharmacology and Chemotherapy*, 1949, 4, pp. 381-400.

70. PFEIFFER, C. C.: *Science*, 1948, 107, pp. 94-96.

71. RICHTER, D., and CROSSLAND, J.: *American Journal of Physiology*, 1949, 159, pp. 247-255.

72. ROSENBLUETH, A.: The Transmission of Nerve Impulses at Neuroeffector Junctions and Peripheral Synapses. New York, John Wiley, 1950.
73. SMITH, S. M.; BROWN, H. O.; TOMAN, J. E. P.; and GOODMAN, L.: *Anesthesiology*, 1947, 8, pp. 1-14.
74. WELLER, J. M., and TAYLOR, I. M.: *Annals of Internal Medicine*, 1950, 33, pp. 607-612.
75. WELSH, J. H.: *Bulletin of Johns Hopkins Hospital*, 1948, 83, pp. 568-579.
76. WELSH, J. H.: *American Scientist*, 1950, 38, pp. 239-246.
77. WELSH, J. H., and TAUB, R.: *Science*, 1950, 112, pp. 467-469.

A Confession of Ignorance

WARREN S. MCCULLOCH, M.D.

I had hoped to have something very exciting to say, but, as usual, I have run into a blind lead.

Because of Dr. Meduna's perennial dislike for his firstborn, shock therapy, we have for years been trying, first, to make out how it worked, and thereafter to find a substitute for it. In the attempt to find out how it worked we used convulsant after convulsant and found with all of them the same general story as far as the shift in carbohydrate metabolism was concerned. With every seizure there was a fall in the energetic phosphate bonds—phosphocreatine and adenosine triphosphate—and with all convulsants there was an accumulation of lactic acid.

We then undertook to find other ways of producing the same chemical changes. We used cyanide which, to a lesser extent, causes the same shift in the carbohydrate metabolism of brain. That turned out to be of no use as an agent in curing patients.

Now, as it was clear that the peripheral motor seizure was of no value in curing patients, we wondered whether the cortical seizure was of any value, and we began to look for other agents. The literature disclosed that the compound which was known to produce seizures in the cerebellum contained chlorine atoms; we then began to look for other characteristics that might be useful. At that time we undertook an investigation of agenized breadstuffs, thinking these might have chlorines in a position beta to a nitrogen. You—at least the chemists—are more familiar with that story than I am. It turned out that while the NCl^3-breadstuffs initiated seizures in the cerebellum, they destroyed the cerebellar nuclei and were therefore useless. We then tried another group of compounds, the so-called nitrogen mustards, of which we investigated eighty in all. Those which are capable of producing seizures are bis beta chlor-nitrogen mustards, in which the remaining radical is more than a hydrogen. I am told by my friends in chemistry that this is the condition (that it should contain more than a mere hydrogen here) for its being able to be converted to a tetravalent nitrogen, and that we may be playing again with our old friend, the tetravalent nitrogen, cropping up in a new form.

The interesting point concerning all of the convulsants that start seizures in the cerebellum was that the seizures were precipitated by breathing carbon dioxide; whereas with every cortical convulsant that we have tried the seizure has been prevented by feeding carbon dioxide.

Investigation of the nitrogen mustards, however, proved to be a blind lead because these compounds also caused degeneration of the nuclei of the cerebellum (most marked in the nucleus dentatus) and were consequently of no use in experiments on man as possible substitutes for ordinary shock therapy.

I began looking for other agents. Among those tried was eserine. With this agent I did not know where the seizures would start. During the investigation with this compound a peculiar phenomenon was noted. Those of you who are electrically minded will remember a long series of experiments that Dusser de Barenne and I carried out in New Haven on the ancient problem of facilitation and on extinction. If an area of cortex is stimulated following a prior stimulation of the same area, a larger or a smaller response is obtained according to the interval between the first and second period of stimulation. If the cortex of an animal under barbiturates is eserinized and then stimulated electrically, it is found that the eserine has produced no change in the threshold to electrical stimulation. If that area is atropinized, it is found that there is no change in the threshold to electrical stimulation. Yet eserine in large doses is a good convulsant, and convulsions can be stopped with large doses of atropine, which a cat can tolerate in enormous amounts.

There are three known factors entering into the facilitation and extinction of the motor response to stimulation at one point in the cortex. The first of these, an obvious one, is concerned with after-discharge. If the initial stimulus stirs up an after-discharge, a greater response is obtained than if the second stimulus falls in the silence after the after-discharge. That after-discharge turned out to be difficult to dodge in an eserinized cortex. The second factor is that if many cells lying close together are stimulated repeatedly there results a large change in the pH of that area, it being initially alkaline and subsequently acid, the alkalinity being associated with increased and the acidity with decreased responsiveness.

By familiarity with a given preparation and careful study, one can dodge both the after-discharge and the pronounced change in the pH of the area; thus the remaining facilitation is associated merely with a negativity of the surface of that cortex, with respect to its depth, in the excited area and nowhere else.

If, now, that area of cortex is eserinized, it is found that the period of negativity endures more than twice as long, and that the time the response is facilitated is enormously protracted. If the area is atropinized, the period of facilitation and the period of surface negative are cut approximately in half, although the size of the first motor response is unaffected.

Placing an interpretation on the behavior of the cortical elements very similar to that demonstrated by Dr. Lloyd in the cord, we have here motor neurons with apical dendrites and basal dendrites, and an axon going elsewhere. If the cell is stimulated repeatedly, there are stirred up impulses which as they play out into the dendritic end of that cell cannot possibly go all the way to the end following the first impulse, because the length of the impulse increases as the fiber-diameter decreases and when it dies its sink fades slowly. The time of fading will be too long to allow the rapid succession of aftercoming impulses to proceed as far. The process will end in a relatively depolarized state of the dendrites. A period of positive after-potential should supervene in the axon, and there should be, because of these polarizations, a polarization of the cortex—dendrite negative, axon positive—during which time the clear negativity of the surface could be recorded. During this time the superior part of the cell, being somewhat depolarized, might be more excitable, but the axon in hyperpolarization could deliver a greater kick. This is a very neat and simple theory, and if it were true the role of eserine and acetylcholine in the process would be relatively uncomplicated.

We went, therefore, next to Lloyd's preparation for the potentiation of the monosynaptic arc, and here we ran into a peculiar difficulty, which accounts for the fact that I have nothing exciting to report.

If the experimental animal is prepared by a high spinal transection, cutting only the dorsal roots in the lumbar enlargement necessary to reach the ventral roots, picking up the dorsal root or the motor nerve to be stimulated, and sectioning the ventral root and recording from it, it is found that the potentiation is enormously enhanced under eserine and reduced under atropine.

If, however, the cord is transected in the thoracic region and all of the dorsal roots, except the one to be stimulated or the one bringing impulses in from the muscle in question, are cut, and recordings are made from the motor root after it is cut, then there is obtained no change in potentiation on atropinization or on eserinization. In other words, at the present moment I can make neither head nor tail of the findings, and two preparations in which I can see no reason for any difference are giving diametrically opposite results.

This is the sort of obstacle I have encountered almost every time I have experimented with drugs in the spinal cord, above all with eserine, atropine, or DFP.

CHAPTER 13

Physiologic Development of the Cortex of the Brain and Its Relationship to Its Morphology, Chemical Constitution, and Enzyme Systems

LOUIS B. FLEXNER, M.D.

As FAR AS I KNOW, the physiologist Tarchanoff in the 1870's was the first person to apply a method of modern physiology to a study of the brain before birth. Tarchanoff's experiments were designed to test a thesis held at that time, namely, that the brain becomes organized for its control of muscular movements only after the eyes of the newborn animal have been opened for several days and the animal has received sufficient visual impression of its environment. In 1870 Fritsch and Hitzig demonstrated that localized muscular responses can be produced by electrical stimulation of the cortex. Tarchanoff argued that these responses are dependent upon cerebral organization and proceeded to study the effects of stimulation of the cerebral cortex in guinea pigs before birth and before their eyes were opened. He obtained positive results, that is, cortical stimulation evoked muscular contraction; thus he concluded that the brain is organized before birth and before the eyes are opened.

Our interest in the development of the brain has had a different origin. We have wanted to know when evidences of function could first be detected but we have in addition been concerned with underlying structural and chemical changes. An approach of this kind in which an effort is made to correlate the beginnings of function with structural and chemical change represents to me one of the most fascinating aspects of embryology. An organ of the fetus may be lacking in one or many of its typical activities up to a certain stage of development; then rather suddenly it may begin to function in a manner similar to that of the adult. The investigator is consequently presented with a situation in which he can analyze the structural and chemical changes which occur in cells when they change from a passive to an active functional state and in this manner, it is fair to assume, he

A report of investigations carried out largely with the collaboration of J. B. Flexner and V. B. Peters at the Department of Embryology, Carnegie Institution of Washington.

may gain insight into the mechanisms which underlie cellular activity. This is the viewpoint which has directed our studies on the developing cerebral cortex.

My introduction to this field came from a collaborative study with J. B. Flexner and W. L. Straus, Jr.,[8] on the developing cerebral cortex of the fetal pig. We found that there is a critical period about half way through gestation when there is an abrupt increase in the number of Nissl bodies, a rapid increase in size of the nerve cells, and a sudden rise in the activity of the respiratory enzyme cytochrome C. Further work showed that succinic dehydrogenase begins to increase rapidly in activity a few days after this period.[5]

The fetal pig is an inadequate experimental animal for a broad approach to this problem and we have consequently used the guinea pig for our more recent studies confining our attention so far as possible to the frontal cortex, areas f and f' of Fortuyn.[10] The microscopic studies which I shall first present were made by Peters.[14] The first aim of these cytologic studies was to determine how early in development the processes of the nerve cells of the frontal cortex make their appearance. The guinea pig has a gestation period of about sixty-six days. At the forty-first day of gestation, about two-thirds of the way through pregnancy, only a few of the nerve cells have processes. At the forty-fifth day, long processes are evident in most of the cells; when the whole depth of the cortex is viewed under the phase-contrast microscope the change is a very dramatic one. The cells were next examined for clumps of basophilic material, the Nissl bodies. Here again the forty-first to the forty-fifth days of gestation are critical ones. Before the forty-first day Nissl substance is absent; at about the forty-first day it appears for the first time and then rapidly accumulates during the next four days. And finally, using the ingenious methods of Chalkley for quantitative morphologic analysis as well as direct measurement, the average volume of the nuclei of the nerve cells was estimated during development. These measurements gave the surprising result that the nucleus apparently ceases to increase in volume at the critical stage of forty-one to forty-five days. This finding suggests the possibility that the nucleus reaches a considerable degree of maturity before the onset of fundamental changes in the cytoplasm evidenced by the rapid accumulation of Nissl bodies and the intense elaboration of processes.

With clear-cut and abrupt structural changes of this kind one immediately asks the question: Do fundamental biochemical changes occur at the same period? One of the first investigations of J. B. Flexner in a continuing study of metabolic relationships during growth and differentiation was on the enzyme apyrase[3] or ATPase believed by some to be involved in making energy available to the cell for its many activities from the energy-rich molecule ATP. This enzyme has a low activity up to the forty-second day of gestation; it then begins sharply to increase to the adult level. Changes of the same kind found in collaborative work with J. B. Flexner and E. L.

Belknap[1] have been found in the activities of respiratory enzymes. Thus succinic dehydrogenase and cytochrome oxidase follow the same pattern as does apyrase. It is clear, consequently, that microscopic changes which include rapid sprouting of the processes of the nerve cells, appearance of Nissl substance, and growth of the nucleus to its final volume are accompanied by sudden changes in the activities of certain enzymes.

What can be said of the beginnings of function in the nerve cells of the frontal cerebral cortex? Can the onset of function be correlated with the sudden structural and chemical changes which have just been described? We have approached this problem in two ways: first by recording the spontaneous electrical activity of the cortex and second by observing peripheral muscular response to electrical stimulation of the cortex. In a study of great interest and aid to us, Jasper, Bridgman, and Carmichael[12] found that they were first able to record electrical activity from the cortex of the fetal guinea pig at about the same time that we observed structural and chemical changes. Tyler, Gallant, and I[9] have confirmed these results with the addition that we have to our satisfaction demonstrated that these electric potentials arise in part at least from the cortex itself and not wholly at any rate from the underlying brain. In these experiments the spinal cords of pregnant animals were transected at the mid-thoracic level and then in the absence of anesthetic the fetuses were delivered into a saline bath at body temperature, with great care to disturb minimally the placental circulation and so to maintain the oxygen supply to the fetal brain. Potentials were recorded from bipolar leads taken from the surface of the cortex. As suggested by Jasper, Bridgman, and Carmichael, to test for artefact the umbilical cord was clamped; in absence of artefact the potential changes promptly disappeared as a consequence of the anoxia produced by clamping the cord. The cortical origin of the potentials was tested for by applying a small piece of filter paper wet with strychnine to the surface of the cortex and observing the prompt appearance of strychnine spikes. Potential changes were clearly evident with a fetus at the end of the critical period we have talked about, forty-six days of gestation. After application of strychnine there were typical spikes of activity. When the cord was clamped, all activity except a small artefact disappeared. By contrast, at the forty-fourth day of gestation no spontaneous activity could be recorded and application of strychnine was without effect. The evidence consequently indicates that spontaneous electrical activity can first be recorded from the frontal cerebral cortex at the end of the period critical for morphologic and certain biochemical changes, and that this activity arises in part at least from the cortical cells themselves.

Cortical stimulation carried on in our laboratory by Kimel and Kavaler,[13] again without anesthesia and with care to maintain the placental circulation, also indicates that the frontal cerebral cortex becomes organized for function at this time. Before this period the facial musculature which is represented in that part of the cortex we have studied fails to respond to electrical stimulation of the cortex. At about the same time that the cortex becomes spontaneously active, electrical stimulation for the first time evokes contraction of the facial musculature.

The appearance of brain potentials and of a positive response to cortical stimulation can be correlated with indications of the onset of function in higher parts of the central nervous system revealed by changes in the behavior of the fetus, as noted by Jasper, Bridgman, and Carmichael.[12] The appearance of spontaneous electrical activity occurs at about the same time as "the striking reduction of stimulus-released activity characteristic of late stages of fetal life" and at about the same time when there is a marked increase in responses after high transection of the spinal cord.

We have made an observation which possibly may give considerable insight into an event responsible for the onset of spontaneous electrical activity. Hodgkin and Katz[11] as well as other investigators now have evidence that the action potential of nerve may be due to the sudden development, as the nerve impulse is transmitted, of a selective permeability to sodium ions. This permits the positively charged sodium ions to move selectively from the fluid surrounding the nerve fiber into the fiber and in this way to set up a potential change. There is evidence that much the same thing may happen in the cortex when it first becomes electrically active. The demonstration depends upon the concept that the bulk of the chloride of the cortex is extracellular and that the cells themselves are relatively free of chloride. The extracellular space can consequently be estimated from the ratio of the concentration of chloride in the cortex to that in the blood plasma. This has been done during gestation.[6] The volume of tissue in which radiosodium is distributed is apparently the same as that of chloride up to forty days of gestation. At forty-six days, however, and thereafter sodium is distributed in a considerably larger volume than chloride. This, we believe, possibly may mean that nerve cells at this time become permeable to sodium, and since this is the same time as that at which electrical activity appears, we believe it possible that increase in permeability to sodium may be causally related to the appearance of electrical activity in conformity with the thesis of Hodgkin and Katz.

We next became interested in certain other aspects of the chemical composition of the cellular phase of the cortex during growth and differentiation. Let me first speak about the water, protein, and fat of the cellular phase during development. You will note that I used the term "cellular phase" and not "nerve cells." This is because we cannot distinguish among nerve cell bodies, nerve fibers, and glia in these studies. The question for experimental study was: Do the concentrations of water, protein, and fat of the cellular phase change during development? The approach depends upon the orthodox concept already alluded to, namely, that the chloride of the cortex is very largely extracellular, that the weight of the extracellular space can therefore be estimated from the ratio of concentration of chloride in the blood plasma to that in the cortex, and that the weight of the cellular phase can be obtained by difference. The fluid filling the extracellular space is assumed to be equivalent to an ultrafiltrate of plasma in equilibrium with it. With these assumptions one is in position to estimate the concentrations of the constituents of the cellular phase. The total water of a unit weight of cerebral cortex diminishes by about 10 per cent from the early stages of gestation to term.[4] This loss of water is accounted for by diminution in weight of the extracellular water, a reflection of the great increase in size and number of nerve processes. Total cellular water, over this same period, shows an over-all gain. The cellular phase increases in weight, however, more rapidly than does intracellular water with a consequent decrease in the concentration of cellular water as gestation advances. Additional studies showed that extractable fatty substances increase greatly in concentration, the rise beginning between the forty-first and forty-fifth days. This is the same period during which nerve processes start to grow in large numbers, and suggests that even in early stages of development cortical fibers have a fatty sheath such as has been demonstrated in the adult cortex by Brodal and Harrison.[2] The single constituent which appears to be at a constant level of concentration during gestation is protein.

The apparently constant level of concentration of cellular protein means to us that increase in size of the nerve cells as well as their elaboration of processes involves the synthesis of new protein molecules at such a rate that the over-all concentration of protein is unaltered. This raises a question, which I shall now briefly discuss. Energy-rich phosphate groups have been demonstrated to be essential for many synthetic reactions. Is their intracellular concentration altered when the synthetic activity of the nerve cell is greatly increased as evidenced by the intense elaboration of processes? The sum of the labile phosphorus of adenosine triphosphate plus ADP as well as that derived alone from phosphocreatine shows large fluctuations during gestation.[7] The decline in labile phosphate from ATP+ADP is particularly pronounced from the fortieth to the fiftieth day of gestation. Here as at other ages the decline in labile phosphate from one source is compensated for by an increase from the other source, so that the sum of energy-rich phosphate from ATP, ADP, and PC remains essentially constant throughout gestation and in the adult. We were considerably surprised by this finding. We had anticipated that increased synthetic activity of the nerve cells, evidenced as I have said by the appearance and rapid growth of fibers, as well as the increase in activity of ATPase to which I have referred, would result in a diminished level of energy-rich groups. The maintenance of a constant level of energy-rich groups from early in development to the adult indicates that throughout their life the nerve cells possess a mechanism which nicely balances the quantity of energy-rich phosphate which is synthesized against that which is dissipated. In calling attention to the increase in activity of ATPase and of synthetic activity by the cells during and after the critical period, I have emphasized factors which may be assumed to dissipate energy-rich phosphate. During the same period there is, however, an increase in the activity of respiratory enzymes which may be assumed to lead to an increase in the rate of synthesis of energy-rich groups. This viewpoint implies that although the concentration of energy-rich phosphate remains constant during development its rate of turnover increases coincident with the appearance of the factors which have been mentioned.

To fit the observations which I have given into a working hypothesis is not difficult. Cessation of growth of the nucleus at the critical period may be taken as evidence that a considerable degree of nuclear maturity precedes the beginning of rapid maturation of the cytoplasm signaled by the appearance of Nissl bodies and of processes. The neuroplasm synthesized during prenatal development contains a constant concentration of protein nitrogen and a progressively diminishing concentration of water; increase in extractable fatty substances which begins at the critical period is perhaps due in part to the deposition of fat in the sheaths of even the young processes. The increase in the activities of enzymes concerned with providing energy to the cell is correlated with greatly increased synthetic activity by the cells as shown by the rapid growth of processes. The level of energy immediately available to the cell from energy-rich phosphate compounds remains unaltered in spite of large variations in the demand made upon it for synthetic processes; there is reason to suppose, however, that the rate of turnover of energy-rich phosphate compounds may vary in accordance with changing circumstances. Not all of the available energy goes into synthetic processes; part is used to produce a typical activity of nerve cells, rhythmic changes in potential which themselves may be dependent upon alterations in the cell membrane permitting sodium ions to pass it. We do not at this time attempt to evaluate the scientific worth of this hypothesis. Its value to us, working together in this field, lies in the many studies it suggests to test each of its component parts.

REFERENCES

1. BELKNAP, E. L., and FLEXNER, J. B.: *Unpublished observations.*
2. BRODAL, A., and HARRISON, R. G.: *Quarterly Journal of Microscopic Science,* 1948, 89, p. 89.
3. FLEXNER, J. B., and FLEXNER, L. B.: *Journal of Cellular and Comparative Physiology,* 1948, 31, p. 311.
4. FLEXNER, J. B., and FLEXNER, L. B.: *Anatomical Record,* 1950, 106, p. 413.
5. FLEXNER, L. B., and FLEXNER, J. B.: *Journal of Cellular and Comparative Physiology,* 1946, 27, p. 35.
6. FLEXNER, L. B., and FLEXNER, J. B.: *Journal of Cellular and Comparative Physiology,* 1949, 34, p. 115.
7. FLEXNER, L. B., and FLEXNER, J. B.: *Journal of Cellular and Comparative Physiology.* In press.

8. FLEXNER, L. B.; FLEXNER, J. B.; and STRAUS, W. L., JR.: *Journal of Cellular and Comparative Physiology*, 1941, 18, p. 355.
9. FLEXNER, L. B.; TYLER, D. B.; and GALLANT, L. J.: *Journal of Neurophysiology*. In press.
10. FORTUYN, A. B. D.: *Archives of Neurology and Psychiatry*, 1950, 6, p. 221.
11. HODGKIN, A. L., and KATZ, B.: *Journal of Physiology*, 1949, 108, p. 37.
12. JASPER, H. H.; BRIDGMAN, C. S.; and CARMICHAEL, L.: *Journal of Experimental Psychology*, 1937, 21, p. 63.
13. KIMEL, V. M., and KAVALER, F.: *Journal of Comparative Neurology*. In press.
14. PETERS, V. B., and FLEXNER, L. B.: *American Journal of Anatomy*, 1950, 86, p. 133.

The Differentiation of Motor Neurons

DONALD H. BARRON, PH.D.

Nothing I could say would add luster to the beautiful things that you have heard described by my friend, Dr. Flexner, but I would like briefly to draw your attention to a question which arises out of a consideration of his findings, a question in which we have been interested at New Haven: Are these developmental changes in the histochemistry of the cells of the cerebral cortex a consequence of the expression of their genetic organization or are they the result of the interaction of the environment and that genetic pattern; that is to say, is the differentiation of a potential neuroblast into a full-blown neuron determined in part by the position of the cells within a community—a community that may be composed of cells destined to form neurons, glands, smooth or striated muscle?

The question seems to me to be an important one for it may very well be that the interaction of cells—interaction at their interfaces—during development may play the primary role in the determination of the final configuration of neurons and so in the direction of the pattern of neuronal organization and selectivity that is reflected in the control of the final effectors by the afferents of the nervous system.

Our experiments have not been upon the cortex. Flexner's studies have now opened the way for an experimental analysis of the forces involved in the differentiation of these elements and it should be done, but we have worked with the motor horn cells in the brachial and lumbosacral enlargements that supply the limb musculature in the chick.

We have taken advantage of the demonstration by Shorey,[5] Hamburger,[4] and others that the development of the full complement of motor cells in the lateral portion of the ventral horn is dependent upon the normal growth and differentiation of the limb; if the limb is removed before the axons of the motor neuroblasts most precocious in their appearance reach its tissues, the final number of motor neurons in the lateral or appendicular cell column is reduced, though the total number of cells in the ventral portion of the associated cord segments is, according to Hamburger and Keefe, unaffected by the operation. The inference is that the proportion of the total differentiating into neurons is regulated by the periphery. Our studies give some indication of the manner in which this cellular differentiation is controlled.

Using the silver impregnation methods of Cajal (Barron[1]), we have been able to distinguish at least two types of cells in the basal lamina of the cord of the chick as early as the end of the third day of incubation: cells—neuroblasts—that are impregnated by the silver and already in the course of differentiation into neurons; and other cells, spherical in form, that do not take up the silver; these that, for want of a better term, we've called indifferent cells, lie interspersed between the neuroblasts and form a larger

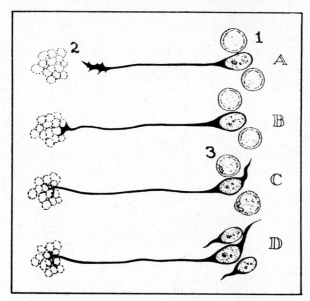

Fig. 53. Schematic representation of the sequence of events through which the cell body of the unipolar neuroblast (1), following its contact with appropriate primyoblasts (2), increases in volume and puts forth dendrites—a process which is accompanied by the differentiation of adjunct indifferent cells (3) into neuroblasts.

portion of the population of the mantle as development advances through the fourth and fifth days of incubation. The motor neuroblasts mentioned above send their axons out toward the periphery with advancing age and, at or about the time the axon reaches its destination, a series of changes is initiated in the cell body. The amount of cytoplasm begins to increase; the cell increases in total volume and the ratio of surface to volume is altered by putting forth an apical dendrite as development advances.

At or about the time these changes are occurring in the neuroblast, with its axon anchored, so to speak, in the periphery, changes quite as remarkable are initiated in the indifferent cells lying in close association with the differentiating neuroblast. They begin to take up silver and lose their spherical form and put forth axons that grow peripheralward and into the limb. This sequence of events is illustrated schematically in Figure 53.

All this might be considered a coincidence if it were not for the fact that when the limb is removed before the axons of the initial or primary neuroblasts reach them, the cytoplasm in the cell body appears to remain unaltered and so too the surface-volume relationship, for dendrites fail to appear. Hence there is good ground for assuming that the changes in the cell are initiated through the association of the neuroblast with the appropriate tissues of the limb via its axon. That is to say, in this case, the differentiation of the motor neuron is not completely determined by genetic action; the final form is a consequence of the reaction of the cell with elements of its environment.

The development of the indifferent cells, described above, into neuroblasts likewise appears to be dependent upon their association with specific members of their cell community, i.e., those neuroblasts in the process of altering their surface-volume ratio by putting forth dendrites—the reaction that follows the arrival of the axon at the periphery. If, as a consequence of the removal of the periphery, the primary neuroblasts fail to put forth dendrites, the associated indifferent cells remain in the mantle unaltered. Their differentiation into neuroblasts is either delayed for several days or never does take place, and it appears to be controlled through the periphery by a sort of chain reaction acting first on the primary neuroblast and then through it on the indifferent cell.

These morphologic changes, though valuable indices of the importance of the interaction of the cells of the limb bud, the neuroblasts, and the indifferent cells, do not give clues as to the nature of the chemical processes, regulated through cellular interaction, which are finally expressed in the geometry of the neurons. In an effort to discover the nature of these processes we (Barron and Mottet[3]) have studied the normal changes in histochemistry of the cells in the lateral portion of the ventral horn of the spinal cord and compared them with those that occur in the cells of this same region when the limb bud has been removed before any axons reached its tissues. We used the Feulgen, Nissl, and Gomori technic to demonstrate the presence and approximate concentration of the desoxyribonucleic acid, ribonucleic acid, and acid phosphatase respectively. These preparations indicate that the nuclear desoxyribonucleic acid reaction diminishes as differentiation advances in cells developing into motor neurons. Concomitantly, the cytoplasmic ribonucleic acid and acid phosphatase reactions increase in intensity. These cytochemical changes parallel morphologic differentiation—increase of cytoplasmic volume and axonal and dendritic growth. When the limb bud is removed the cells that normally differentiate into motor neurons remain cytologically indistinguishable from the indifferent mantle cells. Clearly the inference is that the periphery regulates chemical reactions within the neuroblasts and through them those of indifferent cells.

These few remarks must serve to present the line of thought that has led to the experiments and they will indicate how limited our progress has been. But I hope they will raise new questions associated with these beautiful studies of Dr. Flexner. Are these changes which he has described also timed and directed through the position of the cortical neuroblast in its community?

REFERENCES

1. BARRON, DONALD H.: *Journal of Comparative Neurology*, 1946, 85, pp. 149-170.
2. BARRON, DONALD H.: *Journal of Comparative Neurology*, 1948, 88, pp. 93-218.
3. BARRON, DONALD H., and MOTTET, N. KARLE: *Anatomical Record*, 1951, in press.
4. HAMBURGER, V.: *Journal of Experimental Zoology*, 1934, 68 pp. 449-494.
5. SHOREY, M. L.: *Journal of Experimental Zoology*, 1909, 7, pp. 25-64.

Human Fetal Activity

DAVENPORT HOOKER, PH.D.

It is generally agreed that the human embryo begins to respond to external (i.e., exteroceptive) stimulation by a light hair at about seven and one-half weeks of menstrual age (20 to 23 mm., CR). There also appears to be rather general acceptance of the following phenomena antedating the first reflex activity:

1. The muscles as they differentiate in a cephalocaudal direction become capable of being excited to contraction by electrical or mechanical means before the nerves supplying them are capable of function.

2. Motor nerves precede the sensory in their ability to transmit nervous impulses. Shortly after the appearance of electrically or mechanically excited contractility in a muscle, similar stimulation of its motor nerve will also cause contraction of the muscle.

3. The last elements of the reflex arc to become functional are the sensory receptor neurons and the internuncial cells. However, it is as yet unknown which, if either, of these attains functional capacity first.

In the Pittsburgh studies, 128 human embryos and fetuses have been examined to date. They cover an age range from five and one-half weeks of menstrual age to term. Of this number, eighty-four are considered unanesthetized and relatively uninjured in extraction. The cases are secured by hysterotomy or by spontaneous premature delivery. They are examined in Tyrode's solution, physiologic saline, or water (depending on age) warmed to body temperature in a constant temperature bath. The stimulators used are hairs, calibrated to bend readily at pressures of 10, 25, 50, and 100 mg., or at 2 gm., the tips being protected by a rounded globule of inert material to prevent penetration of the delicate integument of the younger specimens. These are effective only when the skin is gently stroked with the hair (spatial summation).

The first response secured in these studies was in a seven and one-half weeks' (MA) embryo, 20.7 mm. CR. Stimulation by gentle stroking with a light hair in the maxillary area gave rise to contralateral flexion of the head. This was exhibited once only. No other seven and one-half weeks' (MA) embryo in our series gave any response, probably because the mother had received morphine and/or a general anesthetic in each of these cases.

Five unanesthetized embryos at eight and one-half weeks (MA) gave responses to stimulation in the maxillomandibular area of the face. All of these gave identical responses repeatedly during several minutes. The response consisted of a contralateral flexion of the trunk and neck, an extension of the upper arms at the shoulder, and a slight rotation of the pelvis. Each response from each embryo was identical, within the limits of biologic variation, until responses could no longer be secured. Heavy stimulation with a stiff hair elsewhere on the body produced local responses caused by mechanical stimulation of the muscle beneath the integument. Spontaneous movements, those caused by unknown stimuli, were observed at this age.

During the age period from nine to ten weeks (MA), six unanesthetized young fetuses again gave unvarying responses to stimulation by stroking with a light hair in the maxillomandibular region. These responses consisted of contralateral flexions of the neck and trunk, and extension of both upper arms at the shoulder, but the pelvic rotation had become more marked with increasing age. Here also, the responses follow the same pattern and are automatic. Muscle stretching in the upper extremity gave flexions at wrist or elbow, and sudden changes in position caused typical responses of vestibular origin by nine and one-half weeks (MA). In this age range, as deterioration set in later in the observations, there was a tendency for the rump rotation to decrease in extent, a return to a previous level of response noted throughout the entire series of fetuses under this condition.

By ten and one-half to eleven weeks (MA) certain new types of responses gradually appear. The contralateral trunk and neck flexion is at first combined with, then supplanted by, trunk extension, until advancing deterioration returns it to its earlier form. Stimulation of the palm causes partial finger closure, in which the pollex may or may not participate. Forearm stimulation causes its pronation. Stimulation of the upper eyelids causes contraction of the eyelid muscle and scowling. Plantar stimulation causes plantar flexion of the toes. These newer types of reflexes are very sensitive to advancing deterioration and disappear early.

At eleven and one-half to twelve and one-half weeks (MA) trunk extension almost completely replaces lateral flexion, except when deterioration is advanced; contraction of the eyelid muscle may follow stimulation in the maxillomandibular region; digital closure is still incomplete in the hand, but something approaching a true Babinski reflex follows plantar stimulation.

By thirteen to thirteen and one-half weeks the entire surface of the body, except the top, sides, and back of the head, has become sensitive to stimulation and a wide variety of movements at practically all joints may be elicited.

By fourteen weeks the fetus exhibits a wide repertoire of specific reflexes: there is complete and maintained finger closure, but no grasp as yet; tongue responses may be observed and deglutition often follows stimulation of tongue or lips. A true Babinski reflex is definitely present.

Additional reflexes appearing with increasing fetal age must be summarized briefly: Respiratory contractions of the chest and gasping have been observed by twelve and one-half weeks, but true respiration, with phonation, has not been seen before twenty to twenty-two weeks. True hand grasp appears between fifteen and eighteen and one-half weeks and can support the weight of the body by twenty-seven weeks. Lip protrusion occurs at seventeen weeks, lip pursing and active suckling reflexes by twenty-two weeks. After the fetus has been induced to breathe, the grosser tendon reflexes (ankle clonus, knee jerk, and the like) have been observed at twenty-two weeks. Conjugate deviation of the eyes has been seen with opened lids by twenty-five weeks, though downward movement of the eyeballs has been seen to occur by twelve and one-half weeks through the closed eyelids.

In the Pittsburgh studies, we have secured a series of responses maturing in unbroken sequence from seven and one-half weeks (MA) to birth. When breathing can be established, it has been our experience that the nature of the responses elicited does not change in kind from those secured before respiration. Because of this unbroken sequence we believe that these observations are of significance in the development of normal behavior, but we do not claim that the embryos and fetuses observed are unaffected by the changes in their surroundings and conditions from those *in utero*. Interference with placental fetal-maternal relations, even opening of the uterus *per se*, starts a slowly progressive asphyxia which is little relieved by the administration of oxygen to the fetal placenta. Intrauterine pressures are disturbed and temperature changes are inevitable, although this last change can be countered by a constant temperature bath. Nevertheless, we are certain that the responses elicited are true reflex movements not too seriously affected by the slowly progressing asphyxia for a period of several minutes in the younger subjects and for somewhat longer periods with increasing age. We are by no means certain that asphyxia is the sole cause of the deterioration observed. It would be interesting to know, specifically, more about the local variations in acetylcholine-cholinesterase and other chemical and enzymatic factors. However, although careful selection has been made, we cannot avoid progressive asphyxia or some delivery trauma. The latter, in our experience, tends to produce a very brief initial period during which few activities are exhibited except with stiff stimulators which may cause local mechanical stimulation of the muscles.

REFERENCES

1. HOOKER, DAVENPORT: *Proceedings of the Association for Research in Nervous and Mental Disease*, 1939, 19, pp. 237-243.
2. HOOKER, DAVENPORT: Origin of Overt Behavior, p. 38. Ann Arbor, University of Michigan Press, 1944.

CHAPTER 14

Patterns of Localization in Sensory and Motor Areas of the Cerebral Cortex

CLINTON N. WOOLSEY, M.D.

FOR A number of years, and with various collaborators, we have been studying patterns of localization in afferent and efferent areas of the cerebral cortex. We now wish to review some of this work, to present certain new findings, and to offer our present interpretation of the phylogenetic development of the rolandic region as seen in a series of representative mammals. The results should have significance for understanding the organization of the human brain; they are of basic importance for several types of experimental study of brain function.

For a long time a good deal has been known about the arrangement of sensory and motor centers in the postcentral and precentral gyri of man. We have had correspondingly abundant information about the precentral gyrus of other primates, but data on the sensory systems of primates and the sensory and motor systems of other forms have been less satisfactory. A striking feature of the sensory and the motor localization patterns in the precentral and postcentral gyri, which has never been satisfactorily explained, is the separation of the face from the rest of the body by the intervening arm area. Figure 54, from Penfield and Rasmussen,[5] illustrates the current view of the arrangement of sensory centers in the postcentral gyrus of man.

Study of afferent systems in animals has become possible by adapting electrical amplification and recording technics to the problem. As a consequence, comparative studies on a variety of mammals have not only yielded detailed information on the topographic organization of cortical fields, but a previously unsuspected duality of fields has been demonstrated in somatic afferent, visual, and auditory systems.[7] Figure 55 summarizes in outline the findings for monkey, cat, rabbit, and rat.

Supported in part by the United States Public Health Service through grants to the Johns Hopkins University and to the University of Wisconsin, and by the Research Committee of the University of Wisconsin from funds supplied by the Wisconsin Alumni Research Foundation.

When a peripheral receptor system is stimulated in an anesthetized animal, potential changes can be detected at the surface of the exposed cortex and the relations of the periphery to the cortex can then be determined.[9] Figure 56 shows the responses recorded from a single point in the hand area of the postcentral gyrus of the monkey, when various spots on the skin of the contralateral hand were stimulated mechanically. Each numbered

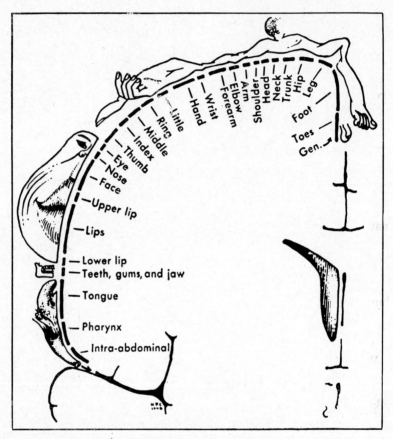

FIG. 54.   Arrangement of sensory centers in the postcentral gyrus of man according to Penfield and Rasmussen.[5]

response was produced by stimulating the correspondingly numbered part of the hand. With this method it was possible to work out carefully the relationship of each cortical point to the area of skin from which it received impulses. With data of this sort, figurine charts were then prepared to illustrate the findings.

Figure 57 shows a part of the pattern of tactile localization in the postcentral gyrus near the midline and in the paracentral "lobule" of the monkey. It reveals certain features of the sensory sequence which had not previously been known. One is the representation of the occipital aspect of the head in the lateral part of the trunk area. Another is the splitting of the leg area into postaxial and preaxial portions by the intervening digital area.

The results of this study led to an analysis of the sensory pattern in terms of Sherrington's dermatomes of the monkey. The results of this analysis are shown in Figure 58. It was deduced that an *en bloc* reversal of

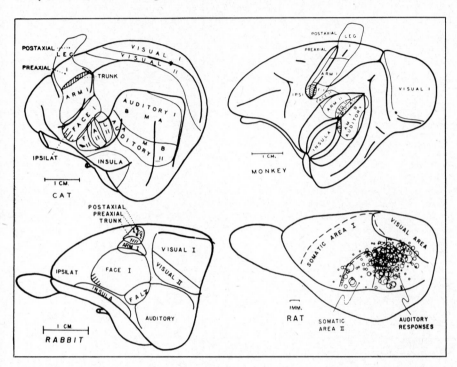

FIG. 55. Somatic, visual, and auditory areas of cat, monkey, rabbit, and rat based on studies previously summarized[7] and on data for the rat obtained by Le Messurier (*Federation Proceedings of the American Societies for Experimental Biology,* 1948, 7, p. 70) and by Woolsey and Le Messurier (*Federation Proceedings of the American Societies for Experimental Biology,* 1948, 7).

the cervical segments had occurred on their projection to the cerebral cortex. Thus a satisfactory explanation of the separation of face from occiput by intervening arm seemed at hand. It also appeared to account for the sharp separation of face, arm, and leg subdivisions which had been revealed by the strychninization technic of Dusser de Barenne.[1] We now believe that this analysis is partly incorrect and that the *en bloc* cervical reversal hypothesis is no longer tenable.

Reorientation toward this problem came from a study with Dr. Le Messurier[8] of the tactile area of the rat. It was quite clear in this animal that there was no reversal in projection of the cervical segments to the cerebral

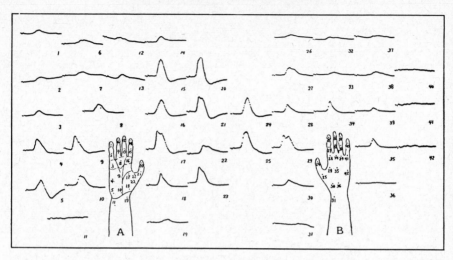

Fig. 56. Surface positive electric potential changes evoked at a single point in the hand area of the left postcentral gyrus of a monkey by punctate stimulation of the palmar surface (A) of the right hand with a cat's vibrissa and of the volar surface (B) with a camel's-hair brush. Reference electrode on occipital cortex. Cutaneous spots stimulated and the recorded responses are numbered to correspond. (From Woolsey, Marshall, and Bard: *Bulletin of the Johns Hopkins Hospital*, 1942, 70.)

cortex. At about the same time Mountcastle and Henneman[4] found no evidence for a cervical reversal in the tactile nuclei of the thalamus of the cat, although the data available at that time indicated that the cortical pattern in this animal was similar to that of the monkey.[3]

Figure 59 illustrates the tactile patterns of the rat. There are actually two tactile areas shown in this diagram. Somatic area II is at the lower right and joins, without any interval, the main tactile area (somatic area I), which is homologous with the postcentral area of primates. Study of the chart will show that the face portion of somatic area I is not separated from the trunk area by an intervening arm area; rather there is direct continuity from tail through trunk and neck to face along the caudal border of the

---

Fig. 57. A portion of the left postcentral tactile area of the monkey. The double figurines are intended to illustrate the skin areas of the right side of the body which sent impulses to cortical points corresponding in position to the arrangement of the figurines in the figure. The upper part of the chart illustrates the arrangement on the medial wall of the hemisphere between the sulcus cinguli (e) and the dorsomedial edge of the hemisphere (d). The lower part of the chart shows the pattern of representation in the medial portion of the postcentral gyrus near the midline (d). The upper part of the central sulcus (a) and the whole of the superior postcentral sulcus (c) are shown. The total area corresponds to leg area I of Figure 55. (From Woolsey, Marshall, and Bard: *Bulletin of the Iohns Hopkins Hospital*, 1942, 70.)

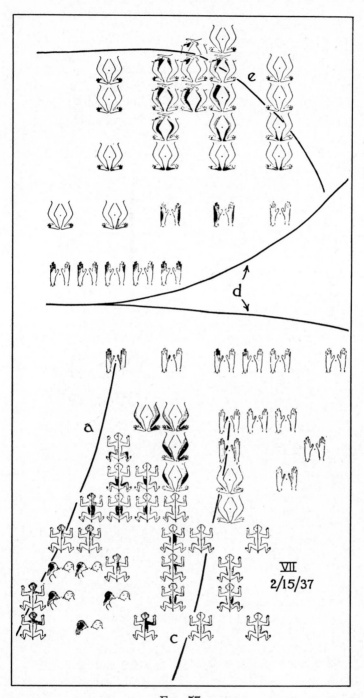

Fig. 57

tactile field. The leg and the arm areas extend forward in the cortex from the trunk area. The general arrangement is shown in a simplified way in Figure 61, which depicts a somewhat distorted image of a rat with its various parts related to one another in much the same way as in the actual animal.

Figure 60 shows the pattern of localization in the motor cortex of the rat.[6]

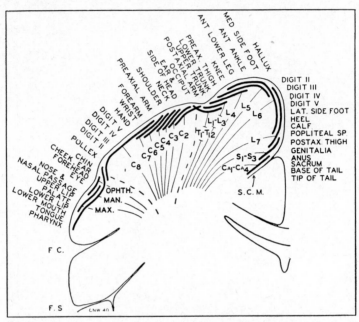

Fig. 58.   Schematic frontal section through the postcentral gyrus and paracentral "lobule" of the monkey, giving the sensory sequence and its analysis in terms of dermatomes according to Woolsey, Marshall, and Bard.[9] Caudal (*Ca*), lumbar (*L*), thoracic (*T*), and cervical (*C*) segments are indicated. *F. S.*, fissure of sylvius; *F. C.*, central sulcus; *S. C. M.*, sulcus cinguli. Broken lines separate face, arm, and leg subdivisions. (From Woolsey, Marshall, and Bard: *Bulletin of the Johns Hopkins Hospital*, 1942, 70.)

Each of the figurines indicates the peripheral location of the muscles activated by stimulating electrically the cortical point (see inset) to which the figurine corresponds. The responding muscles are in the right half of the body, contralateral to the cortex stimulated, but, in order to keep the desired orientation within the pattern, left-sided figurines were used. It will be seen that the epaxial musculature of the back is represented in sequence, from tail to neck, along the medial part of the dorsal surface of the hemisphere, in its rostral half. The limb areas are more lateral, while the head area fills the rostral part of the cortical field and extends laterally to the rhinal sulcus. The general arrangement of the motor pattern is shown in relation to the sensory pattern in Figure 61. They are, in essence,

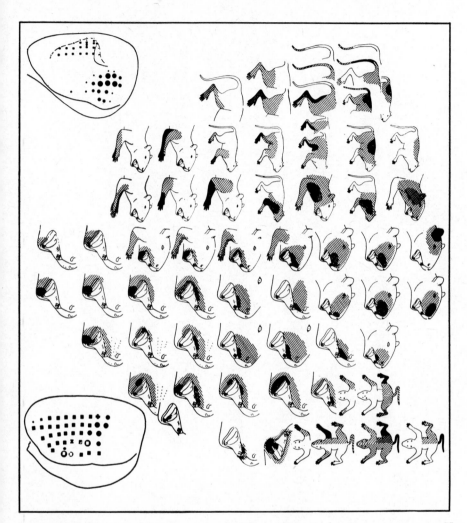

Fig. 59. Pattern of tactile representation in the rat, showing somatic area *II* at the lower right and somatic area *I* in the rest of the figure. The pattern is a composite of two experiments. The lower five lines of figurines correspond to the squares in the lower key figure, the rest to squares in the upper key figure. Circles in both key figures, either alone or combined with squares, mark points responsive to auditory stimuli. The lower key figure is a direct lateral view of the brain; the upper key figure is a dorsolateral view. Points are 1 mm. apart in most instances. (From Woolsey and Le Messurier: *Federation Proceedings of the American Societies for Experimental Biology*, 1948, 7.)

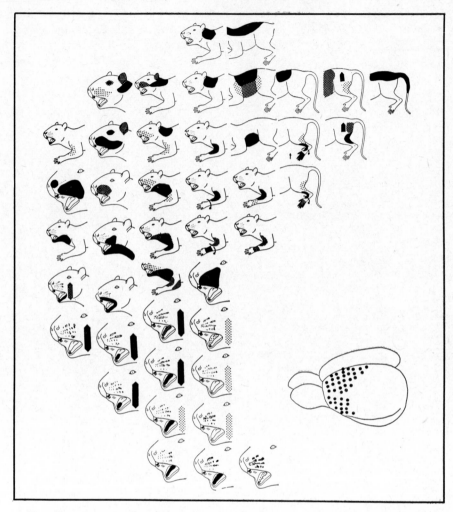

Fig. 60.   Pattern of representation in the motor area of the rat. The figurines correspond to the points marked on the key figure. The intervals between cortical points are approximately 1 mm. The shaded and hatched areas indicate location of musculature activated by threshold 60 cycle alternating current stimulations of two seconds' duration. (From Settlage et al: *Federation Proceedings of the American Societies for Experimental Biology*, 1949, 8.)

mirror images with the apices of the limbs and snout touching one another, while the dorsal parts of the body are represented along the anteromedial and the caudolateral boundaries of the sensory-motor region.

Since with increasing phylogenetic development of the brain the face, hand, and foot obtain increasing cortical representation, while more proximal portions of the limbs and the trunk are allotted relatively less cortex, it is fairly clear that mechanical factors must force upon the cortical patterns extensive distortions and rearrangements. This should affect the sensory and motor hand areas most, since these are in the most central portion of the rolandic field. The final result will depend not only upon differential growths within the sensory-motor region but also upon the development of other and neighboring portions of the cerebral mantle. With expansion of the cortical areas for the apices of the limbs, the cortex either must fold, as in the formation of the central sulcus; or the pattern must be-

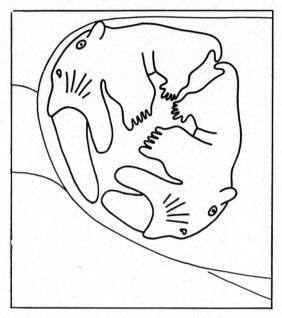

Fig. 61.   Simplified figures outlining the relations of the "rolandic" motor (left) and the sensory (right) localization patterns of the rat, showing the mirror image relationships, based on data of Figures 59 and 60.

come distorted and perhaps torn apart, to produce, for example, separation of the face from the occiput; or the tissue which represents some parts may be stretched so thin that high thresholds result in the motor area, from a decreased density of neurons related to a part, or small potentials occur in the tactile area for the same reason.

These ideas, aroused by the findings on the rat, led to further inquiry. Since at this stage of the work an oscillograph was temporarily unavailable, the pattern of localization in the precentral motor cortex of the monkey was re-examined.[10] Surprisingly the pattern here was found to be very similar to that discovered in the rat's motor area. Since the detailed findings are being presented elsewhere[11] only a general diagram of the pattern will be given now. It will be seen from Figure 62 that there is continuity from the head through the neck to the trunk and that the arm and the leg are related to the trunk in a natural manner. As compared with the rat pattern, that of the monkey shows relative enlargement of the areas for the distal portions of the limbs along the central sulcus. The epaxial musculature is represented in the rostral part of the area. Here the threshold for electrical stimulation is much higher than in the digital centers. This doubtless ex-

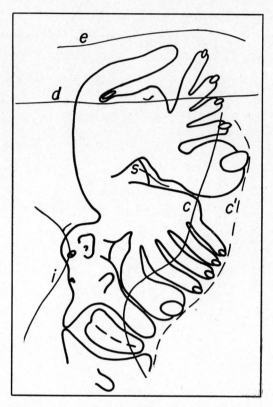

Fig. 62.   Precentral motor area of the macaque showing in simplified outline the general arrangement of the localization pattern. *C*, central sulcus; *c′*, bottom of central sulcus; *d*, medial rim of hemisphere; *e*, sulcus cinguli; *i*, inferior precentral sulcus; *s*, superior precentral sulcus. (From Woolsey et al: *Federation Proceedings of the American Societies for Experimental Biology*, 1950, 9; and *Proceedings of the Association for Research in Nervous and Mental Disease*, December, 1950.)

plains in part the failure of previous workers to define the complete pattern, although some evidence for it can be gleaned from the literature. Attention may be called to an ipsilateral motor face area at the lateral end of the precentral gyrus. This lies adjacent to the ipsilateral tactile face area of the postcentral gyrus which is illustrated as the hatched area in Figure 55.

    The results on the precentral motor area of the monkey suggested strongly that the map of the postcentral tactile area of this animal might be

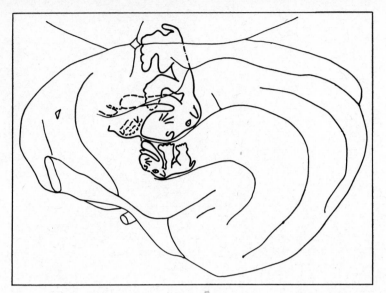

FIG. 63.   General outlines of the tactile areas of the dog. Upper figurine shows the localization pattern in somatic area *I* (postcentral homologue). The lower figurine outlines the pattern in somatic area *II*. (From Hamuy, Bromiley, and Woolsey: *American Journal of Physiology,* 1950, 163.)

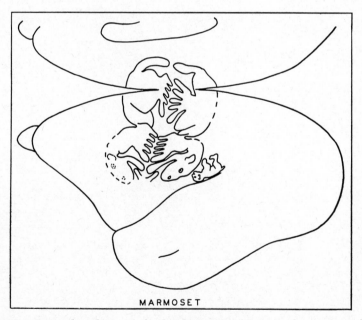

MARMOSET

FIG. 64.   General outlines of the localization patterns in the precentral motor area (left) in the postcentral tactile area (upper right) and in the second somatic area (lower right) of the marmoset. From unpublished data.

incomplete. We, therefore, undertook to re-examine the pattern of localization in this area in several species.

A study begun in Baltimore and recently completed in Madison[2] shows that the "postcentral" tactile area of the dog is similar to that of the rat. It is difficult under certain conditions to demonstrate continuity of the tactile pattern from tail through back to occiput and face along the caudal

Fig. 65. Evolution of the pattern of localization in the postcentral tactile area as defined in a series of mammals. The dotted areas show the extent of the areas devoted to hand and foot. The figures are not all to the same scale, but the proportions of each are approximately correct.

margin of the area. Nevertheless, this has now been satisfactorily accomplished. The general arrangement of the patterns in somatic afferent areas I and II is shown in Figure 63. It may be mentioned in passing that study of the dog has also added to our knowledge of localization in somatic area II. For the first time it has been possible to show that this area possesses a high degree of somatotopic organization.

Figure 64 summarizes results obtained in unpublished studies on the tactile areas and on the precentral motor area of the smooth-surfaced brain of the marmoset monkey. Data for the motor field are incomplete, particularly with respect to the face, as suggested by the broken lines. More information also is needed for the posterior border of the postcentral tactile area. The story, so far as it has been worked out, suggests very definitely the mirror relationship of sensory and motor areas found in the rat. The areas for the apices of the limbs and the mouth touch one another along a line corresponding to the central sulcus. In the motor area there is continuity along the rostral border for the epaxial musculature. In the postcentral field the digital area does not completely split the leg area into preaxial and post-axial divisions, as in the macaque, but continuity of foci for the dorsal aspect of the body has not been satisfactorily demonstrated for the lower back and for the connection from occiput to face.

In Figure 65 we have undertaken to summarize the present status of the evolution of the pattern of localization in the postcentral sensory area. At the upper left is the hypothetic arrangement which might be found in an animal without limbs. The rat pattern would resemble this if the limb areas were removed. In the dog the areas for the apices of the limbs have increased, as indicated by the dotted portion of the figure. In the cat the pattern is similar, but the area for the forepaw has enlarged considerably. This may, in part, account for the difficulty encountered in demonstrating continuity from back to head in the cortical pattern of this animal. There is also lack of continuity from the base of the tail to the back. In the marmoset, invasion of the limb areas by the areas for hand and foot has proceeded still further and there is greater distortion of the total pattern. The areas for hand and foot reach greatest development in the macaque, where they constitute more than half of the total field and produce the greatest deformity of the pattern. Further study will be required to determine whether the pattern has actually been ruptured between occiput and face and between lower sacrum and dorsal trunk, as present data suggest, or whether the missing parts of the pattern result from stretching of the cortex and consequent difficulty in recording electrical potentials in these parts of the pattern. The results on the precentral motor area of the monkey incline one to expect the latter.

REFERENCES

1. Dusser de Barenne, J. G.: *Proceedings of the Royal Society*, 1924, 96B, pp. 272-291.
2. Hamuy, T. Pinto; Bromiley, R. B.; and Woolsey, C. N.: *American Journal of Physiology*, 1950, 163, pp. 719-720.
3. Hayes, G. J., and Woolsey, C. N.: *Federation Proceedings of the American Societies for Experimental Biology*, 1944, 3, p. 18.
4. Mountcastle, V., and Henneman, E.: *Journal of Neurophysiology*, 1949, 12, pp. 85-100.
5. Penfield, W., and Rasmussen, T.: The Cerebral Cortex of Man, 248 pp. New York, The Macmillan Co., 1950.

6. SETTLAGE, P. H.; BINGHAM, W. G.; SUCKLE, H. M.; BORGE, A. F.; and WOOLSEY, C. N.: *Federation Proceedings of the American Societies for Experimental Biology*, 1949, 8, p. 144.

7. WOOLSEY, C. N.: *Federation Proceedings of the American Societies for Experimental Biology*, 1947, 6, pp. 437-441.

8. WOOLSEY, C. N., and LE MESSURIER, D. H.: *Federation Proceedings of the American Societies for Experimental Biology*, 1948, 7, p. 137.

9. WOOLSEY, C. N.; MARSHALL, W. H.; and BARD, P.: *Bulletin of the Johns Hopkins Hospital*, 1942, 70, pp. 399-441.

10. WOOLSEY, C. N., and SETTLAGE, P. H.: *Federation Proceedings of the American Societies for Experimental Biology*, 1950, 9, p. 140.

11. WOOLSEY, C. N.; SETTLAGE, P. H.; MEYER, D. R.; SENCER, W.; HAMUY, T. PINTO; and TRAVIS, A. M.: *Proceedings of the Association for Research in Nervous and Mental Disease*, December, 1950.

Discussion

DR. PERCIVAL BAILEY: May I ask a question? It just occurred to me that, since we know in stimulating the motor cortex of the macaque monkey, if you choose the proper parameter of stimulation without changing the intensity, you can get the thumb immediately following the tongue and no movements from the face at all, perhaps Dr. Woolsey might be able to fill in some of the defects in his schema by properly changing the parameters of stimulation. He knows that, and has probably done it, but I would like to be reassured.

DR. WOOLSEY: I should like to say in reply to Dr. Bailey that it is not in the motor pattern but in the sensory pattern that deficits appear to exist. These cannot be related to parameters of stimulation. However, as we have already pointed out, level of anesthesia may be an important factor underlying the apparent deficits in the sensory patterns.

Forms and Figures in the Electrical Activity Seen in the Surface of the Cerebral Cortex

JOHN C. LILLY, M.D.

In the investigation of the activity of the central nervous system by electrical methods, there is a particular direction of development long desired but not yet realized. This direction is the investigation of more and more zones of activity simultaneously, and, conversely, the electrical stimulation of great numbers of zones with patterned stimuli presented simultaneously. The detailed work which has generated the desire for this direction for

This research was supported, initially, by a grant from the Coyle Foundation; recently, the United States Public Health Service Division of Research Grants and Fellowships has supported the work. Of those who have made the project possible, the author wishes to thank particularly Professors D. W. Bronk and Britton Chance for their interest and encouragement. Among those aiding in the designing and re-designing of apparatus, J. P. Hervey and J. B. Busser were the most active. George Iavecchia has done the bulk of the construction. Dr. W. W. Chambers has assisted in these experiments. Several people have helped in record analysis, as follows: George Iavecchia, Ruth Cherry, Allen Yeakel, and J. C. Lilly, Jr. To these organizations and individuals and the many others who have offered suggestions, advice, and criticism the author wishes to express his thanks and gratitude.

neurophysiologic research is, in part, as follows. The work of Gerard, Marshall, and Saul[8] in 1936 showed that responses in the central nervous system could be evoked by normal end-organ stimulation. Adrian[2] and Woolsey, Marshall, and Bard[19] mapped some of the cortical regions giving responses to tactile stimuli. Talbot and Marshall[17] have mapped the visual system in the cat and the monkey. Woolsey and Walzl[22] mapped the cochlear projection to the cortex. Tunturi[18] has found a cortical map related to the frequency of the sound stimuli. Mountcastle and Henneman[14] have mapped the thalamus for tactile responses. Morison and Dempsey[7, 13] showed that stimuli in the thalamus can give rise to radical changes in the cortical pattern. Jasper and Droogleever-Fortuyn[9] have made further contributions concerning the thalamic effects. All of the above work was done under relatively deep anesthesia. At lighter anesthetic levels, Bishop and O'Leary[3] have examined the responses within the cortex itself. In unanesthetized cats, Bremer and Bonnet[4] have examined some of the relations between the primary acoustic region and the posterior ectosylvian region in terms of fast and slow after-discharges.

Thus, maps taken under deep anesthesia have been constructed showing the relation between some peripheral end-organ sheets and the cortical sheet. These maps are of the cortical zones giving a maximum electrical response to stimulation of a given peripheral zone under deep anesthesia. As Bremer and Bonnet's[4] work suggests, these maps may possibly not be so obvious without anesthesia.

The complementary motor maps of the peripheral regions responding to electrical stimuli applied to single cortical zones have been recently presented in great detail by Woolsey and his co-workers.[16, 20, 21]

This is a small part of the background for future research on many zones simultaneously. This work hints that if we can work with many zones at once we can begin to understand the brain mechanisms more thoroughly. Some of the implications of future work with several thousands or millions of zones at once or their equivalent can be imagined as follows. Given the necessary technical advances it may be possible to by-pass the usual inputs and outputs through the body to and from the central nervous system. At that time with, say, a million sub-micro-electrodes or their equivalent, it may be possible for the first time to see and record enough of the electrical action of the brain concurrently with bodily behavior to begin to offer evidence useful in psychiatric research. Pushing this fantasy a little further than is cautious, we may imagine the day when one brain can electrically "look" into parts or the whole of another brain directly without interposing the confusion inherent in communication by speech and hearing.

To come back to today and be more cautious, we do not have even 100 electrodes or their equivalent nor have we yet solved the basic problem of how to achieve complete reciprocity of electrical stimuli and electrical activity in the central nervous system. To bring us to present realities,

I wish to present a very small step, a relatively crude one, in the direction of recording the activity in many zones at once. In the perspective created by the above fantasy the new step is crude, but in the perspective of past electrophysiologic work, it is an advance.

Apparatus, Technic, and Responses

In our work we are looking at twenty-five zones, at their simultaneous activity in time samples taken at 128 times a second. This is neither enough zones nor rapid enough sampling to satisfy either myself or the electrophysi-

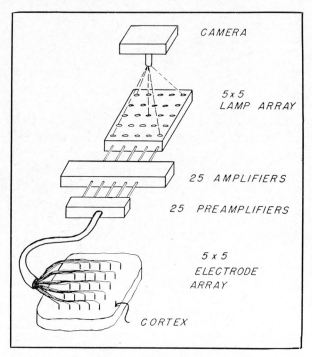

Fɪɢ. 66.   Diagram of apparatus.

ologists participating in this symposium. Figure 66 shows a diagram of the apparatus.[10] In the lower left is a diagrammatic section of cortex with a square array of twenty-five electrodes on the surface, five on a side. In all subsequent records this square array covers 1 sq. cm. of cortex. The electrodes are connected to twenty-five preamplifiers and twenty-five amplifiers which amplify the potentials picked up from the cortex and feed a square array of twenty-five glow tubes. Each electrode drives one glow tube. The camera is a motion picture camera photographing at the rate of 128 frames per second. With this equipment we transpose waves of activity in the electrical sense on the cortex to waves of varying light intensity in the camera field.

Figure 67 shows one of our electrode arrays for implantation through the skull (Clark and Ward[6]). The openings are of small glass tubes imbedded in lucite. Plastic tubes are connected to the glass ones at one end and to a set of twenty-five reversible silver-silver chloride electrodes at the other end. Normal saline is used as the conductor from the pia to the electrodes. A ¾-inch trephine hole is cut through the skull. The dura is removed in the region of the electrodes and the electrode array is screwed into place with a tapered, threaded, stainless steel barrel which surrounds the electrodes.

Fig. 67. Photograph of an electrode array.

Thus we keep the cranium closed and avoid the pathologic effects of exposing the brain to a changed environment during the experiment.

Figure 68 shows the position on the cat cortex of the electrode array for the subsequent response records. The electrodes lie over the posterior ectosylvian region and the sylvian region in the acoustic cortex of the cat. The posterior ectosylvian sulcus penetrates the region covered by the array as does the suprasylvian sulcus. The responses and the structure of this region are discussed in detail by Rose and Woolsey.[15]

Figure 69 shows a series of responses to click stimuli in this region under deep dial anesthesia.[12] These records are prints from an original motion picture. Time goes from the top to the bottom of the picture. In the first vertical strip the click stimuli are reoccurring at one per second, in the second strip at 2.5, in the third strip at 5.8, and in the fourth strip at 10.7 clicks per second. These responses are samples taken from the middle of a long train of such clicks. The maximum spread of the response can be seen in the one per second click column. As the frequency of the clicks increases the extent of the response diminishes as can be seen in row 5 (counting from the top of the picture). The posterior boundary of this maximum spread corresponds approximately with the border between posterior ecto-sylvian and acoustic I and II shown by Rose and Woolsey.[15] Thus, by this technic we can outline functional areas on the surface of the cortex and indicate the boundaries between functionally different areas by recording a single response sequence.

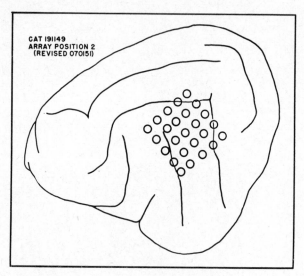

CAT 191149
ARRAY POSITION 2
(REVISED 070151)

FIG. 68.   Array locus on cat cerebrum.

If the frequency is decreased below one per second the extent of the response does not increase any farther. The decrease in the extent of the response with increased click frequencies may mean that the systems responsible for the spread of the click response have different refractory periods and excitability cycles as one moves from the area which responds first (as seen in row 4) posteriorly into the area over which the response spreads. The refractory period would be shortest in the region which responds first and gradually lengthens with distance from this point. Likewise, the excitability cycle changes in a uniform fashion away from this original zone (cf. Chang[5]).

Figure 70 shows the responses of Figure 69 prepared by means of a rubber-dam model.[11] Original records of Figure 69 were measured by means of a photocell, an amplifier, and an ink writer. The resulting quantitative data of the density for each image of each glow tube in each frame of the record are fed into the model by hand as vertical displacements of rods over whose upper end is stretched a rubber dam. The surface of the rubber dam is

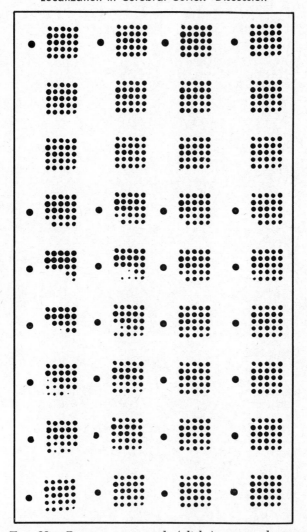

Fig. 69.   Responses to sounds (clicks) at several rates.

marked with a grid of lines to show the displacement of the surface between the electrode or rod positions. Relative surface positivity is represented by upward displacements; surface negativity, by downward displacements. Thus, an averaged picture of the potential gradients at the surface of the cortex is generated for each motion picture frame.

The left-hand column of Figure 70 shows the reference levels or the zero gradient state. The second column shows the one per second click responses; the third, the 2.5 per second; the fourth, the 5.8 per second; and the fifth, the 10.7 per second. (Row 3 in Figure 70 corresponds to the fourth row in Figure 69.) Row 3 shows that the initial phase of the response at each

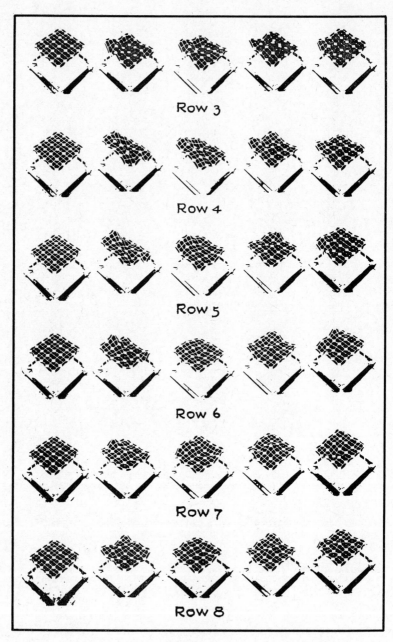

FIG. 70. Differential potential surfaces during the responding forms of Figure 69.

frequency is practically the same except for some small background distortion of the field. Rows 4 and 5 show the variation of the maximum extent of the response with frequency of stimulation. As can be seen by looking down along each column the recovery is more rapid with higher frequencies of stimulation.

Figure 71 is a print of records of some responses and spontaneous waves.[12] Two spontaneous waves and one response are shown. The signal light to the left of each frame signals the occurrence of a click by being extinguished for about ten milliseconds. The click occurs at the instant the light is extinguished. The first strip shows the beginning of the spontaneous wave, the occurrence of the click, and the dying away of the spontaneous wave. By comparing this figure with Figure 68 showing the electrode locus, it can be seen that the spontaneous wave begins posteriorly in the posterior ectosylvian gyrus, spreads in that gyrus and moves out anteriorly and ventrally downward along the gyrus. Against the background of this very large deformation the response cannot be seen very well in this strip. The slow rate of travel of the spontaneous wave compared to the response (Fig. 69) can be seen in this figure.

A spontaneous wave without a superimposed response is shown in the next thirty frames. It can be seen that in this case the spontaneous wave encroaches only into the more ventral part of the area responding to clicks —that area surrounding the upper end of the posterior ectosylvian sulcus (Figs. 68 and 69).

Thus, we may see in Figures 69 and 71 that there is a boundary at this level of anesthesia between the upper part of the responding region and an area generating spontaneous activity. Referring to the map of Rose and Woolsey[15] it can be seen that this boundary is probably that between acoustic I and the posterior ectosylvian region (Ep). (The spontaneous wave may enter acoustic II, but the response in acoustic II does not enter Ep.) Thus, for the first time one may be able to demonstrate the existence of a boundary between the two separate functional regions by single responses and by means of single spontaneous waves. At this level of anesthesia no spontaneous waves are seen originating in acoustic I and acoustic II. The origins of these waves are restricted to the posterior ectosylvian region.

Figures 72 and 73 show the same waves as in Figure 71, analyzed and placed in the model.[12] Figure 72 shows the wave of the left-hand side of Figure 71; Figure 73 shows that of the right-hand side; time goes downward in columns from left to right, following the order of the numbers at the left and bottom of each half of each sequence of thirty frames.

In Figure 72, a click stimulated the ears during frame 12. The response (cf. Fig. 70, the second column from the left) tilts the sheet (frames 16, 17, and 18) an additional amount over that caused by the spontaneous wave (cf. Fig. 73). The spontaneous wave itself develops as a "dome" of relative surface positivity moving from right to left (ventral to middle suprasylvian

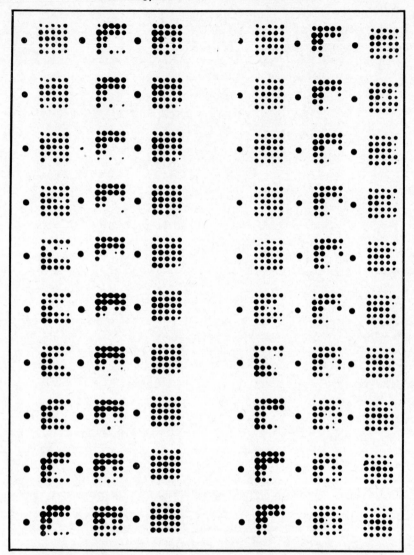

Fig. 71. Spontaneous forms: a responding form occurs in the left hand se-quence during the spontaneous form. Surfaces for these two sequences are given in Figures 72 and 73.

sulcus, and moving from posterior suprasylvian sulcus toward posterior ectosylvian sulcus, Figure 68).

Figure 73 shows another spontaneous wave (dome) starting (frame 6) near the posterior ectosylvian sulcus, moving quickly to the right (frame 7), then slowly to the left (frames 8 through 21).

Motion pictures of these responses and spontaneous waves shown at the original symposium show the movement and travel of the responses and of the spontaneous waves in original records and on the moving model. In these motion pictures it can be seen that the responses start in the lower left-hand corner of the array, progress out over the array, and die away in place after their maximum extent has been reached. The spontaneous waves can be seen to build up in the middle of the posterior ectosylvian region of the array and move downward along the gyrus. A response wave can be seen traversing the distorted field of the slower spontaneous wave. The above static figures lose these essentially kinetic effects.

Other records not presented here show that as the anesthetic level is decreased the responses give rise to "wavelets" which travel back over the posterior ectosylvian region. Concurrently the duration of the spontaneous waves in the posterior ectosylvian region is very much decreased and the waves reoccur much more frequently. As the anesthetic level is further decreased the responses can be lost in a complex, continuous play of spontaneous activity over this whole region. At this level the animal begins to move and attempts to rise to its feet.

At present, it looks as if the effect of the anesthetic is to separate and to simplify the activities of each of these regions and to abolish interactions across the boundaries. We have a few examples at a lesser level of anesthesia, in which the responses in acoustic I and II give rise to these large spontaneous waves in the posterior ectosylvian region. At a critical level of anesthesia, a response causes a "spontaneous" wave to travel away from the boundary and to travel downward along the posterior ectosylvian region. At the same anesthetic level, purely spontaneous waves without any relation to responses in acoustic I and II arise in posterior ectosylvian in the same manner as seen in Figure 71 and travel downward along the posterior ectosylvian region. Thus there seem to be at least two mechanisms involved here, one of which is the primary afferent response system; the other, a posterior ectosylvian spontaneous "system" which can be fired by the response systems and by unknown mechanisms (Ades[1]).

The tendency for responses to evoke activity over large cortical areas at a lighter level of anesthesia or with no anesthesia is shown even more clearly in a series of experiments on unanesthetized monkeys. In a dozing monkey in a quiet environment we have found responses to acoustic stimuli (clicks) as far away from the acoustic region as the sensorimotor cortex. These responses are stereotyped and repeatable. The response starts with a very rapid "flash" traveling under the region of the electrodes in the face and hand area and extending to the leg area. This initial quick component is followed by a series of slow waves which travel around over the sensorimotor cortex in determinable paths over time intervals as long as one second. These slow waves resemble very closely the less regularly organized so-called "sleep" waves. These experiments will be reported in detail in another place.

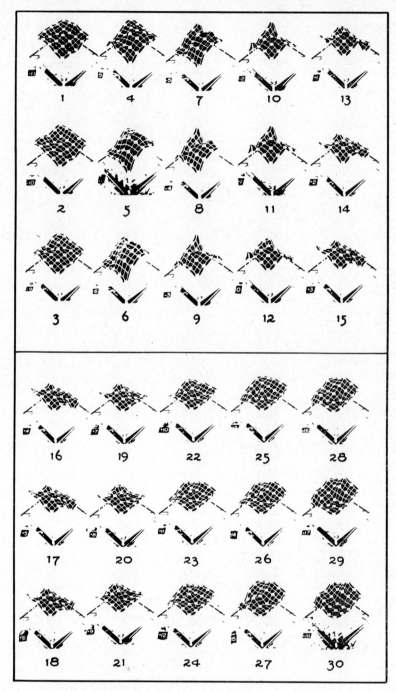

FIG. 72. Differential potential surfaces during a spontaneous form and a responding form. The click occurred during frame 12.

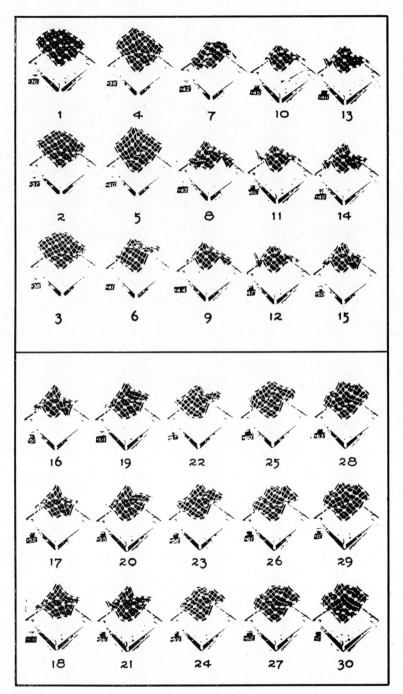

FIG. 73.   Surfaces during a spontaneous form.

In conclusion, it can be seen from these experiments that visualization of the activity of twenty-five electrodes simultaneously allows us to see the forms and figures of the activity of the cerebral cortex on a surface and under suitable conditions to localize regions by their characteristic behavior in response to stimuli and during spontaneous activity. By the easy correlation of events in contiguous regions more meaning can be attached to the waveform in each zone. In other words, the value of the results increases with the number of zones that can be observed simultaneously.

Summary

1. The work reported here is the result of a first attempt to record the activity at the surface of the cerebral cortex in twenty-five zones simultaneously.

2. Using a square array of electrodes, five on a side, lying over 1 sq. cm. of the acoustic region of the cat, responses to clicks and the spontaneous activity of the region have been recorded at a fairly deep level of anesthesia.

3. The click responses are shown to originate in a zone near one corner of the array, to spread out posteriorly to a definite boundary, and then to die out in place.

4. Posterior to this boundary, single spontaneous waves are seen to originate and to travel downward along the posterior ectosylvian gyrus.

5. At lighter levels of anesthesia, it is possible for the responses to excite so-called spontaneous waves across the boundary.

6. As the anesthesia is lightened, spontaneous waves decrease in duration and increase in their repetition frequency in the posterior ectosylvian region.

7. At still lighter levels of anesthesia, additional spontaneous waves travel across the boundaries for the first time; concurrently, spontaneous activity in the primary acoustic afferent receiving area begins to be seen.

8. In another series of experiments on unanesthetized monkeys in a dozing state, it can be seen that the responses to click stimuli spread even farther, to the sensorimotor region and there excite stereotyped, long-lasting patterns of activity.

9. Thus, it can be seen that the effect of anesthesia is to isolate functional regions from one another in the cortex, to simplify their activity, and to prevent interactions between contiguous regions.

REFERENCES

1. ADES, H. W.: *Journal of Neurophysiology*, 1943, 6, pp. 59-64.
2. ADRIAN, E. D.: *Journal of Physiology*, 1941, 100, pp. 159-191.
3. BISHOP, G. H., and O'LEARY, J.: *Journal of Neurophysiology*, 1938, 1, pp. 391-404.
4. BREMER, F., and BONNET, V.: *Electroencephalography and Clinical Neurophysiology*, 1950, 2, pp. 389-400.
5. CHANG, H.-T.: *Journal of Neurophysiology*, 1950, 13, pp. 235-257.

6. CLARK, S. L., and WARD, J. W.: *Archives of Neurology and Psychiatry*, 1937, 38, pp. 927-943.

7. DEMPSEY, E. W., and MORISON, R. S.: *American Journal of Physiology*, 1942, 135, pp. 301-308.

8. GERARD, R. W.; MARSHALL, W. H.; and SAUL, L. J.: *Archives of Neurology and Psychiatry*, 1936, 36, pp. 675-735.

9. JASPER, H. H., and DROOGLEEVER-FORTUYN, J.: *Proceedings of the Association for Research in Nervous and Mental Disease*, 1946, 26, pp. 272-298.

10. LILLY, J. C.: AIEE-IRE Conference on Electronics in Nucleonics and Medicine. (S-33), New York. American Institute of Electrical Engineers, 1950, pp. 37-43.

11. LILLY, J. C.: *Electroencephalography and Clinical Neurophysiology*, 1950, 2, p. 358.

12. LILLY, J. C., and CHAMBERS, W. W.: *Federation Proceedings of the American Societies for Experimental Biology*, 1950, 9, p. 78.

13. MORISON, R. S., and DEMPSEY, E. W.: *American Journal of Physiology*, 1943, 138, pp. 297-308.

14. MOUNTCASTLE, V., and HENNEMAN, E.: *Federation Proceedings of the American Societies for Experimental Biology*, 1949, 8, p. 115.

15. ROSE, J. E., and WOOLSEY, C. N.: *Journal of Comparative Neurology*, 1949, 91, pp. 441-466.

16. SETTLAGE, P. H.; BINGHAM, W. G.; SUCKLE, H. M.; BORGE, A. F.; and WOOLSEY, C. N.: *Federation Proceedings of the American Societies for Experimental Biology*, 1949, 8, p. 144.

17. TALBOT, S. A., and MARSHALL, W. H.: *American Journal of Ophthalmology*, 1941, 24, pp. 1255-1263.

18. TUNTURI, A. R.: *American Journal of Physiology*, 1944, 141, pp. 397-403.

19. WOOLSEY, C. N.; MARSHALL, W. H.; and BARD, P.: *Bulletin of the Johns Hopkins Hospital*, 1942, 70, pp. 399-441.

20. WOOLSEY, C. N., and SETTLAGE, P. H.: *Federation Proceedings of the American Societies for Experimental Biology*, 1950, 9, p. 140.

21. WOOLSEY, C. N.; SETTLAGE, P. H.; SUCKLE, H. M.; and BINGHAM, W. G.: *Federation Proceedings of the American Societies for Experimental Biology*, 1949, 8, p. 172.

22. WOOLSEY, C. N., and WALZL, E. M.: *Bulletin of the Johns Hopkins Hospital*, 1942, 71, pp. 315-344.

Ascending Reticular Activating System

HORACE W. MAGOUN, PH.D.

Prerequisite to cerebral integration is a state called wakefulness, an introspective condition of alertness or attention, which had been difficult to study objectively until electroencephalography revealed it to be associated, in both animals and man, with a characteristic type of electrocortical activity, differing from that in the antithetic state of sleep.

This can be illustrated (Fig. 74) by records of the electrical activity of the cerebral cortex of a cat, in which the electroencephalogram in sleep is seen to be synchronized, or composed of large, slow waves and spindle bursts (left), while in alert wakefulness it is desynchronized and consists of low-voltage, fast activity (right).

This latter waking or activation pattern of the electroencephalogram has been attributed to bombardment of the cortex by asynchronous afferent volleys from peripheral receptors and, in seeming agreement, is the obvious advantage of reducing sensory impressions in predisposing to sleep and the commonplace capacity of afferent stimulation to awaken a sleeping subject.

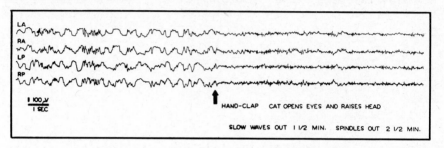

FIG. 74. Activation of the EEG of a normal sleeping cat by auditory stimulation (hand-clap) at arrow. (From Lindsley, Schreiner, Knowles, and Magoun: *Electroencephalography and Clinical Neurophysiology*, 1950, 2.)

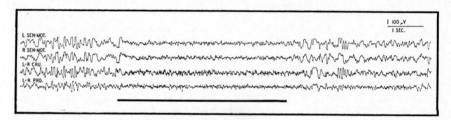

FIG. 75. The EEG of a cat under light chloralosane anesthesia desynchronized during direct electrical excitation of the brain stem reticular formation (heavy line). (From Moruzzi and Magoun: *Electroencephalography and Clinical Neurophysiology*, 1949, 1.)

In the instance shown in Figure 74, auditory stimulation at the arrow aroused the sleeping cat behaviorally and activated or desynchronized its electroencephalogram.

A series of recent studies of the neural management of wakefulness[1-8] began with the observation that direct stimulation of the length of the reticular core of the brain stem, outside the course of classical sensory paths, reproduced the alterations in cortical electrical activity just seen to occur in natural awakening or arousal. In Figure 75 is seen the electrocortical activation induced by such brain stem stimulation (heavy line) against a background of electroencephalographic synchrony in an anesthetized cat. The area whose excitation elicits such responses is indicated in Figure 80, in the shaded region occupying the central reticular core of the brain stem. The

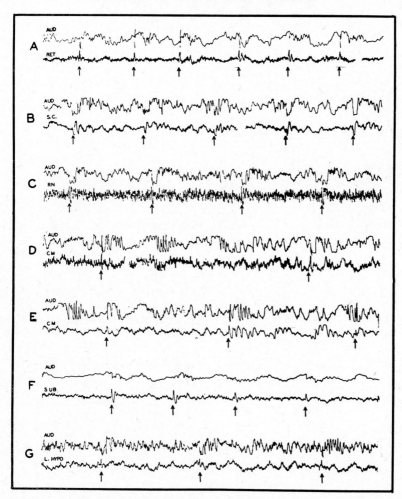

Fig. 76. Potentials evoked by click stimuli (arrow) at the auditory cortex (upper channel in each strip) and at various sites in the activating system in the brain stem (lower channel). (From Starzl, Taylor and Magoun: *Journal of Neurophysiology*, 1951.)

ascending direction and the generalized distribution of its influence upon the cortex is suggested by the arrows present.

Upon the identification of this subcortical activating system it became of interest to see whether afferent connections were made with it in the brain stem. Brief auditory (click) stimuli were delivered to the waking cat and, under local anesthesia, the distribution of evoked potentials in its brain was determined. In each of the records seen in Figure 76, the upper channel picks up discharge from the auditory area of the cortex, for control, and the lower from various sites in the reticular activating system in the brain stem.

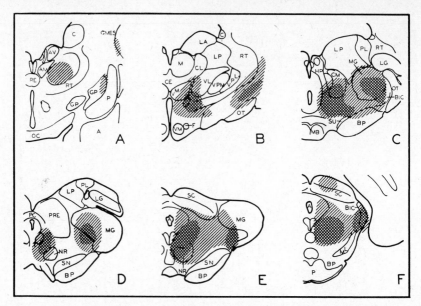

Fig. 77. Transverse sections through the right half of the cephalic brain stem of the cat, with shading indicating the areas from which evoked auditory potentials were recorded. (From Starzl, Taylor, and Magoun: *Journal of Neurophysiology,* 1951.)

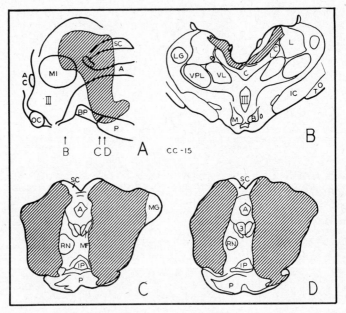

Fig. 78. Midsagittal reconstruction (A) and three transverse sections (B-D) showing the distribution of lesions (shaded) interrupting the classical auditory paths bilaterally. (From Lindsley, Schreiner, Knowles, and Magoun: *Electro-encephalography and Clinical Neurophysiology,* 1950, 2.)

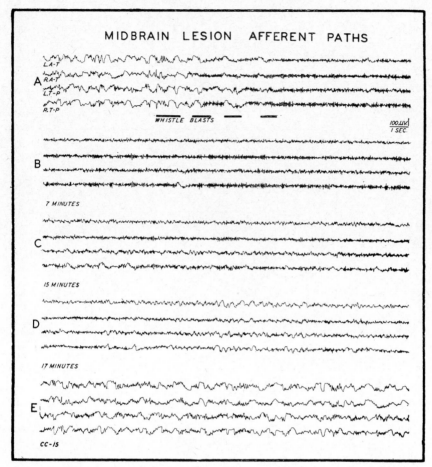

MIDBRAIN   LESION   AFFERENT   PATHS

A

L.A-T
R.A-T
L.T-P
R.T-P

WHISTLE BLASTS

100μV
1 SEC.

B

7 MINUTES

C

15 MINUTES

D

17 MINUTES

E

CC-15

Fig. 79.   EEG records from cat with lateral midbrain lesions (Fig. 78), showing arousal from sleep by whistle blasts. Strips *A* and *B* are continuous; succeeding
time intervals are indicated. (From Lindsley, Schreiner, Knowles, and Magoun:
Electroencephalography and Clinical Neurophysiology, 1950, 2.)

Upon each auditory stimulus (arrow), discharge is seen to be recorded from
both sites.

In a series of sections through the cephalic portion of the brain stem,
shading in Figure 77 marks the subcortical area from which such evoked
auditory potentials were recorded. The classical auditory pathway to the
cortex—the brachium of the inferior colliculus, the medial geniculate, and
the auditory radiation—is of course involved and is marked by the laterally
placed shading at each level. It is clear from the medially placed shading—
in the midbrain tegmentum, the subthalamus and hypothalamus, and the
ventromedial part of the thalamus—that, in addition, auditory connections
are made in abundance with the ascending reticular activating system.

When the classical auditory paths are interrupted in the midbrain, by laterally placed lesions on each side (Fig. 78), sound stimuli are no longer capable of exerting direct influences upon the cerebral cortex, but the intact, centrally placed reticular formation, and auditory connections with it, still provide a potential route for ascending, arousing influences. This route can be demonstrated to be a functional one for, when an animal with such injury is asleep, auditory stimulation, which it presumably cannot hear, is still

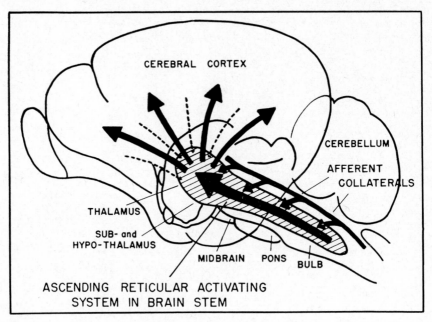

CEREBRAL CORTEX

CEREBELLUM

AFFERENT COLLATERALS

THALAMUS

SUB- and HYPO-THALAMUS

MIDBRAIN PONS BULB

ASCENDING RETICULAR ACTIVATING SYSTEM IN BRAIN STEM

FIG. 80. Outline of the brain of the cat with the ascending reticular activating system marked by shading. The distribution to it of afferent "collaterals" is indicated. (From Starzl, Taylor, and Magoun: *Journal of Neurophysiology*, 1951.)

capable of awakening the cat behaviorally and activating its electroencephalogram. In the instance seen in Figure 79, a series of whistle blasts arouses the sleeping cat, with typical activation of its electroencephalogram, and some fifteen minutes elapse before the animal returns to sleep.

Acknowledging then the demonstrable capacity of afferent stimuli to awaken a sleeping subject, and the importance of diminution of afferent impulses in predisposing to sleep, recent investigation has identified an ascending reticular activating system in the brain stem (Fig. 80). Its direct stimulation reproduces the electrocortical events observed in natural awakening or arousal. Both old and recent observations have shown that injury to its rostral portion results in somnolence. Into it passes such a wealth of afferent collaterals as to indicate that sensory involvement in the waking process is managed indirectly, and at a subcortical level, by modifying its activity.

REFERENCES

1. LINDSLEY, D. B.; BOWDEN, J. W.; and MAGOUN, H. W.: *Electroencephalography and Clinical Neurophysiology*, 1949, 1, pp. 475-486.
2. LINDSLEY, D. B.; SCHREINER, L. H.; KNOWLES, W. B.; and MAGOUN, H. W.: *Electroencephalography and Clinical Neurophysiology*, 1950, 2, p. 483.
3. MAGOUN, H. W.: *Physiological Review*, 1950, 30, pp. 459-474.
4. MAGOUN, N. W.: *Research Publication, Association for Research in Nervous and Mental Disease*, 1951.
5. MORUZZI, G., and MAGOUN, H. W.: *Electroencephalography and Clinical Neurophysiology*, 1949, 1, pp. 455-473.
6. STARZL, T. E., and MAGOUN, H. W.: *Journal of Neurophysiology*, 1951, 14.
7. STARZL, T. E.; TAYLOR, C. W.; and MAGOUN, H. W.: *Journal of Neurophysiology*, 1951, submitted for publication.
8. STARZL, T. E.; TAYLOR, C. W.; and MAGOUN, H. W,: *Journal of Neurophysiology*, 1951, submitted for publication.

CHAPTER 15

Electrical Activity and Mechanisms of Cerebral Integration

HERBERT H. JASPER, M.D.

NEUROPHYSIOLOGY HAS made considerable progress in the analysis of the mechanisms for the differential function of the nervous system, namely, the manner in which stimuli from without and within the body are translated into nerve impulses which become the basic specific signals providing the information upon which the nervous system must react. Much less progress, however, has been made in our understanding of the integral functions of the brain which transform the multitudinous signals into unified thought and action.

In Sir Charles Sherrington's classic treatise on the *Integrative Action of the Nervous System,*[34] the basic principles of integrative action are derived largely from a study of spinal reflexes. With all of the advances made possible by modern technics in investigation, we still have a great deal to learn about the integrative mechanisms in a single segment of the spinal cord, as has been pointed out by Dr. Lloyd. However, Sherrington did not confine his investigations to spinal reflexes, but continued his systematic studies and thought on to higher level functions found in the cerebellum and in the cerebral cortex. There he sought the basic mechanism for the coordination of reflex action with studies and arguments designed to clarify the problems of the unity of conscious thought and action. The questions posed by Sherrington in regard to the mechanisms of higher level integrations still remain largely unanswered, except for neurophysiologic speculations carried out chiefly by psychologists. I do not pretend to be able to answer many of these questions today but there have been a few observations in neurology and neurophysiology which bear upon them, and which may make it possible for us to see a little more clearly the direction our search must take toward an understanding of the neurophysiologic mechanisms of the central integrative processes of the brain.

A discussion of integration within the central nervous system must first consider levels of integration. In a sense, integrative function begins with the lowest and simplest reflex, in the reciprocal innervation of antagonistic muscles. At this level we still have only the vaguest notion of how an antagonistic muscle becomes inhibited during the contraction of its agonist in synergistic movement. Even at a lower level of integration than this, a single muscle appears to have a reflex regulatory system controlling the intensity of its contraction.[17] Proceeding upward in the levels of motor integration we arrive at the first supersegmental level in the medulla and midbrain where we find a remarkably powerful balanced integrative system in the brain stem reticular formation, whose facilitatory and inhibitory properties have been so beautifully elucidated by Magoun and his colleagues during recent years.[24] Beginning at the bulbar and mesencephalic level, proceeding upward into the diencephalon, we find a reticular system which may exert its effects, not only downstream upon the excitability of spinal segments, but also upstream upon the excitability and activity of the cerebral cortex.[26] It is the properties of this highest level central integrative system which I wish to discuss in further detail. But first let us consider briefly lower levels of integration in afferent systems.

In Adrian's classical investigations of the physical basis of sensation[1, 2] we have portrayed the basic nature of the volleys and trains of nerve impulses which are initiated in different types of sensory nerve fibers subserving not only signals from the skin and muscle senses but from visceral afferents and the more specialized receptors of vision, hearing, and smell. In all of these the principle appears to be the same, namely, that more intense stimulation produces a higher frequency response in individual nerve fibers and usually a stimulation of a greater number of fibers. Except for velocity of conduction the impulses themselves seem to be similar for all sensation. We find, however, that there is opportunity for modulation of these signals, some smoothing and interacting between signals from different nerves or sense organs in the first synaptic pool, which, in the case of the eye, for example, is in the retina (see Granit,[16]) and for the olfactory receptors is in the olfactory bulb.

The olfactory bulb has been the object of Adrian's most recent penetrating analysis.[3] Here he has found that the response to odors may be modified by the state of activity of the cells of the olfactory bulb where some interaction may take place between the signals arriving from different types of odor. To quote from a recent paper by Adrian: "In man vision is dominant and it is difficult for us to become inattentive to sights, but we soon cease to hear uninteresting sounds though we can force ourselves to listen to them again. Smells fade even more readily and in man olfactory adaptation cannot be overcome by voluntary effort. After a time no amount of sniffing will recover the lost sensation. But it is not unreasonable to compare adaptation to smell with adaptation to uninteresting sound and to suppose that both are based on the same kind of competition between the signals and the activity of the region they have to traverse."[3]

Proceeding upward we then find another intermediate level of sensory integration located principally in the thalamus, with the exception of the olfactory system. Here we find another way station in the specific thalamic nuclei where sensory signals may undergo rather minor modifications or modulations, while at the same time retaining their rigid spatial differentiation with accurate point-to-point projection of the retina, for example, or from small areas of the skin. From here we proceed also in the precise topographically localized fashion to the primary receiving areas of the cerebral cortex. Of course, there are side chains in the afferent circuits where a true afferent-efferent integration at the intermediate level takes place, providing for basic postural and autonomic adjustments of the body proceeding on an unconscious level.

The arrival of the volleys of afferent impulses after some modulation and smoothing in the relay nuclei is supposed to reach its highest level in the cerebral cortex where presumably we should look for conscious sensation. Electrophysiologic study of the evoked potentials in the various sensory-receiving areas of the cortex have repeatedly shown, however, that these discharges are most readily seen, not in the conscious alert individual but in the anesthetized individual who, according to most accepted criteria, would be considered rather deeply unconscious. The meticulous mapping of evoked potentials in the various sensory receiving areas of the cortex as carried out by Adrian, Woolsey, and others has yielded much of value to our knowledge of the detailed anatomic projection of most all sensory receptors. I hope Dr. Woolsey will pardon me, however, for expressing the opinion that such studies are largely of anatomic interest, revealing the primary cortical projection but not the mechanism of conscious sensation. They reveal another intermediate level where afferent signals may become modulated on their way toward centers which must represent the receiving areas for conscious sensation.

We find, however, that at the cortical level in the sensory receiving areas the electrical pattern of response may be varied by factors which do affect the level of consciousness. In addition there is evidence for variation in local responses to a given sensory stimulus depending upon the simultaneous or preceding stimulation of other types of sense organ. For example, the magnitude and form of the local response to a flash of light may be modified by a concurrent sound stimulus as was shown by Gerard and his colleagues[14] and more recently in unpublished work of Bickford at the Mayo Clinic. At the cortical level at least, therefore, we begin to see evidence of a form of intermodal integration between different types of sensation.

There is another type of regulation of the cortical response to afferent volleys which can be shown to arise from a cortical projection system which is distinct from that of the principal specific afferent projection systems. This system, which is located in the diencephalon and midbrain, has been shown to exert a rather remarkable regulatory action, not only upon the responses of the cerebral cortex to afferent impulses but also upon the resting electrical activity of the cortex. It is closely related to the system which seems most directly concerned with the functional states of the brain which are commonly regarded as conscious, unconscious, sleep or waking, coma or excitement, and arousal or attention. Perhaps by consideration of the possible relationships between these specific afferent systems, the specific motor systems, and the central integrating or regulatory system which seems more directly related to conscious processes as such, we may at least approach somewhat nearer to the problem of conscious sensation. In this approach we come upon a central integrative mechanism which may subserve a level of integration which may be considered in one sense higher than that found in the cerebral cortex.

With this survey or outline of a way of looking at the problem let us now review a few facts and experimental observations which bear upon its solution. I shall confine my remarks to evidence gained from a study of the electrical activity of the brain. Other speakers in this symposium present evidence from other ways of watching the brain at work.

Resting Rhythms of the Brain

The electrical activity of the brain may be divided into two general types: (1) the resting rhythms, and (2) evoked responses. (We should mention a third electrical property of the brain, namely, polarization potentials which reflect the electrical charges on the surfaces of cell membranes. The importance of these large resting potentials which can be measured across masses of nerve cells of parallel orientation has been emphasized by Gerard and Libet,[13] and more recently by Bishop, O'Leary, and their co-workers.[4, 15] Their relationship to nerve metabolism and to excitatory states in nerve centers seems well established, though complex, as might be anticipated from the structural complexity of centers, such as those found in the cerebral cortex.)

The resting electrical rhythms of the brain probably represent periodic fluctuations in the "steady state" electrotonic membrane potential of nerve cells (see Fig. 81). Such rhythmic cell potentials may be initiated by nerve impulses arriving at their synapse, and they may result in the discharge of a train of nerve impulses propagated along their axons, but this is not necessarily so. They may also occur in cells completely deprived of afferent inflow owing to the marked tendency for intrinsic or autonomous rhythmicity in nerve cells of the central gray matter, if their excitatory state is maintained optimal either through nervous mechanisms or by variations in the biochemical nature of their environment.

Rhythmic cell potentials may not always be associated with the discharge of impulses along their axons. They seem most closely related to fluctuations in excitability, which, when sufficiently intense, may also signal the propagation of volleys or trains of nerve impulses into, or away from, the group of cells from which the electrical waves are derived. With this brief consideration of what the resting electrical rhythms of the brain may represent, let us consider some of the factors controlling them.

In the first place these electrical rhythms of the brain are exquisitely sensitive to chemical factors affecting nerve metabolism and excitability,[9] such as glucose, oxygen, carbon dioxide, electrolytes, and others including acetylcholine. The importance of these factors in the regulation of brain function is being emphasized by other speakers. They form the background for the more rapid and differential action of nervous regulatory systems.

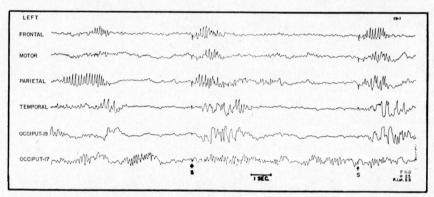

FIG. 81.   Bursts of rhythmic electrical activity as recorded from various areas of the cortex in the cat under barbiturate anesthesia. At S a brief electrical shock has been given to the intralaminar system of the thalamus which serves to initiate bursts similar to those occurring spontaneously.

The electrical rhythms which have been recorded from the human brain in the electroencephalogram, although in quantity of record probably sufficient to stretch several times around the world, have yielded surprisingly little of definite and critical value to our knowledge of human brain function. They have become of definite practical value in locating cerebral lesions, and in the analysis of the location and form of excessive neuronal discharge found in patients with epilepsy, and they have helped to locate the projection of different types of sensory inflow upon the cerebral cortex. Their possible significance, if any, in relation to the more complex functions of the brain has remained largely in the realm of speculation, although some of this speculation is now becoming sufficiently concrete to be subjected to experimental verification.

Relations to States of Consciousness

It may seem presumptuous to speak in this symposium about such ill-defined phenomena as states of consciousness, although I am sure we all have a fairly clear idea of what we mean by this expression. In subjective terms, of course, we mean the clarity of our awareness of our internal and external environment. In objective terms, consciousness seems most clearly described as "readiness to respond" but not just readiness of any portion of the nervous system to respond. The state of consciousness must be related to the excitatory state of that portion or system within the brain most closely concerned with the highest integrative functions. At any rate, what we wish to consider is the variations in the electrical rhythms of the brain with such conditions as sleep, drowsiness, waking, alertness, and acute tension states or arousal of the individual organism as a whole. It has been disappointing to find the pattern of the electroencephalogram relatively normal in patients with severe mental disturbances of various kinds—disturbances sufficiently severe to classify the subjects as psychotic. However, any disturbance in mental activity, which might be related to the level or state of consciousness, is immediately reflected in changes in the spontaneous electrical rhythms of the cortex (see Fig. 82). The well-known alpha rhythm which dominates the normal pattern of the electroencephalogram from parieto-occipital regions disappears and is replaced by slower irregular waves with the gradient of electrical activity moving forward to occupy the frontal and central regions.[5, 12] There is a slow irregular pattern with some specific spindles of 14 per second waves which characterize certain stages of sleep. The electrical rhythms of the entire brain become altered in drowsiness and sleep as they do in any other form of impairment or loss of consciousness such as that due to anoxia or to anesthesia. The most dramatic change occurs in the sudden momentary loss of consciousness seen in petit mal seizures of epilepsy. All normal brain rhythms become extinguished suddenly over both hemispheres and are replaced by the familiar wave and spike discharge which is synchronized over wide areas of both hemispheres by a central pacemaker[19, 29] as shown in Figure 83. One might assume that these impaired states of consciousness represent some impairment in the metabolic functions of the brain as a whole. However, it is possible to produce similar changes by specific and restricted lesions in the brain stem in regions which do not affect necessarily the metabolism of the brain as a whole and in regions which do not impair the inflow of afferent impulses to the cerebral cortex.

Lindsley, Bowden, and Magoun[22] have recently shown that the changes in the electrical activity of the cortex, comparable to that of sleep, can be reproduced by lesions of the upper brain stem well localized in the basal diencephalon and midbrain tegmentum. These discrete lesions were without effect on the principal ascending sensory pathways.[23] This brought to light, following the previous evidence of Ranson and others, the existence of an ascending reticular activating system which served to produce changes in electrocortical activity similar to that of arousing the animal from sleep, when local stimulation was administered to this region. Changes in the electroencephalogram similar to sleep were produced by lesions in this restricted area. It has also been shown that stimulation within this area may produce a marked change in the cortical response to afferent stimuli

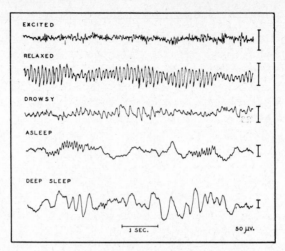

Fig. 82. Human electroencephalograms during excitement, relaxation, drowsiness, and deep sleep. (From Penfield and Erickson: Epilepsy and Cerebral Localization, p. 401. Springfield, Charles C Thomas, 1941.)

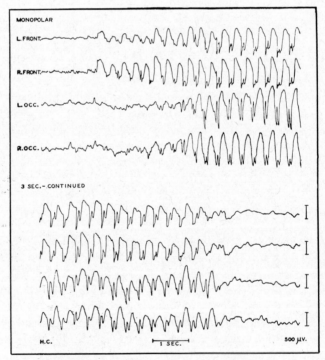

Fig. 83. Electroencephalogram from left and right frontal and occipital regions at the beginning and end of a petit mal seizure in an epileptic patient. The patient was apparently unconscious throughout the attack, with slight flickering of the eyelids.

and may alter the apparent excitability of the motor cortex to electrical stimulation.[9, 27, 28]

Neurologists and neurosurgeons have long been aware, from clinical observations, that there existed a very critical area in the region of the third ventricle or midbrain in which small lesions produced states of coma, prolonged unconsciousness, or, what has been termed by Sir Hugh Cairns, "akinetic mutism."[7] Bremer[6] first thought that lesions of the brain stem which produced a change in electrocortical activity resembling sleep were due to an interruption of the main incoming afferent pathways upon which depended, he thought, the arousal of the cortex to a waking state or a condition of readiness to respond, which he termed "tonus corticale." It is now clear, from the work of Magoun and his associates[23] particularly, that the nervous mechanisms responsible for this waking state of the cortex are not the principal afferent pathways but a separate projection system which is independent in its projection pathways from the basal diencephalon and midbrain to the cortex, since interruption of the afferent pathways themselves does not alone produce this state resembling sleep, either as judged by the electrocorticogram or as judged by the behavior of the animal. Since anesthetic agents such as the barbiturates are known not to block conduction of afferent impulses to the cerebral cortex, it is proposed that their action on consciousness may be related to more specific effect on the brain stem reticular system.

Studies of the relationship between the thalamus and cortex have also revealed a separate projection system which is capable of exerting an even more direct and specific regulating action on the electrical activity of the cerebral cortex. While recording the resting electrical rhythms simultaneously from many areas of the cerebral cortex, one may explore the local nuclei of the thalamus with a minute pair of stimulating electrodes which excite only about one square millimeter or less of tissue in the immediate vicinity of the tip of the electrode in the thalamus. A systematic exploration of the entire thalamus in this manner has shown that there exists a separate and well-restricted system, concentrated mostly in nuclei which are usually described within the internal and external medullary lamina of the thalamus, a system which may exert a regulatory action upon the rhythmic activity of wide areas of the cortex in both hemispheres (see Fig. 84). Portions of it exert their principal influence only on one hemisphere and some may be shown to affect principally one lobe of one hemisphere with activity spreading slowly to other regions. The existence of this diffuse thalamocortical projection system was first pointed out by Morison and Dempsey[8, 25] and later studied with Droogleever-Fortuyn.[18, 19]

The thalamic reticular system does not seem to be related definitely to the specific thalamocortical projection systems within the thalamus. In many experiments, displacement of the point of the stimulating electrode as much as one-half a millimeter, or less at times, would abolish the recruiting response characteristic of this system. When one stimulates the specific thalamocortical projection nuclei, local cortical responses are obtained upon the specific and well-localized topographic projection of this portion of any specific nucleus. These physiologic studies, therefore, have brought to light a separate and centrally placed projection system from the higher brain stem to the cortex which is capable of exerting a powerful effect upon

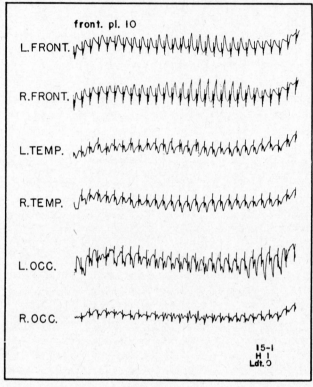

front. pl. 10

L.FRONT.

R.FRONT.

L.TEMP.

R.TEMP.

L.OCC.

R.OCC.

15-1
H I
Ldt. 0

Fig. 84.   Cortical electrical responses to repetitive stimulation of the thalamic reticular system (n. Centralis Medialis) in the cat.

cortical activity—a system which can exert this effect independent of the principal afferent pathways to the cortex. There is, however, an interrelationship between these afferent pathways and the diffuse projection system —an interrelationship both at a subcortical and cortical level.

Interrelationships between Specific Cortical Functions and the Central Integrating System

The electrical sign of response of the cerebral cortex to an afferent stimulus is composed of several parts. One records first an extremely well-localized small potential wave of positive sign which marks the arrival of the volley of afferent impulses to the cortex and which is sometimes called the radiation potential, as shown in Figure 85. Following this, there is a larger surface positive wave known as the evoked potential. This wave has been used to great advantage in mapping of sensory representation in the cortex. It represents the first primary discharge of cortical cells in response to the afferent volley. In lightly anesthetized or unanesthetized animals, this initial positive deflection is rapidly followed by a variable large negative wave which seems to represent the local elaboration of the

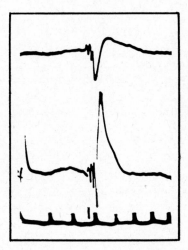

FIG. 85.   Evoked potential complex recorded from the visual cortex in the cat following a brief shock to the lateral geniculate body. In the upper record, a characteristic response is shown consisting of the three small irradiation spikes followed by the larger surface positive (down) wave and a small surface positive (up) wave. In the second record, a conditioning shock was administered to the thalamic reticular system about 20 msec. before the geniculate shock. Note the enhancement of the surface negative wave. Time line at bottom, 10 msec.

afferent volley in the cortex of the receiving area (Fig. 85). This primary local response complex may be followed by a series of oscillating potentials which may spread somewhat farther in the local receiving area of the cortex and be shown as a damped oscillation, somewhat as shown in Figure 86.

In addition to these local effects on electrocortical activity, which seemed fairly well confined to the receiving area and sometimes spread to surrounding elaborative areas, there are more widespread effects of a sensory volley upon the electrical activity of the brain as a whole. Two such more general responses have been described, the arousal response[31] and the secondary sensory discharge.[10] The latter was shown by Forbes and Morison[11] to be mediated by a subthalamic system in a structure in the vicinity of the amygdaloid nucleus beneath the temporal lobe. The arousal response causes a diminution in the slow rhythmic activity of the widespread areas of the brain depending upon the arousal value of a given stimulus.

Simultaneous activation of the diffuse and specific projection systems has been shown to cause marked changes in the cortical response to an afferent volley (Fig. 85). By careful timing of electrical impulses applied within the thalamic reticular system and to a sensory relay nucleus such as the lateral geniculate body, it can be shown that the negative phase of the sensory-evoked potential of the cortex may be enhanced by appropriate timing of the stimulus to the reticular system. Rapid stimuli within this system, however, may block or depress the negative sensory response and completely abolish the rhythmic sensory after-discharge or the response which is sometimes called the repetitive sensory discharge.

It seems, therefore, that the diffuse thalamocortical projection system may exert a regulatory action, either by enhancing or depressing the elaboration of nerve impulses after they reach their primary projection in the cortex, even though it cannot apparently exert any effect upon the arrival of such volleys to the cortex. The elaboration of cortical response to incoming afferent signals is, therefore, modified by the regulating influence of this separate central integrating system. The thalamic portion of this system may exert its effect only on a small restricted area of the cortex, while the more caudal portions of this system in the brain stem have a more diffuse and undifferentiated action on the cortex as a whole.

It is possible to demonstrate that the spontaneous electrical rhythms of the brain, which are probably analogous to the alpha rhythm of the human electroencephalogram, are distinct from the transient responses induced by afferent stimulation, including the repetitive or rhythmic responses from a local sensory receiving area. There seems, therefore, to be a separate regulating system in the thalamus which may time and control the resting rhythms of the cortex analogous to the alpha rhythm in man. Therefore, this particular portion of the central reticular system may be thought of as bearing some special relation to other factors which seem to be related to the alpha rhythm. We have mentioned before that this rhythm is most susceptible to variations in the state of consciousness and towards sleep or drowsiness. We wish to emphasize now the well-known relationships of the alpha rhythm to conscious attention. The alpha rhythm is blocked readily by concentration of attention, especially when such concentration has some emotional tone. Also it has been shown that the neural mechanism underlying the regulation of the alpha rhythm is susceptible to conditioning and that practically all varieties of Pavlovian conditioned reflexes can be shown to manifest themselves in changes in the alpha rhythm of the human cortex.[17, 20, 32, 33] In the alpha rhythm we have demonstrated, therefore, a relationship between attentive processes and conscious learning (Fig. 87). It seems to involve the same nervous mechanisms which exert such a direct control over the resting rhythms of the cortex.

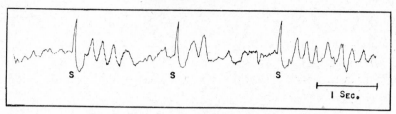

FIG. 86.   Sensory after-discharges following evoked potentials from the
auditory cortex in the cat in response to click stimuli (S).

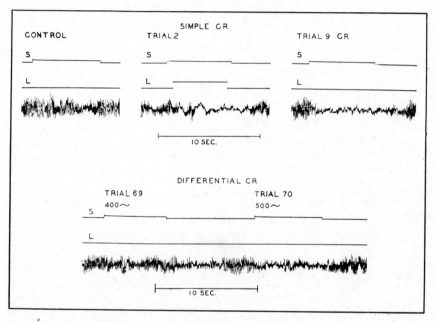

FIG. 87.   Examples of records showing conditioning of the alpha rhythm in
man. S indicates a sound stimulus, and L a light stimulus. Simple conditioning of
the blocking of the alpha rhythm to sound after nine trials is shown above. Differential conditioning of the blocking reaction to a tone of 500 cycles, as compared
to 400 cycles, is shown in the record below. (From Jasper and Shagass: *Journal
of Experimental Psychology*, 1941, 28, pp. 503-508.)

There have been also clearly demonstrated projections from the cortex
to the thalamus. These corticothalamic projections were first shown clearly
to return directly to the specific thalamic nuclei from the primary sensory
cortical projection areas. There are also projections from other cortical
areas to the elaborative nuclei, and more recently there have been shown to
be connections between the elaborative areas of the cortex and this central
reticular system of the diencephalon from which direct stimulation is shown
to exert such control over the resting rhythms of the cortex itself. The

significance of these cortical diencephalic connections is not entirely clear but their existence is necessary for an understanding of the integration of cerebral activity. Details of these projections are only now being worked out and their functional significance is at present largely a matter of speculation. However, I would like to propose a schematic diagram to serve as a working hypothesis (Fig. 88).

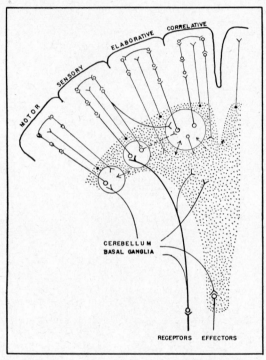

Fig. 88. Schematic diagram of relations between specific thalamocortical projection systems and the brain stem (including diencephalic) reticular system. Collaterals from the afferent pathways into the reticular system are shown, as discussed by Magoun. Separate projections from the thalamic reticular system are shown overlapping those of the specific systems. Projections from the elaborative (e.g., peri- and parastriate visual cortex) and correlative ("association areas") back into the central reticular system are indicated, as well as the return connections to the specific nuclei.

In this diagram we have pictured the principal sensory pathways with their relay nuclei. Along their course there are collaterals to the lower levels of the brain stem reticular formation. On the whole, however, the intensity and the temporal and spatial pattern of afferent stimuli proceed through these two synaptic pools to the cortex in a relatively unaltered form. In the cortex we have then an elaboration of these impulses from the primary to the surrounding elaborative cortical areas (such as, for example, to areas 18 and 19 of the occipital cortex).

This process of elaboration is apparently not simply a direct spreading of impulses outward into cortex surrounding the receiving areas, but involves cortico-thalamo-cortical circuits of to-and-fro projections. The impulses then enter a complex network of circuits which have been labeled "correlative" to signify the process of integrating or abstracting from specific sensory channels the perceptual images and universal concepts which give meaning to conscious thought and experience. Here again cortico-thalamo-cortical circuits play an important role. We now find, however, a far more important participation of the diencephalic reticular system, which receives its most important projections from areas of cortex which have correlative functions, particularly from portions of the frontal and temporal lobes. In addition, the separate projections from the reticular network exert an independent regulatory action upon the reactivity of the cortex as a whole.

We present this schema as a working hypothesis. It is grossly oversimplified, of course, to clarify our present conceptions of how a centrally placed reticular network in the diencephalon and brain stem may interact with specific thalamocortical and corticothalamic systems to provide a mechanism for a central unity of cerebral function, a unity which has been a major problem of philosophers since the time of Descartes, and which today may be approached more objectively by neurophysiologists and neuroanatomists.

REFERENCES

1. ADRIAN, E. D.: The Basis of Sensation, 122 pp. London, Christophers, 1928.
2. ADRIAN, E. D.: The Physical Background of Perception, pp. 1-95. London, Oxford University Press, 1947.
3. ADRIAN, E. D.: *Electroencephalography and Clinical Neurophysiology*, 1950, 2, pp. 377-388.
4. BISHOP, G. H. and O'LEARY, J. L.: *Electroencephalography and Clinical Neurophysiology*, 1950, 2, pp. 401-416.
5. BRAZIER, M. A. B.: *Electroencephalography and Clinical Neurophysiology*, 1949, 1, pp. 195-204.
6. BREMER, F.: *Comptes rendus des séances de la Société de biologie*, Paris, 1935, 118, pp. 1235-1242.
7. CAIRNS, H.; OLDFIELD, R. C.; PENNYBACKER, J. B.; and WHITTERIDGE, D.: *Brain*, 1941, 64, pp. 273-290.
8. DEMPSEY, E. W., and MORISON, R. S.: *American Journal of Physiology*, 1942, 135, pp. 293-300.
9. DUBNER, H. H., and GERARD, R. W.: *Journal of Neurophysiology*, 1939, 2, pp. 142-152.
10. FORBES, A.; BATTISTA, A. F.; CHATFIELD, P. O.; and GARCIA, J. P.: *Electroencephalography and Clinical Neurophysiology*, 1949, 1, pp. 141-175.
11. FORBES, A., and MORISON, B. R.: *Journal of Neurophysiology*, 1939, 2, pp. 112-128.
12. GERARD, R. W.; KLEITMAN, N.; and BLAKE, H.: *Journal of Neurophysiology*, 1939, 2, pp. 48-60.
13. GERARD, R. W. and LIBET, B.: *Journal of Neurophysiology*, 1941, 4, pp. 438-455.

14. GERARD, R. W.; MARSHALL, W. H.; and SAUL, L.: *Archives of Neurology and Psychiatry*, Chicago, 1936, 36, pp. 675-738.
15. GOLDRING, S.; WETT, G.; O'LEARY, F.; and GREDITZER, A.: *Electroencephalography and Clinical Neurophysiology*, 1950, 2, pp. 297-308.
16. GRANIT, R.: Sensory Mechanisms of the Retina, 412 pp. London, Oxford University Press, 1947.
17. GRANIT, R.: *Journal of Neurophysiology*, 1950, 13, pp. 351-372.
18. JASPER, H. H.: *Electroencephalography and Clinical Neurophysiology*, 1949, 1, pp. 405-420.
19. JASPER, H., and DROOGLEEVER-FORTUYN, J.: *Research Publication, Association for Research in Nervous and Mental Disease*, 1947, 26, pp. 272-298.
20. JASPER, H. H. and SHAGASS, C.: *Journal of Experimental Psychology*, 1941, 28, pp. 373-388.
21. JASPER, H. H. and SHAGASS, C.: *Journal of Experimental Psychology*, 1941, 28, pp. 503-508.
22. LINDSLEY, D. B.; BOWDEN, J.; and MAGOUN, H. W.: *Electroencephalography and Clinical Neurophysiology*, 1949, 1, pp. 475-486.
23. LINDSLEY, D. B.; SCHREINER, L. H.; KNOWLES, W. B.; and MAGOUN, H. W.: *Electroencephalography and Clinical Neurophysiology*, 1950, 2, pp. 483-498.
24. MAGOUN, H. W. and RHINES, R.: Spasticity: The Stretch Reflex and Extrapyramidal Systems, vii, 59 pp. Springfield, Ill., Charles C. Thomas, 1947.
25. MORISON, R. S. and DEMPSEY, E. W.: *American Journal of Physiology*, 1942, 135, pp. 281-292.
26. MORUZZI, G. and MAGOUN, H. W.: *Electroencephalography and Clinical Neurophysiology*, 1949, 1, pp. 455-473.
27. MURPHY, J. P. and GELLHORN, E.: *Journal of Neurophysiology*, 1945, 8, pp. 341-364.
28. MURPHY, J. P. and GELLHORN, E.: *Journal of Neurophysiology*, 1945, 8, pp. 431-448.
29. PENFIELD, W. and JASPER, H.: *Research Publication, Association for Research in Nervous and Mental Disease*, 1947, 26, pp. 252-271.
30. PENFIELD, W. and RASMUSSEN, T.: The Cerebral Cortex of Man. New York, The Macmillan Company, 1950.
31. RHEINBERGER, M. and JASPER, H. H.: *American Journal of Physiology*, 1937, 119, pp. 186-196.
32. SHAGASS, C.: *Journal of Experimental Psychology*, 1942, 31, pp. 367-379.
33. SHAGASS, C. and JOHNSON, E.: *Journal of Experimental Psychology*, 1943, 33, pp. 201-208.
34. SHERRINGTON, C. S.: The Integrative Action of the Nervous System, 433 pp. Cambridge, The University Press, 1947.

Discussion

MARY A. B. BRAZIER, PH.D.

It is my task to draw the work just reported to you into the framework of this symposium and to examine what it means for the subject whose name this symposium bears: Biological Aspects of Mental Health and Disease.

I wish I were able to remember verbatim the opening paragraph of Dr. Kety's address. He indicated to us the great accumulation of knowledge which had resulted from *in vitro* experiments on cerebral metabolism, and then went on to show us how much could be added by a method applicable to studies *in vivo*.

I think there is a parallel here to electrophysiology. We have learned a great deal about the structure of the brain from the microscopist and about its constituents from the chemist, but electrophysiology tells us about the interconnections and integration of this communication system *in vivo*. And isn't this what the title of the symposium is really asking us for? Mental health and mental disease are conditions of living brains and any method which allows us to study the living brain should take us nearer to our goal.

The growth and development of electrophysiology has worked a profound change in neurophysiology in the last twenty-five years. I do not mean only the experimental advance but the change in concepts of the nervous system. In brief, it is a change from the concept of a passive, static nervous system to an active, dynamic one. In the old concept, the nervous system was bound in space by the paths of neurons, in direction by the Bell-Magendie law, and was bound in time by the conduction rate of nerve fibers and the delay time at synapses. No persistence in time was accounted for and the parameters of its activity were thought to be rigorously imposed by the all-or-nothing law.

The new neurophysiology looks at things very differently. Temporal summation, spatial summation, inhibition, electrotonus all give flexibility of response. These properties were known (Gotch published a description of electrotonus many years ago) but they were not yet incorporated in the concepts of the integration of the brain. After-potentials, after-discharge, and self re-exacting loops release the nervous system from the fetters of time. No longer does anybody think of the nervous system as responding only at the moment when stimulated. It is clear, as Judson Herrick[4] has pointed out, that simple reflexes are not the elementary units of behavior and that the "actual conduct of animal and human bodies is not fabricated by monumentally piling up of simple reflexes."

No longer do we think of the nervous system as having to respond only when it is stimulated. If the hypothesis of self re-exciting chains of neurons is accepted, we can see how the nervous system can seize and retain stimuli and respond to them at a later time. We realize now that it is also emancipated in space, for the discovery of moving fields of DC potentials makes possible the use of other parts of the brain than those directly served by the direct incoming nervous pathway.

All this is consistent with the central nervous system being, not a mere relay station which when unstimulated is at rest, but a system which is in itself a hive of activity, clues to which can be found in the "spontaneous" activity of all neuron aggregates, both in the cord and in the brain.

Dr. Jasper has given us some insight into some of the possible mechanisms for integration of activity in the brain. You will have noticed how well supported by experimental evidence his hypotheses are. This cannot be said for all the hypotheses that have been advanced for the alpha rhythm.

I would like to refer to one of these. It is that this rhythmic electrical activity is the electrical sign of a scanning process. This is a very attractive hypothesis, published first, I think, by Craik,[3] although several people had been thinking along these lines. It could account for most if not all the characteristics of the alpha rhythm. This hypothesis (in one of its forms) allots a facilitating role to the alpha rhythm for it is suggested that it may represent the activity of a process resembling a scanning sweep of the visual receiving area by rhythmic impulses from the association areas; when no visual impulses are coming in, the sweep follows its cyclical sequence and its rhythm is recordable in its purest form (this would represent the alpha rhythm of the waking subject with eyes closed); when the sweep encounters the spatial pattern of visual impulses in the cortex, the periodicity is disrupted (as when the eyes are opened). Thus in the integration of the brain's activity, another signal system is introduced in the form of the "on" and "off" periods of the sweep.

A scanning process of this kind would not necessarily demand reverberating circuits but would invoke pathways other than those primarily concerned with incoming visual impulses. One would expect to find the generator of its impulses in the visual association areas, and, in fact, it is here that the main foci of the alpha rhythm are found.

Now this is a very difficult hypothesis to test experimentally and this may account for the fact that there is practically no direct experimental evidence to support it or to deny it.

Bremer,[2] who is perhaps the dean of the polemicists on this subject, holds the view that the electroencephalogram consists of a combination of primary sensory responses and of efferent cortical discharges against a background of the fluctuating membrane potentials of the cortical cells. He suggests that this subliminal oscillation of potential serves to maintain an optimal level of excitability at cortical synapses and thus to ensure effective response to all messages.

A statement such as the last one, which suggests that the role of the cortical rhythms is to maintain an optimal state of preparedness for appropriate facilitation or inhibition of incoming stimuli does, however, imply that the cortical neurons have information as to what would in fact be the appropriate level of excitability at any given moment. One may infer that the delivery of this information to the cortex would necessitate some form of feed-back circuit from an integrating center or network. Already the demonstration by Bates that, for a fraction of a second before a voluntary movement is made, the electroencephalogram assumes a definite pattern, indicates that the alpha rhythm carries a signal before the efferent impulse is discharged. It would therefore be an error to underestimate the importance of the subcortical connections in the composite picture of the alpha rhythm

In closing, may I say how much I appreciated Dr. Jasper's fine contribution; it is work such as his which will elucidate for us the dynamics of nervous intercommunication and further our search for the signals which by their timing and their grouping produce order in place of randomness, and integration instead of scatter. It is interesting to consider what the behavior of an organism might be if all the cells of its nervous system were to discharge at random.

To the search for changes in structure in the brains of the mentally ill we can now add a search for clues to the integration of these signals, the integration which decides whether behavior is to be reliable, predictable, and appropriate, as demanded by society, or whether it is to be random, unpredictable, and uncertain and lead to the clinic and the hospital.

REFERENCES

1. BATES, J. A. V.: *American Journal of Physiology*, 1951, 113, p. 240.
2. BREMER, F.: *Electroencephalography and Clinical Neurophysiology*, 1949, 1, p. 177.
3. CRAIK, K. J. W.: The Nature of Explanation. London, Cambridge University Press, 1943.
4. HERRICK, C. J.: The Problem of Mental Disorder, Chapter 8. New York, McGraw Hill, 1934.

CHAPTER 16

Functional Organization of the Brain in Relation to Mentation and Behavior

HARRY F. HARLOW, PH.D.

EXPERIMENTAL WORK in the last twenty years has led authorities to propose theories concerning the cortical localization of intellectual functions ranging from complete nonspecificity to extreme specificity. Thus, Lashley,[7] in 1929, advanced the hypothesis that intellectual functions, in contrast to motor and sensory functions, are equally represented throughout all parts of the cerebral cortex. Carlyle Jacobsen,[6] on the other hand, shortly afterward presented evidence that a particular intellectual function, presumably immediate memory, is specifically located in the frontal lobes. This conclusion was based on his findings that, following extirpation of the prefrontal areas, chimpanzees and monkeys lost the ability to solve delayed response problems. The significance of his results, however, was rendered indeterminate when a number of different investigators—Finan,[3] Malmo,[8] Campbell and Harlow,[1] and Wade[9]—independently demonstrated that monkeys could solve delayed reactions after bilateral destruction of the prefrontal areas.

During this same twenty-year interval, a considerable number of human cases was studied, following very large cortical lesions, including bilateral destruction of the prefrontal areas, hemidecortication, and unilateral removal of the dominant occipital and temporal lobes.

The data on bilateral destruction of the frontal lobes in man gave no evidence of anything approaching total loss of immediate memory. Most investigators, however, did find evidence indicating some intellectual loss, deficits usually described in such terms as loss of abstract attitude, inability to shift sets, and inability to synthesize the component parts of complex problems.

Recently, Hebb has reviewed these human data and has concluded that none of the studies convincingly demonstrated any intellectual loss spe-

The researches reported in this paper were supported in part by the Research Committee of the Graduate School from funds supplied by the Wisconsin Alumni Research Foundation, 1945 to 1951.

cifically attributable to loss of frontal lobe tissue. By this Hebb[5] did not mean to imply that there was no loss following bilateral destruction of the frontal areas; he meant, merely, that the studies were not definitive. Either the tests were inadequate, or proper controls were not maintained, or the possibility of continued pathologic process after operation was not excluded.

Theoretic interpretations have been further complicated by the recent publication of the results of the Greystone Project.[2] In that investigation, frontal lesions were made on human beings having no organic pathologic condition, and a very extensive battery of psychologic tests was given. A year after the operations, no significant differences could be demonstrated between members of the group subjected to operation and their controls.

Equally puzzling are the human data investigating the effect, on intellectual processes, of large lesions other than those in the frontal areas. The human cases of hemispherectomy—none of which has been adequately studied from the psychologic point of view—suggest a range of intellectual loss from comparatively slight to almost totally disabling. Furthermore, many of the symptoms reported are strikingly similar to those attributed in the clinical literature to the frontal syndrome.

The psychologic symptoms reported following the destruction of the dominant occipital lobe in man range from none to almost total alexia and severe visual agnosia.

It is difficult to effect completely adequate controls on these complex problems with human subjects. Basic data concerning the cortical localization of intellectual functions may best be obtained from studies of the subhuman primates; taking this point of view, we are conducting a research program at the University of Wisconsin, designed to determine the effect of large cortical lesions upon certain intellectual functions of rhesus monkeys.[4] Special emphasis is given to the effect of large bilateral lesions. Three fundamental questions are asked. What evidence is there for cortical localization of specific kinds of intellectual functions? Is any intellectual function completely destroyed by large cortical lesions? If the obtained intellectual loss is only quantitative, how persistent is this deficit?

Experimental Work

Methods: Though results from twenty monkeys will be presented, the data which we report come chiefly from a group of twelve monkeys continuously tested for a period of over five years and having completely known and equivalent learning histories. Four of these animals, the Normal Group, have never undergone any brain operation. The other eight monkeys were first subjected to extensive unilateral lesions. The frontal pole was amputated at a coronal plane passing through the rostral limit of the superior limb of the inferior precentral sulcus, and the remaining cortex on the lateral surface anterior to this sulcus was removed by suction. A large portion of the hemisphere was removed in a dissection passing through a coronal plane located 3 to 4 mm. rostral to the sulcus lunatus. Part of the remaining temporal lobe tissue was removed by an incision located a few millimeters below, and parallel to, the lateral fissure. The remainder of the lateral surfaces of the temporal and parietal lobes was removed with the exception of a small area at the tip of the temporal lobe and a strip of cortex approximately 2 to 3 mm. caudal to the central sulcus. The eight monkeys, following this operation which involved removal of most of the neocortex on one-half of the brain except for the motor and the primary somatic areas, are described as the Unilateral Group.

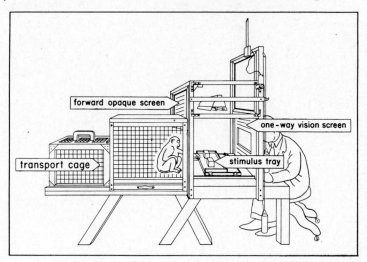

Fig. 89. Wisconsin general test apparatus. A delayed response trial is illustrated.

After more than two years of testing on a wide variety of learning problems these eight monkeys were divided into two equal groups. The Frontal Group underwent extirpation of the lateral surface of the contralateral prefrontal region. The Posterior Group was subjected to a lesion which began near the midline at the junction of the lunate sulcus and the vein representing continuation of the intraparietal and superior temporal sulci. The lesion, produced by aspiration of cortical tissue, followed laterally along the lunate sulcus and caudal to the vein and broadened into and completely destroyed the lateral surface of the temporal cortex.

The basic test apparatus used throughout the experiment is illustrated in Figure 89 and consisted of a restraining cage, a stimulus tray with two or more foodwells which could be appropriately baited and covered by stimuli, an opaque screen which could be lowered in front of the monkey, and a one-way vision screen which could be interposed between the animal and the experimenter.

Three fundamental kinds of tests used were discrimination learning, delayed response, and oddity. Discrimination learning involves training the monkeys to select the one of two objects which is consistently rewarded with food, even though its position on the test tray is continually shifted in an irregular manner. Individual problems involving a particular pair of stimuli were usually run for only six trials. Long series of such problems were run during various phases of the test program, and proficiency was measured by performance on these problem series. The stimuli used differed in many dimensions and should have been easily differentiated by an animal in spite of considerable visual-field defect.

A basic direct-method delayed-response technic was used. One of two stimuli, usually identical, was baited while the monkey watched, the one-

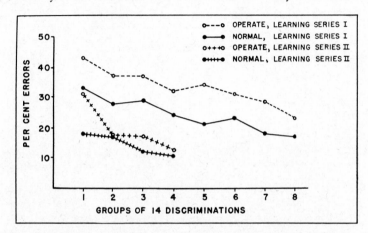

Fig. 90.   Comparison of Normal and Unilateral (Operate) Groups on two series of discrimination problems.

way vision screen was lowered, and, after a predetermined period of delay, the subject was permitted a choice. Many variations of this technic were used, including interposition of discrimination trials between delayed response trials, lowering of the forward opaque screen during various stages of the trial-setting and delay period, and varying the number of trials before shifting the position of the rewarded foodwell.

Oddity testing involved use of a tray containing three foodwells covered by two identical and one odd object, the latter covering a small piece of food. Two pairs of objects were used for each problem, and both the object singly represented and its position varied from trial to trial in a balanced order. Sixty problems of twenty-four trials each—with every problem utilizing new stimuli—comprised the test series presented in this paper.

Results: Behavioral comparisons of the Normal Group and the Unilateral Group (with lesions which destroyed all association areas on one side of the brain) revealed relatively little permanent difference. The performance of the Unilateral Group (described as Operate in Fig. 90) was significantly inferior to that of the Normal monkeys when tested initially on a series of 112 discrimination problems, but the difference was less marked when the animals were tested a year later on fifty-six discrimination problems.

The compensatory effect of learning in animals with large unilateral cortical lesions is illustrated in Figure 90 by the finding that the half-brained monkeys performed more effectively on the second test series than did the full-brained monkeys on the first series.

Inconclusive evidence that the Unilateral Group might be inferior to the Normal Group on delayed response tests appeared in experiments carried

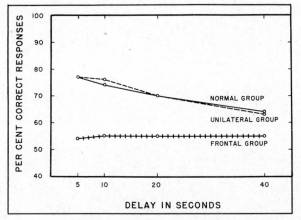

FIG. 91.   Performance of Normal, Unilateral, and Frontal Groups
as a function of delay.

out a few months after operation. But extensive delayed response tests made a year later revealed no differences in the Unilateral and Normal Groups, as is shown in Figure 91.

The Unilateral monkeys were significantly inferior to the Normal animals as measured by a series of oddity tests (see Fig. 92), but the design of our experimental program made it impossible to assess the degree of permanence of this impairment.

Our primary concern in this program is the comparison of performances among the Normal, the Frontal, and the Posterior Groups, for the subjects at the time they formed the latter two groups had large bilateral lesions. The results presented in Figure 93 are typical of those obtained on ten different series of delayed response tests. Very serious loss was suffered on these delayed response tests by the Frontal animals, but little loss was suffered by the Posterior Group. Furthermore, these results were persistent even after two years of frequent retesting on a wide range of delayed response problems.

In contrast to these data were the performances obtained when dis-

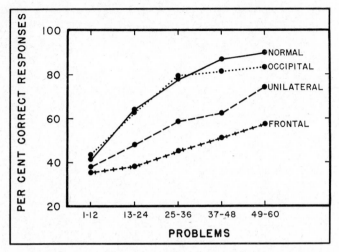

Fig. 92. Comparison of Normal, Unilateral, Frontal, and Occipital Groups on a series of oddity problems. (Members of the Occipital Group had undergone unilateral occipital lobectomy.)

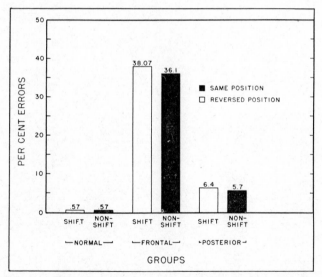

Fig. 93. Comparison of Normal, Frontal, and Posterior Groups on a delayed response test.

crimination learning problems were presented. On all such series of measures the Frontal Group showed little or no loss, whereas the Posterior Group consistently exhibited severe loss (see Figs. 94-97). Continuous testing over a year's duration indicates that these deficits are either permanent or, at least, extremely persistent.

Both Frontal and Posterior Groups showed deficit on the oddity tests

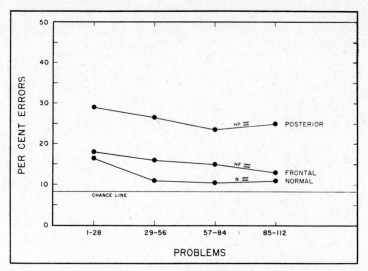

Fig. 94.   Performance of Normal, Frontal, and Posterior Groups on a series
of object quality discriminations.

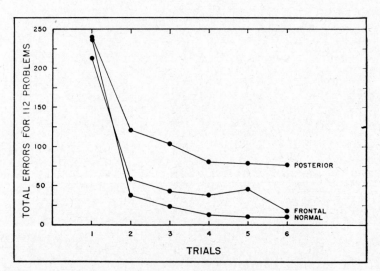

Fig. 95.   Intraproblem discrimination learning by Normal, Frontal, and
Posterior Groups.

(Fig. 98), and here no difference in error scores was found for members of the group upon which operation was performed. Observational data suggest, however, that the kinds of errors made by the two groups may differ.

Conclusions: The data which we have obtained give strong support to the thesis that different kinds of intellectual functions are differentially sus-

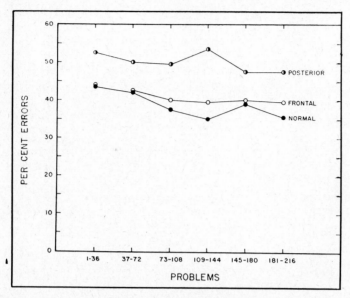

Fɪɢ. 96.   Performance of Normal, Frontal, and Posterior Groups on a series
of pattern discrimination problems.

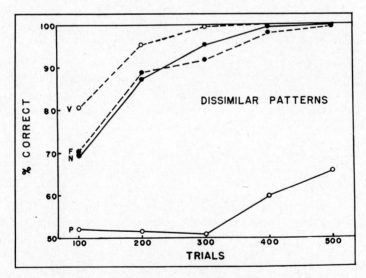

Fɪɢ. 97.   Performance of Normal, Frontal, Posterior, and Visual Groups on a
single pattern discrimination problem. (Members of the Visual Group had undergone extensive bilateral damage to the periparastriate areas.)

ceptible to lesions located in the frontal and the posterior association areas. Delayed-response–type tests—which may measure memory but which we have reason to believe basically measure some attentive function—are primarily impaired by lesions in the frontal association areas. Visual-discrimination–type functions are little affected by bilateral frontal lesions but very seriously impaired by bilateral lesions in the posterior association areas.

Bilateral frontal association lesions impair, but do not completely destroy, performance on delayed-response–type tests; bilateral posterior association

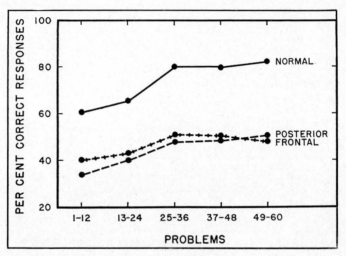

FIG. 98.   Comparison of Normal, Frontal, and Posterior Groups on a series of oddity problems.

area lesions impair, but do not completely destroy, performance on visual-discrimination-type functions. In no cortical association area have we found a lesion that completely destroys any intellectual function. The losses obtained—as of the present—have been merely quantitative rather than of an all-or-none character.

Even though the deficits are only quantitative, the impairment following bilateral lesions is very persistent, if not permanent. The operated groups of animals improve with practice, but their performance levels relative to each other and to the normal animals remain unchanged on the various problems. The monkeys with bilateral posterior lesions are comparatively inept at visual discrimination learning, and the monkeys with bilateral frontal lesions are relatively ineffective on delayed response tests.

Our theoretic position is that, although no specific intellectual function is localized in any single cortical area, the different cortical areas play markedly unequal roles in the mediation of our diverse intellectual processes.

REFERENCES

1. CAMPBELL, R. J., and HARLOW, H. F.: *Journal of Experimental Psychology*, 1945, 35, pp. 110-126.
2. COLUMBIA-GREYSTONE ASSOCIATES: Selective Partial Ablation of the Frontal Cortex: A Correlative Study of Its Effects on Human Psychotic Subjects. (Mettler, F. A., Editor.) New York, Paul B. Hoeber, Inc., 1950.
3. FINAN, J. L.: *American Journal of Psychology*, 1939, 52, pp. 1-15.
4. HARLOW, H. F., *et al.*: Detailed accounts of the experimental studies of this project will appear as a series of papers in the *Journal of Comparative and Physiological Psychology*, and the *Journal of General Psychology* in 1951 and 1952.
5. HEBB, D. O.: *Archives of Neurology and Psychiatry*, 1945, 54, pp. 10-24.
6. JACOBSEN, C. F.: *Comparative Psychological Monographs*, 1936, 13, No. 63, pp. 3-60.
7. LASHLEY, K. S.: Brain Mechanisms and Intelligence—a Quantitative Study of Injuries to the Brain. Chicago, University of Chicago Press, 1929.
8. MALMO, R. B.: *Journal of Neurophysiology*, 1942, 5, pp. 295-308.
9. WADE, M.: *Journal of Neurophysiology*, 1947, 10, pp. 57-61.

Discussion

HEINRICH KLÜVER, PH.D.

Judging by the number of discussers of this paper, there must be something wrong. But I assume that the large number of discussers is not so surprising if you consider that the paper you just heard is the first paper of the whole symposium which refers to the "mental" and to "mentation" in its title. It is perhaps significant that the organizers of this symposium, in formulating a four-day program on biologic aspects of mental health and disease, could not quite avoid—and, I hope, did not even wish to avoid—reference to the word "mental."

It remains true, however, that "mental," unlike isotopes, is something we wish to forget about nowadays. Why?

The psychologist, McDougall, who claimed in his autobiography that he had had perhaps a more intensive and varied training in the natural sciences than any other living man, reached the conclusion at the end of his life that psychology is "the most difficult of the sciences, and the most unsatisfactory of all fields of research."[8] It does not seem surprising, therefore, that many of the present-day generation of "psychologists and their fellow travelers" are no longer concerned with behavior as something to think about as a point of departure for a difficult scientific analysis, but only with behavior as something they should "do something about." If it is abnormal—and it apparently always is—it should be "normalized"; if it is maladjusted—and it apparently always is—it should be "adjusted."[4]

Obviously, Dr. Harlow's paper does not fall into the category of papers purporting to introduce improved or new psychotherapeutic "technics" for human or subhuman primates; it merely deals with various attempts to specify at least some of the conditions under which certain behaviors or behavior alterations occur. Unfortunately, as much as I would like to forget about the "mental," my colleagues in physiology, neurology, or neuropathology always prevent my doing so. For instance, Dr. Katzenelbogen quoted Sherrington on the mind-body problem. It is true that he quoted him quite correctly since Sherrington really did insist that sensible "space-time energy" and insensible "unextended mind" or "energy and mental experience" are disparate and incommensurable.[9] However, I should like to have the privilege of finishing the quotation which Dr. Katzenelbogen did not finish. It is a fact that Sherrington went on to inquire gloomily whether mind and matter have, then, really nothing in common. And he finally concluded that this at least they have in common: they are both "concepts." It is true, of course, that "ham" and "cigars" (whether smoked or unsmoked), "cabbage" and "sealing wax," "dianetics" and "cybernetics" as well as "mind" and "body" are concepts.

Indeed, if the most eminent neurophysiologist alive can ultimately say nothing about "mind" and "matter" except that they are both concepts, I submit that you may be forgiven for drawing the conclusion that physiologists should leave psychology strictly alone. Unfortunately, this seems to imply that psychologists, in turn, should not bother with physiology, biochemistry, or neuroanatomy. I, for one, am very reluctant to draw such a conclusion. In fact, whenever I hear reports made by physiologists, biochemists, or other investigators in the biologic sciences I cannot help wondering about the implications of their findings for the study of behavior. To give just one example: in connection with Dr. Tschirgi's interesting report on the blood-brain barrier I have been wondering about the implications of Cammermeyer's rather recent study of the area postrema. Cammermeyer is of the opinion that this nucleus presents conditions resembling those in the vegetative nuclear groups of the diencephalon and that it even contains cells producing a "neurosecretion."[1] If Cammermeyer's anatomic findings are related to available data on the permeability of the capillaries in this region, the area postrema appears to be one of the most unique portions of the central nervous system.

If I were to discuss brain mechanisms and behavior mechanisms before psychologists I would be tempted to dwell on the great and somewhat unexpected role rhinencephalic structures play in the relations between animal and environment, particularly in subhuman and human primates,[5] but since I am speaking chiefly before physiologists, biochemists, and neurologists I shall be content with emphasizing two points in regard to the study of behavior.

It is the aim of any behavior analysis to relate facts of behavior, let us say, a particular response, to conditions or stimuli in the external environment, i.e., to isolate the relevant or effective stimulus properties related to or responsible for a given response. Thus the ultimate goal of such a behavior analysis is to arrive at a specification of stimulus properties or stimulus constellations capable of influencing or eliciting a given form of behavior. The first point I wish to emphasize is that behavior can be studied and analyzed in such a way and that behavior can even be predicted on the basis of such an analysis without bothering to consider whether the skull contains a vacuum or a brain, whether it contains one of the hemi-semi-decorticated brains Dr. Harlow has occasionally talked about or merely McCulloch's cybernetic conception of a brain.

The second point I wish to emphasize concerns one of the most fundamental facts about behavior and is one with far-reaching implications. Briefly stated, this point is that any given form of behavior may be elicited by numerous and widely different stimuli. Since the most heterogeneous stimuli may produce the same behavioral or psychologic effect, a scientific analysis of behavior requires, first of all, the determination of the particular stimulus aspect or aspects responsible for a given effect. It is for purposes of such an analysis that I introduced about twenty-five years ago "the method of equivalent and non-equivalent stimuli."[2, 3] Once you have fully understood the implications of the facts of equivalence you will also understand why so few investigators have ever succeeded in determining and specifying the factors responsible for the directions and turns of behavior.

In closing, I should like to remind you that a monkey does not do many things a human being does; for instance, he does not do any "work" and is, as Mrs. Kohts insisted about twenty years ago, "incapable of work." In fact, her researches[6, 7] have left no doubt that monkeys cannot be made use of in any five-year plan formulated in Moscow or anywhere else. I took the occasion, a few years after Mrs. Kohts' publications, to point out that one of the many things which a monkey does not do is to write a *Critique of Pure Reason* while at the same time it may be asserted that he can think "categorically."[2]

If I wanted to embarrass Dr. Harlow (which I have, of course, no intention of doing) I would ask him to name at least a few of the "principles" or "categories" on which a monkey relies in reacting to the external environment. At the present time, I believe, there are no definite answers to such embarrassing questions; however, to gauge the degree of our ignorance in this matter, another symposium, namely, one on the behavioral aspects of biology, seems clearly indicated.

REFERENCES

1. CAMMERMEYER, J.: *Acta Anatomica*, 1946/47, 2, p. 294.
2. KLÜVER, H.: Behavior Mechanisms in Monkeys, 387 pp. Chicago, University of Chicago Press, 1933.
3. KLÜVER, H.: *Character and Personality*, 1936, 5, p. 91.

4. KLÜVER, H.: *Journal of Psychology*, 1949, 28, p. 383.
5. KLÜVER, H., and BUCY, P. C.: *Archives of Neurology and Psychiatry*, 1939, 42, p. 979.
6. KOHTS, N.: Adaptive Motor Habits of the *Macacus rhesus* under Experimental Conditions; a Contribution to the Problem of "Labour Processes" of Monkeys, 368 pp. Moscow, Scientific Memoir Museum Darwinianum, 1928.
7. KOHTS, N.: *Journal de psychologie*, 1930, 27, p. 412.
8. MURCHISON, C. (Ed.): A History of Psychology in Autobiography, Vol. I. (*cf.* pp. 191-223). Worcester, Clark University Press, 1930.
9. SHERRINGTON, C.: Man on His Nature, 413 pp. Cambridge University Press, 1940.

Discussion

DONALD O. HEBB, PH.D.

I would like to say first that the work we have been doing in Montreal supports the general conclusion that Dr. Harlow has reached concerning differential contributions of parts of the cortex to problem-solving, and that our work indicates pretty strongly (this is not true merely of the primates but also of the rat) that "mass action" may well be an expression of ignorance. The theory that all parts of the cortex contribute equally to problem-solving may mean only that the problem-solving contains so many diverse elements that on the average all parts of the brain contribute to total performance equally. Sometime we may get to a point of being able to make our analysis of behavior do the kind of thing that Dr. Klüver asked for. We may be able to make our analysis more satisfactory, ask the proper questions, and we may then find that we have to go even farther, perhaps, than Dr. Harlow suggested in saying that a component in intellectual performance only has its focus in one part of the brain. These unknown components may each be restricted to one part of the brain. That is a possibility in view of our present ignorance.

Another aspect of Dr. Harlow's work that I cannot dwell on is one feature of a recent development of psychologic knowledge that is turning things pretty well upside down. That is the long-term study of behavior and Dr. Harlow's conception of "learning to learn." It appears that there may be profound and irreversible changes in the organization of the cortico-diencephalic system with sensory experience, particularly during the infantile period. It can even be shown that there are lasting changes in intelligence, as far as one can identify that elusive substance in the rat, with variations of experience.

My last point: Dr. Bishop asked what his place was, as a neurophysiologist, in such a meeting aimed ultimately toward the psychiatric problem. I am prepared to say what the role of the psychologist is here. I think it is the willingness to be wrong.

Some twenty years or so ago Lashley, I believe, suggested that a psychologist in the present state of knowledge must be either wrong or vague. We have tried being vague for twenty years, and look at the situation we are in. I suggest that perhaps we had better try being wrong, but in somewhat more specific and intelligible terms.

Relation of Structure to Function in the Cerebral Cortex

PERCIVAL BAILEY, M.D.

Profiting by the example of my predecessors, I shall ignore the subject under discussion and "stick to my own theme."

Having been obliged, by my profession, to intervene surgically on the brain over a long period of years, naturally I was very much interested in its structure and also in its function, particularly when I began to operate with the intention of altering somewhat the function of the cortex of the brain.

I was also very much perturbed by the fact that I could not orient myself very well by inspection of the surface of the brain. Furthermore, when I tried to still the qualms of my own conscience afterward by examining under the microscope what I had removed, I developed an even greater anxiety because I couldn't recognize what it was that I had removed even when I had it under the microscope.

As a result of that difficulty, I began to study the literature very arduously and, in those periods when I wasn't too tired from working in the operating room and had the misfortune to remember what I had read (which was not easy, I assure you), I was very much worried by the fact that there were continuous contradictions in that literature. For example, Economo contradicts a prior statement within the space of three pages; therefore I concluded that, if he couldn't remember for three pages, perhaps what he was talking about was not very important.

I was also worried by a phenomenon that the French psychiatrists call *le phénomène du déjà vu*. Actually, when I would compare a certain page with another description three pages before, I realized that the author had said exactly the same thing, only in other words.

So I came reluctantly to the conclusion that I had to make my own cytoarchitectonic study of the cerebral cortex.

Being "brought up" by Dr. Bartelmez, I knew that the material used by my predecessors was not suitable for such study. Brains were used (taken out as long as twenty-four hours post mortem) which were fixed by simply dunking them into a vat of formalin solution. Any cytologist knows that cytologic work cannot be done on such material. The problem was to obtain a good brain for such a study. About that time World War II broke out, affording, so it seemed, an opportunity to acquire a normal brain on which to make such a study. I began to bombard the Surgeon General with letters and telegrams concerning this until he finally became very much annoyed with me, but, along about VJ Day, a can appeared in my laboratory containing the most perfect human brain that I have ever seen, with a simple statement that it had come from a young, healthy adult who had died in an accident, without any injury to the head, and without any previous illness. It had been injected through the arteries, as I had wished, with 4 per cent aqueous solution of formaldehyde within an hour after death.

I began the laborious process of preparing it. After the young men came back from the Army, and I didn't have so much clinical work to do, I settled down to the task of looking through these sections, and then I really developed an inferiority complex because, with that perfect brain before me, I still couldn't distinguish a section from the frontal cortex from one of the parietal region. I became quite psychoneurotic concerning this dilemma until, one day, I adopted a well-known psychologic mechanism: I transformed my inferiority complex into a superiority complex and decided that my predecessors were all wrong.

Since then, that delusion has been growing on me steadily, and I believe that my predecessors have operated on false premises. Their fundamental theory, stated clearly by Brodmann, was that the brain was a mosaic of organs. Therefore it was the anatomist's duty to outline those organs, and the physiologist's job to determine the function of each one of those organs.

At present, however, we do not look upon the brain in this manner. We think of it as a machine, perhaps not merely a machine but, at least, a machine dealing with communications, functioning for handling signals. As such, of course, it has to have an input as well as an output. For a long time the anatomists have been able to recognize the input stations, in which all of the cells become very small, whereas in the output stations all of the cells become large. From the time when Betz first looked at the cortex, all workers have been able to find those stations. The regions between them, however, have led workers astray and they went astray because, I think, of the fundamental hypothesis upon which they were working; they had to find organs in those other areas and in looking for them, naturally, they found them. The problem was not too complicated as long as we had only Brodmann's fifty-three areas but, when Economo listed 102 and Vogt and his co-workers found about 200 on the superior surface of the temporal lobe alone, it became a *reductio ad absurdum*. The physiologists became alarmed and would much rather cling to the old, simpler system of Brodmann. I think that is the reason they do not want to give it up, and become anxious whenever this is suggested.

At any rate, a much simpler system corresponds better with newer ideas concerning the function of the cortex and also, I believe, better with the actual structure of the cortex because, after all of these years of study, my colleague, Dr. Bonin, and I[4] cannot recognize the difference between sections from the parietal cortex, the temporal cortex, and large areas of the frontal cortex under the microscope if we do not know in advance from whence they came. If we know their source, we can place two of them side by side and describe differences between them but those differences are so small that they cannot have any great significance.

I am certain that there are vast areas of the cortex in which any difference in the function from that of another area depends on the external connections of the areas in question rather than upon the intrinsic structure. Therefore, I believe that nothing is to be gained by trying to subdivide the cortex into different organs on the basis of its intrinsic structure.

REFERENCES

1. BRODMANN, K.: Vergleichende Lokalisationslehre der Grosshirnrinde, 324 pp., Leipzig, Barth, 1925.
2. ECONOMO, C. VON.: The Cytoarchitectonics of the Human Cerebral Cortex, 186 pp. Oxford University Press, 1929.
3. VOGT, C., and VOGT, O.: Allgemeinere Ergebnisse unserer Hirnforschung, 190 pp., Leipzig, Barth, 1919.
4. BAILEY, P., and BONIN, G. VON.: The Isocortex of Man, 301 pp., Urbana, University of Illinois Press, 1951.

Some Observations on the Organization of Higher Functions after Penetrating Brain Injury in Man

HANS-LUKAS TEUBER, PH.D.

The problem of localizing psychologic functions in the cerebrum has at least two aspects: it is necessary (1) to know how to subdivide the neural structure, and (2) to know how to identify the functions to be localized. As Dr. Bailey has just indicated, a very large portion of our problem is the question of how to subdivide the cerebral structure. We do not know, *a priori*, which parcellations of the brain are relevant for the study of relationships between structure and function. We do not know what particular portions of the structure should be destroyed if we work with animals, nor do we know on what particular lesions we should concentrate when we study the effects of accidental injury or of surgical ablations in man. These difficulties are increased by the doubts which have recently arisen concerning the reliability and validity of cytoarchitectonic methods.

On the other hand, we do not know—and I think Dr. Klüver has stressed this point in more than one way—which particular functions we should try to attribute to various portions of the cerebrum. For these functions, again, are not given *a priori* but depend upon the experimental procedures used to demonstrate their presence or absence. Every change in procedure of testing is bound to lead to a different classification of cerebral function. The one definite result of current work, on monkey or man, is essentially negative: we are agreed that functions are not lost according to preexisting logical categories, as if the organism would fall apart according to the subdivisions of our textbooks. Our efforts are still limited, therefore, to attempts at localizing symptoms rather than functions. In most instances, we are merely trying to show failures on specific tests, not knowing of course what functions we are testing. The question of localization of function is thus reduced, temporarily, to the much simpler issue: Can we define certain test situations in which animals or patients, with particular lesions, are bound to fail?

Dr. Harlow has just shown that he can approximate such test situations for macaques; but he has added some important qualifications to which we agree. He has stressed that we cannot at present demonstrate any particular test situation that would be uniquely difficult for animals with certain lesions. Thus, disregarding the effects of radical removals from primary afferent and efferent areas of the cortex, we cannot set up tasks in which there is always failure by animals with one type of lesions, and always success by animals with another type of lesion. Instead, as Dr. Harlow puts it, deficits are quantitative rather than all-or-none. The same situation exists in another species—one that has been unnecessarily neglected in this work—in man. Here, too, losses after various cerebral lesions are quantitative rather than all-or-none.

Dr. Harlow has suggested, furthermore, that there are gradients of localization. In his monkeys, a frontal lesion will affect performance on the delayed response test more than will any other lesion studied. Conversely, a parieto-occipital lesion, in the macaque, interferes much more with solution of complex visual problems than does a frontal lesion. Is there anything in man corresponding to such gradients of localization for "higher" functions? On this point there is, I believe, a serious controversy in the field.

Until recently, the tendency has been to expect the most marked disturbances of "higher" intellectual functions in man after frontal lesions. Current studies, notably the Columbia-Greystone project, have singularly failed in fulfilling this expectation. We would therefore agree with Dr. Hebb in stressing that thus far we do not have any tests which would be uniquely difficult for human beings with frontal lobe lesions. On the other hand, our own recent work has convinced us that it is possible to define certain complex visual tasks which human beings with lesions in the posterior lobe substance—the parieto-occipital regions—perform very poorly. The difficulties of these patients appear to be similar to those described by Dr. Harlow for his monkeys.

The work to which I want to refer is carried out jointly by Dr. M. B. Bender and myself in the Psychophysiological Laboratory at the New York University College of Medicine. For the last three years we have been studying a group of veterans of World War II—all with penetrating gunshot wounds of the head, and with proved loss of brain substance.

The lesions in these subjects are distributed nearly at random over different parts of the cerebrum. Grouped according to wounds of entrance, there are forty frontal and frontoparietal, thirty-two parietal and temporal, and thirty-eight parieto-occipital and occipital cases. In the absence of autopsies, we do not know the exact localization and extent of these lesions. However, by relying on a fairly random distribution of major lesions, we can by-pass, for the present, this problem of localizing the lesions and concentrate instead on a study of symptomatology *per se*. We have felt, however, that it would be permissible, for a provisional comparison of data, to classify our cases further according to a threefold scheme: according to wound of entrance we distinguished anterior penetrations (frontal and frontotemporal), posterior penetrations (occipital, occipitoparietal), and intermediate penetrations (temporal, parietal). By comparing the performance of these three groups with each other and with our controls (veterans with peripheral nerve injuries), we have an experimental situation roughly similar to Dr. Harlow's, although not nearly as well controlled, since we lack anatomic data.

The use of this design can be illustrated with reference to simple and complex visual discriminations. In the case of a presumably simple visual discrimination, such as the recognition of flicker in an intermittent light, the patients report whether an electronically regulated flickering patch of light, pulsed at different rates, is subjectively flickering or steady. Fusion thresholds are obtained for the center of the field of vision and for different areas in the periphery of the visual field. In the group with posterior lesions and visual field defects the fusion thresholds are reduced as compared with the thresholds for normal controls. This depression of fusion thresholds is not large, but is statistically significant even in areas of the field where vision appears to be normal according to all other tests.

By contrast, we have been unable to confirm earlier statements in the literature according to which fusion thresholds are depressed in patients with frontal lesions. The work of Dr. Battersby in the Psychophysiological Laboratory, New York University, has shown that there is no difference between men with anterior lobe penetrations and their matched controls. Thus, we have here a regional gradient of a simple sort, related to the primary sensory deficit but not reducible to such simple deficit. This is similar to Harlow's findings in lower primates with posterior lobe penetration. On the other hand, we do not find any lasting deficits in this function following frontal lesions.

Turning now to the more complex visual discriminations, we have administered to our groups of patients with anterior, intermediate, and posterior lesions, a number of "masked" or hidden figure tests. In all of these tests the subjects' task is to discover one outline figure in another more complicated figure in which the first figure is embedded. On those tests patients with posterior lobe lesions, as a group, do worst; those with anterior (frontal) lesions do slightly better; and men with intermediate lesions do best. The poor performance of the posterior lobe group is not explained by primary visual deficits. The same is true for a number of highly complex tests of sorting and "categorizing" of visual material (tests involving equivalent and nonequivalent stimuli after Klüver; matching from sample technics; conditional reactions). Many of these procedures are experimental versions of the clinical sorting tests of Goldstein and his students, and these tests, in turn, are obviously similar to those used by Dr. Harlow in working with his monkeys. With these procedures, patients with posterior lobe lesions exhibit the poorest performance, those with anterior penetrations are somewhat better, and those with intermediate lesions do best.

In conclusion, if we compare our data obtained in man with Dr. Harlow's data obtained in the monkey, we can say that there are similarities with regard to the role of the posterior cerebral area: there are a number of deficits which appear, not uniquely, but maximally with lesions in the posterior lobe substance, in particular the parieto-occipital convexity, and these deficits cannot be fully explained in terms of primary sensory deficits. On the other hand, we have been unable to find, thus far, any task which is as difficult for human beings with frontal lobe lesions as the delayed response test seems to be for those of Dr. Harlow's monkeys that have prefrontal ablations. Thus, in contrast to the data available for the macaque, we have yet to find any one deficit characteristic of losses of frontal lobe tissue in man. This does not mean that in our group frontal lobe lesions due to gunshot wounds produced no deficits. The deficits are there, and can be demonstrated in some instances by variants of the classical "frontal-lobe tests"; but the deficits are not specific for frontal lobe lesions, since they appear in equal fashion, and often more markedly, after involvement of the posterior lobe substance. In fact, some of the changes in performance which we have noted in the parieto-occipital series are precisely those which have heretofore been described among the typical frontal lobe symptoms.

Remarks on Psychological Findings Attendant on Psychosurgery

CARNEY LANDIS, PH.D.

What I have to say may be summarized very rapidly, and can be organized under five general headings.

The work on which these conclusions are based is mainly that which has been reported by the Columbia-Greystone Associates.[4, 5, 6] As you may or may not know, the psychologists in those projects tried almost everything in the way of psychologic experiments and tests prior to brain operations carried out on the frontal lobes and then repeated the same test procedures following operation, trying to find out what differences, if any, could be attributed to the extirpation of bilaterally symmetrical areas of the human frontal lobes.

Our first finding gave us endless trouble. Our difficulty with the data and measurements was that we found samples of almost everything that anybody had ever reported or attributed to the frontal lobes, but we did not obtain such changes in all patients nor did we obtain them with any sort of regularity or degree. Practically every test or every experiment which we conducted showed postoperatively changed scores as transient phenomena, these transient changes disappearing during two, three, or four months after operation.

The second conclusion is that these transient changes can for the most part be regarded as phenomena which may be brought together under the concept of vigilance, as Henry Head[1] used that term. That is, the patient during the first six weeks or two months postoperatively is somewhat dull, sleepy, or "dopey." The changes in test performance are reflections of the decreased vigilance.

The third point is the observation that many of the patients following the operation were less ambitious or less zealous in their approach to their everyday tasks, in their social relationships, and in their attitude toward life. This loss in zeal may or may not be permanent. There is a certain amount of doubt as to the reality of this change and whether the change is a "primary" alteration. In any event it certainly is not marked in all patients.

My fourth point is that in spite of all present-day views and beliefs that frontal lobe damage *must* be accompanied by intellectual deficit, deficit in categorical attitude or the ability to abstract, such deficits occur in only a few patients. They do not occur in all patients. They are not very pronounced when they do show themselves. They are altogether unimpressive, and, in my opinion, our critical experiments definitely prove that these functions are not primarily connected with frontal lobe tissue.

The really astounding change which no one has mentioned so far in this symposium is the alteration in affect—in emotion—which takes place after the extirpation of the frontal lobe tissue or cutting of frontothalamic fiber tracts.[2, 3] Psychosurgery relieves the patient of intolerable anguish or pain —either physical pain in the case of the intractable pain cases, or mental pain in the psychotic or neurotic patients. Such relief does not take place in every patient who undergoes psychosurgery but when it happens, the patient is sure of it, the doctors are sure of it, the nurses are sure of it, the family is sure of it. There is no argument about it. No refined test is needed to prove it. Being obvious, it is somehow overlooked. But there can be no argument on the point that surgical intervention with frontal lobe tissue produces a radical emotional alteration in many patients while all other changes are of minor importance in contrast.

Dr. Harlow mentioned that some of his monkeys were quite tame following frontal lobe operations. Psychosurgery patients are "tame" in somewhat the same fashion, that is, they have lost anguish. This tameness is the most astonishing fact that evolves from all frontal lobe investigations. Moreover it is the change which no one would have predicted on the basis of anything which had been reported in the literature previous to the advent of psychosurgery.

REFERENCES

1. HEAD, H.: *British Journal of Psychology*, 1923, 14, pp. 126-147.
2. LANDIS, C.; ZUBIN, J.; and METTLER, F. A.: *Journal of Psychology*, 1950, 30, pp. 123-138.
3. LANDIS, C.: *Journal of Nervous and Mental Disease*. (In press.)
4. LEWIS, N. D. C. (Ed.): Studies in Topectomy. New York, Nervous and Mental Disease Publishing Co. (In press.)
5. METTLER, F. A. (Ed.): Selective Partial Ablation of the Frontal Cortex. New York, Paul B. Hoeber, Inc., 1949.
6. METTLER, F. A. (Ed.): Studies in Psychosurgery. Philadelphia, Blakiston. (In press.)

CHAPTER 17

Endocrine Influence on Personality and Behavior

ROBERT A. CLEGHORN, M.D.

IN CONSIDERING the influence of the endocrines on personality and behavior I am extending a previous review in which altered autonomic and humoral functions in psychoneuroses were considered.[15] Advances in the past two years make the task more topical.

In my present presentation I wish first to draw attention and pay tribute to Beach's monograph.[6] Whereas his comprehensive review included much detail on subprimates, my remarks will be confined almost exclusively to observations on man. I recognize the difficulty of defining personality[49] and differentiating it from behavior. The latter can be isolated and observed while the former represents the integration of behavior and attitudes over a considerable period and in many situations.

Knowledge of the influence of the endocrines on behavior is derived first from clinical observations, and secondly from experimental studies. From the former approach, observations on deficit states arising spontaneously or by incidental human intervention yielded a good description of cardinal clinical states such as hypothyroidism, but little understanding. With the development of the experimental approach, more has been accomplished in the last fifty years than in the preceding five thousand. It has been possible to reproduce both deficit and excess hormonal states and to unravel, to some extent, the complexities of the interdependence of the endocrines and their various effects on form and function.

Role of Endocrines in Maintaining Normal Behavior

Deficit States: The simplest demonstration of the influence of the endocrines in maintaining normal behavior is provided by the personality changes which often accompany deficit states. Eunuchoidism is, of course, the most ancient of these.

Hypothyroidism, recognized more recently, yielded first to experimental study. In 1888, the Committee of the Clinical Society of London, reporting on myxedema, stated: "Delusions and hallucinations occur in nearly half the cases, mainly where the disease is advanced. Insanity . . . takes the form of acute and chronic manias, dementia or melancholia, with a marked predominance of suspicion and self-accusation."[5] More recently, this aspect seems to have been largely lost sight of, though Means[56] in his book, published in 1948, does mention psychosis as an accompaniment of hypothyroidism. Impaired memory, nervousness, and emotional instability are listed as symptoms. Probably, internists do not often see the psychotic cases which find their way into mental hospitals. Asher[5] has recently drawn attention again to this condition in his recent report on fourteen such patients seen over a four-year period. Nine of these showed a dramatic and complete improvement with thyroid medication. He observed no constant pattern in the mental derangement.

Hypoparathyroidism emerged as a rare complication of thyroidectomy, and the recognition of its effects was at first difficult. Recently, however, psychoses have been reported in a group of such patients. The usual picture is that of a toxic delirium with anxiety, depression, delusions, and hallucinations. Recovery follows restoration of the serum calcium level.[30] Cyclical changes in behavior and mood related to parathyroid deficiency in monkeys and in human beings have been described by Richter et al.[62]

Hypogonadism, due to removal or to imperfect development of the gonads before puberty, leads to a variety of clinical pictures, of which the best known is eunuchoidism. Here there are obvious developmental defects in skeletal and secondary sexual characteristics. Those interested in the complicated physiologic variations of developmental aberrations and their endocrine interrelationships may find them well described by Albright[1, 48] and others.[19] It is only necessary to point out here that all the changes are not due to gonadal defects, but to secondary functional changes in other glands, e.g., the adrenal.[33]

In prepuberal eunuchs, the normal psychosexual maturation does not occur. Castration in adult life often leads to a loss of interest in sex, but by no means always, as Tauber[72] points out. Not all the symptoms[55] in these cases can be assigned to hormonal defects, for castration is a psychic trauma which leads to an altered endopsychic concept of the self.[73] Psychoanalytic studies of castrates[18] have shown that psychotherapy alone may enhance sexual expression, a result also achieved by testosterone.

Studies on chimpanzees substantiate the view that the sex hormones have other effects on personality. Among female chimpanzees, greatest social dominance occurred when the estrogen level was highest,[13] and in a castrate, male dominance over an intact companion was achieved through treatment with methyl testosterone.[12]

The endocrine changes of the climacteric provide little convincing evidence of the importance of endocrines in behavior.

In women the declining ovarian function in mid-life is probably not the cause of psychiatric disturbances seen then. The hot flush and cessation of menses are the only symptoms definitely related to the declining ovarian function.[32] There is no correlation between hot flushes and serious emotional disturbances. Recent studies indicate that the mental and emotional upsets occurring about this time of life are of the same character as at any other age.[71]

The mental picture of "menopausal depressions" is that of a reactive depression developing naturally out of previous maladjustment, concerning marriage and reproduction. Hence, Stern and Prados[71] consider it to be a "reactive depression" rather than a true involutional melancholia, as defined by Henderson and Gillespie.[38]

In men, the situation regarding the psychiatric aspects of the so-called male climacteric is even more confused. Almost every physical or psychoneurotic complaint in middle-aged men has been ascribed casually to declining gonadal function. McCullagh,[53, 54] however, indicates the difficulty of making a reliable diagnosis to support this. Heller and Myers,[39] in their review, conclude that it is rare for men even in late mid-life to show somatic symptoms due to interstitial cell failure. On the other hand, certain psychiatrists,[32] feel that some middle-aged men show psychiatric symptoms due to interstitial cell deficiency. This latter verdict must be considered "not proved," however, until more thoroughgoing studies correlating mental upset and testicular hormone function have put it on a sound basis, by the use of testis biopsy and hormone excretion studies. Meanwhile, it is advisable to insist on a thorough investigation of life situations in disturbed middle-aged men before prescribing testosterone.

In *adrenal insufficiency* there is more impressive evidence of the importance of hormones in maintaining both normal mental activity and the physical stamina to support normal behavior. The clinical syndrome representing the effects of almost total destruction of the adrenal cortex was described by Addison one hundred and one years ago. He noted the pigmentation, hypotension, asthenia, and gastrointestinal upsets which characterize this disease, but only within recent years has attention been directed to the personality changes so often seen in these patients—apathy, negativism, and paranoid attitudes. In some cases, frank psychoses with hallucinations have been reported.[22, 29] In two cases with associated diabetes mellitus,[17, 76] the patients seemed to have better dispositions. So far, intensive psychologic studies have not been reported, but associated electroencephalographic findings have been described.[22, 42] The electroencephalogram was not affected by DCA, but was by 100 cc. of aqueous cortical extract.[22] Cortisone improves the outlook of these patients[11, 25] as well as the abnormal electroencephalographic pattern.[75]

In *pituitary cachexia*, or Simmond's disease, the features of thyroid and gonadal hypofunction are added to the adrenal insufficiency, and there appears a more overwhelming picture of vegetable-like apathy, which is susceptible to correction by therapy with thyroid, testosterone, and cortisone.

Developmental and Cyclical Changes: At first thought, the developmental changes of adolescence and of precocious puberty would seem to provide an opportunity to study the place of gonadal and adrenal steroids in producing adult behavior. However, concomitant serial studies of endocrine function and psychologic status are difficult to carry out, and the part played by the parallel influence of social pressure is not easily unraveled. It is not surprising, therefore, that we must await adequate studies of this part of the problem.

In like manner we might expect to gain information from serial studies of psychologic changes during the menstrual cycle. Here, a start has been made. Benedek and Rubinstein[7] claim that certain types of dreams and desires were correlated with hormonal changes during the cycle. Others[26] feel that these results are inconclusive and conflicting. We can say with some confidence, therefore, only that premenstrual tension and irritability seem to be associated with sodium and water retention, as a result of the action of estrogens and progesterone.

Role of Endocrines in Producing Pathologic Behavior

Turning from the above hints that the endocrine glands do, in fact, help to maintain normal behavior, we now consider the production of abnormal behavior by hormone excesses. Here again, our first information comes from clinical studies.

Hyperfunctional States: Hyperthyroidism is historically the longest recognized endocrine disorder of excess secretions. The clinical picture of the autonomously hyperfunctioning toxic adenomatous goiter is identical with that elicited by excessive doses of thyroxin, while the picture in exophthalmic goiter has added features.[56] Mental symptoms such as irritability, restlessness, hyperactive cooperativeness, euphoria, crying, and hypomania are common.[56] Psychoses as an accompaniment have been known since 1870, but are rarer. Means[56] believes that in these cases there has been a latent susceptibility to psychosis. In the majority of cases, the psychosis disappears with a lowering of the metabolic rate. In others, it continues unabated. The form of the psychosis depends on pre-morbid personality.[21, 27]

Hypercorticalism or abnormally increased secretion of the adrenal cortex is associated with certain tumors of that tissue or excessive stimulation by the pituitary body, typically in association with a basophilic cell tumor of the anterior lobe.[67] Women are principally affected and show signs of virilism such as hirsutism, amenorrhea, clitoral hypertrophy, acne, and a change in somatic configuration towards the masculine form.[67] Not all hirsute women have demonstrable hyperfunction of the adrenal cortex[8] though recent work indicates an abnormal increase in ketosteroid excretion in the middle of the menstrual cycle.[50] Holmes[43] was one of the first to point out the altered psychologic outlook in a girl with a masculinizing adrenal tumor, remedied by removal of the growth. Subsequently others have confirmed this[10] and noted marked psychotic trends in women showing signs of virilism.[67] Several writers have published accounts of patients developing a paranoid psychosis with physical masculinization, improved following unilateral adrenalectomy.[2, 3, 9, 31] Homosexual trends were observed in some. Masculinizing ovarian tumors may have a similar effect.[64] Feminization in the male is occasionally seen due to adrenal cortical hyperactivity[77] and may be associated with psychical abnormalities.[14] The relative part played by the hormonal dysfunction, and by the altered appearance in producing the psychologic changes, remains unsettled, though some evidence is available from recent work with ACTH which will be considered later.

There are many cases of spontaneous *hypoglycemia* associated with asthenia, syncope, and even convulsion not due to islet cell tumors.[20, 59] Portis[59] emphasizes the frequent association of neurosis in patients with spontaneous hypoglycemia, but points out that this exaggerates many of the neurotic symptoms.

Administration of Hormonal Agents: The role of unusual amounts of hormones in producing abnormal behavior is elucidated further by the administration of hormonal agents.

Thyroxine or thyroid extract administered in gross amounts reproduces the symptomatology of nodular toxic goiter. In several cases of myxedema, psychoses have been precipitated during the therapeutic restoration of metabolism towards normal levels.[56] Neither estrogen, nor testosterone, nor desoxycorticosterone has been reported to produce outstanding psychologic deviations when given in excess to normals. ACTH and cortisone, in contrast, have produced some striking changes in behavior and personality. Euphoria was seen early in arthritics receiving cortisone[37, 61] and in other patients given either agent.[24, 40, 74] Recent reports confirm these observations.[68, 70] Hench et al[70] maintain that there was less euphoria in patients receiving ACTH than in those receiving cortisone. Mood changes to the extent of mania have also been described[41, 43] severe enough to warrant ECT, to which they responded. Depression has also been described[63] as a reaction to ACTH and cortisone treatment. These reactions, some of them psychotic, accompanying the alleviation of the physical symptoms in psychosomatic conditions are disappointing but not surprising to those familiar with the profound emotional problems of these people.[46] The psychotic factors in certain patients with arthritis, asthma, and ulcerative colitis have been reported on recently by Appel and Rosen[4] who feel that when the physical manifestations improve, psychologic aberrations increase. There is also some evidence that in asthma and arthritis, there is a reduction in adrenal cortical function.[45]

Summary

To summarize what has been reviewed so far, we see that:

1. Normal behavior requires the integrated action of optimal quantities of a variety of hormones.

2. Both endocrine deficits and excesses sometimes produce mild aberrations in behavior and personality, and more rarely psychotic states.

3. There is little, if any, specificity of reaction in the abnormality which occurs.

4. The same disease state or hormonal agent may produce different disturbances in different individuals, e.g., ACTH may produce mania or depression. Dr. Bernheim's comment would be appreciated.

All this emphasizes that we cannot isolate the influence of changes in the internal chemical environment from genetic endowment and previous experience.

Psychiatric Illnesses in Which Endocrines Are Implicated

Without trespassing too far on the fields assigned to Drs. Hoagland and Gildea, it seems appropriate to include reference to psychoses in which endocrine disturbance is indicated, whether as a cause or result is not known.

Schizophrenia: Evidence for thyroid and gonadal deficits in this state has been summarized by Hoskins.[44] The work of Gjessing,[28] Hardwick and Stones,[34] and Hemphill and Reiss[36] implies an adrenal cortical disturbance in catatonics. The defective response of the adrenal gland to stress and ACTH described in recent years by Pincus and Hoagland[58] has been the most exciting recent contribution.

Alcoholism: Smith[65, 66] has described constitutional data which are suggestive of an adrenal origin of alcoholism. He has shown that in acute alcoholic states, ACTH provides effective treatment.

Manic Depressive Psychosis: Hemphill and Reiss[36] have presented data which indicate altered adrenal cortical activity, in some respects enhanced, in the depressed phase. Lehmann et al[51] have reported corroborative evidence. Altschule et al.[16] have reported testosterone to be helpful in certain depressions. Intensive ACTH therapy did not significantly alleviate or increase depression in our hands[16] nor alter the electroencephalographic pattern.

Involutional Melancholia: Several writers have claimed improvement with ACTH.[35, 69] Rome and Braceland's findings[63] do not agree.

Endocrine Disturbances in Which Emotional Factors May Be Causal

Although my presentation has been restricted to the influence of endocrine glands on behavior and personality, no one can work in this field without noting the obverse of this topic—the influence of emotion and psychologic stress on endocrine function. In some ways, this is even more interesting and complicated than what we have considered, and would take us on to an examination of the onset and aggravation of hyperthyroidism, diabetes, hyperinsulinism, hypothalamic amenorrhea, anorexia nervosa, premenstrual tension, pseudocyesis, asthma, and arthritis. But this must await another occasion.

REFERENCES

1. ALBRIGHT, F., et al.: *American Journal of the Medical Sciences,* 1942, 204, p. 625.
2. ALLEN, C. G., and BROSTER, L. R.: *British Medical Journal,* 1945, 1, p. 696.
3. ALLEN, C. G.; BROSTER, L. R.; VINES, H. W. C.; PATTERSON, J.; GREENWOOD, A. W.; MARRIAN, G. F.; and BUTLER, G. C.: *British Medical Journal,* 1939, 1, p. 1220.
4. APPEL, J., and ROSEN, S. R.: *Psychosomatic Medicine,* 1950, 12, p. 236.
5. ASHER, R.: *British Medical Journal,* 1949, 2, p. 555.
6. BEACH, F. A.: Hormones and Behavior. New York, Paul B. Hoeber, Inc., 1948.
7. BENEDEK, T., and RUBINSTEIN, B. B.: *Psychosomatic Medicine,* 1939, 1, p. 245.
8. BISSELL, G. W., and WILLIAMS, R. H.: *Annals of Internal Medicine,* 1945, 22, p. 773.
9. BROSTER, L. R.: *Proceedings of the Royal Society of Medicine,* 1946, 40, p. 35.
10. BROSTER, L. R., and VINES, H. W. C.: The Adrenal Cortex. London, H. K. Lewis & Company, 1933.
11. BROWNE, J. S. L.: Personal communication, 1945.
12. CLARK, G., and BIRCH, H. G.: *Psychosomatic Medicine,* 1945, 4, p. 321.
13. CLARK, G., and BIRCH, H. G.: *Federation Proceedings,* 1946, 5, p. 16.
14. CLEGHORN, R. A.: Unpublished observations.
15. CLEGHORN, R. A., and GRAHAM, B. F.: Recent Progress in Hormone Research, IV, pp. 323-362. New York, Academic Press, 1949.
16. CLEGHORN, R. A.; GRAHAM, B. F.; SAFFRAN, M.; and CAMERON, D. E.: *Canadian Medical Association Journal,* 1950, 63, p. 329.
17. CLEGHORN, R. A. and KERR, R. B.: Unpublished observations.
18. DANIELS, G. E., and TAUBER, E. S.: *The American Journal of Psychiatry,* 1940, 97, p. 905.
19. DEL CASTILLO, E. B.; TRABUCO, A.; and DE LA BALZE, F. A.: *The Journal of Endocrinology,* 1947, 7, p. 498.
20. DUNBAR, F.: Synopsis of Psychosomatic Diagnosis. St. Louis, C. V. Mosby Company, 1948.
21. DUNLAP, H. F., and MOERSCH, F. P.: *American Journal of Psychiatry,* 1935, 91, p. 1215.
22. ENGEL, G. L., and MARGOLIN, S. C.: *Archives of Neurology and Psychiatry,* 1941, 45, p. 881.
23. FARQUHARSON, R. F.: Simmonds Disease. Springfield, Ill., Charles C. Thomas, 1950.
24. FINLAND, M.; KASS, E. N.; and INGBAR, S. H.: Proceedings of the First Clinical ACTH Conference, p. 595. Philadelphia, The Blakiston Company, 1950.
25. FORSHAM, P. H.: Personal communication, 1945.
26. FREED, S. C., and KROGER, W. S.: *Psychosomatic Medicine,* 1950, 12, p. 229.
27. FREEMAN, W.: *Annals of Internal Medicine,* 1935, 9, p. 444.
28. GJESSING, R.: *Journal of Mental Science,* 1948, 84, p. 605.
29. GORMAN, W. F., and WORTIS, S. B.: *Diseases of the Nervous System,* 1947.
30. GREEN, J. A., and SWANSON, L. W.: *Annals of Internal Medicine,* 1941, 14, p. 1233.
31. GREENE, R.; PATTERSON, A. G.; and PILE, G. C. L.: *British Medical Journal,* 1945, 1, p. 698.

32. HAMBLEM, E. C.: Endocrinology of Women. Springfield, Ill., Charles C Thomas, 1945.
33. HAMILTON, J. B.: *Anatomical Record*, 1943, 85, p. 314.
34. HARDWICK, S. W., and STOKES, A. B.: *Proceedings of the Royal Society of Medicine*, 1941, 34, p. 733.
35. HEMPHILL, R. E., and REISS, M.: *Journal of Mental Science*, 1944, 90, p. 410.
36. HEMPHILL, R. E., and REISS, M.: *International Congress of Psychiatry*. Paris, 1950.
37. HENCH, P. S.; KENDALL, E. C.; SLOCUMB, C. G.; and POLLEY, F.: *Proceedings of the Staff Meeting of the Mayo Clinic*, 1949, 24, p. 181.
38. HENDERSON, D. K., and GILLESPIE, A.: Textbook of Psychiatry. VIth ed. London, Oxford University Press, 1944.
39. HELLER, C. G., and MYERS, C. B.: *Journal of the American Medical Association*, 1944, 126, p. 472.
40. HOEFFER, P. F. A., and GLASER, G. H.: Proceedings of the First Clinical ACTH Conference, p. 536. Philadelphia, The Blakiston Company, 1950.
41. HOEFER, P. F. A., and GLASER, G. H.: *Journal of the American Medical Association*, 1950, 143, p. 620.
42. HOFFMAN, W. C.; LEWIS, R. A.; and THORN, G. W.: *Bulletin of the Johns Hopkins Hospital*, 1942, 70, p. 335.
43. HOLMES, G.: *Quarterly Journal of Medicine*, 1925, 18, p. 143.
44. HOSKINS, R. G.: The Biology of Schizophrenia. New York, W. W. Norton & Company, 1946.
45. HOWARD, R. P.; VENNING, E. H.; and FISK, G. H.: *Canadian Medical Association Journal*, 1950, 63, p. 340.
46. JOHNSON, A.; SHAPIRO, L. B.; and ALEXANDER, F.: *Psychosomatic Medicine*, 1947, 9, p. 295.
47. KLEIN, R.: *Journal of Mental Science*, 1950, 46, p. 293.
48. KLINEFELTER, H. F., JR.; REIFENSTEIN, E. C., JR.; and ALBRIGHT, F.: *The Journal of Clinical Endocrinology*, 1942, 2, p. 615.
49. KLUCKHOHN, C., and MURRAY, H. A.: Personality in Nature, Society and Culture. New York, Knopf, 1948.
50. KOETS, P.: *The Journal of Clinical Endocrinology*, 1949, 9, p. 795.
51. LEHMANN, H.; TURSKI, M.; and CLEGHORN, R. A.: *Canadian Medical Association Journal*, 1950, 63, p. 329.
52. MACLAY, W. S.; STOKES, A. B.; and RUSSELL, D. S.: *Journal of Neurology and Psychiatry*, 1938, 1, p. 110.
53. McCULLAGH, E. P.: Recent Progress in Hormone Research, II, New York, Academic Press, Inc., 1948, p. 295.
54. McCULLAGH, E. P.: *Bulletin of the New York Academy of Medicine*, 1948, 24, p. 341.
55. McCULLAGH, E. P., and RENSHAW, J. F.: *Journal of the American Medical Association*, 1934, 103, p. 1140.
56. MEANS, J. H.: Thyroid and Its Diseases. Philadelphia, J. B. Lippincott Company, 1948.
57. PINCUS, GREGORY (Ed.): Recent Progress in Hormone Research, IV, New York, Academic Press, Inc., 1949, p. 291.
58. PINCUS, G., and HOAGLAND, H.: *The American Journal of Psychiatry*, 1950. 106, p. 641.
59. PORTIS, S. A.: *Journal of the American Medical Association*, 1950, 142, p. 1251.
60. PRADOS, M., and RUDDICK, B.: *Psychiatric Quarterly*, 1947, 21, p. 410.

61. RAGAN, C.; GROKOEST, A. W.; and BOOTS, R. H.: *The American Journal of Medicine*, 1949, 7, p. 741.
62. RICHTER, C. P.; HONEYMAN, W. M.; and HUNTER, H. J.: *Journal of Neurology and Psychiatry*, 1940, 3, p. 19.
63. ROME, H. P., and BRACELAND, F. J.: *Proceedings of the Staff Meeting of the Mayo Clinic*, 1950, 25, p. 495.
64. SELYE, H.: Textbook of Endocrinology. Montreal, University of Montreal, 1947.
65. SMITH, J. J.: *Quarterly Journal of Studies on Alcohol*, 1949, 10, p. 251.
66. SMITH, J. J.: *New York State Journal of Medicine*, 1950, 50, p. 1704.
67. SOFFER, L. J.: Diseases of the Adrenals. Philadelphia, Lea and Febiger, 1946.
68. SPIES, T. D., and STONE, R. E.: *Lancet*, 1950, 1, p. 11.
69. SPIES, T. D.; STONE, R. E.; DREIZEN, S.; and MORTON, B. F.: *Southern Medicine and Surgery.* 1949, 42, p. 991.
70. SPRAGUE, R. G.; POWER, M. H.; MASON, H. L.; ALBERT, A; MATHIESON, D. R.; HENCH, P. S.; KENDALL, E. C.; STOCUMB, C. H.; and POLLEY, H. F.: *Archives of Internal Medicine*, 1950, 85, p. 199.
71. STERN, K., and PRADOS, M.: *The American Journal of Psychiatry*, 1946, 103, p. 358.
72. TAUBER, E. S.: *Psychosomatic Medicine*, 1940, 2, p. 74.
73. TAUBER, E. S., and DANIELS, G. E.: *Psychosomatic Medicine*, 1941, 3, p. 72.
74. TAYLOR, S. G., III, and MORRIS, R. S., JR.: Proceedings of the First Clinical ACTH Conference, p. 331. Philadelphia, The Blakiston Company, 1950.
75. THORN, G. W.: Proceedings of the First Clinical ACTH Conference, p. 536. Philadelphia, The Blakiston Company, 1950.
76. THORN, G. W., and CLINTON, M., JR.: *Journal of Clinical Endocrinology*, 1943, 3, p. 335.
77. WILKINS, L.: *Journal of Clinical Endocrinology*, 1948, 8, p. 111.

Role of the Hypothalamus in Release of ACTH

DAVID M. HUME, M.D.

As Dr. Cleghorn has said, the problem of central nervous system influence over the endocrines is a vast subject, and there is wide difference of opinion among workers in this field as to the actual mode of control. The mechanism in the case of the neurohypophysis and adrenal medulla is readily apparent, but it is less so for the adenohypophysis.

For the purposes of brevity I will confine my remarks to the concept held by us at present of hypothalamic control of ACTH release by the anterior lobe of the pituitary body (Fig. 99). There is an interaction between the anterior lobe of the pituitary and the adrenal cortex to maintain a fairly constant blood level of adrenal cortical hormones, as proposed by Sayers.[5] Superimposed on this is an emergency mechanism under the control of the nervous system and mediated by a humoral substance, formed in the hypothalamus and carried in the general circulation, which increases the rate of ACTH production in response to psychic or physical trauma. This hypothalamic center is postulated to be sensitive to a wide variety of stimuli, both endocrine (insulin and epinephrine) and nervous (afferent impulses from traumatized areas and from the cerebral cortex). Thus certain hypothalamic lesions will abolish the increased release of ACTH (as measured by eosinopenia) which is normally seen following the injection of epinephrine or insulin, and decrease that seen after operative trauma.[3] Spinal cord section above T_1 will abolish the eosinopenic response to surgical trauma if the area traumatized is below the level of cord section.

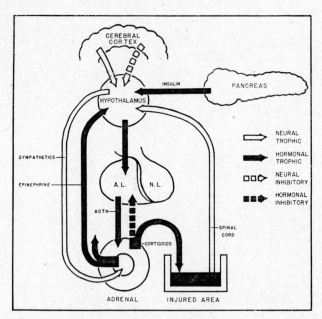

Fig. 99. Diagram to show the theory of hypothalamic control of ACTH release from the anterior lobe of the pituitary body, superimposed on a self-regulatory mechanism whereby increased ACTH secretion leads to increased output of ACH, which in turn inhibits excessive ACTH production.

It has been shown that hypothalamic stimulation in the conscious animal by means of induced current in implanted coils will produce a marked release of ACTH from the pituitary body[4] (Fig. 100). This response is not altered by sympathectomy, nor is the eosinopenic response to other stresses altered by sympathectomy. Hence it is felt that the release of epinephrine by hypothalamic stimulation is not an important factor in the subsequent secretion of ACTH.

It is known that fear and other psychic trauma can produce ACTH discharge from the pituitary body, and this is apparently on the basis of hypothalamic stimulation, because it can be abolished by hypothalamic lesions.[2] It has been found that manic depressive psychotics in the manic phase may show no eosinopenia at all in response to an amount of apparent agitation that would produce a definite fall in eosinophils in normal persons, but these same patients have normal reactions to ACTH and epinephrine

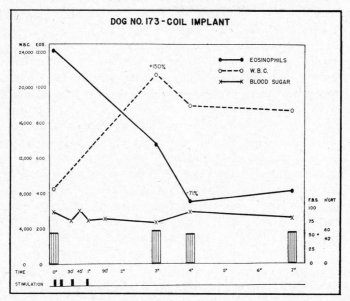

Fig. 100. Anterior hypothalamic stimulation. The changes in the leukocytes, eosinophils, blood sugar, and hematocrit following four three-minute stimulations over the course of one hour in the conscious dog are charted. Note the marked eosinopenic response. (From Proceedings of The First Clinical ACTH Conference (J. R. Mote, ed.). Philadelphia, The Blakiston Company, 1950.)

tests.[1] It may be possible that this phenomenon can be explained by an inhibition of impulses at some level between the hypothalamus and cerebral cortex.

It appears, then, that the hypothalamus plays an important role in translating emotional, peripheral nervous, and endocrine stimuli into altered anterior pituitary secretion of ACTH.

REFERENCES

1. Gildea, E. F.: Personal communication.
2. Harris, G. W., and de Groot, J.: *Federation Proceedings*, March, 1950, 9, p. 57.
3. Hume, D. M.: *Journal of Clinical Investigation*, 1949, 28, p. 790.
4. Hume, D. M., and Wittenstein, G. J.: Proceedings of the First Clinical ACTH Conference (J. R. Mote, ed.), p. 134. Philadelphia, The Blakiston Company, 1950.
5. Sayers, G.: *Physiological Reviews*, 1950, 30, p. 241.

Discussion

GREGORY PINCUS, SC.D.

I will try to be sparing of words concerning two topics: steroid euphoria and the adrenal cortex.

Steroid euphoria is a phenomenon which has not been mentioned by Dr. Cleghorn and is one about which a great deal may be heard in the future. With the advent of the use of rather heroic doses of steroids, particularly of cortisone, for therapeutic purposes in the human subject, it has become obvious that larger doses than those which have been hitherto used are tolerable. In some experiments which we have conducted, in which we have given quite large doses—up to 2 Gm. per day—of one steroid or another, including those with no particular hormonal activity, to a group comprised mainly of arthritic subjects, one of the phenomena we have observed is this euphoria.

The euphoria has a degree of nonspecificity which makes observations in respect to cortisone somewhat suspect. It may be that cortisone is euphoric in the same sense that progesterone, testosterone, and pregnenolone have been found to be euphoric.

As the result of recent work (some of which Dr. Hoagland will tell you about), we have come more and more to feel that the secretory processes of the adrenal glands are more complex than the simple terms ACTH or cortisone would indicate. It is true that ACTH is a remarkable stimulant of the adrenal cortex, but our recent work has shown that it is much more remarkable than was at first believed. The original observations of the chemists extracting the adrenal glands for steroids show that there are twenty-eight substances of a steroid nature which could be extracted; this was looked upon as a chemical curiosity.

In our recent work with the isolated adrenal glands, we have obtained evidence that fifteen different corticosteroids are produced by that isolated gland.[2] Therefore we believe that a number of simple statements will have to be elaborated in order to explain what is actually secreted by a highly activated adrenal gland under the influence of ACTH.

This places the problem of what one might call "replacement therapy" in an entirely different light, because, if the adrenal gland normally does produce a variety of steroids and if these have separate and distinct functions, then replacement with a single substance is not replacement therapy. This would apply to cortisone therapy and presumably will lead us, in the future, to the observation of the effects of substances hitherto neglected. It is fortunate that our chemical knowledge is keeping pace with the physiologic knowledge and that such substances will be available.[1]

REFERENCES

1. HECHTER, O., and others: Recent Progress in Hormone Research, VI. New York, Academic Press, Inc., 1951, 6, p. 215.
2. PINCUS, G.; HECHTER, O.; and ZAFFARONI, A.: Second Clinical ACTH Conference. Philadelphia, The Blakiston Company, 1951, Vol. I, p. 40.

CHAPTER 18

Genetics and Normal Mental Differences

R. RUGGLES GATES, D.SC.

THOSE WHO study dispassionately the inheritance of mental differences, normal or pathologic, must conclude, I believe, that these differences are inherited in exactly the same way as are physical (bodily) differences. The evidence is much too extensive even to summarize here, but much of it is discussed in Chapters XXII to XXV of *Human Genetics*.[2] That mental and physical differences are inherited in the same way only seems strange or uncertain because for three centuries we have been misled by the Cartesian separation of body and mind as different realms of existence which in some mysterious way meet and interact. Many modern psychologists and philosophers have now repudiated the Cartesian point of view. Although the relation between mind and body has been discussed since the time of Aristotle, and every conceivable view of that relationship has been expressed in the last two thousand years, yet there seems now a reasonable hope that scientists at least can reach an agreed point of view regarding this fundamental question.

Modern physics has helped to dispel this fatal bifurcation between mind and matter. Modern physics recognizes that the atom can be analyzed in terms of particles, or in terms of wave patterns, both approaches being equally necessary and complementary in any understanding of all the experimental results. Like the two sides of a coin, both being essential to a recognition of what the coin is, neither mind nor matter can be repudiated because they both refer to different aspects of the same thing. Bridgman[1] has recently stated that in physics there is no sharp line between the purely instrumental and the purely mental (paper and pencil) operations. Dingle thought rather that the distinction is between concepts associated with measurements and those which are pictorial, such as action at a distance, or empty space. In any case, what we commonly call mind enters into all physical observations and operations as an essential element.

May we not say then that mind and body, so long separated in our common thought, are the two aspects of psychosomatic existence, in much the same way that waves and particles are different aspects of atomic analysis?

277

Ryle[4] has recently developed this point of view at length, attacking the Cartesian theory of body and mind as distinct entities—an external physical and an internal mental world harnessed together in life. The polar opposition between mind and matter is thus dissipated, not by the absorption of either into the other as many philosophers have tried to reason in the past, but by recognition that they are different aspects of a psychosomatic unity.

Once we adopt this point of view it becomes inevitable that mental and physical differences will follow exactly the identical laws of inheritance. In *Human Genetics* (Chapter XXIII) it was shown that innumerable abnormalities of the nervous system are inherited, like physical abnormalities of the skeleton or the muscular system, as simple gene differences— dominant, recessive, or sex-linked as the case may be.[2] In many of these hereditary diseases the ultimate abnormality is one of metabolism, as in amaurotic idiocy or Schüller-Christian disease. In many others, such as Huntington's chorea or Niemann-Pick disease, there is a degenerative process of demyelination of certain parts of the central nervous system which may not begin until middle age, yet the inheritance is perfectly unitary and definite. The metabolic nature of phenylketonuria with its accompanying mental defect is already well known and its inheritance as a simple recessive genic difference is clear. The inheritance of such conditions as schizophrenia, epilepsy, and mongolism is receiving full attention at this meeting.

Inheritance of Normal as Apart from Pathologic Mental Differences

I wish to stress the inheritance of normal as apart from pathologic mental differences. The latter are generally based upon single genes or mutations and their inheritance is generally traced relatively easily. On the other hand, the inheritance of normal mental differences is much more complicated because many factors are involved, and the matter of environmental effect is also a source of disturbance.

The modern analysis of human abilities is based upon the work of Spearman,[7] which was first described in his classical paper published in 1904 in which he discussed a hierarchy of mathematical relationships among the results of mental tests. The coefficients of correlation between tests tended to fall into a hierarchic order which he found could be explained by his two-factor theory, a factor G, which he at first regarded as representing general intelligence, and a second factor S. In the immense amount of later work, which is much better known to some of you than it is to me, there have been many interpretations of the nature of G, but its stability and consistency have become increasingly impressive. In the matrix of correlations and tetrad differences G represents something innate, but the real nature of G seems to remain anybody's guess. In the latest treatment of this subject,[8] G is regarded as a general factor, while there are many narrow special (S) factors and a very few broad group factors. The word "intelligence" is discarded as an unprofitable term. An earlier view of Thomson[9] is that "the factors are not real but as it were fictitious tests which represent certain aspects of the whole mind." As regards the I.Q., it is evidently a good measure of learning ability. Whether this is equivalent to "intelligence" is immaterial, as all children in civilized countries are required to attend school.

Thurstone introduced the method of multiple factor analysis in 1931, and has recently summarized the extensive results of his school.[10] There appears indeed to be no limit to the amount of psychologic analysis which can be carried out by these and similar methods. Most psychologists appear to be willing to grant that men are not all equal in intellectual endowments or in temperament. The differences are conceived in terms of traits, parameters, or factors, some of which may be expected to be basically physiologic, some anatomic, and some influenced more by the social or educational background.

Notwithstanding the immense amount of work in this field, there has not, so far as I am aware, been any extensive comparison of parents and their children as regards these parameters. If any of the factors could be traced through individuals from generation to generation it would add greatly to their reality and significance as elements of the mind. If they cannot be so traced, then the nature and meaning of these factors remain obscure. In the meantime, the inheritance of mathematical ability is well recognized and need not be considered here, except to point out that in test scores arithmetic and geometry share no common factor other than G. Seashore[5] has shown that the power to discriminate pitch dominates the entire sphere of musical talent, although it is obvious that various other independent traits are concerned as well in different types of musical ability.

Another line of approach to analysis of the mind is through Sheldon's method of somatotyping. From this extensive line of work it appears that certain somatotypes are more or less associated with certain types or features of mentality. Much more evidence will be required to determine in detail the nature of these correlations. Sheldon's latest study[6] of 200 delinquent youths provides a further approach to an analysis of these relationships. Dr. Sheldon was brought up in an atmosphere of expert judging of poultry and dogs. In one aspect, somatotyping is the application of similar methods applied to mankind. It has the advantage of dealing with components, while anthropologists generally deal with linear measurements or indices. The relation of these components to genetically determined unitary differences of body and mind can only be investigated by comparing the somatotypes of parents and offspring. This has not yet been done. Even one such analysis would add greatly to the value of the somatotyping method. A hypothetic analysis in terms of assumed genes is of no genetic value. Sheldon's study of delinquency has led to a new approach to psychiatric classification in which the classic types of psychosis are replaced by quantifiable components.

Racial Differences in Mentality

Finally, I wish to refer briefly to another aspect of the genetics of normal mental differences. All those who have any respect for the facts will agree that men differ in their mentality at least as widely as in their physique. All mental analysis and testing is based on the assumption that minds differ. Otherwise psychologic tests would have no meaning. It may be pointed out that if individuals differ in intelligence—I use this word for lack of a better —or in other mental qualities, then groups and races of mankind may be expected to differ in similar respects, because they have evolved from different groups of ancestors. That such differences exist is abundantly clear to the unbiased observer. For instance, who will deny that the Welsh and the Negroes are more than usually endowed with musical ability?

This subject of racial differences in mentality has been so bedeviled by propaganda that it has become invidious even to compare the races in this country. Therefore let us compare races which are as remote as possible from our present population. One of the very few wholly unbiased studies of comparative racial intelligence is that of Porteus,[3] who investigated chiefly the Australian aborigines and the Bushmen of the Kalahari desert. Each race was studied in relation to its environmental setting, and the results are worthy of much wider recognition than they have yet received.

From extensive travels in Australia and South Africa, and from many performance tests, including that of the maze, Porteus draws a number of clear and interesting conclusions. He shows that the conditions in the desert of Central Australia are the most extreme under which man can survive. Yet the tribes living there, such as the Arunta, were superior according to practically all tests to those of Western Australia where the conditions are much less severe. I think one is justified in concluding that the severity of the conditions in the extreme desert had a selective effect on the mentality of the natives, placing a premium on such items as memory of topographic features and close observation of the habits of animals, as well as powers of endurance over long periods.

The only other people living under equally severe climatic conditions are the Eskimos. Everyone who has made contacts with the Eskimos knows that they are lively extroverts, unlike their more southerly neighbors, the introvert Indians. One gains the impression of a vigorous intelligence for everything connected with their Arctic surroundings, and here again it is reasonable to conclude that there has been positive selection for good judgment regarding probable weather conditions and the many other hazards of Arctic life, and also perhaps for a happy rather than a morose disposition under the long Arctic night.

As regards the Bushmen, Porteus shows that they live under much more favorable conditions than the Australians. The Kalahari has a relatively abundant vegetation and considerable game. Australians living under such conditions would consider themselves in a paradise. Yet notwithstanding these better conditions the Bushmen were at the bottom of the list in all comparative mental tests. On the other hand, they are well known to be superior to the Australians in graphic art.

From these and similar results it seems clear not only that races differ in their mentality and in what we call intelligence, but also that the mental conditions are in part a result of the climatic and physical environment in which the race has evolved.

REFERENCES

1. BRIDGMAN: *Nature*, 1950, 166, p. 91.
2. GATES, R. R.: Human Genetics, 2 vols., 1518 pp. New York, Macmillan Company, 1946.
3. PORTEUS, S. D.: Primitive Intelligence and Environment, 325 pp. New York, The Macmillan Company, 1937.
4. RYLE, GILBERT: The Concept of Mind, 334 pp. London, Hutchinson, 1949.
5. SEASHORE, C. E.: The Psychology of Musical Talent, 288 pp. Boston, Silver, Burdett and Co., 1919.
6. SHELDON, W. H.: Varieties of Delinquent Youth, 899 pp. New York, Harper and Brothers, 1949.
7. SPEARMAN, C.: *American Journal of Psychology*, 1904, 15, pp. 201-293.
8. SPEARMAN, C., and WYNN JONES, L. L.: Human Ability, 198 pp. London, 1950.
9. THOMSON, G. H.: The Factorial Analysis of Human Ability, 326 pp. Boston, Houghton, 1939.
10. THURSTONE, L. L.: Multiple-Factor Analysis, 535 pp. University of Chicago Press, 1947.

Discussion

JAMES V. NEEL, M.D.

Dr. Gates has reviewed a few of the various data relating to the genetics of normal mental differences. He has stressed, and I believe rightly so, that if we are willing to accept intrinsic or genetic factors in the etiology of all manner of neurologic disorders, we cannot logically deny the operation of such factors in the development of the mind. On the other hand, the geneticist of today has no inclination to discount the significance of the extrinsic or environmental factors which in a multitude of obvious and not-so-obvious ways mold the functioning of the brain. The interplay of intrinsic and extrinsic forces in the etiology of the normal and the abnormal, the evaluation of which is certainly a cardinal problem of human biology, is nowhere more complexly seen than in the development of mentation and mental ability.

What has been largely lacking in the past has been an objective evaluation of the component parts of these extrinsic and intrinsic factors. As a geneticist, I would scarcely be so presumptuous as to suggest how those interested in the extrinsic factors should proceed to define them. However, I may perhaps be permitted to comment on the need of clearer definition of the intrinsic factors in mental ability. The observation of a parent-offspring correlation in I.Q. or social competence is interesting but so far as a knowledge of the mechanisms involved goes, we are today only a little further ahead than was Galton with reference to the inheritance of stature when, in 1889, he published his well-known observations on parent-offspring correlations.

I am sure we will all agree as to the outstanding need for an identification of the various attributes and qualities that enter into what we call intelligence. Not until this has been accomplished and, further, agreement reached as to the degree to which each is susceptible to modification, can the geneticist begin to move with assurance. In this connection, the studies of Dr. L. L. Thurstone and his students, to which Dr. Gates has alluded, would appear to a rank outsider to hold particular promise. There appears to be clear evidence for a number of more or less distinct components in mental ability, each of which can be measured by appropriate tests. An individual's performance on tests designed to evaluate any one of these factors may be altered by training, but there is some evidence that intrinsic base lines and capacities set the boundaries within which training must operate, and that these base lines are genetically determined. This recognition of primary mental attributes, each of which may be inherited in some independence of the others, suggests broad possibilities for research.

In closing, I will say just a word about inherent mental differences between the races of man. Dr. Gates' views would not find universal acceptance among geneticists. Speaking again as an outsider, I cannot escape the impression that so much needs to be done to develop mental tests the results of which are in no way influenced by cultural factors that it will be some time before the question of innate racial differences can be more than a subject for speculation.

CHAPTER 19

Genetic Aspects of Psychoses

FRANZ J. KALLMANN, M.D.

IN A REVIEW of the genetic aspects of severe mental disorders, especially those of schizophrenic, manic-depressive, and involutional psychoses, it is advisable to set out from a few plain and generally acceptable premises. One of them is that certain persons exist, who seem capable of adapting themselves to varying combinations of distressing circumstances without the development of a progressive psychotic process. The list of frustrations, known to produce no severe psychosis in some people, is practically unlimited and extends to physical hardships such as starvation, complete exhaustion, and prolonged malignant disease, to extreme emotional stress, and to a great number of behavioral inadequacies of the parents.

The observation that certain types of psychosis are precipitated by unfavorable environmental influences only in a limited number of persons by no means minimizes the psychodynamic significance of these constellational factors in potentially vulnerable individuals. However, the given limitations would seem to make it rather difficult to insist on considering human adaptability to be so flexible in nature as to justify the principle of explaining any deviation from normal adjustive patterns entirely on the grounds of past emotional experiences, that is, without the assumption of variable individual vulnerabilities. In the last analysis, such codified explanations of maladjustment as the currently rather popular one, ascribing almost every known variety of psychopathology to maternal imperfection during the child's early life, merely serve to affirm some basic biologic truisms. No one has ever denied that a person must have a mother, and must pass through infancy, in order to have any earthly chance of demonstrating genetically controlled variations in his capacity for physical adaptation, emotional stability, and social adjustment.

Much corroborative evidence is available in support of the observation that similar personality deviations are not found to be associated consistently with similar environments or, more precisely, that a psychosis of the schizophrenic, manic-depressive, or involutional variety is not apt to be developed by all the persons in an environment that produced a psycho-

283

sis in another member of their group. It is certain, for instance, that the failure of some persons to respond with a severe psychosis to a known constellation of unfavorable environmental circumstances, extends to many siblings and dizygotic twin partners of psychotic patients, who are known to have had an incompetent mother. It is even more significant that statistical investigations of the incidence of these different types of psychosis reveal a highly consistent pattern of distribution in comparable population samples.

With respect to the prevalence of schizophrenia, no general population survey has as yet resulted in an expectancy rate in excess of approximately 1 to 2 per cent. It is also a fact that irrespective of the diagnostic system used, very few investigators have found manic-depressive psychosis—in the absence of special conditions of inbreeding—to occur as frequently in the general population as is true of schizophrenia. On the other hand, no analysis of a statistically representative group of blood relatives of schizophrenic or manic-depressive patients has so far been completed in any country without showing a significant increase in the expectancy rate for either psychosis.

From a genetic standpoint there is reason to believe, therefore, that some persons, namely, the carriers of a specific type of predisposition or potential vulnerability, have the biologic capacity for reacting to precipitating environmental stimuli with either a schizophrenic or another type of psychosis, while this capacity is not possessed by a number of ordinary people. In other words, the ability to respond with such a severe psychosis cannot be considered to be part of a person's normal biologic equipment and, therefore, should not simply be classified as "determined constitutionally," that is, as part of the normal constitution of man or as a potentially "norm-directed" human trait.

In order to substantiate this theory, geneticists have to demonstrate that the tendency to develop a severe psychosis increases in proportion to the degree of blood relationship to a family member showing the given type of psychosis, since organic inheritance cannot operate without the factor of blood relationship. Another requirement would be that it is the incidence of schizophrenia, rather than that of a manic-depressive or another type of psychosis, which is apt to be increased in the blood relatives of schizophrenic index cases, and vice versa. If it is possible to procure adequate evidence for a sliding scale of specific morbidity rates, correlated with the degree of consanguinity, advocates of purely environmental theories should make an attempt to provide plausible explanations for a few plain implications of the genetic hypothesis. One of the inferences is that many members of psychotic index families are expected, in accordance with the laws of statistical probability, to be sufficiently protected against a psychosis-producing environment by the absence of a specific genetic predisposition, without which a person under stress is assumed genetically to be incapable of reacting with such a psychosis.

It is safe to state that the clarification of these rather important etiologic problems of psychiatry was delayed by a number of practical difficulties, especially by the lack of comparative family data based on a uniform diagnostic system with respect to schizophrenic, manic-depressive, and involutional psychoses. Obvious inconsistencies in diagnostic classification gave rise to the widespread belief that the symptomatologies of the three types of psychosis were either overlapping or variable expressions of the same basic disturbance. In fact, the frequently reported alternation of schizophrenic and manic-depressive psychoses within individual family units found its reflection in the genetically rather confusing idea that the children of manic-depressive parents were likely to be either schizophrenic or manic-depressive, while manic-depressive psychosis was not believed to occur among the children of schizophrenic parents.

Another theory was that a manic-depressive patient may become schizophrenic, but that a schizophrenic would not become manic-depressive, because it was presumed to be "easier to fall down a cliff than to fall up a cliff." In some schools, extreme oversimplification of psychodynamic interpretations actually threatened to lead to the relegation of the given psychotic syndromes to the obscure status of "semantic conventions."

Analysis of Distribution of Different Types of Psychosis in Cotwins, Siblings, and Parents of Psychotic and Senescent Twin Index Cases

However, most of these time-honored theories seem entirely incompatible with the results of our recently completed analysis of the distribution of psychoses observed in the cotwins, siblings, and parents of a total of 1232 psychotic and over 2500 senescent twin index cases. The analysis was based on strictly unselected, fully observed, and consistently diagnosed samples of patients distinguished by both their twinning status and verified evidence either of a schizophrenic (953), manic-depressive (75), or involutional (96) psychosis or of survival until the beginning of the senium (2618). The main objective of this investigation was to procure a longitudinal and controlled series of observational data on normal and abnormal personality development by combining the original twin study method and Weinberg's sampling method, as applied to the study of siblings, with the general principles of a procedure approximating a statewide population census of twins in certain age brackets and deviant population groups (twin family method).

The most essential diagnostic feature of our investigative procedure may be seen in the restriction of the classification of manic-depressive psychosis to patients showing acute, self-limited, and unadulterated mood swings before the fifth decade of life and no progressive or residual personality disintegration before or following manic or depressive episodes. Strictly ieactive or neurotic depressions were not included in the analysis, while primary menopausal and presenile depressions, agitated anxiety states, and other nonperiodic forms of depressive behavior in the involutional period (50 to 69 years) were placed in the category of involutional psychosis, together with the typical cases of involutional melancholia characterized by agitated depression with paranoid features.

The uniform application of this diagnostic scheme resulted in the distinct impossibility of finding any pair of monozygotic twin partners, whose clinical symptomatology would have warranted their placement into two different diagnostic categories within the range of psychoses studied. Whenever there were diagnostic difficulties with respect to the symptomatology of one member of a psychotic index pair distinguished by monozygocity, they inevitably recurred in the classification of the other twin partner.

In the dizygotic series of index pairs the only diagnostic discrepancies overriding the dividing lines among our main groups of psychoses were presented by four opposite-sexed pairs showing varying combinations of schizophrenic, involutional, and senile psychoses. Otherwise, our sample includes neither a dizygotic pair with a schizophrenic psychosis in one member and a manic-depressive psychosis in the other nor a single manic-depressive index family with an authentic case of schizophrenia among the parents and siblings of the index cases.

The general trend of the comparative data summarized in Tables 18 and 19 is clearly in the direction of specific genetic mechanisms for the different types of psychosis. As a rule, the incidence of schizophrenia is found to be increased in the consanguinity of schizophrenic index cases, and that of manic-depressive psychosis in the consanguinity of manic-depressive index cases. It seems significant, however, that the blood relatives in involutional

TABLE 18. SURVEY OF PSYCHOTIC TWIN INDEX FAMILIES
(twin family method)

Type of Twin Index Family	Number of Psychotic Twin Index Cases		Number of Adult Members of Twin Family Unit (over Age 14)				Total Number of Persons
	Mono-zygotic	Dizy-gotic	Cotwins	Full Siblings	Half Siblings	Parents	
Schizo-phrenic	268	685	849	2,461	109	1,432	5,804
Manic-de-pressive	23	52	68	184	12	122	461
Involu-tional	29	67	78	256	14	159	603
Senile	33	75	48	172	7	144	479
Total number	353	879	1,043	3,073	142	1,857	7,347

TABLE 19.   DISTRIBUTION OF PSYCHOSES AMONG THE PARENTS AND SIBLINGS
OF PSYCHOTIC TWIN INDEX CASES

Type of Psychosis in Twin Index Cases	Expectancy of Respective Psychosis in General Population	Collective Psychosis Rate for Single-Born Members of Index Family Unit°			
		Schizo-phrenia	Manic-depressive Psychosis	Involu-tional Psychosis	Schizoid and Cycloid Types of Emotional Instability
Schizophrenia	0.9	9.7	0.1	6.6	29.9
Manic-depressive psychosis	0.4	—	21.2	1.8	13.4
Involutional psychosis	1.0	4.3	0.8	10.0	6.8

* Related to all parents and siblings over age 14 years with respect to schizophrenia, manic-depressive psychosis, and emotional instability, and related to all persons over age 44 with respect to involutional psychosis.

cases show an increase in both involutional and schizophrenic psychoses, which is paralleled by a moderate increase in involutional and senile psychoses among the blood relatives in schizophrenic cases. Schizoid personality types are preponderant in the consanguinity in both schizophrenic and involutional cases, but cycloid types prevail among the blood relatives in manic-depressive cases.

The analysis of age-specific expectancy figures (Table 20) reveals a monozygotic concordance rate of 60.9 per cent with respect to involutional

TABLE 20.   EXPECTANCY OF PSYCHOSES IN PSYCHOTIC TWIN INDEX FAMILIES

Type of Psychosis in Twin Index Case	Expectancy in General Population	Corrected Expectancy Rates in Relation to Original Psychosis°				
		Parents	Half Siblings	Full Siblings	Dizygotic Cotwins	Mono-zygotic Cotwins
Schizophrenia	0.9	9.3	7.1	14.2	14.5	86.2
Manic-depressive psychosis	0.4	23.4	16.7	23.0	26.3	95.7†
Involutional psychosis	1.0	6.4	4.5	6.0	6.0	60.9

* Related to one-half of the persons in the age group 15 to 44 years and to all persons over age 44 with respect to schizophrenia and manic-depressive psychosis, and related to all persons over age 44 with respect to involutional psychosis.
† Uncorrected since the corrected percentage exceeds 100.

psychosis. This finding indicates that monozygotic twin partners are more likely than dizygotic twins or ordinary siblings (6.0 per cent) to be alike in those factors which favor the occurrence of a psychosis in the involutional period. Evidently, the development of such a psychosis presupposes not only the capacity for survival until the later years of maturity, but also the ability to live through the preceding years without succumbing to another type of psychosis. In addition, however, the developmental process is apt to require varying combinations of etiologic components, which individually would not be sufficient to produce a psychotic reaction syndrome.

The scheme of interacting causative elements includes progressive impairment of general adaptability, cumulative emotional strain and insecurity due to increasingly conspicuous signs of aging, and the coexistence of certain basic personality traits such as rigidity, compulsiveness, or oversensitivity. The long-range effect of these traits is toward a reduction of the adjustive plasticity of aging persons and, thereby, toward an impairment in their faculty of adaptation to involutional changes.

From a genetic standpoint, most of these cases of eventually overflowing emotional instability seem identifiable with schizoid personality traits, although it is probable that some involutional psychoses are actually late-developing and attenuated processes of schizophrenia precipitated only by the impact of involutional experiences. A few other cases are possibly related to the emotional vulnerability of cycloid personality types during the period of senescence. However, our data provide no evidence of a specific or single-factor type of genetic mechanism as far as the usual symptomatology of involutional psychoses is concerned.

The extent of adjustive differences in the involutional period, found to be typical of genetically dissimilar (dizygotic) twin pairs, despite very similar environmental and existential conditions, may be illustrated by the twin sisters shown in Figure 101. Throughout their lives, they had differed as much in their personalities and adjustive patterns as they did in their general appearance and physical signs of aging. The younger-looking twin, described as sociable, placid, and kind, remained active and well adjusted until she died in her eighties of a heart attack, a few months before the death of her taller and more intelligent twin sister. The latter, who had always been moody, ill-tempered, and vindictive, developed a depressive-paranoid psychosis as an old maid under equally protected circumstances and finally died in a mental hospital.

By contrast, the monozygotic A. twins (Fig. 102) remained strikingly similar until and throughout senescence, although their histories were distinguished by very unusual differences. They were 18 years old when they were separated through the marriage of one of them to a local farmer. While the married twin continued to live in a small rural community where she raised a large family, the other twin entered a Bible School and, a few years later, left as a missonary for the Orient where she remained until her

Fig. 101.   Dizygotic twin sisters at the age of 80.

retirement. When the twin sisters were reunited after forty-seven years of separation, they were still very much alike not only physically but also in their emotional patterns of adjustment to senescent decrepitudes. It would not be difficult to multiply indefinitely whatever documentary material is required for demonstrating essential genetic differences between one-egg and two-egg twin index groups in relation to adaptive variations during the involutional period.

Genetically, it is indicated by this part of our analysis (Fig. 103) that the principal causal relationship of involutional psychosis is to the group of schizoid personality traits and, therefore, indirectly to the schizophrenic disease entity (heterozygous genotype) rather than to that of manic-depressive psychosis. Psychiatrically, it may be assumed that the development of an involutional psychosis is precipitated by a strained situation posing a threat of insecurity to the rigid attitudes of a schizoid person with compensatory superiority feelings and a perfectionist self-esteem. Since such

Fig. 102.   Monozygotic twin sisters at the age of 67.

persons require an inordinate amount of protection throughout their adult lives, they break down in the involutional period, because they gradually experience an irresistible decline in those resources, which previously facilitated a sufficient degree of adaptation and compensation.

With respect to the other two diagnostic categories, schizophrenia and manic-depressive psychosis, which generally occur before the involutional period of life, the available evidence is conclusively in support of specific and basically single-factor types of inheritance. According to an analysis of age-corrected expectancy rates, the chance of developing either psychosis increases strictly in proportion to the degree of blood relationship to the respective type of index case.

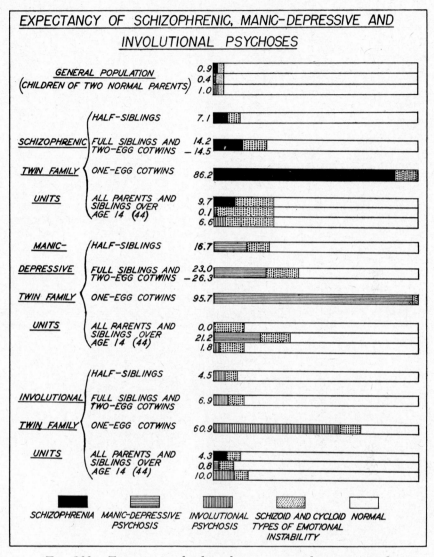

F I G. 103.   Expectancy of schizophrenic, manic-depressive, and
involutional psychoses.

The comparative rates for manic-depressive psychosis vary from 16.7 per
cent for the half-siblings to 95.7 per cent for the monozygotic cotwins and
indicate a very high degree of penetrance of the given genotype. The
observed morbidity rate for the parents of manic-depressive index cases
is only 23.4 per cent, but approximately 60 per cent of the index cases have
been found to come from matings between one normal and one manic-
depressive or cycloid parent. This distribution seems best explained by an

TABLE 21. REPRODUCTIVE TRENDS IN NORMAL AND
PSYCHOTIC TWIN FAMILY UNITS

Type of Family Unit	Rate of Celibates				Rate of Married Persons without Children				Number of Children per Fertile Married Person			
	Twins		Siblings		Twins		Siblings		Twins		Siblings	
	With Psychosis	Without Psychosis	With Psychosis	Without Psychosis	With Psychosis	Without Psychosis	With Psychosis	Without Psychosis	With Psychosis	Without Psychosis	With Psychosis	Without Psychosis
Schizophrenic (over age 45)	50.7	33.3	43.5	17.1	9.8	24.3	24.6	19.9	2.4	2.5	2.0	2.6
Manic-depressive (over age 45)	27.8	14.3	26.6	6.1	22.2	7.1	26.6	13.6	1.7	2.0	2.0	3.1
General twin population (over age 60)	—	13.3	—	11.7*	—	19.2	—	15.5	—	3.0	—	3.2

* Celibacy rate for the general population over age 60 of the State of New York (U.S. Census 1940): 11.6 per cent.

irregularly dominant mode of inheritance, especially since no instance of a consanguineous marriage has been discovered among the parents of our manic-depressive index cases, as compared with an increase to 5.0 per cent in the rate of such matings in our schizophrenic sample.

The relative infrequency of manic-depressive psychosis is largely due to factors of selection, which are liable to reduce the reproductive rate of the trait-carriers. According to our fertility data (Table 21), both manic-depressive twins and siblings marry less frequently, tend more often to remain childless when married, and produce fewer children if fertile, than is true for the nonpsychotic persons among their cotwins and siblings as well as for the general population. In fact, the fertility rates of our manic-depressive index cases are even lower than the corresponding rates of schizophrenic index cases.

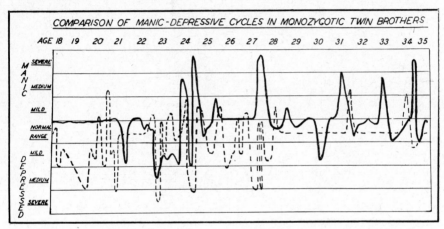

FIG. 104. Comparison of manic-depressive cycles in monozygotic twin brothers.

The extent to which manic and depressive cycles may vary on the basis of the same genotype, is graphically illustrated in Figure 104 for a seventeen-year period in the histories of twin brothers included in our series of concordant one-egg pairs. The twins are unmarried men who are active in similar professions, but have frequently displayed pathologic mood swings in opposite directions, irrespective of whether they lived together or apart.

The childhood pictures of these twin brothers are shown in Figure 105. Current photographs are withheld in order to prevent identification of the twins as members of our profession.

Clinically it may be of particular significance that the affective instability and biochemical dysfunction produced by the manic-depressive genotype seems to be correlated with the genetic factors for gout and diabetes and especially with a tendency to obesity. If concordant one-egg twin pairs show a definite dissimilarity in the severity of their psychotic symptoms, the display of a milder or more easily controllable manic-depressive syndrome has generally been found by us to be associated with a lesser degree of overweight.

For instance, in the development of those originally completely similar and equally pyknic-obese twin sisters shown in Figure 106, a pronounced difference in the present severity of their clinical symptomatology corresponds with a considerable discrepancy in the degree of their obesity as indicated by a weight difference of over 35 pounds. While the stouter twin is still subject to an almost continuous succession of depressions, the slimmer twin has been free of severe depressive attacks for several years.

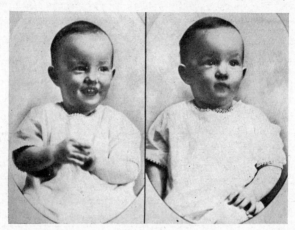

Fig. 105.   The B. twins at the age of 1 year.

The situation is completely different with respect to the constitutional ability or inability to resist the development, or to counteract the progression, of a schizophrenic psychosis, the main genotype of which is usually transmitted in the collateral rather than in the direct line of descent and, therefore, is believed by us to follow a recessive mode of inheritance. In this group it is the rule that if one twin remains free of schizophrenic symptoms or shows a milder form of the disease than his cotwin, there is always a difference between the twins in regard to physical development, the difference being consistently in favor of the more resistant twin.

According to the results of our most recent analysis (Fig. 107), the total expectancy of the different forms of schizophrenia varies from 7.1 per cent for the half-siblings, through about 14 per cent for the full siblings and dizygotic cotwins, to 86.2 per cent for the monozygotic twin partners. The differences in concordance between one-egg and two-egg groups of twin index pairs show no positive correlation with corresponding degrees of environmental similarity or dissimilarity. About one-quarter of one-egg pairs have been found to develop schizophrenic psychoses in the absence of similar environments, and close to one-half of two-egg pairs remain dis-

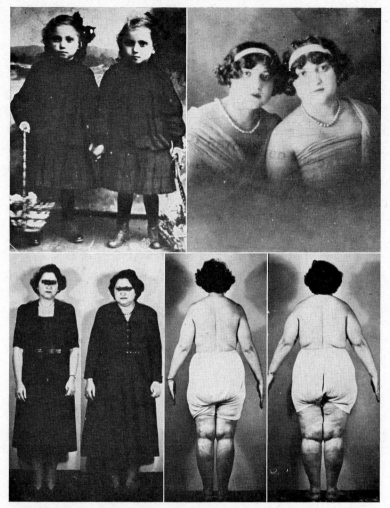

FIG. 106.   The C. twins at the ages of 3, 17, 40, and 46 years.

cordant despite similar environments. The incidence of schizophrenia among the parents of schizophrenic index cases is 9.3 per cent.

Deficient resistance to the effect of the recessive unit factor for schizophrenia seems to be determined by a nonspecific and certainly multifactorial type of secondary genetic mechanism. Measurable correlates of this mechanism may be seen in the capacity for mobilizing effective mesodermal defense reactions, in the compensatory power of the athletic component of physique, and in the ability to maintain a stabilized level of body weight.

The variable effect of this constitutional defense mechanism is demonstrated by the fact that the largest possible difference from extreme deterioration in one twin to complete absence of a schizophrenic psychosis in the other twin does not occur in our sample of monozygotic pairs, although it is observed in every sixth dizygotic pair. For a while, the monozygotic pair shown in Figure 108 seemed to be disposed to become the only exception to this rule. The physically weaker twin, who had shown a deficit of at least five pounds in weight throughout childhood and adolescence, developed a severe type of hebephrenic psychosis before she reached the age of 20. Despite a full course of insulin treatment, she went downhill rapidly and, following her third admission in 1938, required continuous hospitalization for ten years, apparently in a chronic state of dilapidation and indifference.

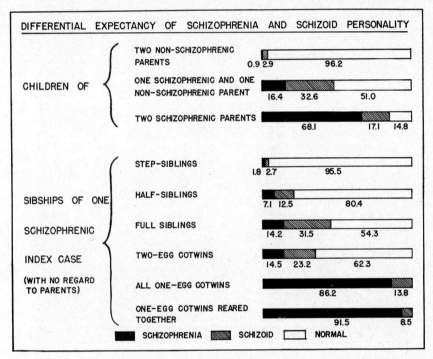

Fig. 107.   Differential expectancy of schizophrenia and schizoid personality.

However, while we were keeping the twin sister under close observation for the earliest symptoms of an impending breakdown, the patient improved slowly, and unobtrusively except for a steady gain in weight. She gradually reversed the original weight difference and in 1948, when she was 22 pounds heavier than her continuously normal twin sister, was found to be free of psychotic symptoms. Her physical and mental condition has been satisfactory ever since. Therapeutically it is justified to infer, therefore, that one of the guiding principles in the management of schizophrenia should be to keep a potential or convalescent patient on a stabilized level of constitutional resistance.

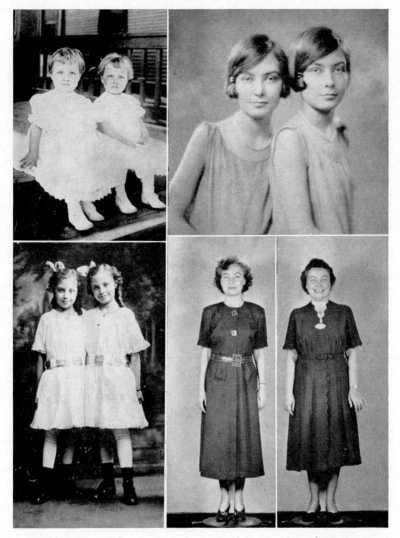

FIG. 108.   The N. twins at the ages of 3, 10, 18, and 42 years.

Conclusion

In conclusion it may be stated that the biologic implications of this inference are still a challenging proposition with respect to all of the psychoses discussed in this rather condensed review. For obvious reasons, the ultimate objective cannot be accomplished without a full understanding of the interaction of gene-specific biochemical dysfunctions with general constitutional (adaptational) modifiers and those precipitating outside factors arising from the effect of uncontrolled imperfections in the structure of modern human societies. There is reason to believe, however, that gradual advancement of our insight into the varying genetic and constitutional background factors will not only be useful in developing a consistent system of diagnostic classifications, but will also help in improving the therapeutic, social, and preventive management of the various psychoses.

In any case, a concession of our still incomplete knowledge about the biologic aspects of psychotic reaction syndromes seems preferable to an attitude of optimistic complacency and, I hope, will prove to be conducive to a steady progress of psychiatry.

REFERENCES

1. BISCHOF, G.: *Zeitschrift für Neurologie*, 1939, 167, p. 105.
2. BROCKHAUSEN, K.: *Allgemeine Zeitschrift für Psychiatrie*, 1939, 112, p. 179.
3. ESSEN-MÖLLER, E.: *Monthly Review of Psychiatry and Neurology*, 1946, 112, p. 258.
4. HOSKINS, R. G.: The Biology of Schizophrenia. New York, W. W. Norton, 1946.
5. HOTH, T. A.: *American Journal of Psychiatry*, 1922, 78, p. 365.
6. KALLMANN, F. J.: The Genetics of Schizophrenia. New York, J. J. Augustin, 1938.
7. KALLMANN, F. J.: *American Journal of Psychiatry*, 1946, 103, p. 311.
8. KALLMANN, F. J.: Failures in Psychiatric Treatment (P. H. Hoch, ed.). New York, Grune and Stratton, 1948.
9. KALLMANN, F. J. *Congrès International de Psychiatric* (Hermann & Cie, éd.) Paris, 1950, 6, p. 1.
10. LUXENBURGER, H.: *Zeitschrift für die gesamte Neurologie und Psychiatrie*, 1928, 116, p. 297.
11. SCHULZ, B.: *Zeitschrift für Neurologie*, 1940, 168, p. 332.
12. SCHULZ, B.: *Zeitschrift für Neurologie*, 1940, 169, p. 311.
13. SCHULZ, B.: *Aerztliche Monatshefte*, 1949-50, 5, p. 299.
14. SLATER, E.: *Zeitschrift für die gesamte Neurologie und Psychiatrie*, 1938, 162, p. 794 and 163, p. 1.
15. STEVENSON, G. H.: *Psychiatric Quarterly*, 1949, 23, p. 71.

Counseling in Human Genetics

SHELDON CLARK REED, PH.D.

It is clear to me that genetics is indebted to Dr. Kallmann for the majority of the usable data which are available concerning the heredity of the major psychoses. There are many papers with information which might be employed by the geneticist in the specialized analyses he can make. Unfortunately, some essential group of figures is usually missing or cannot be disentangled from the tables given. Consequently, it is with extreme gratitude that the geneticist receives the tables which Dr. Kallmann has presented, in addition to those obtained previously from the German population studied by him.

At the Dight Institute of Human Genetics at the University of Minnesota, much time is given to what is called "Counseling in Human Genetics." We have a continuous flow of questions from troubled people or their troubled physicians who want facts about heredity.

It is most difficult to supply the facts about mental diseases. Without Dr. Kallmann's data, we would be very badly off indeed. Even with it, there are great difficulties. For instance, each psychiatrist warns the geneticist that the diagnosis in mental disease is extremely tricky and that it is often incorrect. I have a better opinion of the psychiatrist than he has of many of his fellows, and generally accept the diagnosis from the staffs of reputable institutions. Furthermore, we have discovered that this difficulty of diagnosis can be overcome for pedigrees collected many years ago which we have at the Dight Institute.

This validation can be done by means of subsequent diagnoses, from the frequency of suicides in the family, and diagnoses of other relatives. The diagnoses for the other members of the family turned out to be surprisingly consistent. With a family size of 300 persons or better in each family, a very clear majority of the diagnoses will indicate whether we are dealing with schizophrenia or manic-depressive psychosis.

About one million dollars was spent in collecting the pedigrees concerned with mental deficiency and mental diseases, which the Dight Institute received as a gift from the Carnegie Institute at Cold Spring Harbor. These pedigrees were collected by intelligent people who were trained in the proper methods of extracting personal information. The pedigrees were collected thirty to forty years ago and provide a unique opportunity to follow up the descendants of large numbers of the mentally ill of two and three generations ago. It would be impossible today to reconstruct detailed statistics which were recorded for us between 1910 and 1920.

The State of Minnesota, through its Mental Health Commissioner, Dr. Ralph Rossen, is generously supporting this follow-up work. It is a source of amazement both to us and to the head social worker at the State Institution that so many of the patients turn out to have a common affected ancestor. The various branches of the large families of the rural Middle West are quite often unaware of their rather close blood relationship.

In the genetic counseling which we do for individuals and the county and state welfare agencies, we need such follow-up data on the expectations for schizophrenia and manic-depressive psychosis. We need it very badly and soon! I cannot wait out my lifetime for the 100 per cent perfect diagnosis.

Dr. Kallmann's data answer our questions well enough for the brothers and sisters of the psychotic patient. However, the question most often asked concerns the children, or the nieces and nephews, or the grandchildren of the affected person. What are the chances that each grandchild of a manic-depressive will eventually develop the psychosis? The only way these answers may be obtained directly is from a longer-time, longitudinal study of individual families. The only way that this can be accomplished is for the geneticist to live to be well over 100 years old, or to check and bring up to date the pedigrees collected two generations ago. At present, the latter procedure seems the more likely to occur.

It should be obvious that in genetic counseling we are interested in rough percentages only. The client is usually not much interested in the distinction between a 23 per cent chance of having a manic-depressive descendant and a 50 per cent chance. But the client should and does want to know whether the chance of having a defective offspring is one in ten or one in 10,000. The only person in a position to supply such information is the geneticist, and he must have the assistance of the psychiatrist in arriving at roughly correct answers. We will continue to give free answers to clients at the Dight Institute; and, with the aid of Dr. Kallmann's data, those of many others, and what we are collecting ourselves, we are likely to be able to give proper counseling to the many that ask for it.

My function today has been that of pointing out the very practical uses of genetic data. The problems are very real to the families involved and the members are extremely grateful for whatever information we can give them.

Discussion

JAN A. BÖÖK, M.D.

Judging from the extensive studies of Dr. Kallmann and others who have applied genetic methods in a critical manner, it is quite evident that the schizophrenic syndrome should be recognized as a genetically controlled disease. The question as to whether only one or several genetic entities are involved is not yet clear and will be difficult to decide. However, at the present stage of psychiatric research it is important to realize that genes are instrumental in the etiology. This statement does not mean that environmental factors are immaterial. It is implied, however, that these factors must act upon a specific genotype in order to produce a schizophrenic psychosis. Further research into the given environmental factors is needed for the purpose of determining whether they are specific or not. If it were possible to identify them adequately and to change their individual effect, we would have a good chance of prophylaxis and treatment. This objective has not yet been achieved.

In any case, it should be borne in mind that primarily specific gene actions are involved. If a safe approach resembling causal therapy is to be accomplished, research into these gene actions is required. The genes participate in, or set in motion, biochemical processes. A special discipline of biochemical genetics is needed in the study of genetically determined psychoses. In other words, the ordinary biochemical approach to an understanding of these disorders should be combined with genetic investigations.

What has been achieved so far is the procurement of adequate evidence for the conclusion that the major psychoses, schizophrenia and manic-depressive psychosis, are genetically controlled disorders. In relation to the magnitude of this discovery, it is only of secondary importance whether these psychoses are inherited as dominants or recessives. Any possible disagreement as to the mechanism of transmission should not be allowed to overshadow the really important fact of a genetic basis of the given disease entities.

In a recent study of psychoses in a North Swedish community of about 9000 individuals, the expectancy of schizophrenia was found to be approximately 2.8 per cent. As the normal expectancy of general populations has usually been estimated at somewhat below 1 per cent, one may assume either that the latter figure is too low or that the composition (inbreeding) and particular environment of this community tend to favor schizophrenia By comparison, manic-depressive psychosis was found to be extremely rare. Of course, all cases in this community were studied without any selection. Within this sample, however, data from about 100 selected family units reveal approximately the same morbidity rates for the different degrees of blood relationship to schizophrenic index cases as were observed in Kallmann's study published in 1938.[1] This fact seems to rule out major environmental influences as an explanation of the increased expectancy of schizophrenia in this population, so that it seems preferable to ascribe this increase either to a higher gene frequency or to a more thorough method of investigation.

Beyond question, an adequate understanding of the implications of a genetic disorder will lead to a proper appreciation of the contributions of genetics to medical research.

It is obvious that the genetic approach to the problems of schizophrenia and manic-depressive psychosis is not so pessimistic, deterministic, or sterile as many psychiatrists are still inclined to believe. It is highly desirable that the two major schools of psychiatry, the organically minded and the psychoanalytic, discontinue a controversy which is largely based on mutual misunderstandings. No one wants to deny the importance of psychologic factors or that of psychotherapy. However, in regard to schizophrenia and manic-depressive psychosis the need of a systematic search for a basic etiology should be comprehended. The genetic aspect of psychoses does not interfere with the application of the methods of conventional treatment of these disorders as long as more direct or more effective procedures are not available. Nor is there any conflict between a genetic theory and the idea that psychologic and other factors may precipitate or impair the symptomatology of psychoses, which appear in persons having a specific genotype. The genetic theory explains that only some individuals develop these psychoses and why they do so. The psychodynamic approach has not been able to give a satisfactory answer to this question (*cf.* Rosenberg[2] and Shulman[3]). Many observational facts contradict theories based on sociologic or psychic contamination, and there is much evidence in support of a theory of fundamental biological differences.

REFERENCES

1. KALLMANN, F. J.: The Genetics of Schizophrenia. New York, J. J. Augustin, 1938. 291 pp.
2. ROSENBERG, R.: *American Journal of Psychiatry*, 1944, 101, pp. 157-165.
3. SHULMAN, A. J.: *Psychiatric Quarterly*, 1950, 24, 3, pp. 515-531.

CHAPTER 20

Mental Disorders Arising From Organic Disease

WALTER L. BRUETSCH, M.D.

THE INCREASED ATTENTION of present-day psychiatry to social ills, such as the milder psychoneurotic conditions, juvenile delinquency, and tension in the international field, has created the impression that psychiatry and mental hygiene are mainly concerned with social and psychologic implications. In recent years it has almost been forgotten that psychiatry is also a biologic science, dealing with biochemical and pathologic processes in the cerebral tissue which may affect mental health.[32]

In the United States alone, more than half a million individuals are confined with a mental disorder in state and government institutions. Generally speaking, in approximately 50 per cent of these patients organic changes are present in the brain, which can be demonstrated with histologic methods.

But the microscope and the histologic technic leave us far short of our goal, although in the past fifty years they have been among the important mainstays of sound research in the field of the major psychoses. It is most likely that biochemistry will take up, where histopathology fails to furnish new information. It is, therefore, most gratifying to see on the program of this symposium so many excellent papers on various phases of brain chemistry.

Some neuropathologic observations in psychiatry are as puzzling today[37] as they were to the earlier investigators.[29] There are individuals with gross defects in the brain exhibiting few or no obvious mental abnormalities during life. Some of these persons may live a completely normal existence[37] or even attain a certain degree of "fame," as in the instance of the young woman who was afflicted with a large porencephalus and who at the age of 12 years was known throughout eastern Europe for her abilities in clairvoyance and mental healing.[29]

On the other hand, there are the mental patients with gross psychiatric abnormalities in whom the most minute microscopic examination reveals little or nothing of tangible evidence of an organic nature. In the latter

303

group may be included some of the markedly deteriorated schizophrenic patients and some instances of the senile psychoses.

A particularly interesting example in this regard is general paresis. It is usually conceded that the cerebral alterations in this psychosis are the cause of the mental manifestations. The difficulty of the relation of the anatomic changes to the clinical picture is exemplified by the fact that individuals have died in whom a fully developed general paretic brain process was present, but these persons had not shown any psychiatric or neurologic symptoms.[46] Here the question comes to the fore: How long and to what degree must general paretic alterations in the brain be present before they express themselves in mental symptoms, and on exactly what pathophysiologic mechanisms does the appearance of psychic disturbances depend? General paretics who were treated with malaria or penicillin have furnished additional material for the same conjectures. Some of these patients show a complete disappearance of all psychotic symptoms while still under malaria or penicillin therapy or shortly afterwards, i.e., at a time when there is no anatomically perceptible regression in the pathologic state of the brain. It is surprising that this intriguing problem never aroused more than a cursory discussion, and it is doubtful whether these phenomena will ever be answered with any degree of accuracy.

In the past, the American Psychiatric Association has been conscious of the importance which physical disease plays in the causation of psychiatric illness. It classifies unhesitatingly as organic, the psychoses due to infection, intoxication, trauma, disturbance of circulation, and several other conditions.[13] Three-fifths of mental disorders are now accepted as being organic.[48] Further research may establish definite organic bases for some of the remaining psychoses now considered due to a psychologic background.

Since World War II, American psychiatry has become psychoanalytically oriented and the revised classification of mental disorders, which is about to appear, has been constructed to suit the concepts of dynamic psychiatry. How far this new orientation has carried was vividly described by Levine[31] at the International Congress of Psychiatry in 1950. However, important as psychoanalysis is and as much as it has contributed to the understanding of personal and social dynamics, it does not give an answer to most psychiatric problems which are seen in the average mental hospital.

Since there are a considerable number of persons in the audience who are not psychiatrists, I will make you first familiar with the official classification of the psychoses now in use by hospitals for mental diseases. The following condensed classification is taken from the tenth edition (published in 1942) of the *Statistical Manual for the Use of Hospitals for Mental Diseases* (pp. 14-16). It was prepared by the Committee on Statistics of the American Psychiatric Association in collaboration with the National Committee for Mental Hygiene.

Condensed Classification of Mental Disorders

00-1 *Psychoses due to, or Associated with, Infection*

Psychoses with syphilis of the central nervous system
    Meningo-encephalitic type (general paresis)
    Meningo-vascular type (cerebral syphilis)
    Psychosis with intracranial gumma
    Other types. Specify
Psychoses with tuberculous meningitis
Psychoses with meningitis (unspecified)
Psychoses with epidemic encephalitis
Psychoses with acute chorea (Sydenham's)
Psychoses with other infectious disease. Specify
Post-infectious psychoses. Specify organism when known

00-3 *Psychoses due to Intoxication*

Psychoses due to alcohol
    Pathologic intoxication
    Delirium tremens
    Korsakoff's psychosis
    Acute hallucinosis
    Other types. Specify
Psychoses due to a drug or other exogenous poison
    Psychoses due to a metal. Specify
    Psychoses due to a gas. Specify
    Psychoses due to opium or a derivative
    Psychoses due to another drug. Specify

00-4 *Psychoses due to Trauma (Traumatic Psychoses)*

Delirium due to trauma
Personality disorders due to trauma
Mental deterioration due to trauma
Other types. Specify

00-5.0 *Psychoses due to Disturbance of Circulation*

Psychoses with cerebral embolism
Psychoses with cerebral arteriosclerosis
Psychoses with cardio-renal disease
Other types. Specify

00-5.5 *Psychoses due to Convulsive Disorder (Epilepsy)*

Epileptic deterioration
Epileptic clouded states
Other epileptic types. Specify

00-7 *Psychoses due to Disturbances of Metabolism, Growth, Nutrition or Endocrine Function*

Senile psychoses
    Simple deterioration
    Presbyophrenic type
    Delirious and confused types
    Depressed and agitated types
    Paranoid types

Presenile sclerosis (Alzheimer's disease)
Involutional psychoses
    Melancholia
    Paranoid types
    Other types. Specify
Psychoses with glandular disorder. Specify
Exhaustion delirium
Psychoses with pellagra
Psychoses with other somatic disease. Specify disease

00-8 Psychoses due to New Growth

Psychoses with intracranial neoplasm. Specify
Psychoses with other neoplasm. Specify

00-9 Psychoses due to Unknown or Hereditary Cause but Associated with Organic Change

Psychoses with multiple sclerosis
Psychoses with paralysis agitans
Psychoses with Huntington's chorea
Psychoses with other disease of the brain or nervous system. Specify disease

00-X Disorders of Psychogenic Origin or without Clearly Defined Tangible Cause or Structural Change

Manic-depressive psychoses
    Manic type
    Depressive type
    Circular type
    Mixed type
    Perplexed type
    Stuporous type
    Other types. Specify
Dementia praecox (schizophrenia)
    Simple type
    Hebephrenic type
    Catatonic type
    Paranoid type
    Other types. Specify
Paranoia
    Paranoid conditions
    Psychoses with psychopathic personality
    Psychoses with mental deficiency.

Limitation of time precludes the discussion of all diagnostic subgroups. I will select, therefore, from the more important organic groups some facts which illustrate the practical and especially the therapeutic importance of the concept of the organic psychoses, which is about to be swept away by the overenthusiasm of dynamic psychiatry.

Psychoses due to, or Associated with, Infection

Since we are living in the "golden era of the treatment of infectious diseases," this group of mental disorders will be the first to disappear.

The most important infection capable of producing mental disorders has been syphilis. Neurosyphilis appears under two main forms, as a meningo-encephalitic type, better known as general paresis, and as a meningovascular type, referred to as cerebral syphilis.

When I entered psychiatry twenty-five years ago, the incidence of general paresis was at its peak. To give an idea of the magnitude of the problem at that time, I may mention that on the men's service of the Central State Hospital in Indianapolis the admission rate was 30 per cent. In other words, one out of three male mental patients had general paresis.

There has been a steady decline in the incidence of general paresis, which has been due to three factors. The first was the introduction of the malaria or fever treatment. The second was the national campaign against syphilis. And the last and most important reason has been the advent of penicillin. In contrast to the older forms of antisyphilitic therapy, consisting of arsphenamines and heavy metals, penicillin, when given in appropriate amounts, will eradicate the syphilitic infection entirely in most instances, and in this way forestall any later nervous system involvement.

Until a little more than fifty years ago mental diseases were explained mainly on the basis of philosophic or psychologic speculation. As for general paresis the same psychic factors, which today are supposedly the cause of the so-called psychogenic psychoses, were then given as the causes of general paresis. In 1877, v. Krafft-Ebing,[27] the famous Viennese professor of psychiatry, gave the following etiologic possibilities for general paresis: dissipation in alcohol and love, heredity, smoking of ten to twenty Virginia cigars, excessive heat and cold, trauma to the head, exhaustive efforts of making a living, weak nerves, and fright. Among women, the menopause was given as the most important factor because the onset was frequent between the age of 40 to 50 years. Strikingly, v. Krafft-Ebing in 1877 did not mention syphilis among the possible causes, although Esmarch and Jessen[18] had published the now famous paper on syphilis and insanity in 1857.

Among the first patients with general paresis, described by French psychiatrists, were many former soldiers and officers of the armies of Napoleon. In these it was speculated that the terrors of war were the precipitating factors.

In the face of the popular theories in modern psychiatry on the "emotional etiology" of the psychoses, the history of general paresis lends significant coloring. The assumption that general paresis was the result of psychic causes enjoyed credit as late as the turn of the last century. The greater frequency of general paresis in males was explained by the preponderance of intellectual work in men and by their more frequent contact with the strains of the world, with ambitions and frustrated hopes. The small number of general paretics in the peasant class was explained on the grounds that they were relatively free from emotions and passions. The fact was that syphilis was less prevalent in the rural than in the urban areas.

It is also an interesting commentary that as eminent an authority as Virchow in discussion before the Berlin Medical Society as late as 1898 denied vehemently its syphilitic origin.[50]

It was not until the trend of investigations shifted from the clinic to the laboratory that the physical causation of general paresis was definitely established. In 1904, Alzheimer[2] and Nissl,[39] using new methods of staining, gave a detailed description of the microscopic changes in the brain of general paretic patients. In 1906, the Wassermann reaction was introduced, revealing that in almost all cases the reaction of the blood and spinal fluid were positive for syphilis. In 1913, Noguchi and Moore[40] were able to demonstrate *Treponema pallidum* in the brain of general paretics.

Until 1917, when Wagner-Jauregg introduced the malaria treatment, general paresis was a fatal disease. With the use of malaria fever about half of the patients were benefited, the benefit ranging from arrest of the disease to complete recovery. By now it has been fairly well established that penicillin, when given in sufficiently large amounts, is equal if not slightly superior to malaria therapy.

It is of the greatest therapeutic interest that the general paretic who during his illness is inadequately adjusted to his environment—as psychologists call it—becomes following malaria or penicillin therapy a well-adjusted personality without any psychotherapy whatsoever. Physical treatment and not mental healing, that is, talking or lecturing to the patient, relieves the patient of his abnormal behavior, his emotional disturbances, and his delusions and hallucinations. This simple fact cannot be too strongly emphasized in present-day psychiatry, where the dogma is propounded that psychoses are nothing but maladaptive attitudes of the individual to environment.[10]

I have devoted a large portion of this discussion to general paresis because it illustrates so clearly what can be accomplished by persistent research along biologic lines, in contrast to fruitless philosophic and psychologic speculations.

With general paresis we have merely scratched the surface of mental disorders arising from physical disease. Broadly speaking, any affliction of the cerebrum, particularly of the cortex, may express itself in mental abnormalities.

In the classification of mental disorders there is listed a psychosis with tuberculous meningitis. Tuberculous meningitis, being a rapidly fatal disease, has up to now been of little psychiatric significance. With the use of streptomycin, the psychiatric implication of tuberculous meningitis has changed. The slowing of the tuberculous process, brought about by streptomycin, permits in some instances the appearance of a subacute tuberculous meningo-encephalitis. In adults, the clinical picture is reminiscent of general paresis. In the child who recovers one may observe disturbances of mood and personality, with instability and fits of anger, analogous to those noted in postencephalitics.[41] Only the future will tell whether a complete cure of tuberculous meningitis, associated with restoration of normal function of the brain, can be accomplished with streptomycin.[22]

Encephalitis, particularly the so-called von Economo type, which occurred in several epidemics following World War I, has come to take an important place in psychiatry.[33] During the acute stage there is delirium, stupor, psychomotor excitement. In the chronic stage, which one sees today in mental hospitals, apathy or emotional indifference is a leading symptom. Some of these cases, in the absence of Parkinsonian symptoms, have been mistaken for catatonic dementia praecox and hysteria.

Next in the classification are the psychoses with acute, or Sydenham's chorea. It is realized now that most cases of acute chorea in the child are due to rheumatic fever. The underlying pathologic condition in Sydenham's chorea is a mild rheumatic encephalitis. Rheumatic chorea may be followed, in some instances, by mental retardation and other abnormal behavior. The emotional disturbances are usually attributed to psychologic factors, such as child-parent separation. It has been felt that these problems can be avoided when "the child as a whole" is treated and not simply the illness.[49] The fact, however, remains that from 5 to 7 per cent of all patients with rheumatic chorea later find their way to state hospitals as chronic mental patients because the personality disturbance is organically conditioned.

In childhood, infections such as measles and pertussis leave in a small percentage some sequelae. The emotional difficulties may be so severe and persistent as to compromise permanently the competitive status of the child.[9]

The febrile period of some of the infectious diseases is occasionally characterized by a delirious stage. Such transitory infectious psychoses are apt to arise particularly in association with influenza, pneumonia, typhoid fever, and rheumatic fever. In most of these diseases, with the exception of rheumatic fever, the psychotic manifestations are of short duration and there are usually no sequelae.

But rheumatic fever, particularly in its chronic or subclinical form, has recently been found to be an important factor in the production of chronic mental illness.[6, 7] There have been two important developments in the study of rheumatic fever: (1) In the past, rheumatic fever has been viewed as a disease taking place within a short period of time. The newer concepts, however, emphasize that the rheumatic infection may endure through the entire life of the patient. (2) As the result of the continuation of the rheumatic infection, vascular changes may occur in later life in any organ and at any time, when the patient is otherwise in good health. If in this development the cerebral vessels take part, gross and microscopic infarctions will result, due to rheumatic obliterating endarteritis, producing a variety of mental and neurologic symptoms. From postmortem examinations it has been estimated that between 4 and 5 per cent of the patients in mental hospitals have rheumatic brain disease, associated with rheumatic heart disease.

The importance of these studies lies in the fact that for the first time in almost forty years a new major factor has been established, which is responsible for the production of a large number of mental cases each year. It was Alzheimer who in 1907 last added a new entity, a type of presenile psychosis, called "Alzheimer's disease."

The confirmation of this work by an eminent group of research workers, such as Kernohan et al.,[26] Dublin,[16] Castex,[11] Neubuerger,[15, 38] van der Horst,[21] Luzzatto,[35] Benda,[5] Manguel,[36] Whitman and Karnosh,[52] and Sim- maro Puig,[44, 45] has put the stamp of permanency on this work.

In particular, Dr. L. van der Horst, professor of psychiatry of the University of Amsterdam, Netherlands, describing similar cases, is most emphatic as to the concept of rheumatic brain disease.[21] In the beginning of one of his papers he mentioned that the last thirty years have seen the almost complete disappearance from the psychiatric vocabulary of the description of psychotic manifestations due to rheumatic fever. In concluding his paper van der Horst says: "We must ally ourselves with Bruetsch and other workers in distinguishing a form of rheumatic brain disease as an idiopathic psychosis with a specific anatomic basis."

The sequence of events in a clinically and histologically well-observed case of psychosis with rheumatic brain disease is given in the following paragraphs.

At the age of 21 years the female patient had rheumatic fever. When 51 years old, she developed mental symptoms characteristic of involutional melancholia. Seven years previously she had a slight stroke leaving no obvious residue.

Physical examination revealed chronic rheumatoid arthritis of both hands and knees and a systolic blow in the mitral and aortic area. The blood pressure was 145/80. Since the patient was only depressed and showed insight, saying that all her trouble was due to her crippled condition as the result of arthritis, it was felt that this patient might have an involutional psychosis on a psychologic basis and that the rheumatic heart disease, which had followed an attack of rheumatic fever earlier in life, was incidental.

The patient died at the age of 60 of tuberculous spondylitis.

The mitral and aortic valves revealed gross and microscopic rheumatic changes. In addition to old quiescent vegetations on the mitral and aortic leaflets, there was a rim of fibrin on the mitral valve into which young dividing fibroblasts were growing. This finding was interpreted as mild activity. Rheumatic fever in this patient had therefore continued in a chronic or subclinical form throughout the entire life of the patient, as could be shown by histologic examination of the heart valves.

In the brain, there was an area of infarction involving a large part of the right occipital lobe (Fig. 109). There were also softened convolutions in the parietal and frontal areas. A small cystic area in the putamen, close to the internal capsule, was present, most likely dating back to the stroke antedating the onset of the psychosis. In both middle cerebral arteries and in other vessels at the base of the brain, not a single arteriosclerotic plaque was observed.

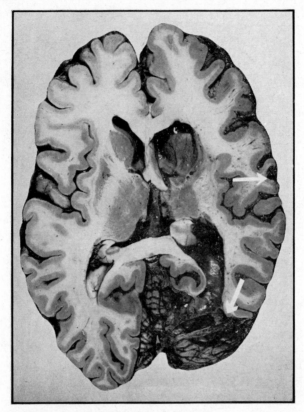

Fig. 109.   Psychosis with rheumatic brain disease. The arrows point to the softened right occipital lobe and to a partially infarcted convolution in the central parietal region.

Seventy tissue blocks from various regions of the brain were examined histologically. Twenty-eight cortical blocks were free of obvious changes. In the remaining forty-two tissue blocks, from one to several acellular areas were present, ranging from minute size (Fig. 110) to cortical devastation of a whole convolution. The greatest number of acellular areas was found in the gray matter from the upper aspect of the brain. In spite of the large number of involved convolutions it was difficult to find endarteritic changes on the meningeal and cortical vessels. However, serial sections unearthed an occasional meningeal vessel with endothelial cells in active proliferation.

From a clinical point of view it is interesting to note that in spite of widespread gross and microscopic involvement of the gray matter, the patient showed no global mental deterioration.

With the exception of the lungs, where rheumatic endarteritic vessels were observed, the internal organs were free of definite rheumatic vascular changes.

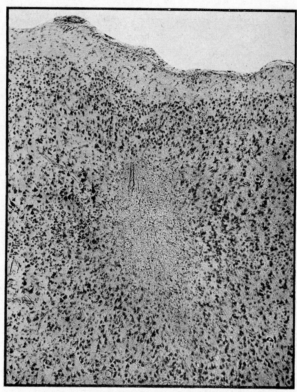

FIG. 110.   Microscopic area of incomplete softening (acellular area) in cerebral cortex in rheumatic brain disease. Toluidine blue stain.

I have used up a great deal of my allotted time with only one group of organic psychoses, and I shall have to continue very rapidly in order to cover the entire field.

Psychoses due to Intoxication

In psychoses due to intoxication, particularly alcohol, the changes in the brain are mostly of a transitory physicochemical nature.

Prolonged exposure to a metal (lead, arsenic, and mercury), and exposure to poisonous gases, in particular carbon monoxide gas, produce chronic mental illness.

Then there are the well-known psychoses due to opium, morphine, and

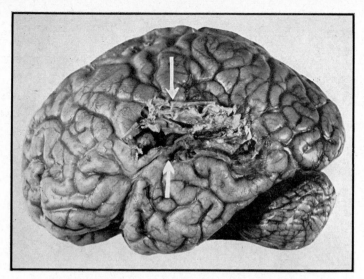

Fig. 111.   Traumatic psychosis associated with mental deterioration. There is a
large cerebral scar in the central parietal region.

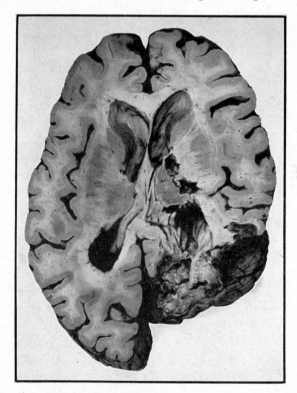

Fig. 112.   Psychosis with cerebral arteriosclerosis. There is complete softening
of the right occipital lobe. An area of infarction is also present in the right basal
ganglia.

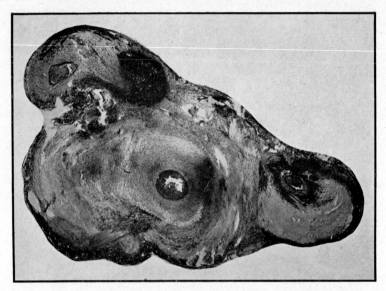

Fig. 113.   Basilar artery from a patient with advanced cerebral atherosclerosis. The outline of the vessel is markedly distorted. Owing to the deposition of large masses of amorphous material there is complete occlusion of the lumen. Toluidine blue stain.

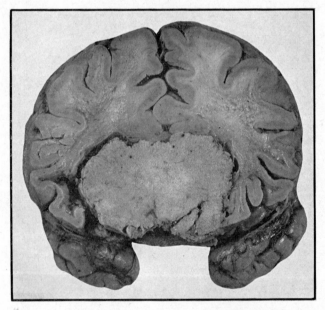

Fig. 114.   Psychosis with brain tumor (meningioma). Section through tumor mass in the frontal lobe area. The white matter above the neoplasm is necrotic.

other drugs, such as cocaine, bromides, and some of the antihistaminic drugs.[53]

Cortisone and ACTH may produce mental changes (euphoria, depression, hallucinations, delusions, stupor),[42] on a physiologic basis.

Psychoses due to Trauma

Fairly characteristic psychotic reactions are brought about by brain injuries. This is usually in the form of a short delirium, but in some cases mental deterioration (dementia) may ensue. In addition to the symptoms due to brain damage there are frequently others referable to psychogenic mechanisms.[25] For optimal therapeutic results both the structural changes and the psychoneurotic state must be treated.

It is not so well known that acute and chronic mental symptoms may be due to subdural hematoma.[30] In Krayenbühl's forty-eight patients with subdural hematoma, 75 per cent displayed changes in the psychic sphere.[28] Following surgical evacuation of the hematoma there is usually marked improvement in the personality disorder.

Even less familiar to psychiatrists are the mental changes following traumatic damage to the carotid arteries, as observed particularly in modern warfare.[19]

Figure 111 shows the brain of a patient with a traumatic psychosis, associated with mental deterioration. The patient was kicked on the head by a horse, when 9 years of age, and he was unconscious for one week. The boy was permanently paralyzed in his right arm and right leg, but adjusted well to his handicap. There were no mental symptoms until the age of 25 years, when he suddenly developed an acute psychosis. He remained in the institution for twelve years. During this time he had periods when he was well behaved. At times he had temper tantrums, during which he became entirely unmanageable.

The patient died quite suddenly at the age of 37 years during one of these episodes, which could well be described as "brain storms." A postmortem diagnosis of acute brain swelling was made and finding nothing else of importance, it was felt that this was the immediate cause of the patient's death. In retrospect, it was speculated whether the recurrent episodes of psychotic behavior may have had the same background. Was it possible that the huge brain injury produced in some obscure way from time to time various degrees of brain swelling?

Possibly, the chairman, Dr. Penfield, who has had much experience with cerebral scars causing traumatic epilepsy, could give us some explanation. This patient did not have epileptic fits. But could these periodic episodes of extreme psychotic behavior possibly be explained on the basis of so-called psychomotor epilepsy, and would surgical excision of the scar[20] have relieved the attacks of abnormal behavior? Delay[14] reported recently on what he called "psychic epilepsy" with temperamental disorders, which as the electroencephalogram showed is a manifestation of epilepsy, thus permitting the adoption of suitable treatment.

Psychoses due to Disturbance of Circulation

In this category are classified the large group of elderly individuals who show evidence of interference with the cerebral circulation as the result of arteriosclerosis.

Figure 112 shows one of the more dramatic effects of cerebral arteriosclerosis in a man 64 years of age. There is softening of the entire right occipital lobe as the result of arteriosclerotic occlusion of the supplying artery.

A brief summary of the case history reads as follows: One night the patient wandered away from home. The next morning he was found in a cattle yard, lying in mud. He was unable to recognize friends or persons whom he had previously known. For several years prior to this episode the patient had what appeared to be epileptiform attacks with a growing tendency to mental dullness and vague ideas of persecution.

Soon after admission the patient had an apoplectic seizure, followed by a hemiplegia of the entire left side, loss of speech, and extreme helplessness. In the months prior to his death there was complete disorientation and marked dementia.

Autopsy revealed softening of the entire right occipital lobe with the area of cystic degeneration extending into the right basal ganglia and internal capsule. In the vessels at the base of the brain were many yellow atherosclerotic plaques. Atherosclerosis was particularly far advanced in the aorta.

As to the etiologic basis of atherosclerosis there are possibly various factors, one of the important ones being a disturbance in fat metabolism, associated with a deposition of cholesterin esters in the intima. As life advances, some persons seem to have difficulty in absorbing fats which continue to circulate in the blood causing damage to the arteries. It is true that not all the facts are known. However, even at this stage it is well advised to recommend to the middle-aged person, particularly if there is a family history of vascular disease, and to the patient with cerebral and coronary arteriosclerosis, to limit the use of eggs, milk, butter, cream, and cheese, which are the main sources of cholesterol and which are apparently implicated in the genesis of this vascular disorder.

How far the deposition of lipoidal matter in the vessel wall may go is shown in Figure 113, which represents the basilar artery of a patient, 69 years of age, with an arteriosclerotic psychosis. There is practically no lumen left, and it is difficult to recognize this structure as a blood vessel.

The problem of the rapidly mounting admission rate of patients with cerebral arteriosclerosis will ultimately be solved by the physician with sound knowledge in the biologic sciences. The "modern psychiatrist" with his predominant training in dynamic psychology will contribute little if anything to the fundamental issue of this mental disorder.

The rate of admission for psychoses with cerebral arteriosclerosis has increased from 5 per cent in 1920 to 11 in 1930 and to 21 in 1940.[12] Fortunately, not all patients with cerebral arteriosclerosis show mental symptoms. In some instances there are well-developed anatomic changes in the brain, yet the patient reveals no intellectual deficit. But as the years go on, almost always some personality change takes place which, however, in most instances can be managed in the home.

With intensified research the chances of survival and possibly even recovery of patients with atherosclerosis will be greatly enhanced in the near future.[17]

Under the heading of psychoses due to disturbance of circulation may be mentioned psychosis with Buerger's disease (thromboangiitis obliterans). In recent years it has been realized that not only the peripheral blood vessels can become affected with this strange disorder, but also the cerebral and any other vessels in the body.[34]

The clinical history of one of my patients was as follows: Three years after amputation of the left foot because of gangrene due to Buerger's disease, mental symptoms appeared. The patient developed fantastic ideas about making money, threatened members of the family, and wandered away from home. Half a year later he had a slight stroke, which was a strong indication that the psychiatric abnormalities were on an organic rather than on a psychogenic basis.

The literature indicates that any neurologic symptom may be produced by thromboangiitis obliterans of the cerebral vessels, ranging from tics to epileptic convulsions, hemiplegia, aphasia, and hemianopsia. Mental symptoms occur less frequently. They range from transient confusion to full-fledged psychosis.

Psychoses due to Epilepsy

The psychoses due to epilepsy are classified under the organic mental disorders. The clinical abnormalities in the idiopathic group of epilepsy are produced by factors yet unknown. In the group of so-called symptomatic epilepsy, approximately seventy to eighty miscellaneous conditions which produce seizures have been mentioned by Walker.[51]

Psychoses due to Disturbances of Metabolism, Growth, Nutrition, or Endocrine Function

The senile psychoses constitute the largest and most important group under this heading. In about 38 per cent of the present admissions to mental hospitals the diagnoses are senile psychoses and psychoses with cerebral arteriosclerosis.[12] From present trends it can be expected that this percentage will increase considerably in the years to come.

In the senile psychoses, contrary to general belief, we are on a less firm basis as far as easily demonstrable changes are concerned. In textbooks one finds the statement that the brain of a senile demented patient is more or less atrophied. Atrophy of the cerebral convolutions, except in extreme cases, is most difficult to judge. Similarly, under the microscope there is at times little to be seen with the usual staining methods.

Drs. Wolf and Cowen in their paper on the histopathology of mental diseases will possibly discuss some of the more important changes in the senile psychoses, such as the senile plaques and the neuro-fibrillary changes of Alzheimer.

The more important psychoses due to glandular disorder are mental disturbances associated with thyroid dysfunction (instability of mood and personality or a confusional syndrome in the course of hyperthyroidism), and the psychoses ascribed to pituitary disease (Simmonds' disease).

In the psychoses with pellagra due to dietary deficiency, accompanied by tissue changes in the nervous system, the condition can be cured by the administration of the appropriate vitamin.

Psychoses due to New Growth

Mental disturbances are present at one time or another in the great majority of patients with intracranial tumor.[1, 24] The mental disorder may range in severity from symptoms suggesting a neurosis to delirium and dementia. Particular physical constellations must arise to produce mental symptoms. How these symptoms are produced is at present unknown.

Occasionally, mental abnormalities are among the earliest manifestations. With the increasing vigilance of neurosurgeons, few patients find their way into mental institutions. If recognized as patients with an intracranial neoplasm, they are directed to the neurosurgical division of general hospitals regardless of any psychiatric symptomatology.

The meningioma arising from the olfactory groove and involving the frontal lobe is probably the most important tumor in psychiatry—important because the tumor frequently produces only mental symptoms, goes unrecognized, and is capable of producing any mental reaction type.

Figure 114 shows such a meningioma, a firm tumor mass, taking up almost half of the frontal lobe area.

The male patient, 68 years of age, was admitted with the history of having shown in recent months loss of memory and having episodes during which he became obscene and violent. He had intercourse with stock and was reported as unsafe to be around women and children. The history in many respects was very much like the one of senile psychosis.

In the hospital he was considered a nice and good-natured patient. This jocularity or "Witzelsucht" was possibly the only symptom suggestive of a frontal lobe tumor. There were no obvious neurologic signs, such as headaches, vomiting, convulsions, choked discs, or optic atrophy.

The patient died of an arteriosclerotic gangrene of the left foot.

Without an autopsy the tumor would have never been diagnosed.

Psychoses due to Unknown or Hereditary Cause but Associated with Organic Change

Under this heading are registered the psychoses occasionally associated with multiple sclerosis, paralysis agitans, Huntington's chorea, and the like.

At this point ends my assignment. There is only one category of psychoses left to cover: disorders of psychogenic origin or without tangible cause or structural change.

Disorders of Psychogenic Origin or without Clearly Defined Tangible Cause or Structural Change

Here we find the large group of the manic-depressive psychoses, which have a significant constitutional component. And lastly, dementia praecox or schizophrenia, the great riddle of psychiatry, and today the most important of mental disorders.

But even here considerable discussion has been going on since the concept was introduced by Kraepelin whether the causative factors of dementia praecox are of essentially somatic or primarily of psychogenic origin. Personally, I feel that in some instances the etiologic factor is of a psychogenic nature, while in other cases the mental disorder is of a somatic origin.

Almost any organic condition of the brain may at times simulate a schizophrenic syndrome. Brain tumors, especially the slow-growing meningiomas involving the frontal lobes, and some of the demyelinating diseases may produce a schizophrenic picture. Every experienced psychiatrist remembers the patient in whom the clinical impression was that of a schizophrenic until spinal fluid examination proved the diagnosis of general paresis. Rheumatic brain disease is a possible factor in the causation of some cases of dementia praecox.[6, 7] There is the small group of dementia praecox patients (about 3 to 5 per cent) with an increase of spinal fluid protein, ranging between 46 and 166 mg. per 100 cc.[8] The pathogenetic significance of the increased spinal fluid protein in these patients has never been explained. In other words, there is not one single factor in this large group of psychotic patients but possibly a multitude of different etiologic causes. European psychiatry has become increasingly aware of this trend of thought, as shown by the symposium of the Clinical Subdivision of the Schizophrenia Syndromes, arranged at the International Congress of Psychiatry in Paris, France, in 1950.[47]

Bellak,[4] who recently has reviewed the entire problem of dementia praecox, also concludes that in principle at least it can be conceived that organic brain disease, or a disturbance in a carbonic anhydrase,[3] or genetically transmissible defects,[23] may be responsible etiologic factors in bringing about the thought disturbances of schizophrenia. Furthermore, it seems probably true that the resultant clinical schizophrenic syndrome is influenced to a large extent by the character structure of the individual, i.e., the prepsychotic personality influences the formation of the psychosis. This has been shown so clearly in general paresis, in which the mental manifestations vary from case to case although the tissue changes in the brain are the same in every paretic patient.

Conclusion

In conclusion one may say that an increasing amount of evidence has been accumulating over the years pointing to the fact that most psychoses are the result of a disturbed physiology of the brain. The psychopathologic phenomena are mainly the expression of the abnormal functioning of the nervous system. The major mental disorders, therefore, have to be explained on a biologic rather than on a psychologic, sociologic, or anthropologic basis.

REFERENCES

1. ALLIEZ, J.; PAILLAS, J. E.; and TAMALET, J.: Annales médico-psychologiques, 1949, 1, p. 67.
2. ALZHEIMER, A.: Histologische Studien zur Differenzialdiagnose der Progressiven Paralyse. Histologische und Histopathologische Arbeiten ueber die Grosshirnrinde mit besonderer Beruecksichtigung der Pathologischen Anatomie der Geisteskrankheiten, vol. 1, p. 18. Jena, Gustav Fischer, 1904.
3. ASHBY, W.: Journal of Biological Chemistry, 1944, 156, p. 331.
4. BELLAK, L.: Psychiatric Quarterly, 1949, 23, p. 738.
5. BENDA, C. E.: Archives of Neurology and Psychiatry, 1949, 61, p. 137. Neuropsychiatric Aspects of Mental Deficiency. North Carolina Medical Journal, 1947, 8, p. 72.
6. BRUETSCH, W. L.: American Journal of Psychiatry, 1938, 95, p. 335; Zeitschrift für die gesamte Neurologie und Psychiatrie, 1939, 166, p. 4; American Journal of Psychiatry, 1940, 97, p. 276; American Journal of Psychiatry, 1942, 98, p. 727; Archives of Internal Medicine, 1944, 73, p. 472; American Journal of Psychiatry, 1947, 104, p. 20; Journal of the American Medical Association, 1947, 134, p. 450; Late Nervous System Sequelae of Rheumatic Fever. IV. International Neurological Congress, Paris, France, September 5-10, 1949, Vol. 3, p. 297, Paris, Masson et Cie, 1951.
7. BRUETSCH, W. L., and BAHR, M. A.: Journal of the Indiana State Medical Association, 1939, 32, p. 445.
8. BRUETSCH, W. L; BAHR, M. A.; SKOBBA, J. S.; and DIETER, W. J.: Journal of Nervous and Mental Disease, 1942, 95, p. 669.
9. BYERS, R. K., and RIZZO, N. D.: New England Journal of Medicine, 1950, 242, p., 887.
10. CAMERON, N.: The Psychology of Behavior Disorders: A Biosocial Interpretation. Boston, Houghton Mifflin Co., 1947.
11. CASTEX, M. R.: La prensa médica argentina, 1943, 30, p. 1401.
12. Committee on Hospitals, Group for Advancement of Psychiatry: The Problem of the Aged Patient in the Public Psychiatric Hospital. Topeka, Kansas, Report No. 14, Aug., 1950.

13. Committee on Statistics of the American Psychiatric Association (in collaboration with the National Committee for Mental Hygiene): Statistical Manual for the Use of Hospitals for Mental Diseases, 10th ed., 1942.
14. DELAY, J.: *La presse médicale*, 1949, 57, p. 1037.
15. DENST, J., and NEUBUERGER, K. T.: *Archives of Pathology*, 1948, 46, p. 191.
16. DUBLIN, W. B.: *Diseases of the Nervous System*, 1941, 2, p. 390.
17. Editorial: *Journal of the American Medical Association*, 1949, 141, p. 392.
18. ESMARCH, F., and JESSEN, W.: *Allgemeine Zeitschrift für Psychiatrie*, 1857, 14, p. 20.
19. FAUST, C.: *Allgemeine Zeitschrift für Psychiatrie*, 1949, 124, p. 243.
20. FORSTER, F. M.: *Journal of the American Medical Association*, 1951, 145, p. 211.
21. VAN DER HORST, L.: *Digest of Neurology and Psychiatry*, Institute of Living, 1947, 15, p. 399; *Folia psychiatrica, neurologica et neurochirurgica, neerlandica*, Jaargang 1948; *Archiv für Psychiatrie und Nervenkrankheiten*, 1949, 181, p. 325.
22. HUEBSCHMANN, P.; POTHMANN, F. J.; and SCHAUKOWSKI, R.: *Zeitschrift für Tuberkulose*, 1950, 96, p. 14.
23. KALLMANN, F. J.: The Genetics of Schizophrenia. New York, J. J. Augustin, 1938.
24. KANZER, M.: *American Journal of Psychiatry*, 1941, 97, p. 812.
25. KARLAN, S. C., and HELLER, E.: *Psychiatric Quarterly*, 1948, 22, p. 487.
26. KERNOHAN, J. W.; WOLTMAN, H. W.; and BARNES, A. R.: *Archives of Neurology and Psychiatry*, 1939, 42, p. 789.
27. V. KRAFFT-EBING: *Archiv für Psychiatrie und Nervenkrankheiten*, 1877, 7, p. 182.
28. KRAYENBÜHL, H., and NOTO, G. G.: Das Intrakranielle Subdurale Hämatom, pp. 11, 35, 119. Bern, H. Huber, 1949.
29. LAMBL, D.: *Archiv für Psychiatrie und Nervenkrankheiten*, 1884, 15, p. 45.
30. LEVIN, S.: *American Journal of Psychiatry*, 1951, 107, p. 501.
31. LEVINE, M.: Trends in Psychoanalysis in America. (In, Évolution et Tendances Actuelles de la Psychanalyse.) *Proceedings of the International Psychiatric Congress*, vol. 5, p. 49. Paris, Hermann & Cie, 1950.
32. LEWIS, N. D. C.: Introduction to Psychiatry. The 1949 Year Book of Neurology, Psychiatry and Neurosurgery, p. 209. Chicago, The Year Book Publishers, Inc., 1950.
33. LINDSAY, D. S.: *American Journal of Psychiatry*, 1950, 107, p. 131.
34. LLAVERO, F.: Thromboendangiitis obliterans des Gehirns: Neurologisch-psychiatrische Syndrome. Basel, B. Schwabe & Co., 1948.
35. LUZZATTO, A.: *Rassegna di studi psichiatrici*, 1948, 37.
36. MANGUEL, M.: *El día médico*, 1948, 20, p. 1501.
37. NATHAN, P. W., and SMITH, M. C.: *Journal of Neurology, Neurosurgery and Psychiatry*, 1950, 13, p. 191.
38. NEUBUERGER, K. T.: *Diseases of the Nervous System*, 1947, 8, p. 259.
39. NISSL, F.: Zur Histopathologie der Paralytischen Rindenerkrankung, vol. 1 p. 315. Jena, Gustav Fischer, 1904.
40. NOGUCHI, H., and MOORE, J. W.: *Journal of Experimental Medicine*, 1913, 17, p. 232.
41. POROT, M., and DESTAING, F.: *Annales médico-psychologiques*, 1950, 108, p. 47.
42. ROME, H. P., and BRACELAND, F. J.: *Proceedings of the Staff Meetings of the Mayo Clinic*, 1950, 25, p. 495.
43. SILVERMAN, M.: *Journal of Mental Science*, 1949, 95, p. 706.

44. SIMARRO PUIG, J.: *Medicina clínica*, Barcelona, 1948, 10, p. 324.
45. SIMARRO PUIG, J., and ROCA DE VIÑALS, R.: *Revista clínica española*, 1950, 36, p. 254.
46. SPIELMEYER, W.: *Zeitschrift für die gesamte Neurologie und Psychiatrie*, 1925, 97, p. 287.
47. Symposium on Clinical Subdivision of the Schizophrenia Syndromes (Chairman: W. L. Bruetsch), held at International Congress of Psychiatry, Paris, France, 1950.
48. TERHUNE, W. B.: *American Journal of Psychiatry*, 1949, 106, p. 241.
49. The Total Treatment of the Rheumatic Child in the Sanatorium. *Bulletin of St. Francis Sanatorium for Cardiac Children*, Roslyn, L. I., 1950, 7, p. 1.
50. VIRCHOW, R.: *Berliner Klinische Wochenschrift*, 1898, 35, p. 691.
51. WALKER, A. E.: *Archives of Internal Medicine*, 1936, 58, p. 250.
52. WHITMAN, J. F., and KARNOSH, L. J.: *Cleveland Clinic Quarterly*, 1949, 16, p. 136.
53. YAPALATER, A. R., and ROCKWELL, F. V.: *Journal of the American Medical Association*, 1950, 143, p. 428.

Some Remarks Concerning the Differentiation of Organic from So-called "Functional" Psychoses

THEODORE LIDZ, M.D.

The discussion which I had prepared was based on the assumption that Dr. Bruetsch would speak concerning the cerebral pathologic changes in rheumatic fever. However, it now seems more important to discuss certain basic concepts lest misconceptions arise from certain implications of the paper. This seems particularly necessary as many of the audience are not psychiatrists.

As a psychiatrist, perhaps more than is the case with some of you, I sometimes receive telephone calls that are not easily understood. There are two general causes for the difficulties in comprehension. Something may be faulty with the mechanism of the telephone system; or the words being uttered by the person speaking into the telephone do not make very much sense. The point I wish to make is this: there is general agreement that the brain is an organ of adaptation and that if this organ is not virtually intact, functioning of the individual both symbolically and behaviorally will suffer disorganization. A large number of the psychoses are due to damage of the brain which decreases the limits of adaptability of the individual, primarily because the areas and pathways essential for symbolic functioning are affected by the lesions. The causes of such damage to the brain are manifold, and therefore the organic psychoses take up a large part of the diagnostic index.

The fact that brain damage is one of the etiologic factors in many psychoses does not permit us to assume that it is the cause of all psychoses. Behavior and mentation can be distorted for reasons other than the destruction or dysfunction of the pathways necessary for such aptitudes.

Dr. Bruetsch's paper tends to take us back to the period when, after a definite etiologic factor for general paresis was found, and because it was difficult at times to differentiate general paresis from schizophrenia clinically, a search for a similar organic factor in schizophrenia was pursued for many years. What was not mentioned in the paper was that this entire list of organic psychoses can be distinguished from the so-called "functional psychoses" by one very obvious fact: in virtually all of these organic psychoses one can find a deficit state, that is, a deficit in the capacity for intellectual functioning, whereas, thus far, it has not been possible to find or, at least, to validate the finding of such defects in the capacity for mentation in the schizophrenic and in the manic-depressive psychotic.

If a general paretic is in a state in which psychologic tests can be utilized, one invariably finds that there is a defect in intellect. If the patient had been tested prior to suffering from general paresis, we find that after the illness has become manifest his intelligence decreases perceptibly. For example, there might be a fall from the mental age of 16 years down to 8 or 9 years, causing a marked diminution in the patient's adaptability. Often, if the patient is treated early enough, a good deal of this deficiency disappears. It has been possible to see on a few occasions that it is when the intelligence level, speaking in very general terms, falls below a certain level that the patient becomes manifestly psychotic. His capacity for symbolic activity is diminished, and his behavior deteriorates. Dr. Bernard Lewis at the Johns Hopkins Hospital has recently concluded a study which showed that all patients suffering from general paresis showed such deficit states, in contrast, even, to some other forms of neurosyphilis. During the World War II we studied atabrine psychoses, and it is important to note that many soldiers suffering from atabrine psychoses were erroneously diagnosed as schizophrenic. However, when such patients could be tested, that is, when they were not wildly excited or totally withdrawn, it was invariably found that there was a severe deficit in their intellectual functioning and that after recovery the intelligence returned to within normal limits. In the senium there is likewise a decline in intellectual ability with a concurrent diminution in the capacity to adapt to new situations. The individual's integration and behavior often rest to a large extent upon capacities learned during earlier age periods. With aging, when the intellectual disorganization becomes very serious, psychoses are likely to ensue.

Dr. Bruetsch's work on rheumatic fever is potentially extremely significant. It is not always simple to differentiate between an organic psychosis and a functional psychosis. Work such as Dr. Bruetsch has carried out which points up the brain damage in rheumatic fever is essential because it must be made clear as to which psychoses may, at least in part, depend on organic defects of the brain and those which do not. As far as I know, Dr. Bruetsch did not demonstrate that these lesions in the brain were sufficient to cause defects in the intellectual capacities of the patients, but it is quite possible that they do. Studies of this type which have shown that brain lesions in brucellosis cause intellectual deficit states help clarify some of the puzzling aspects of the apathy and peculiar mental symptoms in brucellosis. In the psychoses which occur in disseminated lupus erythematosis and related conditions, it has also been possible to demonstrate that at the time of manifestation of the psychosis there is definite intellectual impairment. It may be, as many believe, that eventually similar deficits will be demonstrated in schizophrenic patients. If such deficits exist, they are certainly of a totally different type than is the clear-cut intellectual deterioration which we have been discussing, for I believe enough studies have been carried out to show that schizophrenic patients are not deteriorated in this sense, and, indeed, are often able to make symbolic abstractions of a very high degree even though they are sometimes very fanciful ones. From certain unpublished studies I have gained an impression that rheumatic fever occurs in the lives of schizophrenic patients with a frequency beyond that anticipated in the general population. However, I had considered it likely that the treatment of rheumatic fever and of rheumatic heart disease played an important role in differentiating the patient, tending to isolate him from social participation. It may well be, as Dr. Bruetsch indicates, that the impairment in cortical functioning is a significant factor. At any rate, this type of differentiation of organic states from other syndromes is necessary if we are going to be able to group our psychiatric syndromes properly and go further in our understanding of etiologic basis.

REFERENCES

1. APTER, N. S.; HALSTEAD, W. C.; EISELE, C. W.; and McCULLOUGH, N. B.: *American Journal of Psychiatry*, 1948, 115, p. 361.
2. BRUETSCH, W. L.: *Archives of Internal Medicine*, June, 1944, 73, p. 472.
3. BRUETSCH, W. L.: *Journal of the American Medical Association*, 1947, 134, p. 450.
4. LEWIS, B. I.: *American Journal of Syphilis, Gonorrhea and Venereal Diseases*, 1950, 34, p. 534.
5. LIDZ, T.; GAY, J. R.; and TIETZE, C.: *Archives of Neurology and Psychiatry*, 1942, 48, p. 568.
6. LIDZ, T., and KAHN, R. L.: *Archives of Neurology and Psychiatry*, 1946, 56, p. 284.

Discussion

DR. WILLIAM MALAMUD: Dr. Bruetsch and I have worked with essentially the same material, most of our experience having been with State Hospital patients, and both of us started our neuropathologic studies in the same laboratory. In spite of this, we seem to have reached entirely different conclusions. I should therefore like to ask Dr. Bruetsch the following question: Has he observed in his neuropathologic investigations of senile psychoses the same findings we obtained at Worcester—that there is no one-to-one relationship between the histopathology of senile psychoses and their behavior disturbance? In other words, are there not found occasionally more severe neuropathologic disturbances in brains of seniles who are not psychotic than are found in those who are psychotic, and, vice versa, are there not found a good many psychotic seniles with very mild histologic changes in the brain?

I am asking these questions in relationship to two points that Dr. Bruetsch made. The first one was to the effect that the incidence of general paresis has dropped significantly during the last twenty or thirty years, and the slack has been taken up primarily by two types of conditions: (1) senile psychoses, in which there is a lack of parallelism between histologic and behavior changes, and (2) manic-depressive and schizophrenic psychoses, which Dr. Kallmann just told us are the results of constitutional vulnerability (not disease) inter-acting with environmental stresses. The other point that Dr. Bruetsch made, if I quote him correctly, referred to the "fruitlessness of psychologic, philosophic," (and, I might add, sociologic) "investigations."

From my own observations, I came to the conclusion that the sooner we dis-card the unwarranted dichotomy of mind and body and study human beings as they are, the nearer we will come to the understanding of mental health and mental disease.

DR. STANLEY COBB: I do not believe that we can let this discussion pass without some remarks on semantics. We have heard here in the last half hour the use of many words such as "functional," "organic," "psychosis"—all of them unde-fined. In this audience, I think many have a fairly clear meaning for each of these, but in the psychiatric meetings which I have often attended, much misunderstand-ing arose because we were talking without defining our terms.

I agree with Dr. Malamud that we should stop thinking "either or"—that a disorder either has to be "organic" or "psychogenic." I would like therefore to raise the spirit of Dr. Adolf Meyer who, fifty years ago, began fighting for the idea of multiple etiologic bases in mental disease. He insisted on thinking of the individual and of all of the pertinent facts related to that person—his genes, the lesions he may have in his cerebrum, his chemistry, his hormones, his social situa-tion, his economic situation, and his psychologic experiences. He then would make a summation concerning this individual, showing a concatenation of events at a certain point in time. It is only if we begin thinking in that way concerning the individual's mental breakdown, that we begin to have something like a whole picture. The point is well illustrated by the geneticists—that manic-depressives and schizophrenics have abnormalities of the genes. Of course there are also psychogenic precipitants and hormonal and neuronal disorders that may or may not be genetic.

I wish to emphasize, in short, that there is always a multiplicity of factors in the etiologic background of mental disease.

DR. SOLOMON KATZENELBOGEN: In order to focus the attention on what Dr. Lidz, Dr. Malamud, and Dr. Cobb have said, I would like to ask Dr. Bruetsch the fol-lowing questions:

Does he admit that there are numerous patients with more or less marked cerebral arteriosclerosis who do not show any significant personality disorders?

Does he admit that even in general paresis, that during the treatment there may be and usually there is a tremendous gap between the improvement in the behavior of the patient, sometimes to the extent that it may be, for all intents and purposes, normal; while the serologic study shows persistence of organic changes in the cerebrospinal nervous system?

DR. WALTER L. BRUETSCH: I am very appreciative of the extensive discussion of my presentation, but it will be almost impossible to answer all the questions.

Dr. Malamud has brought up the important problem of the correlation between anatomic changes and clinical manifestations. I admit that we do know of arteriosclerotic patients who had areas of softening in the brain but who did not show what is called an "arteriosclerotic psychosis." However, these persons will develop as the years go by some mild personality changes which are at times only obvious to those who have known the individual in former years.

I have been very cognizant of Dr. Meyer's teachings, not to think exclusively of the patient's illness but of the "person as a whole." But I feel that the psychiatric social worker who had his start through the Meyer school of psychiatry is apt to read into every patient's life a chain of maladaptations. I once made the rule to check on the data gathered by the social worker for my psychiatric cases, because often I could not verify the personality difficulties which had gone into the histories.

What I have just mentioned in reference to maladaptations concerns particularly the patient with cerebral arteriosclerosis. It has been said that the psychologically well-adjusted person can tolerate a large amount of brain damage without developing a psychosis. This is an unproved statement. Not infrequently one sees, after a cerebral insult, severe and prolonged psychotic reactions in previously well-adjusted individuals. On the other hand, persons with odd personalities may show only slightly more abnormal behavior after extensive brain damage. Unknown pathophysiologic conditions are obviously responsible for the appearance and also for the spontaneous disappearance of mental symptoms in the organic psychoses.

In answer to Dr. Cobb, who insists that we should forget about "either or," I may say that for some time I felt the same way. I changed my mind, and now I am quite emphatic that we should say "either or." This is particularly important in teaching because otherwise the student will never learn how to make accurate etiologic diagnoses which are so important for an intelligent treatment program. It is highly important, in my opinion, that a student learn to differentiate, for instance, between a depression as the initial symptom in a brain tumor or in general paresis and a depression of psychogenic basis. Otherwise he will be a confused person the remainder of his professional life.

Finally, I come to Dr. Katzenelbogen's discussion. He noticed that in some patients with general paresis the spinal fluid following treatment has not changed, yet the patient becomes normal clinically. A similar situation exists in so-called asymptomatic neurosyphilis, where there may be a fully paretic spinal fluid formula, with the individual being free of clinical symptoms. These are challenging questions which await a solution.

CHAIRMAN WILDER PENFIELD: Professor Bruetsch flatters me with his question in regard to his patient who had the early brain injury. If this patient had no seizures, as he pointed out, I think we have to assume that the scar probably had nothing to do with the edema that was found in the brain. We would have to assume that the brain edema was produced by some agonal change before he died, or possibly it was associated with the psychosis as its cause. Some of us believe that acute swelling of oligodendroglia is to be found in such cases. Scars do not produce edema.

CHAPTER 21

Anoxia: Its Effect on Structure of the Brain

WILLIAM F. WINDLE, PH.D.

I PROPOSE to review experiments that have been performed in our laboratories in cooperation with a number of my colleagues and students. (I wish to mention especially Drs. R. F. Becker, A. V. Jensen, R. A. Groat, A. E. Sola, H. Koenig, R. Koenig, Chan-nao Liu, H. H. Wilcox, and W. W. Chambers.) These studies have demonstrated that oxygen deficiency can induce some marked structural alterations in the brain that are secondary, in large measure, to certain changes in the vasculature. Correlations with impairment of behavior have been drawn, but there will not be time to describe this aspect of our work in detail. Significant differences in survival of adult and newborn animals after anoxia have been observed, and it is hoped that further study of these differences will point the way to preventive measures. I shall consider first the effects of anoxia and asphyxia on the brains of adult guinea pigs and then proceed to a consideration of asphyxia at birth.

Effects of Anoxia and Asphyxia on Adult Animals

It is well known that structural alterations in the adult brain follow anoxia induced by breathing atmospheres lacking oxygen, by asphyxial degrees of nitrous oxide anesthesia, or by arrest of the cerebral circulation. It is generally held that complete anoxia of nervous tissues need be of brief duration only to bring about profound and permanent changes in neurons. Some investigators have reported that lesser degrees of oxygen deficiency of repeated occurrence can likewise result in permanent brain damage in adult animals. In reviewing the reports of other investigators who have described effects on brain structure of intermittent exposure to reduced oxygen tensions, one is struck by the widespread failure to evaluate adequately postmortem and fixation artefacts and the possibility of confusion of these

The studies reviewed in this article were aided at various times by grants from The Women's Faculty Club and The Clara A. Abbott Funds of Northwestern University Medical School, The National Foundation for Infantile Paralysis, Inc., and Baxter Laboratories, Inc.

artefacts with true changes wrought by the anoxia. Indeed, one investigator recommended that a period of two hours be allowed to elapse after death before fixation of brain tissues, because, he claimed, immediate fixation can bring about histologic artefacts.

We have studied postmortem alterations in neurons of the guinea pig brain.[5] Without burdening you with details, I can say that vascular perfusion was carried out at varying times post mortem after preliminary washing out of the blood. Perceptible changes in neurons of the brain were observed as early as one-half hour post mortem. These consisted of cell swelling, fragmentation of Nissl bodies, and slight loss of basophilia of the cytoplasm. The changes progressed so that by three hours post mortem they were marked in some groups of nerve cells. By ten hours post mortem many neurons were extensively vacuolated. The changes seen at three hours or more after death resemble changes that have been ascribed by some writers to anoxia.

Other experiments were performed to compare the histologic picture after fixation of brain tissue by immersion in formalin with fixation by vascular perfusion with formalin.[2] In the specimens that were immersed in formalin within twelve minutes after death many hyperchromatic nerve cells and occasionally vacuolated cells were observed. The material taken from guinea pigs perfused through the vascular system at a pressure equivalent to blood pressure with an isotonic solution of formaldehyde containing gum acacia presented no such picture of hyperchromatic and vacuolated cells. It is clear that fixation of brain tissue by immersion in formalin, even when performed immediately after death, provides inadequate material for differentiating fixation artefacts in neurons from the effects of anoxia. The perfusion-fixation technic[4] has become a standard in our laboratory in preparation of tissue for controlled staining of nerve cells by the buffered thionin and other methods.[1]

In view of the fact that some investigators have reported pathologic change in the central nervous system in animals subjected to an altitude pressure equivalent to 18,000 feet, our first experiments in adult guinea pigs were carried out at a simulated altitude of 23,000 feet.[12] Fifty-four guinea pigs, weighing 400 to 700 Gm. were used. Thirteen of the group were kept at atmospheric pressure and served as controls. The rest of the animals were placed daily (six days a week) in wire cages in a decompression chamber of 1650 liters capacity and gradually brought to a pressure of 307 mm. Hg (23,000 feet). There they were kept for six hours each day, after which they were gradually returned to atmospheric pressure. After fifty, one hundred, two hundred, three hundred, and five hundred hours, groups of experimental and control animals were killed by the perfusion-fixation technic. Serial sections of the brains were prepared and alternate tenth sections were stained by the buffered-thionin and the Weil methods.

The animals gained weight throughout the period of the experiment and developed no symptoms of brain damage. Careful comparison of the histologic sections of brains of experimental animals and their controls revealed no hemorrhages, no vascular changes, no glia proliferation, no cytologic alterations in nerve cells. There appeared to be no reduction in the number of nerve cells and no changes in the myelin sheaths of nerve fibers. Therefore, we concluded that the degree of anoxia prevailing in the experiments at a simulated altitude of 23,000 feet had no deleterious effect on the brain.

Another group of animals was subjected to a similar routine of reduced barometric pressure and an effort was made to determine whether there was any impairment of memory of a learned task.[6] Their retest performances on a simple alternation type of maze were compared with those of control animals after periods of one hundred, two hundred and fifty, three hundred, and four hundred hours in the decompression chamber. No statistically reliable difference between the performance scores of control and experimental groups was observed. Even after four hundred hours, the retest established such an equality of performance between the groups as to permit the conclusion that the conditions had no effect.

Because the conditions at a simulated altitude of 23,000 feet provided negative results, we performed another group of experiments.[3] Thirty-one animals were used. The pressure in the chamber was reduced to 225 mm. Hg, simulating an altitude of approximately 30,000 feet. Before the series of daily decompressions was begun, twenty-four of these animals were trained to run the simple alternation maze to the point of perfection. Time does not permit a consideration of the details of this psychologic study, but I can say that it was carefully controlled to eliminate factors of personal bias. Histopathologic studies were carried out, as in the preceding group of experiments, using the perfusion-fixation technic and the buffered-thionin and Weil methods for staining.

Structural changes were found in most of the experimental animals' brains. The most striking changes were focal areas of degeneration. These appeared in all the specimens subjected to two hundred hours or more in the altitude chamber, but were found in only three of the seven animals receiving one hundred to one hundred and fifty hours of decompression. With one exception these focal areas of degeneration were confined to the cerebellum, and they rarely extended beyond the confines of the vermis. In the one exception they were found in the cerebrum as well. Appearance varied with the age of the lesions. In early lesions, granule and Purkinje cells of the cerebellum were visible, though in such advanced stages of degeneration that they often appeared as mere shadow forms. In the older lesions the cerebellar neurons disappeared entirely and extensive proliferations of small blood vessels and glia occurred. In all instances the borders between normal brain tissue and degeneration were sharply defined.

Hemorrhages did not occur in cerebellar foci of degeneration. Only in the one instance in which foci appeared in the cerebral cortex, hippocampus, and diencephalon were perivascular hemorrhages observed. It looked as though the foci of degeneration were related to impaired blood flow but not to hemorrhage, in most instances.

Never did degenerative changes involve the whole central nervous system. There was no reduction in total number of nerve cells in the principal groups or layers, and no thinning of the cerebral cortex could be seen. The hippocampus, usually considered to be a region readily affected by lack of oxygen, appeared to be entirely normal except in the one specimen in which hemorrhages occurred. Although generalized changes were not found, careful comparisons of sections from experimental and control animals' brains did reveal slight local disturbances of the normal structural picture throughout various parts of the brain, notably in the cerebral cortex, diencephalon, midbrain, and the medulla oblongata. Without the controls these changes might easily have been overlooked as nothing more than fixation artefacts. They consisted of focal impairment of staining and shrinking of the smaller neurons around blood vessels, especially in the cerebral cortex.

A very striking condition was observed in animals that had been subjected intermittently to reduced barometric pressure for two hundred and fifty hours. Indeed, all the animals that had been in the chamber two hundred hours or more exhibited this condition to some extent. Clumps of leukocytes resembling emboli were encountered in blood vessels not only within the brain substance but also in the meninges. The apparently plugged vessels of the brain were not surrounded by areas of degeneration. Therefore, there could not have been complete occlusion of these vessels during life. It should be noted that the vascular system of the living animal was perfused and as much blood as possible washed out with a saline solution before the fixing fluid was run in. Had leukocytes been sticking to the vessel walls, it is possible that the preliminary perfusion with saline solution would not have washed them free, but the fixing solution could have dislodged them and caused them to form masses resembling emboli.

The main points learned in our experiments on adult animals subjected to intermittent bouts of reduced oxygen tension in the decompression chamber are that nerve cells were unaffected by the anoxia, per se, but groups of them ultimately succumbed, probably due to impairment of their metabolism secondarily induced through changes in the blood and vasculature. When this happened, pathologic change could be demonstrated in the brain and the function of the nervous system was impaired.

In respect to the learning tests of animals in these experiments, no impairment was observed after one hundred hours of intermittent exposure to lowered barometric pressures. Significant impairment of memory occurred only in the animals from the one hundred and fifty-, two hundred-, and two hundred and fifty-hour groups. All experimental animals in the two hundred-hour group required retraining on the retest in the maze, whereas their controls did not. None of the two hundred and fifty-hour group was able to relearn the problem. The impairment occurred without specific correlation with any of the focal pathologic changes in the brain.

The guinea pig may be an animal that is somewhat more resistant to conditions of high altitude than other species. The adult can tolerate simulated altitudes of 40,000 feet and even 45,000 feet for short periods of time without deleterious effects. It readily becomes acclimatized to simulated altitudes of 23,000 feet, with pronounced increase in number of red blood corpuscles and hemoglobin values. It can live in an atmosphere consisting of 3 percent oxygen and 97 percent nitrogen for several hours. In 2 percent oxygen and 98 percent nitrogen its survival time is reduced to approximately eighteen minutes, on the average, but when placed in a chamber containing an atmosphere of pure nitrogen it can survive for only two or three minutes.

Effects of Asphyxia at Birth

The fetus and the newborn are much more resistant to deficiency in their oxygen supply than is the adult. The survival time is greater, and this provides an important factor of safety against the ordeal of birth. Newborn guinea pigs can be resuscitated after periods of asphyxia lasting as long as twenty-three minutes. Nevertheless, the fetus in utero does not normally live in an anoxic state.[8, 9] It has been demonstrated quite conclusively that conditions of respiration before birth are fully adequate; for example, oxygen saturation of the blood reaching the sheep fetus may be as high as 90 to 95 per cent until the latter part of gestation.

Because of factors peculiar to the birth of man and not so often encountered in other species, human fetuses are occasionally subjected to very severe asphyxial conditions at the time of labor. It should be of great interest to know to what extent the newborn's nervous system may be damaged by asphyxia.

One need not look far in the medical literature to be aware that asphyxia in late fetal life and at birth is the cause of death in an alarming number of instances. The neonatal death rate and the stillbirth rate have not been reduced during the last quarter of the century in proportion to reduction in total infant mortality. Conservative estimations have placed asphyxia as the primary cause of death in about one-fourth of these fetuses and infants.

Not only do many infants die each year at birth because of asphyxiation, but many others are deeply asphyxiated and heavily narcotized at birth, and yet survive. From clinical observations it would seem that some of the latter suffer permanent damage to the central nervous system as the result of asphyxia. There is little doubt that many of the so-called palsied children or congenital spastics are in this category.

A third and perhaps even more exciting problem remains to be considered. One may raise the question, do infants suffering asphyxia at birth, but escaping symptoms of permanent brain damage, reach maturity with neural mechanisms fully equal to those of individuals born normally? There is a real possibility that some of them become children and adults of poor learning ability—dullards, if not actually mental defectives.

In order to study the possible effects of asphyxia at birth upon the central nervous system we performed a large number of experiments, in nearly one hundred of which detailed histologic studies were carried out under controlled conditions.[10] Asphyxiation was produced in the following manner: The abdomen of the pregnant guinea pig at full term was opened under local anesthesia. One fetus was delivered to serve as the control for its asphyxiated littermate. The maternal circulation to the placenta was then occluded. After periods of time varying from four and one-half to twenty-three minutes, an asphyxiated fetus was removed and resuscitated. Resuscitation was accomplished by inserting into the trachea a hypodermic needle to which was attached a rubber tube and bag containing oxygen. By rhythmically inflating and deflating the lung of the asphyxiated newborn guinea pig with this gas, resuscitation was accomplished in a few minutes to one and one-half hours, depending on the duration of the asphyxia, to a great extent.

Without exception, the resuscitated animals manifested symptoms of a neurologic nature. They were comatose for varying periods of time. Thereafter, decerebrate states, tremors, convulsive movements, spasticity, paralysis, ataxia, impairment of sensory functions, or other defects appeared. Motor defects, as a rule, failed to persist in marked form throughout life, and were often only transient. Sensory defects were more permanent. The animals that exhibited marked motor impairments were more difficult to rear (they presented serious feeding problems) than those with marked sensory disturbances; consequently fewer of them survived.

A closely graded series of brain specimens from an hour after asphyxiation to several months afterwards was studied histologically.[11] Evidence of structural change was observed in the nervous system of nearly every animal that had been asphyxiated for eight minutes or more, and some of those asphyxiated for less than eight minutes showed similar changes. The histopathology that was encountered may be summarized as follows: Multiple capillary hemorrhages and occasionally larger hemorrhages were found in nearly all animals whose brains were examined an hour to five days after resuscitation. There was great variation in the amount of hemorrhage and its distribution. Cytologic changes were observed in nerve cells between one hour and a half and twenty-one days after resuscitation. The usual sequence of events appeared to be, first, clouding of Nissl granule patterns, then loss of stainability of the nerve cells with thionin at about five hours. A typical chromatolysis occurred in one or two days. Complete destruction of neurons was seen as early as four days. A few specimens showed generalized changes throughout the brain, but in most of them the marked effects were localized and focal areas of degeneration were encountered. The cerebellum and corpus striatum were not affected to any extent. However, the thalamus, the cerebral cortex, substantia nigra, and tegmentum of the brain stem and spinal cord were often severely damaged. The lateral nuclei of the thalamus and the medial and lateral geniculate bodies were more frequently involved in destructive processes after asphyxiation than were any other regions in the nervous system. The brains of the animals that exhibited the most marked and persistent neurologic symptoms also showed the most severe damage.

Observations on behavioral changes induced by asphyxiation were correlated with structural changes in the brain.[7] Complete histologic studies were made in forty-eight animals and their littermate controls, all of which had been subjected to tests in the alternation maze for their ability to learn a problem at approximately eight weeks of age. Of these forty-eight animals, only thirty-one showed structural brain damage. The remaining seventeen therefore can be discarded from consideration of their ability to learn the problem. Twenty-seven of the thirty-one animals showing brain damage were inferior to their littermate controls in tests on the maze. Some of them could not learn the simple problem at all; others quickly forgot the solution once they had learned it. In no instance was an experimental animal superior to its normal control, for which the problem presented no difficulty. These experiments gave us proof that neonatal asphyxia had impaired learning ability.

All of our experimental animals that survived long enough to be tested for their ability to learn the simple problem had the outward appearance of normal guinea pigs. It was exceedingly difficult to observe any overt differences between their behavior and the behavior of the littermate controls at the time of testing. Nevertheless, significant pathologic changes were present in the brains of the experimental animals that failed the maze test, frequently involving the lateral part of the thalamus and geniculate bodies. It appears that interference with these sensory mechanisms of the brain was responsible for the impaired learning ability.

Thus, it may be concluded that we produced animals, surviving asphyxiation and showing no residual motor deficits, in fact, animals of perfectly normal outward appearance, that were dullards, nevertheless. We are prone to blame inferior human mentalities on poor environment and especially on defects of the germ plasm. It is probable that asphyxiation at birth is partly responsible in man as it was in our guinea pigs.

REFERENCES

1. DAVENPORT, H. A.; WINDLE, W. F.; and RHINES, RUTH; Part I, Section C, in Staining Procedures, edited by Conn and Darrow, Geneva, N. Y., Biotech Publication, 1943.
2. GROAT, R. A.: A Comparison of Immersion Fixation and Perfusion Fixation of Brain Tissues. Unpublished, 1945.

3. JENSEN, A. V.; BECKER, R. F.; and WINDLE, W. F.: *Archives of Neurology and Psychiatry*, 1948, 60, p. 221.
4. KOENIG, H.; GROAT, R. A.; and WINDLE, W. F.: *Stain Technology*, 1945, 20, p. 13.
5. KOENIG, R.: An Experimental Study of Post-Mortem Alterations in Neurons of the Central Nervous System. Thesis, University of Pennsylvania, 1949.
6. SOLA, A. E.; BECKER, R. F.; and WINDLE, W. F.: *Journal of Comparative Physiology and Psychology*, 1948, 41, p. 196.
7. WINDLE, W. F.: *Psychosomatic Medicine*, 1944, 5, p. 155.
8. WINDLE, W. F.: The Harvey Lectures, 1945, Series XL, p. 236.
9. WINDLE, W. F.: Asphyxia Neonatorum. Springfield, Ill., Charles C Thomas, 1950.
10. WINDLE, W. F., and BECKER, R. F.: *American Journal of Obstetrics and Gynecology*, 1943, 45, p. 183.
11. WINDLE, W. F.; BECKER, R. F.; and WEIL, A.: *Journal of Neuropathology and Experimental Neurology*, 1944, 3, p. 224.
12. WINDLE, W. F., and JENSEN, A. V.: *Journal of Aviation Medicine*, 1946, 17, p. 70.

CHAPTER 22

Anoxia: Its Effects on the Physiology and Biochemistry of the Brain and on Behavior

ROSS A. McFARLAND, PH.D.

THE PURPOSE of this paper is to discuss the way in which anoxia may give rise to certain physiochemical changes in the brain resulting in very direct and striking changes in behavior.[27] The approach is a biologic one, demonstrating that sensory and mental deterioration and even loss of insight may result from altered metabolism in the nervous tissue. This concept is in sharp contrast to the view that repression or regression influenced by emotional mechanisms form the basis of certain mental diseases. The experimental results will demonstrate how the so-called "psychic" functions appear to be related to the velocities of certain chemical processes in the tissue, the psychologic and physiologic events forming different aspects of the same thing.

One of the most sensitive and direct ways of demonstrating that psychologic phemomena are directly dependent upon the underlying physiologic processes is to deprive the organism of oxygen.[24] It is well known that the nervous tissue is extremely sensitive to a diminished amount of oxygen and to variations in carbon dioxide. There is no storage in the organism, unless the splenic reservoir be considered such, so that without oxygen a person will collapse within a few minutes.[3] Cortical tissue does not recover if it is deprived of oxygen for more than five to ten minutes, while in certain other parts of the brain and spinal cord irreversible changes do not begin to occur for periods of as long as twenty to thirty minutes.

In considering Claud Bernard's well-known statement that "the fixity of the internal environment is the condition of the free life," Barcroft asked the pertinent question for the psychologist or the psychiatrist: "Freedom for what?"[2] In his opinion, it is chiefly freedom for the activity of the higher levels of the nervous system, especially the cerebral cortex. Barcroft said that the organism in gaining constancy of temperature, hydrogen-ion concentration, sugar, salt, water, oxygen, and certain other organic constants ultimately reached a stage of development so man's higher faculties could develop. The constancy of the internal environment is most exact in man and also in man the free life reaches its highest development. The automatic regulation of these internal constants, such as oxygen, enabled man's intelligence to be set free for other services, such as thinking, imagination, insight, and various manual skills. In support of this theory, a marked variation in certain of these organic constants produces striking effects on the central nervous system. This is particularly true of oxygen, since the cortex of the brain is more sensitive to anoxia than are most other organs. Systematic investigations dealing with the effects of oxygen deprivation on sensory and mental functions reveal significant alterations both of a qualitative and quantitative nature.[26] It seems reasonable to assume that some impairment in the oxygen transport or utilization in the tissues may be the basic cause of certain types of mental illness where actual loss of insight occurs.

In the first part of the discussion several studies will be reviewed to show how it is possible to relate in a quantitative way alterations in a sensory function, such as light sensitivity, to the amount of oxygen in the arterial blood. Consideration will then be given to the effects of anoxia on complex mental functions, such as memory, judgment, and insight. Experiments at high altitude in the Andes as well as in low-oxygen chambers at sea level will be reviewed. The final section of the paper will deal with the role of anoxia in certain of the mental disorders and with various suggestions for future research.

Effect of Anoxia on Certain Sensory Functions

The purpose of these experiments was to develop a simple, objective method for appraising the effects of various substances interfering with the oxidative mechanisms of the central nervous system. The alteration of certain visual functions by anoxia has yielded results of considerable theoretic interest and practical significance.[31] The study of vision under such conditions is important because certain visual functions are believed to reflect changes in the central nervous system, of which the retina of the eye is essentially a part. The accuracy of such studies is often limited by the nature of the test employed or the physiologic function which has been used as an index of the effects of an active physiologic stress. To obtain satisfactory results a test should possess certain features, including: (1) a high degree of sensitivity, so that small changes can be readily measured; (2) precision of the physical measurements involved in the test; (3) independence of the results from the degree of conscious or unconscious effort which may be exerted; and (4) stability of the function during control experiments when the physiologic stresses are not applied.

Tests of certain visual functions, particularly light sensitivity, possess all of these desirable qualities. They seem to provide a useful tool with which to measure the effects of anoxia and related stimuli. The changes manifested by the visual mechanism when its oxidative processes are disturbed are of considerable magnitude. The physical measurements of light intensity involved in these tests can be made very accurately. Moreover, the control of such experiments is simplified by the fact that the subject is not aware of changes in his own visual sensitivity or changes in the physical intensity of the stimulus, since at the threshold level the stimulus always has the same appearance. The subject, therefore, cannot mask the impairment by exerting additional effort.

The phenomena under study can be readily demonstrated by observing the changes in the intensity of a light during sudden or acute anoxia or by inhaling oxygen at high altitude. The particular visual function selected for the series of studies reported here was differential brightness sensitivity, i.e., the ability to distinguish differences in brightness or light intensity. By means of a visual discriminometer, the subject's eye was exposed to a dim uniformly illuminated circular field about one-fiftieth of a footcandle, simulating dim moonlight.[5] A small red point of light near the center of the field served as a fixation target. Just below this, on the foveal portion of the retina, a 1 degree by 1 degree square test object was presented in flashes of 0.1 second, and measurements were made of the least intensity that could be distinguished against the illuminated background. A dim field was used because the test is most sensitive to anoxia at low illuminations. The stimulus was applied on the fovea because the adaptive mechanisms are constantly changing if rod vision, i.e., dark adaptation, is primarily involved.

Changes in differential brightness sensitivity imply similar changes in certain other visual functions. Under most circumstances, objects can be seen against a given background only when there is a visible difference between the brightness of the object and that of the background. Thus, visual acuity, or the ability to distinguish the shape and details of an object, also depends on differential brightness sensitivity. If a given physiologic stress affects differential sensitivity, it may be expected to have a corresponding effect on visual acuity under low illumination.

The series of experiments was concerned with four main problems: (1) the effects of oxygen deprivation on differential brightness sensitivity; (2) the effects of insulin hypoglycemia on differential brightness sensitivity; (3) the role of high blood sugar levels in counteracting the effects of oxygen lack; and (4) carbon-monoxide anoxia at sea level and simulated high altitudes.

Effects of Oxygen Deprivation on Differential Brightness Sensitivity: Our earlier experiments on dark adaptation revealed that one's ability to see dim objects against a completely dark background is markedly impaired by oxygen lack.[30] In practical situations, however, it is rarely necessary to distinguish objects against a totally dark background. Even in night flying, the background is more or less illuminated. It was therefore more relevant to investigate the effect of oxygen lack on differential thresholds in relation to the intensity of illumination of the background.[36]

In this study, measurements were made of the sensitivity of the eye to foveal stimuli presented against backgrounds which varied in intensity over a range of about 1:100,000. It was found that anoxia affects visual sensitivity to the greatest extent when the background is most dimly illuminated. The effect becomes less marked as the intensity of the background increases. At very high light intensities, as in sunlight, oxygen lack produces practically no change in visual sensitivity.[37] The findings of one experiment are shown in Figure 115.

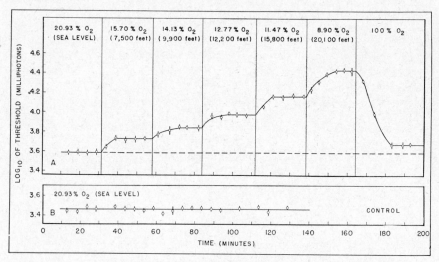

FIG. 115. The effect of progressive degrees of oxygen deprivation on foveal differential brightness sensitivity at a constant field intensity is shown in the upper figure (A). In the control experiment (B) the oxygen tension was not altered. (From McFarland, Halperin, and Niven: *American Journal of Physiology*, 1944, 142.)

The results of this study indicate that oxygen should be used at moderate altitudes during night flights in so far as visual sensitivity is concerned. Under conditions equivalent to a height of only 5000 to 7000 feet, the change in visual sensitivity is quite significant. In so far as visual changes may reflect other alterations in the central nervous system, any significant degree of anoxia might be expected to impair maximal performance.

Effects of Insulin Hypoglycemia on Differential Brightness Sensitivity: The concentration of blood sugar is intimately related to the functioning of the central nervous system. This is true because glucose is the chief substance which can be utilized by the central nervous system as a fuel, or metabolite. If the supply is deficient, the oxidative processes are slowed, and the effect should be equivalent to that of a reduced supply of oxygen.[33]

The retina behaves very much like the central nervous system in regard to its metabolism.

In the present experiments, differential visual sensitivity underwent the same changes when the blood sugar was reduced by intravenous injection of insulin as when the oxygen supply was reduced.[39] The differential threshold was affected most acutely when the background illumination was dim. Furthermore, it was found that inhalation of pure oxygen counteracted a portion of the adverse effect caused by hypoglycemia. Typical results are shown in Figure 116 for three different subjects.

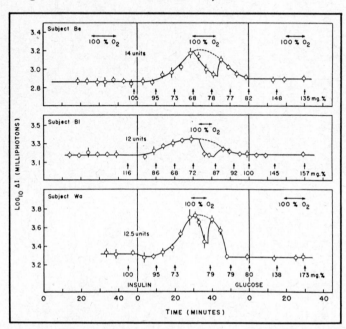

Fig. 116. The figure shows the effect of oxygen on the impairment of visual sensitivity caused by insulin. The various symbols have the same meaning as in Figure 115. The administration of 100 per cent oxygen at the height of the effect of insulin restores the thresholds to nearly normal levels. Reversion to room air results in a rise of the curve, showing that the insulin was still exerting an effect. (From McFarland, Halperin, and Niven: *American Journal of Physiology*, 1946, 145.)

In a normal subject under ordinary conditions, it was found that the blood sugar level does not become sufficiently low to impair visual sensitivity. Such impairment occurs only when the blood sugar concentration falls below about 60 to 65 mg. per 100 cc. However, these findings are important in explaining the results of the following experiments which are more directly applicable to practical situations.

Role of High Blood Sugar Levels in Counteracting the Effects of Anoxia: The results of the preceding experiments suggested the possibility that high blood sugar levels might counteract the effects of anoxia. Studies were made, therefore, of differential sensitivity during exposure to oxygen deprivation equivalent to altitudes of 12,000 to 16,000 feet, before and after the administration of 50 Gm. of glucose. A dim background was again used.

It was found that elevation of the blood sugar level from a fasting value of about 100 mg. per 100 cc. to a peak value of about 180 mg. counteracted about one-third to one-half of the impairment caused by anoxia.[38] The effect of an oxygen tension corresponding to 16,000 feet altitude, for example, was reduced to that ordinarily caused by 10,000 to 12,000 feet altitude. Visual sensitivity varied in a manner parallel with the blood sugar level. Similar results were obtained whether the sugar was given during oxygen deprivation or whether it was given before oxygen deprivation in order to prevent its effect. During control experiments, on the other hand,

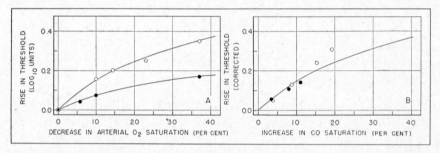

FIG. 117.   The left-hand figure indicates the visual thresholds plotted against the decrease in arterial oxygen saturation as a result of exposure to simulated altitudes while the right-hand figure shows the rise in visual thresholds caused by various concentrations of carbon monoxide in the blood. The open and solid circles represent the data for two experiments on the same subject. (From McFarland, Roughton, Halperin, and Niven: *Journal of Aviation Medicine*, 1944, 15.)

a saccharin solution had no effect. It was found also that high blood sugar levels improved visual sensitivity only when this function had first been impaired by anoxia or hypoglycemia, and then only to its original value.

These results indicate that airmen should not be exposed to oxygen lack in a fasting state. Food should be taken, preferably in small quantities at frequent intervals, in order to maintain the blood sugar at fairly high normal values. While ordinary sugar and similar carbohydrates cause the most rapid rise in blood sugar, other foods, such as proteins, may cause a more prolonged elevation.

Combined Effects of Carbon Monoxide and Anoxia at Sea Level and Simulated High Altitudes: In the case of airmen, carbon monoxide may be absorbed from two main sources: engine exhaust gas and tobacco smoke. When carbon monoxide combines with hemoglobin, the oxygen-carrying capacity of the blood is reduced. Furthermore, carbon monoxide displaces the oxygen dissociation curve to the left, thus inhibiting the release to the tissues of even this decreased amount of oxygen. As a result, there is a marked lowering of the tissue oxygen tension. This would naturally accentuate the anoxia caused by exposure to high altitude.

Theoretic considerations have led to the conclusion that the venous (or even tissue) oxygen tension, which is associated with the loss of a given percentage of the oxygen capacity of the blood due to saturation with carbon monoxide, is the same as that caused by a similar decrease in

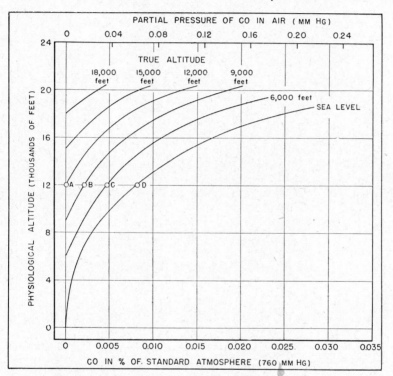

Fig. 118. Physiologic altitude is shown as a function of the amount of carbon monoxide in the air at various true (pressure) altitudes when equilibrium with the blood has been reached. (From McFarland, Roughton, Halperin, and Niven: *Journal of Aviation Medicine*, 1944, 15.)

arterial oxygen saturation at high altitudes. On this basis, 5 per cent saturation with carbon monoxide would be expected to have an effect equal to that of an altitude of about 8000 to 10,000 feet on those functions which depend on the tissue oxygen tension (Fig. 117).

Earlier attempts to determine the least amount of carbon monoxide capable of producing impairment of psychologic functions yielded no clear results. Even with 30 to 35 per cent saturation, causing numerous subjective complaints, such as headaches, there was no clearly demonstrable impairment in various psychologic tests. This was probably caused by the fact that the tests employed were not sufficiently sensitive and that the subject could mask a considerable degree of impairment by exerting greater effort. In the measurement of visual sensitivity, on the other hand, compensation is not a factor. The subject merely reports whether or not he sees a flash of light and is unaware of the intensity required.

A series of experiments was carried out to determine the effect of carbon monoxide on visual thresholds, both in normal air and in combination with varying degrees of oxygen deprivation.[15,40] The results were entirely consistent with the theoretic expectations. It was found, for example, that 5 per cent saturation with carbon monoxide depresses visual sensitivity to as great an extent as anoxia at 8000 to 10,000 feet altitude. Fifteen per

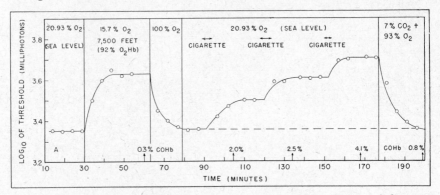

FIG. 119.   The effect of cigarette-smoking on the light sensitivity of the eye is shown in comparison with that of high altitude. The figure indicates that the rise in threshold or impairment of sensitivity after smoking three cigarettes is slightly greater than the effects of 7500 feet altitude. (From McFarland: Human Factors in Air Transport Design, McGraw-Hill Book Co., 1946.)

cent saturation caused an impairment corresponding to that at about 15,000 to 19,000 feet. At various simulated altitudes, the addition of carbon monoxide, causing a given percentage of saturation produced an effect equal to that at an altitude sufficient to produce an additional loss of arterial oxygen saturation of the same amount (Fig. 118).

The test proved to be so sensitive that even the effects of the small quantities of carbon monoxide absorbed from cigarette smoke were clearly demonstrable. Deep inhalation of the smoke from a single cigarette caused a carbon monoxide saturation of almost 2 per cent. After inhaling the smoke of three cigarettes, the saturation of the blood with carbon monoxide was approximately 4 per cent and the effect on visual sensitivity was equal to that at an altitude of about 7500 feet (Fig. 119). The loss of arterial oxygen saturation at this altitude is about 4 per cent. The absorption of a similar amount of carbon monoxide at 7500 feet altitude causes a combined loss of sensitivity equal to that at 10,000 to 11,000 feet.[28a]

The inhalation of oxygen was found not only to accelerate the elimination of carbon monoxide but also to produce an improvement in visual thresholds at any given point after inhalation. The improvement was equivalent to a decrease of about 5 to 7 per cent carboxyhemoglobin when breathing oxygen as compared with room air. If, instead of oxygen, the subject breathed atmospheric air throughout the recovery period, the visual thresholds failed to recover as rapidly as the percentage of carboxyhemoglobin declined.

These studies indicate that carbon monoxide at high altitudes may be harmful in much smaller amounts than previously supposed. The importance of guarding against the entry of exhaust gases into an airplane and of adequate removal of gases liberated by gunfire is therefore intensified. The importance of refraining from excessive inhalation of tobacco smoke and the importance of the use of oxygen in flight is obvious. Theoretic considerations had led to these same conclusions previously, but these studies represent an objective demonstration of the effects of small quantities of carbon monoxide, especially if combined with anoxia or low blood sugar.

Effects of Anoxia on Mental Functions

Other psychologic functions are not influenced until anoxia is fairly marked. The average number of words recalled in standardized tests for immediate memory show a significant decrease at altitudes of approximately 10,000 to 12,000 feet during rapid ascents. During prolonged acclimatization to high altitude during the Andean Expedition which is discussed in following pages, a significant impairment was not observed in the memory test until somewhat higher altitudes were reached. The psychologic deterioration at altitude is characterized not merely as a general slowing up of mental functions and a greater amount of effort needed to carry out a task but also with qualitative changes. The content of the associations is different and the pattern of behavior is altered. Attention appears to fluctuate more easily. Calculations are unreliable and judgment faulty. An airman may feel unduly fatigued or may complain of sleepiness, headache, and breathlessness. Normal inhibitions may be released as in alcoholic intoxication at higher altitudes. Such emotional reactions as euphoria, overconfidence, pugnaciousness, or moroseness may occur, depending on the basic personality traits of the individual and the length of the exposure.[24]

Tests relating to immediate memory in anoxia are of considerable interest in relation to age.[27] It is well known that older persons are poorer in this function than younger ones. The procedure for testing is as follows: A series of ten pairs of four-letter words are exposed for fifteen seconds each. The subject is then shown the first word of each pair in the same order as prescribed and he is instructed to give the second. There are no obvious or meaningful associations between each pair. The average number of words recalled and the number of wrong associations at each altitude are shown in Figure 120 (*left*). The average college student at sea level can remember eight to nine out of ten paired words in the test mentioned above. While inhaling oxygen percentages simulating 10,000 to 12,000 feet he is impaired approximately 10 to 15 per cent. We have observed that the average college student may even excel his professor of 55 to 60 years of age. It is also of interest that older subjects, especially after 50 to 60 years of age, show a significant impairment in dark adaptation or light sensitivity. Although these variations in memory and dark adaptation may be related to many complex factors, it seems reasonable to suppose the factors relating to the delivery or utilization of oxygen by the nervous tissue may be the basic cause.

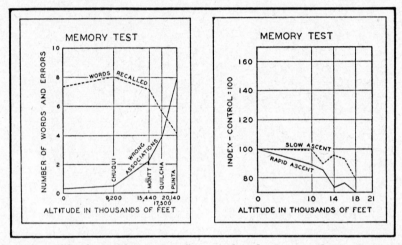

Fig. 120.	The figure shows the effect of altitude on immediate memory. Impairment in words recalled and wrong associations is very marked above 15,000 feet in acclimatized subjects on an Andean high altitude expedition (*left*). There is a significant decrement in objective tests for immediate memory at altitudes of about 10,000 feet and over during simulated flights (*right*). (From McFarland: *Journal of Comparative Psychology*, 1937, 24, and McFarland: C.A.A. Technical Development Report 11, Government Printing Office, Washington, D.C., 1941.)

Precise experiments in regard to such mental functions as judgment or insight are more difficult to carry out owing to the lack of objective tests. Nonetheless, certain evidence is available from mountain expeditions and chamber studies which show that normal individuals lose insight and take on many of the characteristics of a psychotic. Several illustrations will make this clear. Many of you will remember the experiment which Barcroft carried out on himself by living in a low-oxygen chamber for five days at approximately 16,000 feet.[2] Toward the end of the study he lost insight into the objectives of the investigation and those outside of the chamber took corrective action. The illustrations from mountain expeditions and high-altitude flying in aviation are numerous. If the arterial oxygen saturation is as low as 70 to 75 per cent, loss of insight may be very striking in some subjects and behavior may be very irrational.

Possibly one of the best methods of demonstrating loss of insight is to show the handwriting of one of my own subjects in a very acute anoxia experiment. The per cent of oxygen was lowered from sea level to a simulated altitude of 28,000 feet within an hour. Figure 121 shows the marked

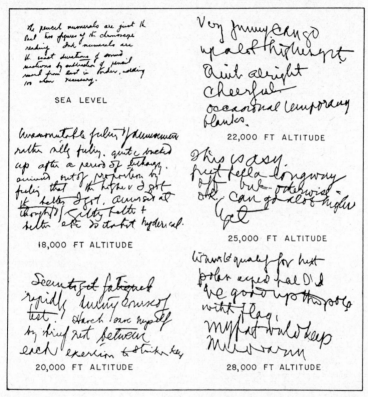

FIG. 121.   The figure shows the gradual deterioration in the handwriting of a subject at progressively higher altitudes (simulated). Note the increase in size from normal, in muscular incoordination, and the omission of letters. From Mc-Farland. *Archives of Psychology*, No. 145, Columbia University, 1932.)

deterioration present. The subject was very amused during the test and wrote that he felt cheerful and quite all right except for occasional temporary blanks. At 23,000 feet (8.5 per cent oxygen) he began to omit letters from common words and his writing became quite illegible. He complained of his feet feeling a long way off and of his inability to orient other parts of his body. At 26,000 feet (7.4 per cent oxygen) he was greatly incapacitated and yet he appeared to be cheerful and was well satisfied with his performance. He became quite annoyed when he was removed from the apparatus and insisted that he could go much higher. He was convinced of his marked deterioration only after seeing his handwriting. The insidious loss of insight as to the nature and extent of his own deterioration was one of the most significant aspects of the experiment.[24]

In an extensive investigation carried out during 1936-1937 at Columbia University an attempt was made to determine the altitudes where the effects of oxygen want are first manifested and where the effects become dangerous for the average passenger of an air transport plane.[28] The study involved the analysis of the response of over 200 subjects, varying in physical fitness and in age (from 18 to 72 years), at different rates of ascent and lengths of exposure to simulated altitudes of 10,000, 12,000, 14,000, 16,000, 18,000, and 21,000 feet. The tests included the recording of the pulse rate and the blood pressure at frequent intervals, the sampling of the alveolar oxygen and carbon dioxide, and the reaction to a series of psychologic tests involving muscular, sensory, and mental functions. In spite of the large individual differences, certain generalizations may be briefly stated concerning the physiologic and psychologic responses. There appeared to be a fairly close relationship between increase in pulse rate and height attained. A well-controlled rise in pulse rate with a gradual return to more normal levels was apparently a favorable response. Subjects in poor physical condition responded with extreme variations in pulse rate, i.e., either an unusually large increase, a sudden decrease, or no change at all. The changes in blood pressure with increasing altitude were not as consistent as the alterations in pulse rate. At the moderate altitudes most subjects reacted with an initial increase in systolic pressure followed by a well-controlled fall to normal values. An extreme rise or fall in blood pressure usually indicated poor acclimatization.

The results of the psychologic tests involving handwriting, choice reaction times, perseveration, code transliteration, and memory indicated a significant impairment for the group at 12,000 feet (13.2 per cent oxygen) where the partial pressure of oxygen in the alveolar air was roughly 50 mm. Hg and the per cent saturation of the arterial blood with oxygen 85. During the rapid ascents to 10,000 feet, there was a significant effect in the more complex mental tests involving perseveration and memory. In Figure 120 B the group means are charted for the memory test at the various altitudes.[28]

There appears to be a marked turning point for the worse in most unacclimatized subjects at 16,000 to 18,000 feet. The handwriting becomes more illegible and words are misspelled, memory is markedly impaired, word associations are altered, and judgments are not to be trusted. Under acute oxygen want the loss of capacity for self-criticism or the capacity for accurate judgments about one's own deterioration is very striking. In this respect there is a close resemblance of anoxia to the progressive stages of alcoholic intoxication. The implications of these observations for pilots while flying above 10,000 to 12,000 feet are significant.[28] At 14,000 to

16,000 feet the subjective complaints become accentuated, while at higher altitudes, i.e., 18,000 feet and above, marked alterations in mood may become apparent, such as heightened irritability, indifference and anger, or, on the contrary, exhilaration and boisterousness. The most frequent complaints reported voluntarily in the experiments discussed above are tabulated in Table 22.

TABLE 22. MOST FREQUENT COMPLAINTS NOTED VOLUNTARILY BY SUBJECTS AT THE ALTITUDES SHOWN FOLLOWING RAPID ASCENTS

| Complaints | Altitude in Feet | | | |
	10,000	12,000	14,000	16,000
	Per Cent			
Headache	10.5	33.3	62.4	66.7
Respiratory changes or difficulties	26.3	16.7	42.5	60.0
Excessive sleepiness	21.1	50.0	37.5	30.0
Vertigo or dizziness	5.3	0.0	32.5	53.3
Difficulty in concentrating	21.1	16.7	15.0	46.7
Sensory impairment	5.3	16.7	30.0	33.3
Lassitude, indifference	21.1	16.7	25.0	13.3
Fatigue	5.3	0.0	27.5	33.3

Experiments at High Altitudes in the Andes

An unusual opportunity was afforded on the International High Altitude Expedition to Chile to study the problems of acclimatization to high altitude.[19] Ten of us spent six months in the Andes studying the effects of the diminished pressure of oxygen on the blood, the circulation, the respiration, the metabolism, the brain, and the sense organs. The itinerary, the barometric pressure, and the altitudes at the various stations of this Expedition are shown in Table 23. A train was equipped at sea level (Anto-

TABLE 23. ITINERARY, BAROMETRIC PRESSURE, AND ALTITUDES AT VARIOUS STATIONS IN ANDES EXPEDITION

Station	Period of Occupation	Corrected Barometric Pressure, MM. Mercury	Altitude in Feet
Chuquicamata	April 8—June 4, 1935	543	9,200
Ollagüe	June 5–13 and June 25—July 18, 1935	489	12,020
Collahuasi (Monti)	June 13–25, 1935	429	15,440
Auconquilcha	June 26—July 15, 1935	401	17,500
Punta de Cerro	June 29—July 14, 1935	356	20,140
Last departure from Chile	August 17, 1935		

fagasta, Chile) composed of two laboratory cars (including compartments for a bicycle ergometer and for animals), a sleeping car, and a kitchen car. Experimental stations were established on the line of the railroad at Chuquicamata (9200 feet), Ollagüe (12,000 feet), and at Collahuasi (15,440 feet). The equipment was then transported by truck to a sulphur mining community at 'Quilcha (17,500 feet). Part of it was conveyed by mule pack and aerial tramway to the mine at 19,000 feet and then by foot to the highest station, Punta de Cerro (20,140 feet).

Except at the highest station, Punta de Cerro, the various psychologic tests were given under comfortable conditions in a room where the light and temperature could be controlled. A snow cavern was constructed at Punta connected with two tents providing protection from the wind and cold. Only six of the ten subjects took the tests at Punta (20,140 feet). Contrary to expectations based on the experience of previous scientific expeditions, the most fit members of the party were able to live fairly comfortably in the snow cavern at 20,140 feet, and especially at 17,500 feet where the main laboratory was maintained.

Of the nine psychologic tests, in five there was shown a significant impairment at 15,440 feet and in six at 17,500 feet. With the exception of the choice reaction times, all of the group means were significantly lower at the highest station (20,140 feet). Of the seven psychologic tests involving complex mental functions, all of the group means at 17,500 feet and above proved to be reliably different compared with the sea level values.[25]

Each subject was asked to mark as to frequency (often, seldom, and never) a list of thirty-five physiologic complaints and thirty psychologic complaints frequently associated with the effects of high altitude. Only a few of these reactions were observed often by all the members of the Expedition. The ten most commonly observed physiologic changes in the order of frequency were: shortness of breath on exertion, or easy fatigability, breathing irregularities, cold extremities, dry skin, disturbed sleep, gas in stomach or intestines, headache, sore throat, irregular pulse, and lassitude. The ten most common psychologic alterations in behavior in the high altitude in order of frequency were as follows: greater effort to carry out tasks, more critical attitude toward other people, mental laziness, heightened sensory irritability, touchy on various subjects, dislike of being told how to do things, difficulty in concentrating, slowness in reasoning, frequent recurring ideas, and difficulty in remembering.

A complete discussion of the results of the various biochemical studies may be found in the original papers of Dill et al,[7] Keys et al,[20] Talbott,[43] Edwards,[8] and Forbes.[9] The critical ratios between sea level and the various altitudes proved to be statistically reliable, with but few exceptions, notably the pH of the serum and the lactic acid. The fairly consistent increase in the group variability and the magnitude of the critical ratios with increasing altitude reflect the greater degree of organic instability known to exist at those altitudes. These measurements are all directly related to the diminished partial pressure of oxygen in the alveolar air and blood. Hence, the greater variations in breathing known to exist at high altitude would naturally be reflected in greater variations in the biochemical determinations. The differences between the results in the various physiologic tests for the Expedition members and the permanent residents were not significant, with the exception of the oxygen capacity, the red cell count, and the alkaline reserve. The mean arterial oxygen saturation was practically the same in both groups (76 per cent). The failure of any of the members of the Expedition to attain as great an oxygen capacity as the average for the miners (30.5 volumes per cent compared with the mean for the Expedition at 17,500 feet of 25.1) may have been related to the miners' more complete adaptation, as well as their more strenuous daily exercise. The red cell count of the miners averaged 7.4 million per cubic millimeter, as compared with the mean for the Expedition members at 17,500 feet of 6 million. The mean resting lactic acid for the miners was 10.2 mg. per cent as compared with 10.7 for the members of the Expedition.

The sulphur mining community at 'Quilcha (17,500 feet) is of interest since it apparently forms the highest permanent community in the world. Approximately 100 men live there all year with their wives and children. The women go down to Ollagüe (12,020 feet) to bear their children, but soon return to the high camp. We were surprised to find that many of the miners were from the lowlands of Chile and Bolivia who had become successfully acclimatized to these great heights. On one occasion an attempt was made to establish the camp at 18,500 feet, nearer the sulphur mine, but they found it impossible to sleep, and general deterioration set in. They now live apparently quite comfortably at 17,500 feet and walk each day to the mine at 19,000 feet. They often run down to the lower camp following a long day's work at the mine (piecework), and after their evening meal play soccer until dark.

Studies of the animals native to the high plateaus of the Andes by Hall et al.[13, 14] furnish excellent examples of complete adaptation to diminished oxygen tension over many centuries. Some species, such as the llama and vicuña, possibly had their evolutionary origin in high altitudes. The arterial blood of these animals has a high oxygen saturation and a high affinity for oxygen in comparison with the blood of human beings and of animals like the sheep and rabbit transported to high altitude from sea level. The arterial oxygen saturation of the sheep at 17,500 feet was 56 per cent; of the llama, approximately 84 per cent; of the vicuña, 82 per cent; and of ten human subjects, 76 per cent. The large number of very small red cells (16 million per cubic centimeter at 17,500 feet) in the vicuña would naturally afford a larger surface area for the diffusion of oxygen to the tissues. This factor may partially account for the unusual ability of these animals to run so fast and for such long distances at 14,000 feet and above. Their red cells are unique among all other animals studied in that the hemoglobin is extremely closely packed in the cells.

In spite of the fact that no single mechanism proved to be of outstanding significance in successful acclimatization or in efficiency in the psychologic tests, an analysis of the individual variations in adaptation revealed that for relatively normal men between the ages of 29 and 44, youth, slow pulse, low normal blood oxygen capacity, low alveolar oxygen pressure and high alveolar carbon dioxide pressure, and high alkaline reserve at sea level were favorable for acclimatization at high altitude.[21]

Alcohol and Oxygen Want

Frequent references may be found in the studies of anoxia carried out on mountain expeditions, during high altitude flights, and in low-oxygen chambers to the similarities in the behavior of a person suffering from oxygen want to one under the influence of alcohol. Barcroft has stated that "acute oxygen want simulates drunkenness, while chronic oxygen want simulates fatigue."[2] Under both conditions a person may become irrational and uninhibited and lose the capacity for self-criticism, memory, sensitivity, and motor control. It has been suggested by Peters and Van Slyke that alcoholism is in fact a form of anoxia (histotoxic) and that "the tissue cells are poisoned in such a manner that they cannot use the oxygen properly."[42] This tends to explain the striking effects of alcohol on the central nervous system, since it is well known that the nervous tissue is particularly sensitive to oxygen want. During the Chilean Expedition that has been discussed in foregoing paragraphs, a study was made of the metabolism of alcohol at high altitude.[32] Drinks of alcohol of approximately 1 Gm. per kilogram of body weight were ingested at 17,500 feet and at 12,200 feet. The tests were later repeated at sea level. At constant intervals, samples of venous blood were taken for the determination of the concentration of alcohol in the blood, and a series of psychologic tests were taken. The concentration of alcohol in the blood rose more rapidly and reached a higher level at high altitudes than at sea level. In one subject at 12,200 feet the concentration of alcohol in the blood was three times as great as at sea level twelve hours after taking the alcohol. The relative impairment in the psychologic tests was also greater in the mountains compared with sea level after the ingestion of alcohol.

Role of Anoxia in Certain of the Mental Disorders

The effects of prolonged exposure to oxygen want, as observed in patients with chronic mountain sickness in the Andes, are of considerable neurologic interest. Based upon extensive laboratory findings and clinical examinations, these patients present a syndrome unlike that of any other disease, justifying the presentation of chronic mountain sickness as a distinct disease entity.[41] In the severe and chronic form of this illness, the patients become cyanotic on the least effort; their faces become blue-violet in color, the skin dry, their fingers clubbed, and their thorax emphysematous. They complain of weakness, insomnia, blurring of vision, frequent vertigo and syncope, and nausea. Vomiting may occur on the least effort and aphonia is common. The psychologic abnormalities are especially noticeable. They exhibit disturbances in emotional behavior, memory, and judgment. One very intelligent engineer at the Cerro de Pasco Mines, for example, had episodes of marked mental confusion, during which it was impossible for him to carry out even the simplest calculations. The most striking fact that characterizes this clinical entity is that the symptoms disappear when the patient is brought to sea level and remains there for a short time.

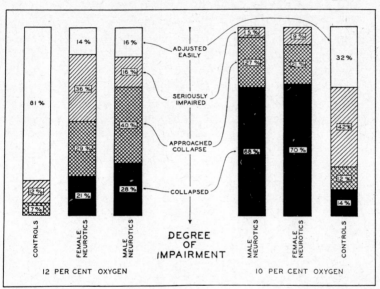

Fig. 122. The figure compares the altitude tolerance of psychoneurotic patients with that of normal control subjects. Note that a larger percentage of both male and female neurotic patients collapsed or approached collapse at simulated altitudes of 14,500 feet (12 per cent oxygen) and 19,000 feet (10 per cent oxygen) than of the normal controls. (From McFarland and Barach: *American Journal of Psychiatry*, 1937, 24.)

Many of the symptoms discussed by Monge in chronic mountain sickness are similar to those exhibited by certain persons roughly diagnosed as "chronically fatigued neurotic" patients, and also in pilots suffering from "aeroneuroses."[1] The outstanding symptoms of such pilots are acute exhaustion and fatigue, shallow, irregular breathing, neurocirculatory failure, nervous irritability, emotional instability, insomnia, and gastric distress. This syndrome is frequently observed in pilots on active combat duty where the combined action of the intense emotional stress and prolonged flights at high altitude apparently has a deteriorating effect on the central nervous system. It is a common observation among clinicians that patients suffering from severe anoxia, as in cardiac insufficiency, neurocirculatory failure, emphysema, pneumonia, carbon monoxide poisoning, or acute alcoholism, simulate many of the characteristics of the psychoneurotic or manifest marked mental and emotional abnormalities.

Because of the fact that psychoneurotic patients with marked symptoms of fatigue and exhaustion manifest certain symptoms of oxygen want, their response was studied to high (50 per cent) and low (10 per cent) concentrations of oxygen.[29] The experiments were carried out in a chamber where the composition of the gases, the ventilation, and the humidity could be carefully controlled. The acclimatization of each subject was followed in terms of the pulse and blood pressure records, as well as their response to sensory, motor, and mental tests. The patients appeared to be more severely impaired in the diminished tensions of oxygen than were the control subjects; approximately 70 per cent of them collapsed in an atmosphere of 10 per cent oxygen (19,000 feet) whereas this occurred in only 14 per cent of the control subjects (Fig. 122). In the 50 per cent oxygen series, the physiologic complaints of the patients, such as headaches and respiratory abnormalities, were less marked and they made better scores in the psychologic tests.

Whether the cause of the illness in these patients is psychologic or physiologic, there appears to be a significant amount of unfitness to account for their complaints of fatigue and exhaustion once they go through a period of chronic emotional stress.[16] It is often suggested that they have impaired sympathico-adrenal systems. These experiments offer some evidence for this view, since the mechanisms involved in adaptation to oxygen lack are closely related to the functions of the sympathico-adrenal system. Cannon has reported that sympathectomized cats are more susceptible to oxygen want following the operation.[3] It is a common observation among pilots that "nervous" passengers are more susceptible to high altitude and are more apt to faint. Normal subjects following loss of sleep are also more sensitive to the effects of oxygen deprivation.

Numerous studies have suggested the presence of oxygen deficiency in certain forms of schizophrenia, and this question has been studied from many angles. The oxygen consumption, as well as the metabolism of nitrogen and carbohydrates, has generally been reported to be below the average, and in some patients, definitely subnormal.[16, 18] A high percentage of schizophrenic and melancholic patients show a diminished excitability of the respiratory centers to carbon dioxide inhalations, a circumstance which would tend to provide a diminished supply of oxygen to the individual.[12] The brains of dementia praecox patients frequently show a deficiency of neutral sulphur and iron, both quantitatively and histochemically.[10, 22] Both of these catalytic agents are involved in the utilization of oxygen by the tissue cells.

Studies of the blood gases in schizophrenia have not shown marked deviations from normal values.[35] The oxygen saturation of the blood drawn from the brachial artery and internal jugular vein of such patients is within the normal range of variation. Further studies should be made of the mechanisms involved in the utilization of oxygen in the nervous tissues, as well as the changes in the blood gases coursing through the brain so as to calculate the respiratory quotient of the brain. The studies which have been made thus far reveal alterations which are too small to account for the mental abnormalities in schizophrenia.

Therapeutic attempts in schizophrenia, either with excess and deficient concentrations of oxygen or excess carbon dioxide, reviewed in detail elsewhere, have not met with striking success.[6, 17, 23, 35] The response of schizophrenic patients to the various shock therapies, such as hypoglycemia, is relative to the above discussion of oxidation in the nervous tissue. In the final analysis, as suggested by Gellhorn, low blood sugar: (1) reduces the oxidation rate in the central nervous system; and (2) possibly stimulates the sympathetic centers as a result of the diminution of the oxidative metabolism.[11] Conclusive evidence is yet to be obtained, however, that impaired oxidation is of primary importance in schizophrenia.[4]

Conclusion

In conclusion, the sensory and mental impairment which occurs in normal human subjects under the experimental conditions of anoxia described in the foregoing pages may be attributed to the diminished partial pressure of oxygen in the blood being delivered to the nervous tissue. These changes are of cellular origin rather than circulatory. The cerebral vasodilatation and increased blood flow known to occur under anoxia cannot fully compensate for the diminished oxygen tension. In unacclimatized man the respiratory adaptation and increase in the oxygen capacity of the blood are also inadequate to compensate for the oxygen deficiency in the nervous tissue. The final result is an impairment of sensory and mental function and integration, the cortical cells apparently suffering more than other parts of the central nervous system. According to concepts presented here, the underlying basis of the physiologic changes in certain forms of mental illness and senescence relates to an interference of normal metabolic processes within individual cells of the brain. This interference may operate through a reduced rate of transference of essential substances to the metabolizing cells, or through inadequacies of the enzyme systems required for normal metabolic processes within cells. Transference may be inadequate because of reduced supply, reduced circulatory delivery, or slower diffusion. The amount of essential substances which reach the cells may be reduced because of greater distances over which diffusion must take place, reduced permeability, or the presence of inert substances through which nutrients diffuse with difficulty.

REFERENCES

1. ARMSTRONG, H. G.: *Journal of the American Medical Association*, 1936, 106, p. 1347.
2. BARCROFT, J.: The Brain and Its Environment. New Haven, Yale University Press, 1938.
3. CANNON, W. B.: The Wisdom of the Body. New York, W. W. Norton and Co., 1932.
4. COBB, S.: *Archives of Internal Medicine*, 1937, 60, p. 1098.
5. CROZIER, W. J., and HOLWAY, A. H.: *Journal of General Physiology*, 1939, 22 (3), pp. 341-364.
6. D'ELSEAUX, F. C., and SOLOMON, H. C.: *Archives of Neurology and Psychiatry*, 1933, 29, pp. 213-230.
7. DILL, D. B.; CHRISTENSEN, E. H.; and EDWARDS, H. T.: *American Journal of Physiology*, 1936, 115, p. 530.
8. EDWARDS, H. T.: *American Journal of Physiology*, 1936, 116 (2), pp. 367-375.
9. FORBES, W. H.: *American Journal of Physiology*, 1936, 116 (2), pp. 309-316.
10. FREEMAN, W.: *Archives of Neurology and Psychiatry*, 1930, 24, pp. 300-310.
11. GELLHORN, E.: *Journal of the American Medical Association*, 1938, 110, p. 1433.
12. GOLLA, F. L.: *Journal of Mental Science*, 1929, 75, pp. 661-670.
13. HALL, F. G.: *Journal of Biological Chemistry*, 1936, 115 (2), pp. 485-490.
14. HALL, F. G.; DILL, D. B.; and GUZMAN BARRON, E. S.: *Journal of Cellular and Comparative Physiology*, 1936, 8 (3), pp. 301-313.
15. HALPERIN, M. H.; NIVEN, J. I.; McFARLAND, R. A.; and ROUGHTON, F. J. W.: *Federation Proceedings*, 1947, 6 (1), pp. 120-121.
16. HENRY, G. W.: *Journal of Nervous and Mental Disease*, 1929, 70, pp. 598-605.
17. HINSIE, L. E.; BARACH, A. L.; HARRIS, M. M.; BRANDT, E.; and McFARLAND, R. A.: *Psychiatric Quarterly*, 1934, 8, pp. 34-71.
18. HOSKINS, R., and SLEEPER, F. H.: *Archives of Neurology and Psychiatry*, 1937, 38, p. 1216.
19. KEYS, A.: *Scientific Monthly*, 1936, 43, p. 289.
20. KEYS, A.; HALL, F. G.; and GUZMAN BARRON, E. S.: *American Journal of Physiology*, 1936, 115 (2), p. 292-307.
21. KEYS, A.; MATTHEWS, B. H. C.; FORBES, W. H.; and McFARLAND, R. A.: *Proceedings of the Royal Society*, London, Series B, 1938, 126, pp. 1-29.
22. KOCH, W., and MANN, S. A.: *Archives of Neurology and Psychiatry*, 1909, 4, pp. 174-219.
23. LOEVENHART, A. S.; LORENZ, W. F.; and WATERS, R. M.: *Journal of the American Medical Association*, 1929, 92, pp. 880-883.
24. McFARLAND, R. A.: *Archives of Psychology*, No. 145, Columbia University, 1932.
25. McFARLAND, R. A.: *Journal of Comparative Psychology*, 1937, 23, pp. 191-258; 1937, 24, pp. 147-188, and 189-220.
26. McFARLAND, R. A.: *Association for Research in Nervous and Mental Disease*, 1939, 19, pp. 112-143.
27. McFARLAND, R. A.: *American Journal of Psychiatry*, 1941, 97 (4), pp. 858-877.
28. McFARLAND, R. A.: CAA Technical Development Report 11, Government Printing Office, Washington, D. C., 1941.

28a. McFarland, R. A.: Human Factors in Air Transport Design, ch. 6, *Carbon Monoxide and Other Noxious Gases*, pp. 209-251, New York, McGraw Hill Book Co., 1946.

29. McFarland, R. A., and Barach, A. L.: *American Journal of Psychiatry*, 1937, 93, pp. 1315-1341.

30. McFarland, R. A., and Evans, J. N.: *American Journal of Physiology*, 1939, 127, pp. 37-50.

31. McFarland, R. A., Evans, J. N.; and Halperin, M. H.: *Archives of Ophthalmology*, 1941, 26, pp. 886-913.

32. McFarland, R. A., and Forbes, W. H.: *Human Biology*, 1936, 8, pp. 387-398.

33. McFarland, R. A., and Forbes, W. H.: *Journal of General Physiology*, 1940, 24, pp. 69-98.

34. McFarland, R. A., and Goldstein, H.: *American Journal of Psychiatry*, 1937, 93, pp. 1073-1095.

35. McFarland, R. A., and Goldstein, H.: *American Journal of Psychiatry*, 1938, 95, pp. 509-552.

36. McFarland, R. A., and Halperin, M. H.: *Journal of General Physiology*, 1940, 23, pp. 613-630.

37. McFarland, R. A.; Halperin, M. H.; and Niven, J. I.: *American Journal of Physiology*, 1944, 142 (3), pp. 328-349.

38. McFarland, R. A.; Halperin, M. H.; and Niven, J. I.: *American Journal of Physiology*, 1945, 144 (3), pp. 378-388.

39. McFarland, R. A.; Halperin, M. H.; and Niven, J. I.: *American Journal of Physiology*, 1946, 145 (3), pp. 299-313.

40. McFarland, R. A.; Roughton, F. J. W.; Halperin, M. H.; and Niven, J. I.: *Journal of Aviation Medicine*, 1944, 15 (6), pp. 381-394.

41. Monge, C.: *Archives of Internal Medicine*, 1937, 59, p. 32.

42. Peters, J. P., and Van Slyke, D. D.: Quantitative Clinical Chemistry, vol. I. Interpretations. Baltimore, Williams and Wilkins, 1931.

43. Talbott, J. H.: *Folia Haematologica*, 1936, 55, pp. 23-26.

Effects of High and Low Oxygen Tensions on Mental Function

Alvan L. Barach, M.D.

I would be very much interested if Dr. Windle could some time study the question of anoxia in monkeys, also. I remember, during World War II, that Morrison in Boston reported significant changes in the frontal lobe cortex of monkeys as a result of relatively moderate degrees of anoxia, when the temporal lobe and the occipital lobe were entirely normal.

I am going to comment on some of the effects of low oxygen and some of the effects of high oxygen in human beings.

In our studies made during and before World War II, it was found that impairment of emotional control took place as early as any impairment of function, with the exception of changes in vision. In other words, a man in a low pressure chamber or breathing low oxygen mixtures at an equivalent altitude, between 12,000 and 13,000 feet, for four hours, might perform tests of neuromuscular control adequately; but he would show either grandiose ideas, would become depressed, or aggressive, or, depending upon the excitant psychologic stimulus, would exhibit sexual strivings. For example, when a man was told he was shirking his work, he became uncontrollably angry. Different manifestations of impairment of emotional control were produced by varying the stimulus, even when all other functions except vision were unimpaired during exposure to altitudes of 12,000 to 13,000 feet for four hours.

An interesting and similar reaction takes place in patients who have had chronic anoxia, when suddenly exposed to 100 per cent oxygen.

Patients with pulmonary emphysema and fibrosis, and some patients with cardiac failure and asthma with severe anoxia, may become irrational and show either grandiose exhibitionistic states, become depressed or aggressive, or manifest paranoid delusions under these circumstances. It is of considerable interest that these paranoid delusions in some cases are permanent; for example, a man who becomes irrational in a hospital as a result of being given 50 per cent oxygen will frequently not want to go back to that hospital.

Of even more interest is the observation first made by Cameron, that patients with cerebral arteriosclerosis, on being given 40 to 50 per cent oxygen, become irrational in the same way. Unfortunately, Dr. Cameron has not published that observation, but we have many times observed people with cerebral arteriosclerosis, but without systemic oxygen want, become irrational in eight to ten hours, and, in some instances, comatose.

If any of these types of patients are given oxygen treatment by gradual increase of the oxygen concentration inspired, such as 22 per cent the first day, and, over a period of ten days increased to 50 per cent, none of them becomes irrational.

Dr. Himwich and I tried this oxygen treatment on a series of patients with cerebral arteriosclerosis. Indeed, it might almost be said that inhalation of 100 per cent oxygen could possibly be used as a test to determine whether or not a patient has cerebral arteriosclerosis. We have kept normal persons for two months in high oxygen concentrations. There is no effect on the individual with intact cerebral circulation, but a person with cerebral arterial disease becomes irrational, paranoid, depressed, or grandiose.

The mechanism by which these changes are effected is still not understood. We believe that in patients with pulmonary emphysema a rise in the arterial carbon dioxide, with a change in pH toward the acid side, is responsible for irrationality and coma. It is not simply a rise in carbon dioxide but a rise in carbon dioxide plus acidosis; but we have no way of knowing at the present time just why patients with cerebral arteriosclerosis become irrational. It is a point of some clinical interest because frequently we have observed spinal taps being made in patients being investigated for brain tumor when either stopping oxygen or giving oxygen gradually caused complete disappearance of symptoms.

It would then appear that modifying the environment either in respect to sudden deprivation of oxygen in a person previously normal, or modifying the environment in a patient who has previously been anoxic by giving him oxygen, may precipitate states that resemble very closely psychotic states.

I only want to make one other observation in regard to schizophrenia. In the cases that Dr. McFarland referred to, the patients who improved —three of them—were those who had carbon dioxide and oxygen to the point of convulsion, but the series of patients with schizophrenia kept in 50 per cent oxygen in a ward at Psychiatric Institute for two months or more showed no alteration in their clinical state.

REFERENCES

1. ARMSTRONG, H. G.: *Journal of the American Medical Association*, 1936, 106, p. 1347.
2. BARACH, A. L.: *The Medical Clinics of North America*. May 1944, p. 704.
3. BARACH, A. L., and KAGEN, J.: *Psychosomatic Medicine*, 1940, 2, p. 1.
4. BARACH, A. L., and RICHARDS, D. W.: *Archives of Internal Medicine*, 1931, 48, p. 325.
5. BARACH, A. L., and RICHARDS, D. W.: *American Review of Tuberculosis*, 1932, 26, p. 241.
6. BARACH, A. L., and ROVENSTINE, E. A.: *Anesthesiology*, 1945, 5, p. 498.
7. COBB, S., and FREEMONT-SMITH, F.: *Archives of Neurology and Psychiatry*, 1931, 26, p. 731.
8. COMROE, J. H.; BALINSON, E. R.; and COOTES, E. O., JR.: *Journal of the American Medical Association*, 1950, 143, p. 12.
9. HIMWICH, H. E.; ALEXANDER, F. A. D.; and LIPETZ, B.: *Proceedings of the Society for Experimental Biology and Medicine*, 1938, 39, p. 367.
10. HOFF, E. C.; GRENELL, R. G.; and FULTON, J. F.: *Medicine*, 1945, 24, p. 161.
11. LENNOX, W. G., and BEHNKE, A. R., JR.: *Archives of Neurology and Psychiatry*, 1936, 35, p. 782; *Journal of the American Medical Association*, 1936, 106, p. 2073.
12. McFARLAND, R. A., and BARACH, A. L.: *American Journal of Psychiatry*, 1937, 93, p. 1315.
13. MORRISON, L. R.: *Archives of Neurology and Psychiatry*, 1946, 55, p. 1.

Remarks on Anoxia

LESLIE F. NIMS, PH.D.

Dr. Barach mentioned some other consequences of anoxic anoxia. I would like to amplify his remarks and present a summary of some of the biochemical responses seen in more or less acute anoxia. We learned a good deal about these as the results of experiments conducted in high-altitude chambers during World War II.

Discussions of anoxia are always somewhat difficult because anoxia is not a state; it is a stress which brings about processes that require time for completion. The body is able to adjust to this stress and can reach a new steady state as long as the blood oxygen saturation is above 60 per cent. At saturations below this, complete adjustment cannot be reached and physiologic processes fail the more rapidly the lower the saturation.

Initially at saturations above 60 per cent, the stress-relieving mechanisms respond in such a way as to drive the pH of the blood more alkaline. There is a progressive loss of carbon dioxide in the blood, and the acid-base balance approaches that of a profound respiratory alkalosis. During this period there is an increased excitability, increased muscular tremor, decreased coordination, and eventual loss of self-critical faculties. This is the region in which Dr. McFarland has made his excellent observations on visual thresholds.

Below 60 per cent saturation in the unacclimatized subject, consciousness rapidly fails, a rise in lactic acid occurs, a rise in blood sugar takes place, and the acid-base balance rapidly approaches one of a profound metabolic acidosis. If this state is prolonged, irreparable damage takes place particularly to the nervous tissues as Dr. Windle has shown. In terms of altitude, Dr. Windle has shown that no damage occurs at prolonged exposures of animals to 23,000 feet. The oxygen saturations of the blood are above 60 per cent on the average in animals until the altitudes are 25,000 feet or above. We can therefore expect changes in function at altitudes below 20,000 feet and change in structure, or death, above altitudes of 25,000 feet.

Man can become acclimatized and live in excellent health up to altitudes of 16,000 feet or so. For shorter periods he can endure altitudes up to 26,000 feet as the mountaineers on Mount Everest have demonstrated. The acclimatized man, owing to compensatory shifts in his acid-base balance and his hematologic and circulatory dynamics, has the capacity to withstand more stringent conditions of anoxic stress than does an unacclimatized subject.

If we examine the responses of various individuals to anoxia there is considerable variation. Owing to our long evolutionary development in an atmosphere of relatively constant oxygen pressure, our reflex protective mechanisms towards a drop in the oxygen pressure of the air we breathe are relatively insensitive and quite variable from person to person. You no doubt noticed the spread of responses in Dr. McFarland's subjects to tests of higher mental functions when exposed to conditions of reduced partial pressures of oxygen. We, in a few experiments inside a high-altitude chamber, asked the question: "Are the men with the higher oxygen saturations at a given altitude in a better functional state than those with the lower oxygen saturations?" That is, are the men who respond to anoxia with hyperventilation, which tends to maintain the oxygen saturation at the expense of reducing the carbon dioxide content of the blood, better fitted to perform the duties of a pilot? To our surprise, we found an inverse correlation at a given altitude between performance tests and the degree of saturation. The men with a 60 per cent saturation and more nearly normal acid-base balance out-performed the men with respiratory alkalosis and 80 per cent oxygen saturation of the blood. This implies that the acid-base balance of the blood is an important variable in determining the functional capacity of men in anoxic states.

In our studies of anoxia and other conditions affecting the functional states of man we are prone to consider the variables we have measured as the primary cause of the disturbance. In anoxia, in the region where function is disturbed, we do not yet have the experimental information to ascribe loss of function to either the drop in oxygen pressure or to the disturbed acid-base balance that rapidly ensues. It is probably a function of both, and further experiments are needed to unravel the complexities.

CHAPTER 23

Effects of Drugs on Metabolism and Physiologic Activity of Brain

J. H. QUASTEL, D.SC.

I PROPOSE, in the first place, to discuss the effects of narcotics on metabolism in the central nervous system. I shall attempt briefly to review the evidence concerning the action of narcotics on animal enzyme systems and to assess to some extent the present standpoint.

The narcotics as a class are, biochemically, inert molecules undergoing but little change, so far as is known, in the presence of the living cell. It is not unreasonable to suppose that their pharmacologic activities are directly related to their surface activities. The Overton-Meyer theory suggested one important factor in the determination of narcotic activity, i.e., the relative solubilities in the lipoid and nonlipoid constituents of the cell or cell surfaces. Traube advanced the theory that narcotics alter cell surface properties by absorption and Hober suggested that permeability of central neurons is depressed by many anesthetic agents. Brink and Posternak, following the work of Ferguson who showed that, for equally effective doses of many narcotics, their thermodynamic activities closely approximate to each other, consider that these substances exert their effects in special regions of the cell. Equal numbers of narcotic molecules, in these special regions of the cell, produce equal degrees of narcosis. This rule does not seem to apply very rigorously, but even if it did, the rule would fail to show more than that the physical characteristics of the narcotic either determine its entry into a cell, or its orientation at a specific surface. It gives no obvious clue to the mechanism of action of the narcotic. It is to be recalled that substances that alter cell permeability or are adsorbed at cell surfaces may be devoid of narcotic power. It has long been known that narcotics as a general rule inhibit enzymic and respiratory processes but until recently there has been reluctance to associate narcosis with a suppression of oxidative events. This reluctance in associating narcosis with oxidative phenomena has been partly due to the fact that the quantities of narcotics required to induce narcosis in an animal are usually of a far smaller order than those required to inhibit enzymic reactions. Moreover, there has not been until recently any clear evidence that during narcosis in an animal there is any fall in respiratory activity in the nervous system upon which the narcotics might be expected to exert their greatest effects.

McClure and associates[27] have, however, demonstrated the existence of anoxia in the central nervous system during the anesthesia brought about by barbiturates and other narcotics; and Himwich and co-workers[16] found that, under pentothal, oxygen consumption of cerebral cortex is decreased more than that of the lower centers. Shaw and associates[44] have shown that ether anesthesia is associated with a decrease in the difference between oxygen contents of arterial and venous bloods. Dameshek, Myerson, and Loman[6] have shown that in the human subject under amytal there is a small but definite inhibition of oxygen uptake and dextrose utilization by the brain. In fact, the depression of cerebral function by barbiturates is found to parallel the reduction of oxygen uptake. It is to be remembered, however, that it is not proved that the *in vivo* depression is directly related to the fall in respiratory activity; probably other factors are involved. These will be considered.

Very many facts point to the profound influence of brain oxidations on its functional activity. These have already been mentioned by previous speakers. Glucose is a principal substrate of the brain, though of course it is not the only one; and oxygen utilized by the brain is mainly concerned with glucose combustion. A deprivation of glucose from the brain has as dire physiologic effects as a deprivation of oxygen. It is known that in hypoglycemia the large decrease in glucose abstracted from the blood in its passage through brain is not equaled by the decrease in oxygen removed, so that it is clear that substances other than glucose are normally burned in such conditions. But we know that a variety of substances, other than those directly involved in glucose breakdown, are burned by brain, as, for example, glutamic acid and a variety of amines. Doubtless such substances assume a greater quantitative importance when availability of glucose has, for some reason, diminished.

The physiologic facts point to a very high degree of dependence of mental function on the maintenance of oxygen and of glucose supply to the central nervous system. Any interference with the respiratory activity of the nervous system or with some important aspect of this by the action of the drug would be expected to disturb its functional activity. The action of the drug, i.e., its biochemical effect, may be highly localized. A large change, therefore, in the respiration or other biochemical activity of the entire central nervous system by biologically active concentrations of the drug might not be anticipated either *in vivo* or *in vitro*. A change of biochemical events at a particular center in the central nervous system, paralyzing its functional activity, and affecting therefore all branches of the central nervous system influenced by this center, would not necessarily be accompanied by similar biochemical changes throughout the entire central nervous system. The brain, of course, is a complex system, and significant and vital chemical changes at a particular center may be quite obscured by a series of other biochemical changes taking place in the brain as a whole as a direct consequence of the paralysis of the center in question. It is for this reason that the biochemical findings obtained in studies of the brain of the intact animal, following drug administration *in vivo*, must be interpreted with great caution. They may have little relation to the direct effect of the drug on the particular nervous center affected.

TABLE 24.　COMPARISON OF ALKYL BARBITURATES AS TO HYPNOTIC ACTIVITY AND EFFECTS ON OXYGEN CONSUMPTION OF MINCED GUINEA PIG BRAIN IN PRESENCE OF GLUCOSE

Barbiturate (0.12 Per Cent)	Hypnotic Activity	Per Cent Inhibition of Oxygen Uptake of Brain
NH–CO CO　　CH·CH(CH₃)₂ NH–CO	0	6
NH–CO　CH(CH₃)₂ CO　　C NH–CO　NH·CO·OC₂H₅	0	4
NH–CO　CH(CH₃)₂ CO　　C NH–CO　CH₂·CHBr·CH₃	Very weak	0
NH–CO　C₂H₅ CO　　C NH–CO　C₂H₅	+	10
NH–CO　CH(CH₃)₂ CO　　C NH–CO　CH₂·CBr=CH₂	++	50
NH–CO　CH(CH₃)₂ CO　　C NH–CO　CH₂·CH=CH₂	++	40
NH–CO　C₆H₅ CO　　C NH–CO　CH₂·CH=CH₂	++	57

Narcosis and Respiration of the Brain in Vitro

The majority of the narcotics have the power of inhibiting at low concentrations the respiration of brain tissue whether this be examined in the form of a mince or in the form of intact thin tissue slices.

If several alkyl barbiturates are compared as to their effects on the oxygen consumption of minced guinea pig brain, it is found[36] that there exists a parallelism between hypnotic and inhibitive powers (Table 24). This parallelism is shown among narcotics of different chemical types. Thus chloral which is a more powerful narcotic than paraldehyde has also a greater inhibitory effect on brain respiration *in vitro*. The same phenomenon holds with hyoscine and atropine. This has been confirmed by later workers.[10]

TABLE 25.   NARCOTIZING CONCENTRATIONS, AND EFFECTS ON THE RESPIRATION
OF BRAIN CORTEX SLICES IN A GLUCOSE MEDIUM

Narcotic	Animal	Estimated Narcotic Dose (Gm./Kg.)	Narcotizing Concentration (M).	Percentage Inhibition of Isolated Brain Tissue Respiration Due to Narcotizing Concentration
Ethyl urethane	Rat	2	0.022	6
Chloral hydrate	Rat	0.22	0.0013	10
Luminal	Rat	0.2	0.00079	15
Chloretone	Rat	0.18	0.0010	20
Evipan	Guinea Pig	0.16	0.00062	17
Avertin	Rat	0.3	0.00106	31
Chloretone	Guinea Pig	0.18	0.0010	32

Using the more sensitive brain slice technic in which brain cortex alone is used, it is possible to show that definite inhibitions of respiration take place in the presence of narcotics at concentrations that produce narcosis in animals. Results[21] in Table 25 make it clear that a variety of narcotics, at their narcotizing concentrations, produce inhibitions of respiration varying from 6 to 32 per cent. The results are consistent with the view that the narcotics considered produce inhibitions of the respiration of brain slices of roughly the same magnitude when they are present at concentrations which in the organism produce an equal fairly deep narcosis. The data, of course, cannot establish this conclusion but they are sufficient to indicate that a definite inhibition of respiration is produced by concentrations of the order of those producing deep narcosis. The inhibitions recorded represent effects of narcotics on the respiration of the entire brain cortex of the animal; they will be much higher at those parts of the nervous system where the narcotic is localized or specifically absorbed or for which the narcotic may have a high affinity. If still diluter concentrations of a narcotic are investigated the effect sometimes, e.g., with pentobarbital,[48] is to bring about a small increase of respiration (of the order of 5 to 10 per cent) of the brain cortex slice. The reason for this is, as yet, unknown, but it seems just possible that the first effect of the narcotic is to affect the cell wall making for changed permeabilities which may result in an increased respiratory activity and this is followed by entrance of the narcotic into the cell where it affects some of the respiratory mechanisms.

TABLE 26. PERCENTAGE INHIBITION BY NARCOTICS (0.12 PER CENT) OF OXYGEN UPTAKES OF MINCED GUINEA PIG BRAIN PRODUCED BY VARIOUS SUBSTRATES

	Allyliso-propyl Barbiturate	Luminal	Chloretone	Hyoscine	Chloral Hydrate
Glucose	73	94	93	79	66
Sodium lactate	71	79	88	73	90
Sodium pyruvate	67	85	84	71	90
Sodium succinate	2	0	0	0	0
Sodium l-glutamate	28	50	59	60	62
p-phenylene diamine	0	0	—	—	—

Narcotics and Specificity of Oxidative Inhibitions

Narcotics do not inhibit all oxidative processes to the same extent. The oxidations of glucose, lactate, and pyruvate are most affected by the narcotics, whilst those of succinate and p-phenylene diamine are undisturbed. Data using the slice technic are shown in Tables 26 and 27 where it will be seen that glutamate oxidation is also affected.[21, 36] Glucose respiration is inhibited to the greatest extent.

TABLE 27. EFFECTS OF LUMINAL (0.08 PER CENT) ON BRAIN RESPIRATION IN PRESENCE OF VARIOUS METABOLITES (RAT BRAIN CORTEX SLICES)

Metabolite	Qo_2 without Narcotic	Qo_2 with Narcotic	Per Cent Effect of Narcotic on Qo_2
Nil	2.9	2.75	−5
Glucose 0.01 M	12.2	5.5	−55
Sodium d. lactate 0.02 M	13.5	8.8	−35
Sodium pyruvate 0.02 M	11.1	8.1	−27
Sodium glutamate 0.02 M	8.0	6.8	−15
Sodium succinate 0.02 M	9.5	10.2	+7

The high sensitivity of glucose oxidation in the brain to the narcotics is a striking feature of narcotic action *in vitro*, and, in view of the great importance of glucose oxidation in the functional activity of the central nervous system, this sensitivity seems to be a highly significant factor in any consideration of the mechanism of narcotic action.

TABLE 28.   EFFECT OF 0.033 PER CENT EVIPAN* ON RESPIRATION OF
GUINEA PIG TISSUES IN PRESENCE OF GLUCOSE

Tissue	Respiration (Qo_2)	Respiration (Qo_2) in Presence of Narcotic	Per Cent Inhibition by Narcotic
Brain	14.2	9.5	33
Spleen	7.7	6.4	17
Liver	4.25	4.15	2
Testis	8.65	7.25	16
Kidney	15.2	15.95	Nil.

* Sodium N-methyl-cyclohexenyl methyl barbiturate.

The total respiration of tissues other than brain is also affected by narcotics though not to the same degree. A result with evipan is given in Table 28. Examination, however, of the inhibitive action of narcotics on the respiration of a variety of tissues has shown that narcotics inhibit the oxidation of glucose, lactate, and pyruvate in tissues such as liver, kidney, or diaphragm to about the same extent as in brain.[21] It would seem that the effects of narcotics at low concentrations are confined, as in brain, to the inhibition of the combustion of substances important in carbohydrate metabolism. With brain, however, in contrast to such tissues as liver and kidney, carbohydrate metabolism is the dominant feature of metabolism and it is this fact which throws into prominence the specific inhibitory effects of narcotics in brain metabolism.

Kinetic Data

The inhibitive effects of narcotics such as the barbiturates or chloretone or hyoscine, or a drug such as mescaline which produces visual hallucinations, on the respiration of rat brain slices are reversible.[37] High concentrations of narcotics, however, produce irreversible effects. Analysis of the kinetic data indicates that two effects of a narcotic on brain respiration *in vitro* take place. There is a rapid attainment of an equilibrium between the narcotic and a constituent of the respiratory system. This follows the mass action law so long as the inhibition does not exceed 40 per cent. This applies to urethane, chloretone, chloral, barbiturates, avertin (tribromethanol), and magnesium ions. There is also a slow development of irreversible changes leading to increased inhibition of respiration that cannot be restored to normal by removal of the narcotic.[20, 21, 22] This takes place with most narcotics but is only observable at relatively high concentrations with narcotics such as barbiturates or chloretone. It occurs, however, at low concentrations with ether or ethanol. Irreversibility of action also occurs with indole which is also a powerful inhibitor of brain respiration. Conceivably this is due to gradual irreversible denaturation of the enzymes with which the drug becomes associated. It is important to remember that the physiologic effects of ether or ethanol on the brain, as shown by the electroencephalographic patterns, differ significantly from those of the barbiturates.

Effects of Potassium Ions

Another phenomenon bearing on the inhibitory effects of small concentrations of narcotics should be considered. The steady rate of the diminished respiration of brain slices brought about by small concentrations of luminal or chloretone is found to be greatly dependent on the concentration of potassium ions.[21] With the concentration of potassium found in blood or at higher concentrations, a steady and constant inhibition of respiration is obtained. But at low concentrations of potassium the respiration falls progressively. It is probable that the phenomenon is due to a leak of potassium from the cell at low external concentrations, and that potassium in the cell is essential for the metabolic changes affected by the narcotic.

Effects of Demerol and Amidone

Elliott and his associates[9] examined the effects of demerol and amidone, which are held to have similar *in vivo* effects to morphine, on brain oxidations. Morphine, to which reference will soon be made, has exceedingly little effect on brain respiration.[42] Demerol and amidone exert powerful effects at the relatively high concentrations tried (Table 29), on lactate and pyruvate oxidations. This and other evidence led Elliott and his co-workers to believe that the drugs inhibit the dehydrogenases involved, though the mechanism may differ from those involved in the inhibitions secured by anesthetics and hypnotics.

TABLE 29. THE EFFECT OF AMIDONE AND DEMEROL UPON THE OXIDATION OF LACTATE AND PYRUVATE BY CEREBRAL CORTEX SLICES

		Controls	Amidone 0.001 M	Demerol 0.001 M
Sodium lactate 0.02 M	Q_{O_2}	2.48	0.64	0.25
	Per cent inhibition		74	90
Sodium pyruvate 0.02 M	Q_{O_2}	2.32	0.47	0.14
	Per cent inhibition		80	94

Each value represents the average wet weight Q_{O_2} of eight vessels sixty minutes after the addition of the drug.

Steroids

An interesting set of results is shown in Table 30 where it is seen that steroids that have anesthetic potency also affect rat brain (homogenate) respiration in presence of glucose but not in presence of succinate.[13] The inhibitions parallel anesthetic action. There is an anomalous action of stilbestrol, which can now be accounted for by special reactions undergone by the substance.[17]

TABLE 30.   EFFECTS OF STEROIDS (INCLUDING STILBESTROL) ON RAT BRAIN (HOMOGENATE) RESPIRATION

			Per Cent Inhibition of Respiration			
	M.P. Degrees C.	A.R.U.* in Mg.	0.2 Per Cent Glucose Substrate	N	0.2 M Succinate Substrate	N
Desoxycorti-costerone	135	1.0†	87	12	15	12
Progesterone	125	2.0	28	10	10	10
Testosterone	151	7.0	24	18	1	10
Stilbestrol	173	20.0	91	19	44	14
α-estradiol	171	>20.0	14	9	3	9
Cholesterol	147	Inactive	14	10	0	10

* Figures from Selye: *Endocrinology*, 1942, 30, 437.
† Selye's value for desoxycorticosterone acetate.
M.P.—melting point.
A.R.U.—anesthetic rat unit.
N—number of vessels.
From Gordan and Elliott: *Endocrinology*, 1947, 41, p. 517.

Narcotics and Glycolysis

Low concentrations of narcotics do not affect the known dehydrogenases. Confirmation of this fact[29] comes from the entire absence of any inhibition by a narcotic such as chloretone on anaerobic glycolysis (Table 31) where an interplay of dehydrogenases is an essential part of this process. There is indeed evidence to show that narcotics increase aerobic glycolysis by sup-

TABLE 31.   EFFECT OF CHLORETONE ON ANAEROBIC GLYCOLYSIS BY BRAIN

	$Q_M^{N_2}$		
Medium without added chloretone	15.2	19.8	16.5
Medium with chloretone 0.033 per cent	15.1	—	—
Medium with chloretone 0.05 per cent	—	17.8	16.4

Rat brain cortex slices in sodium bicarbonate (0.025 M)—Locke solution containing 0.025 M glucose and 0.003 M sodium pyruvate; 95 per cent N_2+5 per cent CO_2; 37° C.

pression of the Pasteur effect. This is in line with the observation of Rosenberg and associates[40] that in presence of narcotics there is an increased rate of breakdown of glucose although there is a suppression of respiration.

Analysis of Respiratory Data

Analysis of the various links in the respiratory chain leading to glucose oxidation has shown that the initial and terminal parts of the chain, i.e., those enzymes that lead to both the activation of glucose and of oxygen, are quite insensitive to the action of the narcotic at low concentrations. If, however, to the mixture of these insensitive enzymes there be added preparations containing the carriers that enable the enzymes to interact, then the system becomes narcotic-sensitive. The indication is that there is a narcotic-sensitive intermediate factor (Table 32) which is taking part in a reaction between

TABLE 32.   NARCOTIC-SENSITIVE RESPIRATORY SYSTEM

Substrate-Dehydrogenase-Cozymase-Flavoprotein-Cytochrome-Cytochrome-
Oxygen Oxidase

Narcotic-Insensitive Region	Narcotic-Sensitive Region	Narcotic-Insensitive Region

reduced cozymase and a cytochrome. The evidence[29] indicates that a flavoprotein is involved and that some such enzyme as this is the narcotic sensitive factor. Grieg,[14] who has confirmed and extended these facts, considers that in the presence of the narcotic there is a binding of reduced flavoprotein with cytochrome 'b' or other intermediate. What seems to be clear is that some special component of the respiratory system is highly narcotic-sensitive and that the effects of the narcotics at biologic important concentrations are not to be attributed, as has been done in the past, to a general inhibition of dehydrogenase by nonspecific adsorption of the narcotics. It would be consistent with much of the data obtained that pyruvic oxidase, which is a flavoprotein, is one important site of narcotic action.[21]

Further Considerations

Although the evidence points to the participation of the narcotics in the respiratory processes of the nerve cell, the problem still remains as to how an effect on a respiratory process, or some important aspect of this, should result in the phenomenon of narcosis. This is understandable only, it seems to me, in terms of cell energetics. A definite rate and direction of energy flow is essential for the normal functioning of the cell, and a diminution or alteration of this, by a drug, may be expected to lead to a paralysis or disturbance of the cells that are affected. Thinking on these lines it may be asked how it is possible to interpret two aspects of narcotic action not hitherto explained: (1) the apparent stimulating action in the nervous system of small concentrations of narcotics, (2) the narcotic action of morphine which has but little action on brain respiration even at relatively high concentrations.

ATP Formation

Let us, in this connection, now consider an important aspect of respiration in the living cell, namely, the synthesis of energy-rich adenosine triphosphate (ATP) at the expense of the energy liberated by oxidations. On the basis of a free energy release of 50,000 to 56,000 calories per gram atom of oxygen consumed and a free energy absorption of 12,000 calories for the conversion of ADP to ATP the theoretic ratio of phosphate bonds formed to atoms of oxygen consumed (P.O. ratio) is 4.2 to 4.7. Experimental ratios of 3.5 to 3.9 and even higher values are recorded.[19, 33] It is known that phosphorylation is coupled with oxidation of reduced DPN,[23] and reduced flavoprotein[18, 23] whose P moiety has a very high rate of turnover, and of participants in the cytochrome system. For the maintenance of nervous activity, a high level of high energy P bonds is presumably of vital importance. My colleagues and I[35] showed nearly fifteen years ago that synthesis of acetylcholine takes place in the brain at the expense of energy derived during the aerobic oxidation of glucose or of its breakdown products lactate or pyruvate (though not of succinate in experiments *in vitro*) (Table 33). Nachmansohn and Machado[31] showed later that ATP is indispensable for acetylcho-

TABLE 33.   SYNTHESIS OF ACETYLCHOLINE BY RAT BRAIN IN
VITRO IN PRESENCE OF VARIOUS SUBSTITUTES

Minced Rat Brain
O_2; 37° C., *Eserine*

Substrate	Acetylcholine Formed γ/Gm.
Nil	2.8
Sodium Lactate	9.5
Sodium Pyruvate	11.4
Sodium Succinate	2.8
Glucose	11.1

Rat Brain Slices

Substrate	Acetylcholine Formed γ/Gm. Aerobic	Anaerobic
Nil	3.5	1.5
Glucose 20 mg. per cent	27.9	2.0
Fructose 20 mg. per cent	7.2	
Mannose 20 mg. per cent	20.0	
Galactose 20 mg. per cent	5.4	

line synthesis; in fact the process can be shown to take place anaerobically in brain homogenates and extracts when ATP is present in excess (Table 34). It is clear that during the aerobic oxidation of glucose, ATP enrichment occurs and that this leads to acetylcholine synthesis. It is also known now that the synthesis of acetylcholine depends on the integrity of the cozymase system present; in fact it is completely dependent, in intact brain, on an active respiratory metabolism involving combustion of glucose or lactate or pyruvate.[15]

TABLE 34.   BRAIN ACETONE POWDER, ANAEROBIC

Adenosine Triphosphate Present (Mg.)	Acetylcholine Formed (γ/Gm.)
0	6
0.01	7.5
0.05	113
0.1	115
0.2	212

It is found that in presence of quantities of narcotics that greatly suppress respiration, acetylcholine synthesis by brain is also greatly suppressed. This was shown very qualitatively over ten years ago[25] using ether (Table 35). It may also be shown that barbiturates will accomplish a similar depression of the synthesis of acetylcholine. McLennan and Elliott have reported a depression of synthesis by 50 per cent, and my colleague W. Johnson and I have obtained similar figures. There is always a concomitant drop in rate of respiration but this need not necessarily be as large.

TABLE 35.   RAT BRAIN (AIR, ONE HOUR, 37° C.)

Substrate	Total Acetylcholine Formed (γ/Gm.)
Phosphate—Locke's solution	5.0
Phosphate—Locke's solution+glucose	10.0
Phosphate—Locke's solution+ether (excess)	4.0
Phosphate—Locke's solution+glucose+ether (excess)	4.0

Narcotics do not diminish the anaerobic synthesis of acetylcholine by ATP in presence of brain extracts (unpublished evidence of Johnson and Quastel), and there is no evidence that any of the known phosphorylations by ATP (e.g., hexokinase, glycolytic reactions) are impeded by narcotics at low concentrations. The most obvious explanation of the inhibitory phenomena aerobically is that the narcotics inhibit those links in the respiratory chain which are responsible for the oxidative synthesis of ATP. On this view, the major effect of a narcotic is not the suppression of respiration as a whole; its effect is mainly concerned with that aspect of the respiratory process which is responsible for the development of high energy phosphate bonds of ATP. It follows from this that narcotics should affect metabolic processes dependent on the oxidative formation of ATP. Acetylations, generally, seem to be examples of such processes. My colleague, Mr. W. Johnson, and I have found (unpublished) that the synthesis of acetyl sulfanilamide in respiring liver, a process dependent on ATP, is markedly inhibited by small concentrations of narcotics and that the inhibition can be neutralized by addition to the system of ATP. This, I think, is the first time that a narcotic inhibition *in vitro* has been neutralized by chemical means.

It is obvious that this hypothesis, that narcotics act by suppressing the rate of oxidative development of ATP in the nerve cell, has wide implications. In this respect, the interesting work of McElroy[27A] should be consulted. Doubtless there are many aspects of metabolism in the nerve cell, equally important for its functional activity, which are controlled by the presence and rate of production of ATP. It should be pointed out that Eiler and McEwen[8] have shown that pentobarbital inhibits the generation of high energy phosphate bonds in brain tissue to the extent that it interferes with oxygen utilization.

Turning once again to acetylcholine, it has been known for some years[25] that this is present in brain in a bound form. It is found that treatment of brain with a small quantity of a narcotic such as ether releases free acetylcholine from the bound form. This may occur at concentrations of the narcotic that do not markedly affect the respiration and presumably, therefore, ATP synthesis of the nerve cell.

It seems possible that the stimulating action of narcotics at low concentrations may be due to release of free acetylcholine from the bound form. It is known, of course, that acetylcholine has highly exciting powers on the magnitudes of brain potentials. With higher concentrations of narcotics or with narcotics acting for long periods of time we may imagine that there occurs a depression of ATP formation (due to an effect on a respiratory component of the nerve cell) with consequent depression of acetylcholine synthesis, or of some other vital synthesis, and an inability therefore to maintain the nervous function associated with the cells affected. Such views are in harmony with what we know of the effects of narcotics on brain potentials[46] and of their effects on respiratory mechanisms.

Morphine

Let us now consider the action of morphine. It seems that, here, an entirely different mechanism from that so far pictured is involved. It is known[34] that morphine competes with acetylcholine for receptor groups in the neuromuscular junction in the leech muscle (Tables 36 and 37), the action being reversible and competitive. Similar phenomena occur with morphine

TABLE 36.   EFFECT OF MORPHINE ON CONTRACTIONS OF LEECH MUSCLE
DUE TO ACETYLCHOLINE

Quantity of Morphine Tartrate Added to the Medium (7 Ml.)	Minimum Quantity of Acetylcholine Chloride Required to Secure a Contraction
Nil	$<0.25\gamma$
250γ	0.025–0.05γ
500γ	0.05 –0.1γ
1000γ	0.1 –0.125γ
2000γ	0.2 –0.3γ
4000γ	0.3 –0.5γ

derivatives (heroin and codeine) but not with apomorphine whose pharmacologic action is quite different. The possibility arises that morphine and its allies act in the brain by competing with acetylcholine for those receptor groups whose combination with acetylcholine is essential for normal functioning of the nerve.

Convulsive Drugs

Let us consider some aspects of the effects of convulsive drugs. It is known that during convulsions there is an increased rate of cerebral circulation and oxygen consumption.[11, 12, 32, 41] In metrazol convulsion there has

TABLE 37.   EFFECTS OF MORPHINE DERIVATIVES ON CONTRACTIONS OF LEECH
MUSCLE DUE TO ACETYLCHOLINE

Morphine Derivatives	Quantity of Alkaloid Added to the Medium (7 Ml.)	Minimum Quantity of Acetylcholine Chloride Required to Give a Contraction
Heroin chloride (diacetyl-morphine)	100γ	0.05 –0.075γ
	250γ	0.1γ
	500γ	0.15 –0.2γ
Morphine chloride	250γ	0.025 –0.05γ
	500γ	0.075γ
	1000γ	0.1 –0.15γ
Codein phosphate (methyl-morphine)	250	$<0.025\gamma$
	500γ	0.05γ
	1000γ	0.075 –0.1γ
Dionine chloride (ethyl-morphine)	500γ	0.05γ
	1000γ	0.075γ
Apomorphine chloride	500γ	$<0.025\gamma$
	1000γ	$<0.025\gamma$

been noticed decreased phosphocreatine and increased inorganic phosphate and lactic acid in the brain.[45] This can be explained by the increased rate of oxygen consumption and by a greater demand and utilization of ATP, so that the phosphocreatine store drops. Whether the ATP level will fall or not simply depends on the balance of reactions leading to its synthesis or breakdown. In spite of the increased blood supply, the increased rate of oxygen consumption leads to a lowering of oxygen tension and possibly increased glycolysis.[7] Such convulsants as metrazol and picrotoxin have little or no effect on oxygen consumption of the isolated tissue[24, 47] and there is no evidence as yet to account for their effects.

The convulsive action of fluoracetate is possibly linked with the fact that it leads to the formation in brain of citrate[4] by an interference with the operation of the tricarboxylic cycle. It is known that convulsions can occur immediately, if citrate is injected intracisternally, presumably because of calcium immobilization. But possibly citrate has other effects that may lead to convulsions; for instance, it greatly influences, in brain extracts, the course of acetylcholine metabolism.

Another very interesting convulsive drug is methionine-sulphoximine, a product formed from proteins by the action of nitrogen trichloride. This substance produces in animals a state resembling human epilepsy.[2, 3, 28, 30] It is tempting to speculate that this substance may act in the brain by a disturbance of the glutamic-acid–glutamine equilibrium, a process known to be affected by methioninesulfoxide itself. It produces no changes in the oxygen uptake of brain and its toxic effect is stated to be overcome by large doses of methionine.

Ammonium ions are said to play a considerable role in the mechanism of convulsive seizures and it is known that they are liberated under such conditions.[38, 39] Ammonium ions have large effects on various aspects of brain metabolism, e.g., respiration, glycolysis, and acetylcholine formation, and it is obvious that the effects of this ion should be investigated more thoroughly. Glutamate injections are reported to inhibit ammonium chloride convulsions and also to reduce attacks in cases of petit mal. Possibly the glutamate reduces the ammonium ion concentrations in the cell by glutamine condensation, but if so ATP once again comes into the picture for the condensation is dependent upon it.

The biochemical effects of benzedrine or amphetamine, an analeptic, with stimulant properties leading to increased wakefulness and euphoria, are of interest. It decreases duration of post-seizure depression following electric shock and seems to compensate to a considerable degree for the adverse effects produced by various lesions of the central nervous system. Biochemically,[26] it is known to have a high affinity for amine oxidase in the brain, an enzyme which oxidizes amines to aldehydes which have a very high toxicity on respiratory systems in the brain. In the presence of benzedrine, the progressive fall in respiration of brain in the presence of amines such as tyramine is halted, and the net result is that respiration of brain is increased. Whether this phenomenon is linked with the narcoleptic action of benzedrine is not known, but the effects take place *in vitro* at concentrations approximately those effective *in vivo*. Benzedrine has also a high affinity for enzymes concerned with choline activations and can compete with choline for choline oxidase, an enzyme, however, which is not present in brain.[5] Doubtless its effects are multiple and only further work will reveal the extent to which it is fully involved in systems in the nerve cell.

Succinate

A final word may be said about succinate as a possible analeptic. The results of Barrett,[1] showing an effect of succinate in reducing the depth of narcosis, have been confirmed by some workers and not by others. It has been reported that succinate can terminate abruptly the visual hallucinations due to mescaline in human beings. It seems possible, in view of what has already been said, that if succinate oxidation could give rise to ATP formation, an effect on the narcotic state might be expected. Results *in vitro* are contradictory. Some claim that succinate can secure ATP synthesis and others have not been successful. It is evident that further factors involved in this phenomenon have yet to be elucidated. In a similar class, perhaps, comes glutamate which has been shown to be capable of replacing glucose in hypoglycemic coma and in experiments on responses of the cord. Further work on these lines is needed, for there seems to be no *a priori* reason why, if our reasoning is correct and our hypotheses have some truth in them, we should not one day be in a much better position to control chemically the narcotic state.

REFERENCES

1. BARRETT, R. H.: *Anaesthesia and Analgesia*, 1947, 26, 74, p. 105.
2. BENTLEY, H. R.; McDERMOTT, E. E.; PACE, J.; WHITEHEAD, J. K.; and MORAN, F.: *Nature*, 1949, 164, p. 438; 1950, 165, p. 150.
3. BENTLEY, H. R.; McDERMOTT, E. E.; and WHITEHEAD, J. K.: *Nature,* 1950, 165, p. 735.
4. BUFFA, P., and PETERS, R. A.: *Journal of Physiology*, 1949, 110, p. 488.
5. COLTER, J. S., and QUASTEL, J. H.: *Nature*, 1950, 166, p. 773.
6. DAMESHEK, W.; MYERSON, A.; and LOMAN, J.: *American Journal of Psychiatry*, 1934, 91, p. 113.
7. DAVIES, R. W., and REMOND, ANTOINE: *Association for Research in Nervous and Mental Disease, Proceedings*, 1946, 26, p. 205.
8. EILER, J. J., and McEWEN, W. K.: *Archives of Biochemistry*, 1949, 20, p. 163.
9. ELLIOTT, H. W.; WARRENS, A. E.; and JAMES, H. P.: *Journal of Pharmacology and Experimental Therapeutics*, 1947, 91, p. 98.
10. FUHRMAN, F. A., and FIELD, J.: *Journal of Pharmacology and Experimental Therapeutics*, 1943, 77, p. 392.
11. GEIGER, A., and MAGNES, J.: *American Journal of Physiology*, 1947, 149, p. 517.

12. GIBBS, F. A.; LENNOX, W. G.; and GIBBS, E. L.: *Archives of Neurology and Psychiatry*, 1934, 32, p. 257.

13. GORDAN, G. S., and ELLIOTT, H. W.: *Endocrinology*, 1947, 41, p. 517.

14. GREIG, M. E.: *Journal of Pharmacology and Experimental Therapeutics*, 1946, 87, p. 185.

15. HARPUR, R. P., and QUASTEL, J. H.: *Nature*, 1949, 164, p. 865.

16. HIMWICH, W. A.; HOMBURGER, EDMUND; MARESCA, ROBERT; and HIMWICH, H. E.: *American Journal of Psychiatry*, 1947, 103, p. 689.

17. HOCHSTER, R. M., and QUASTEL, J. H.: *Nature*, 1949, 164, p. 865.

18. HUMMEL, J. P., and LINDBERG, O.: *Journal of Biological Chemistry*, 1949, 180, p. 1.

19. HUNTER, F. E., JR., and HIXON, W. S.: *Journal of Biological Chemistry*, 1949, 181, p. 73.

20. JOWETT, M.: *The Journal of Physiology*, 1938, 92, p. 322.

21. JOWETT, M., and QUASTEL, J. H.: *Biochemical Journal*, 1937, 31, p. 565.

22. JOWETT, M., and QUASTEL, J. H.: *Biochemical Journal*, 1937, 31, p. 1101.

23. LEHNINGER, A. L., and SMITH, S. W.: *Journal of Biological Chemistry*, 1949. 181, p. 415.

24. MACLEOD, L. D., and REISS, M.: *Journal of Mental Science*, 1940, 86, p. 276.

25. MANN, P. J. G.; TENNENBAUM, M.; and QUASTEL, J. H.: *Biochemical Journal*, 1938, 32, p. 343.

26. MANN, P. J. G., and QUASTEL, J. H.: *Biochemical Journal*, 1940, 34, p. 414.

27. McCLURE, R. D.; HARTMANN, F. W.; SCHNEDORF, J. G.; and SCHELLING, V.: *Annals of Surgery*, 1939, 110, p. 836.

27a. McELROY, W. D.: *Quarterly Review of Biology*, 1947, 22, p. 25.

28. MELLANBY, E.: *British Medical Journal*, 1946, 2, p. 4484; 1947, 2, p. 288.

29. MICHAELIS, M., and QUASTEL, J. H.: *Biochemical Journal*, 1941, 35, p. 518.

30. MORAN, T.: *Lancet*, 1947, 253 (2), p. 289.

31. NACHMANSOHN, D., and MACHADO, A. L.: *Journal of Neurophysiology*, 1943, 6, p. 397.

32. PENFIELD, W.; VON SANTHA, K.; and CIPRIANI, A.: *Journal of Neurophysiology*, 1939, 2, p. 257.

33. POLIS, DAVIS; POLIS, EDITH; KERRIGAN, MAXINE; and JEDEIKIN, LILLIAN: *Archives of Biochemistry*, 1949, 23, p. 505.

34. QUASTEL, J. H., and TENNENBAUM, M.: *Journal of Pharmacology and Experimental Therapeutics*, 1937, 60, p. 228.

35. QUASTEL, J. H.; TENNENBAUM, M.; and WHEATLEY, A. H. M.: *Biochemical Journal*, 1936, 30, p. 1668.

36. QUASTEL, J. H., and WHEATLEY, A. H. M.: *Proceedings of the Royal Society, series B*, 1932, 112, p. 60.

37. QUASTEL, J. H., and WHEATLEY, A. H. M.: *Biochemical Journal*, 1934, 28, p. 1521.

38. RICHTER, D.; DAWSON, R. M. C.; and LEES: *Journal of Mental Science*, 1949, 95, p. 148.

39. RICHTER, D., and DAWSON, R. M. C.: *Journal of Biological Chemistry*, 1948, 176, p. 1199.

40. ROSENBERG, A. J.; BUCHEL, LEYA; ETLING, NICOLE; and LEVY, JEANNE: *Comptes rendus hebdomadaires des séances de l'Academie des sciences*. 1950, 230, p. 480.

41. SCHMIDT, C. F.; KETY, S. S.; and PENNES, H. H.: *American Journal of Physiology*, 1945, 143, p. 33.

42. Seevers, M. H., and Shidemann, F. E.: *Journal of Pharmacology and Experimental Therapeutics*, 1941, 71, p. 373.
43. Selye, H.: *Endocrinology*, 1942, 30, p. 437.
44. Shaw, J. L.; Steele, B. F.; and Lamb, C. A.: *Archives of Surgery*, 1937, 35, p. 1
45. Stone, W. E.; Webster, J. E.; and Gurdjian, E. S.: *Journal of Neurophysiology*, 1945, 8, p. 233.
46. Tucci, J. H.; Brazier, M. A. B.; Miles, H. H. W.; and Finesinger, J. E.: *Anaesthesiology*, 1949, 10, p. 25.
47. Webb, J. L.; and Elliott, K. A. C.: *Federation Proceedings*, 1950, 9, p. 243; *Canadian Journal of Research*, 1948, 26, p. 239.
48. Westfall, B. A.: *Journal of Pharmacology and Experimental Therapeutics*, 1949, 96, p. 193.

Cholinergic Excitation and Adrenergic Inhibition Common to Peripheral and Central Synapses

AMEDEO S. MARRAZZI, M.D.

The hour apparently is rapidly approaching when we do indeed pass from the mental to the physical, or from the cerebral to the gastric. In view of that, I shall attempt to distract you by posing, first, a question with which I had hoped to conclude.

In the study of central nervous system phenomena, the application of the hypothesis that activity could be explained in terms of properties of the peripheral neuron has, as you all know, been very fruitful. I wish to pose the question whether it is not now time to raise a similar question as to the peripheral synapse and whether that sort of inquiry may not indeed be as fruitful and be the second step in the thinking that is now indicated.

Lest you think that my remarks will be entirely divorced from the topic at issue, I will revert briefly to the introduction that I had planned, namely, that it is difficult to think of mental health and disease without being aware that emotion is a conspicuous characteristic feature, and it is difficult to picture emotion without the accompanying autonomic disturbances that characterize it, or the change in internal environment. It is also common knowledge that in some obscure fashion these disturbances tend to perpetuate the emotion that originally engendered them.

Now, since the complex patterns of central nervous system activity can be regarded as an expression of synaptic function, and since the synapse is recognized to be the site that is most vulnerable, some data on aspects of synaptic function may be of assistance and may be pertinent to an analysis of the development of the vicious cycle that I have just described which, when it persists abnormally and is abnormally intense, can be interpreted to constitute mental disease at least in some of its forms.

In order to obtain such data, one has had to make use of a technic that is sufficiently discriminating, accurately localizing, and sensitive.[4, 13] This

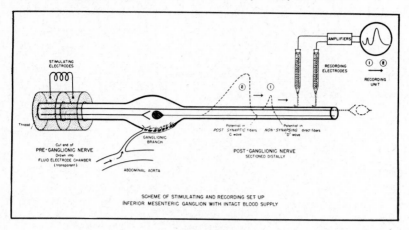

FIG. 123.

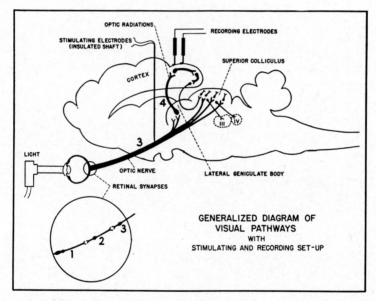

FIG. 124.

was frequently accomplished by applying a test stimulus to a group of synapses, in this case a sympathetic ganglion (Fig. 123) retaining its normal circulation, and recording the electrical activity immediately postsynaptically as an index of what was going on at the site we were interested in, i.e. at the synapse.

In passing, I might point out that in this particular preparation there are fibers running through, such as Lloyd[3] describes, so that one can simultaneously compare transmission phenomena or what occurs at the synapse with what occurs at the fiber or conduction. Let us hark back for a moment to the comments that Dr. Lilienthal has made concerning the possible importance of some cholinesterase being found in the nerve and the interpretation attached to it, that acetylcholine had a role in conduction, but that *in vitro* this had definitely been shown to be very doubtful. We can readily show that *in vivo*, on introducing DFP, one finds a tremendous action on synaptic transmission as indicated by the postsynaptic potentials, and no action on conduction, as indicated by the potentials from the fibers running through without synapsing.

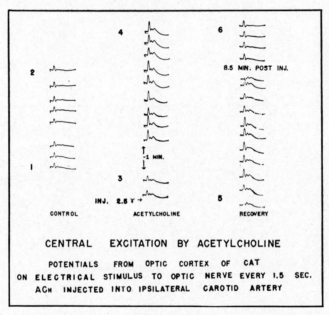

CENTRAL EXCITATION BY ACETYLCHOLINE

POTENTIALS FROM OPTIC CORTEX OF CAT
ON ELECTRICAL STIMULUS TO OPTIC NERVE EVERY 1.5 SEC.
ACh INJECTED INTO IPSILATERAL CAROTID ARTERY

Fig. 125.

To get back to the point, however, our studies with this system indicated to us that the synaptic responses to acetylcholine and to adrenaline are related in a characteristic reciprocal fashion, i.e., excitation by acetylcholine[8] and inhibition by adrenaline[5, 6, 13] and by associated drugs[4, 9]—which I will not go into—in much the same fashion as is true at neuro-effectors. There are apparently the makings of a humoral mechanism capable of operating here, a cholinergic excitatory one and a complementary adrenergic inhibitory one.

Then we went on to stress the question that we had originally posed, namely, whether at other synapses one might not find the same thing. Figure 124 shows an effort to duplicate in the brain the simple preparation that you have seen before, by stimulating the optic tract, passing through two groups of synapses, although we would have preferred to have only one, and

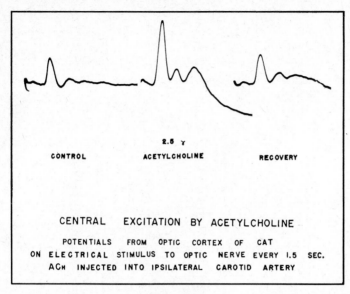

CENTRAL   EXCITATION   BY   ACETYLCHOLINE

POTENTIALS   FROM   OPTIC   CORTEX   OF   CAT
ON   ELECTRICAL   STIMULUS   TO   OPTIC   NERVE   EVERY   1.5   SEC.
ACн   INJECTED   INTO   IPSILATERAL   CAROTID   ARTERY

FIG. 126.

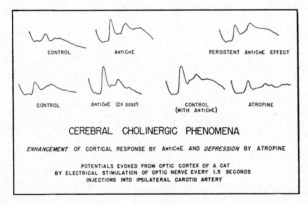

CEREBRAL   CHOLINERGIC   PHENOMENA

ENHANCEMENT OF CORTICAL RESPONSE BY ᴀɴᴛɪCнᴇ AND *DEPRESSION* BY ATROPINE

POTENTIALS EVOKED FROM OPTIC CORTEX OF A CAT
BY ELECTRICAL STIMULATION OF OPTIC NERVE EVERY 1.5 SECONDS
INJECTIONS INTO IPSILATERAL CAROTID ARTERY

FIG. 127.

recording from the optic cortex. We can now determine what happens within this system possibly at the synapses, possibly at the nerve fibers, if we stimulate every one and one-half seconds and use the complex cortical potential merely as a signal of the arrival of the impulse at the optic cortex. Figure 125 shows the results from such an experiment in the cat in which, after controls are obtained, a minute amount of acetylcholine (2.5 gamma— not 10 per cent or even 1 per cent painted on the cortex) is injected into the ipsilateral carotid artery.[10] It may be seen that within a short period of time there is a marked increase in the response. The recovery shows that we are not dealing merely with a fortuitous occurrence associated with a drug, but with a phenomenon that not only can be reproduced at will but from which there is a return to normal. You see this more clearly, perhaps, in Figure 126, which shows enlarged traces of control, maximum effect, and recovery from the same experiment.

The same sort of thing is also obtained by an anticholinesterase suggesting strongly that indeed there must be acetylcholine natural to the site. In Figure 127 it may be seen that the anticholinesterase produces a marked increase over the control which, in this case, cannot return to normal because

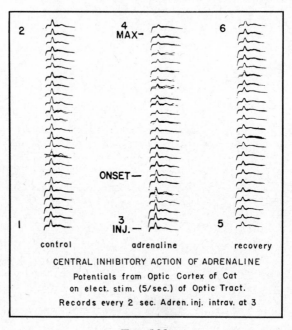

CENTRAL INHIBITORY ACTION OF ADRENALINE
Potentials from Optic Cortex of Cat
on elect. stim. (5/sec.) of Optic Tract.
Records every 2 sec. Adren. inj. intrav. at 3

Fig. 128.

of the persistent nature of the action of this anticholinesterase. Doubling the dose doubles the effect approximately. The persistent effect can characteristically be blocked, as is shown, by atropine.

Inhibition by adrenaline[7] is illustrated in Figure 128. The injection of adrenaline in this case was intravenous and, within one circulation time, there is depression followed by recovery. Figure 129 shows the maximum inhibition compared with the control and recovery.

If the synapses in this system are, indeed, like those in sympathetic ganglia, and in turn like the neuroeffector junction as, for example, those in striated muscle, then curare[11] should have an action in the brain similar to that which it has in striated muscle. As may be seen in Figure 130, it does have a blocking action.

In the system now being demonstrated there is the possibility of an action

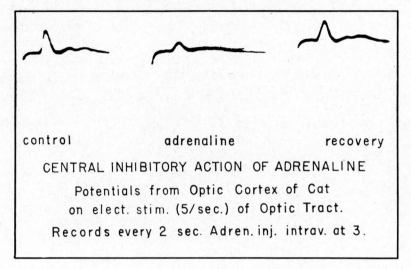

control   adrenaline   recovery

CENTRAL INHIBITORY ACTION OF ADRENALINE

Potentials from Optic Cortex of Cat
on elect. stim. (5/sec.) of Optic Tract.

Records every 2 sec. Adren. inj. intrav. at 3.

FIG. 129.

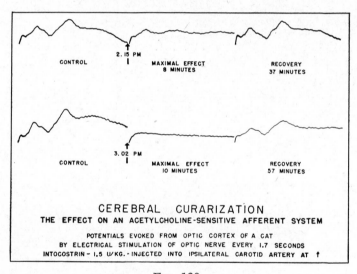

2.15 PM

CONTROL   MAXIMAL EFFECT   RECOVERY
                              8 MINUTES   37 MINUTES

3.02 PM

CONTROL   MAXIMAL EFFECT   RECOVERY
                             10 MINUTES   57 MINUTES

CEREBRAL   CURARIZATION
THE EFFECT ON AN ACETYLCHOLINE-SENSITIVE AFFERENT SYSTEM

POTENTIALS EVOKED FROM OPTIC CORTEX OF A CAT
BY ELECTRICAL STIMULATION OF OPTIC NERVE EVERY 1.7 SECONDS
INTOCOSTRIN - 1.5 U/KG. - INJECTED INTO IPSILATERAL CAROTID ARTERY AT ↑

FIG. 130.

on either or both of two synapses and on the connecting fibers. In order to
localize the effect to one synapse, we resorted to the Curtis and Bard[1, 2]
preparation in which one can stimulate the optic cortex on one side and
record from the cortex on the other side. The impulse passes through the
corpus callosum, through one synapse, and then produces activity in the
contralateral optic cortex. The preparation is illustrated in Figure 131.
As Curtis and Bard pointed out, in a volume conductor the negativity of
the presynaptic neuron reflects itself as a surface positivity, and the nega-

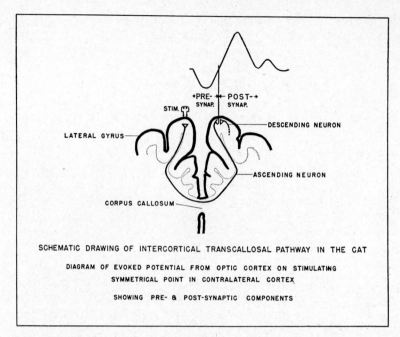

SCHEMATIC DRAWING OF INTERCORTICAL TRANSCALLOSAL PATHWAY IN THE CAT

DIAGRAM OF EVOKED POTENTIAL FROM OPTIC CORTEX ON STIMULATING
SYMMETRICAL POINT IN CONTRALATERAL CORTEX

SHOWING PRE- & POST-SYNAPTIC COMPONENTS

FIG. 131.

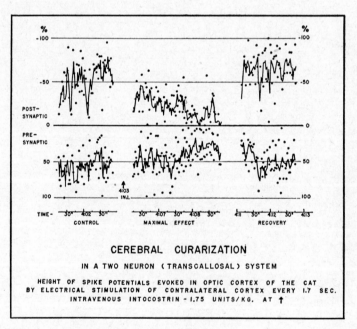

CEREBRAL CURARIZATION

IN A TWO NEURON (TRANSCALLOSAL) SYSTEM

HEIGHT OF SPIKE POTENTIALS EVOKED IN OPTIC CORTEX OF THE CAT
BY ELECTRICAL STIMULATION OF CONTRALATERAL CORTEX EVERY 1.7 SEC.
INTRAVENOUS INTOCOSTRIN - 1.75 UNITS/KG. AT ↑

FIG. 132.

tivity under the recording electrode over the postsynaptic neuron as a surface negativity. We, therefore, have practically a monosynaptic preparation
with a simultaneous record of impulses going in and coming out of this
particular group of synapses. This makes it possible to determine whether
a change in postsynaptic potential originates in the presynaptic neuron or
is a result of changes in synaptic transmission.

Such experiments have shown us[12] that the locus of the cortical excitatory
action of acetylcholine, inhibitory action of adrenaline, and blocking action
of atropine is at the synapse. The results with curare (Fig. 132) are an
example of this technic. In this case, we did not induce an anesthesia sufficiently deep to suppress the spontaneous cortical potentials. The evoked
potentials are, therefore, superimposed upon the spontaneous electroencephalogram. Through the plotted points we have run a moving average
of three consecutive points, dropping one and adding one as we move to each
successive point. It appears that the changes are postsynaptic rather than
presynaptic and that curare produces a marked depression from which
there is eventual recovery to the control level.

In summary, then, it would seem that we have obtained evidence at
least in the systems that we have studied of a cholinergic excitatory system
and an adrenergic inhibitory system.

With respect to the latter, I would like briefly to point out that the
results in the optic system might well give the basis for the well-known
"blindness" with rage. It could readily be conceived that in this state of
extreme emotion the adrenaline liberated into the blood stream might act on
the human optic cortex in the manner we have illustrated in the cat and
thereby produce blackout or temporary "blindness" which would be
terminated by the normal destruction of adrenaline. Perhaps there are
other clinical entities that can be traced to disturbances of this kind where
materials like acetylcholine or adrenaline are liberated in the body, and, if
that is true, it immediately suggests a proper therapy—at least a symptomatic therapy.

REFERENCES

1. CURTIS, H. J.: *Journal of Neurophysiology*, 1940, 3, p. 407, 414.
2. CURTIS, H. J., and BARD, P.: *American Journal of Physiology*, 1939, 126, p. 473.
3. LLOYD, D. E. P. C.: *Journal of Physiology*, 1937, 91, p. 296.
4. MARRAZZI, A. S : *Journal of Pharmacology and Experimental Therapeutics*, 1939, 65, p. 18.
5. MARRAZZI, A. S.: *Journal of Pharmacology and Experimental Therapeutics*, 1939, 65, p. 395.
6. MARRAZZI, A. S.: *American Journal of Physiology*, 1939, 127, p. 738.
7. MARRAZZI, A. S.: *Federation Proceedings*, 1943, 2, p. 33.
8. MARRAZZI, A. S.: *Journal of the Michigan State Medical Society*, 1947, 49, 6, p. 688.

9. MARRAZZI, A. S.: *Bulletin of the School of Medicine of the University of Mary land*, 1949, 33, p. 154.
10. MARRAZZI, A. S., and HART, E. R.: *Federation Proceedings*, 1950, 9, p. 85.
11. MARRAZZI, A. S.; HART, E. R.; and KING, E. E.: *Proceedings of the American Society for Pharmacology and Experimental Therapeutics*, November, 1950.
12. MARRAZZI, A. S., and KING, E. E.: *American Journal of Physiology*, 1950, 163, p. 732.
13. MARRAZZI, A. S., and MARRAZZI, R. N.: *Journal of Neurophysiology*, 1947, 10, p. 167.

Effects of Anesthetics on Oxygen Consumption and Synaptic Transmission in Sympathetic Ganglia

MARTIN G. LARRABEE, PH.D.

The following is a brief report of experiments, performed in collaboration with Dr. J. Garcia Ramos, which are closely related to a question raised by Dr. Quastel. The question is whether the effects of anesthetics on the functional properties of neurons result from a primary interference with oxygen uptake. Difficulties in interpreting existing evidence have been described in a recent review by Butler.[1]

Our objective was to measure simultaneously the rate of oxygen uptake and the functional capacity of nerve cells under conditions in which the activity of the nerve cells was known to be under experimental control. Accordingly our observations were made on sympathetic ganglia of mammals. It has been shown that synaptic processes in these ganglia are significantly sensitive to anesthetic agents, since ganglionic transmission is depressed when an animal is anesthetized to a surgical level, at least with ether and chloroform.[2]

In the experiments to be described, superior cervical ganglia were excised from rabbits and placed in a chamber made of Lucite (Fig. 133). A suitable solution, flowing through this chamber, sustained the tissue for many hours. Close to the ganglion was the tip of a platinum electrode, polarized in such a way that the current flowing through it was directly proportional to the oxygen concentration in the solution. At intervals of five minutes the flow of solution was arrested, and the rate of oxygen consumption measured by the speed with which oxygen disappeared from the solution surrounding the ganglion. Capacity to transmit impulses was tested by stimulating the preganglionic nerve and recording the action potential of the postganglionic nerve.

In the first experiments, volleys of preganglionic impulses were initiated only occasionally so that the results concerned nerve cells which were essentially at rest. The principles found in all such observations on resting cells may be illustrated by an experiment with chloretone. The results are plotted against time in Figure 134. At sufficiently high concentrations there was a marked slowing of oxygen consumption. However, in low concentra-

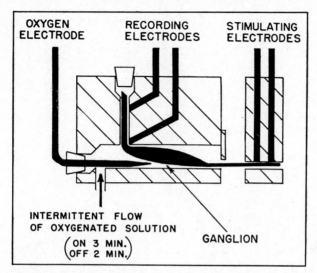

FIG. 133.   Respirometer for excised sympathetic ganglia. The oxygen electrode was insulated except at its tip; the circuit for this electrode was completed through a calomel half-cell which is not shown in the diagram. The oxygenated bathing solution was equilibrated with 5 per cent carbon dioxide, 95 per cent oxygen, and contained sodium chloride, potassium chloride, calcium chloride, magnesium chloride, phosphate, bicarbonate (pH 7.4), and glucose. The respirometer was immersed in a temperature bath at 34° to 37° C.

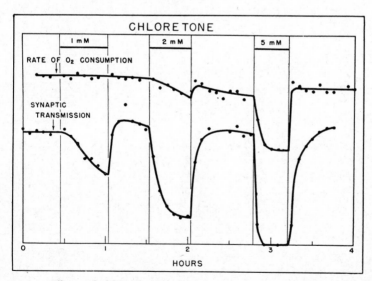

FIG. 134.   Effects of chloretone on rate of oxygen consumption and on synaptic transmission. In this and Figures 135 and 136, transmission was measured by height of postganglionic action potential in response to a volley of presynaptic impulses. Both functions are plotted on a linear ordinate scale with zero at the level of the time scale.

tions there was a range in which synaptic transmission was impaired without detectable effect on oxygen consumption.

Figure 135 represents two experiments using chloroform with results plotted against its concentration. These experiments, like the one with chloretone, reveal marked interference with the capacity to transmit impulses in concentrations too low to depress the rate of oxygen consumption by a measurable amount. A similar independence of functional from oxidative effects was found with all other anesthetics studied, including ether, pentobarbital, urethane, ethyl alcohol, methyl alcohol, and cocaine.[3]

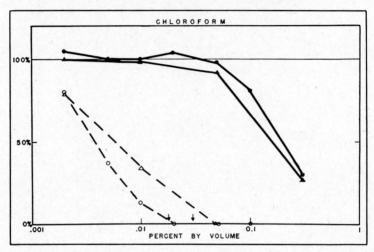

FIG. 135. Depression of rate of oxygen consumption (solid lines) and of synaptic transmission (dashed lines) by chloroform. Observations were made under essentially resting conditions. Both variables are expressed as percentage of their values in the absence of anesthetic. Two arrows above axis of abscissas indicate approximate concentrations of chloroform in blood during surgical anesthesia.

Thus the functional effects of anesthetics on this tissue under these conditions were clearly not ascribable to any effect on oxygen uptake. We may accordingly raise the question, would effects on oxygen consumption of brain tissue be found at the minimal concentrations of anesthetics required to affect function if respiration and functional capacity could be measured simultaneously, and particularly under conditions in which cellular activity is controlled?

Special emphasis may be placed on the requirement that cellular activity should be controlled, for reasons illustrated in the following observations. In these experiments the ganglion cells were not at rest, but the preganglionic nerve was stimulated about ten times per second. Such stimulation elevates the rate of oxygen consumption, typically by about one-half the resting rate.[4] We have compared the effects of a number of agents on this increment in oxygen consumption with their effects on the transmission of nerve impulses. Under these conditions, as shown in Figure 136, urethane and chloretone depressed the oxygen consumption in almost perfect proportion to their effects on synaptic transmission.

Here, then, are results in agreement with the hypothesis that anesthetics limit function by restricting oxygen uptake. This is not, however, the only interpretation which can be made of these observations, for it is quite impossible to tell which is the cause and which is the effect. It is thus equally possible that anesthetics depress cellular activity by some mechanism entirely unrelated to oxygen consumption and that the metabolic changes are merely a secondary result of the changes in activity.

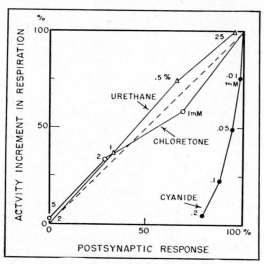

Fig. 136.   Activity increment in rate of oxygen consumption (ordinate) and height of the postsynaptic action potential (abscissa) in presence of various agents during preganglionic nerve stimulation at a frequency of approximately 10 per second. The two variables were affected nearly equally by the anesthetics: cyanide reduced oxygen uptake much more than it did the postsynaptic response. Both variables are expressed as percentage of their values in the absence of anesthetics and cyanide.

These last experiments on sympathetic ganglion cells thus illustrate a difficulty not as yet generally surmounted in attempting to demonstrate a metabolic basis for the depression of brain cell activity by a variety of agents. The difficulty in investigations on the central nervous system arises from spontaneous and experimentally uncontrolled neuronal activity. In the case of sympathetic ganglia it has been possible to make observations on resting neurons, as described in the first part of this discussion. Under these well-controlled conditions, the functional effects of anesthetics were independent of measurable retardation of oxygen consumption.

REFERENCES

1. BUTLER, T. C.: *Journal of Pharmacology and Experimental Therapeutics*, Part II, 1950, 98, pp. 121-160.
2. HOLADAY, D., and LARRABEE, M. G.: *Federation Proceedings*, 1951, 10, p. 310.
3. LARRABEE, M. G.; RAMOS, J. GARCIA; and BULBRING, E.: *Federation Proceedings*, 1950, 9, p. 75.
4. POSTERNAK, J. M.; LARRABEE, M. G.; and BRONK, D. W.: *Federation Proceedings*, 1947, 6, p. 182.

CHAPTER 24

Biologic Implications of Mongolism

THEODORE H. INGALLS, M.D.

MONGOLISM IS NOT A mental disease. It is no more confined to the mind than is general paresis of the insane. Like general paresis, mongolism is an end result and a localized manifestation of illness which overtook the individual earlier in life. To be sure, the manifestations are localized to a degree that justifies classification as a clinical entity. This does not make mongolism a biologic entity. Furthermore, mongolism is a kind of keystone among the congenital defects of mankind, since more observations probably have been recorded on the subject than upon any other congenital disorder. Its curious stigmas, illustrated in Figure 137, have seized the medical imagination and led to numerous investigations during the eighty-five years which have passed since Langdon Downe recognized the disease as a syndrome. As a consequence, sufficient data have accumulated to test provisionally almost any hypothesis that can be advanced concerning causation —even the absurd speculation, which was popularized years ago along with the Jukes and the Kallikaks, that the condition was racial evidence of "the Mongol in our midst." More reasonable suppositions which have received study are the possibilities that mongolism is primarily a genetic disorder,[4,23] or an expression of defective germ plasm,[22, 26] or that it is one of the many manifestations of effects from pathogenic agents which may act on the fetus during intrauterine stages of existence.[14, 15, 16, 19]

Characteristics of Mongolism

Although no single defect is pathognomonic of mongolism, a few signs are constant. As the original and unfortunate name "mongolian idiocy" implied, all patients are mentally retarded, usually to a degree of imbecility rather than idiocy. The skull has never been reported to be other than brachycephalic. There is corresponding restriction of cerebral development, and the forward growth of the face shows constant evidence of arrested growth (Fig. 138). The last characteristic, termed acromicria by contrast to acromegaly, gives the face a bulldog-like flatness, representing suppressed development of the sinuses and acral parts (Fig. 139). Acromicria, together

389

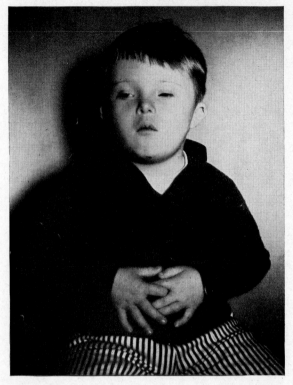

Fig. 137.   Mongoloid boy showing typical facies with depressed nasion and epicanthal folds. Note also the short incurved little finger.

with slight slanting of the palpebral fissures, gives the facies a mongoloid cast, especially when an epicanthus is prominent, a feature which tends to disappear if the patient survives childhood.[3, 21]

Hypotheses of Pathogenesis of Mongolism

The argument that this syndrome is of hereditary origin finds little positive support in the numerous studies of frequency distributions among relatives of mongoloid patients. Benda, for example, found that only two of 255 families with one mongoloid child had a second.[3] This is not to ignore heredity, for genetic factors play some part, however large, however small, in the pathogenesis of all well-understood diseases. Sunburn is determined by the inherited pigment of the skin no less than by exposure to actinic rays. The burn, however, can hardly be considered an inherited condition. Stronger evidence against primary genetic causation in mongolism is that patients do not reproduce. With familial incidence as low as 1 or 2 per cent, and with direct descent playing no part in its propagation, the possibility that mongolism represents a mutation may be considered, only to be

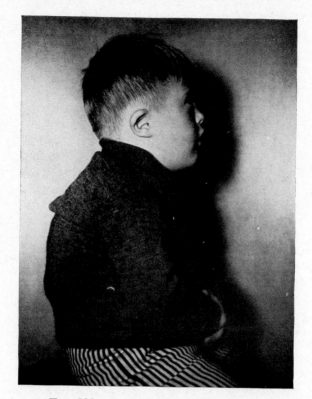

FIG. 138.   Lateral view of the patient.

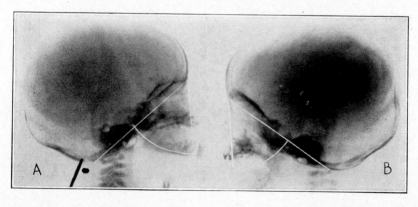

FIG. 139.   A, normal skull; the hiatus between the sphenoid and occipital bones representing the spheno-occipital cartilage may be seen. B, mongoloid skull; dwarfing of the acral parts, representing lack of forward development of the face and the basilar part of the cranium, may be seen. In this particular instance the nasal bones are absent. When present, they will constantly be found to be dwarfed. *Am. J. Dis. Child.* 73: 279, 1947.

abandoned because of the frequency with which the disease occurs, about twice per 1000 births.[2, 6, 24]

The hypothesis that mongolism is due to defective germ plasm is derived from the more than sixty reported occurrences in each of homozygous twins. Recognition in one of homozygous twins is so rare as to be of questionable authenticity.[3, 27] If satisfactorily documented, the circumstance would prove an acquired origin of the disease. The available facts relating to twins argue no more strongly for a genetic or primordial defect of the germ plasm than they do for acquisition of the disease *in utero* when homozygous twins are sharing an environment that is essentially identical. At best, the term "defective germ plasm" in its application to mongolism is a speculation. The challenge to explain what the disease really is and how it propagates is side-stepped.

A third hypothesis is that mongolism is acquired *in utero*. The purpose of this presentation is to examine critically the evidence for that interpretation and its implications.

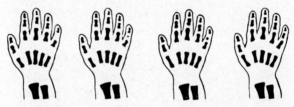

Fig. 140.   Different types of fifth-finger formation in mongoloid patients. A biologic gradient is discernible. *New England J. Med.*, 243: 67, 1950.

Analysis and Implications of in Utero Origin of Mongolism

If the disorder is acquired after fertilization of a healthy ovum, mongolism is to be placed with the other anomalies which have their origin during intrauterine life. It becomes analogous to the mental retardation of the child resulting from German measles of the mother in early pregnancy. The biologic problem is to discover when and how mongolism originates; and the field of investigation is of broad concern to many workers in such diverse disciplines as are represented on this program and in this audience.

A significant clue for setting the time of onset of the disease early in the fetal period of development is the nature of numerous inconstant but, nevertheless, frequent stigmas of mongolism. In addition to the three constant features of mental retardation, brachycephaly, and acromicria, mongoloid persons characteristically possess other congenital defects. Thus, among the soft tissues the ears are usually malformed and a cardiac septal defect exists in from one-half to two-thirds of patients. Opacities in the fetal nucleus of the lens, and speckling and peripheral atrophy of the iris stroma[21] are usually found by ophthalmoscopic examination. The bony skeleton and teeth also partake in the generalized disorder of growth: one or both of the nasal bones are missing in most; the middle phalanx of the fifth finger is stunted in two-thirds (Fig. 140); and the maxillary lateral permanent incisor tooth is missing or dwarfed in approximately a third of mongoloid persons.[17] More than fifty different anomalies have been cataloged in varied combinations with the three constant and about ten to fifteen common defects. Cleft palate in mongoloid children, for example, is not common, but far exceeds expected frequency among newborn infants.

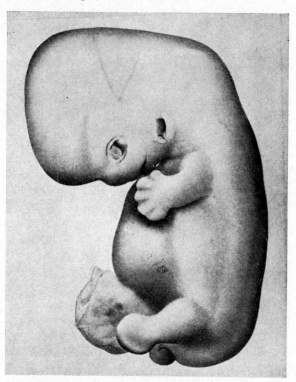

Fig. 141.   Human fetus showing status of development towards the end of the second month of gestation.

It is with the biologic significance of the pattern and not with anatomic and histologic details that this audience is concerned. The anatomic structures characteristically defective have one common feature: derivation from tissues differentiating at approximately the eighth week of fetal life. Towards the end of the second month of gestation, for example, the budding nasal bones, cardiac septum, premaxilla, and tubercles of the ear appear (Fig. 141). For the little finger of a 20-mm. embryo, Figure 142 illustrates the status of development just before the primordial middle phalanx buds off from between the proximal and distal phalanges in the eighth week of gestation.[1] The stigmas of mongolism are morphologic evidence of a departure from the pattern of normal development of the musculoskeletal, cardio-vascular, and central nervous systems, as well as the special sense organs, around the eighth week of prenatal existence.

The mongoloid fetus is visualized as having weathered a critical period of intrauterine stress which has left its permanent impress on budding structures, sparing both the sturdier preformed parts and those portions of the organism yet to come. The fetus has been blighted by what might be called intrauterine drought. The term has the desired connotation that the process is temporary. However, drought has to do with dryness or water lack, while the analogy sought is a metabolic drought, a biochemical upset,

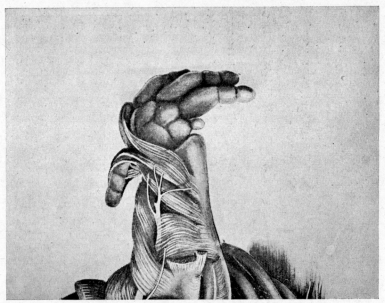

FIG. 142.   Endochondral skeleton right hand of embryo 20 mm. in length. Note status of fifth finger. *Am. J. Anat.* 1: 1, 1901.

transient vitamin or enzyme deficiency, or oxygen lack. This broad concept is suggested by the demonstrable association between mongolism and inter-current infections and vaginal hemorrhage of the mother during the first trimester of pregnancy.[15, 19] The known relation of hemorrhage to anoxia and of anoxia to damage of cerebral tissue suggests that this may be one mechanism operating in the causation of mongolism. The principle that the fetus is susceptible to temporary arrests of growth from which there is no recovery for critically injured parts is clearly proved by the effects of rubella in pregnancy.[11, 29] Whether the virus infecting the mother actually crosses the placental barrier to give the fetus intrauterine rubella, or whether it operates indirectly by producing an impairment of systemic or placental function is not known; nor is it likely that this question will find a ready answer at the bedside. The contribution of clinical medicine must end at the point where more information would mean hazardous experimentation on human beings.

The physician and the biologist are not limited to clinical methods, however, in their study of the effects of intrauterine stresses on the baby. If the individuals studied by the clinician are aggregated as components of populations, the methods of epidemiology may be utilized as another means to further medical knowledge. The technic is illustrated by gains made during the past decade in our understanding of the dangers of German measles during pregnancy. As is so often the case with important discoveries in medicine, a crucial clinical observation was the first step in a new direction. Appreciation of the fact that rubella causes congenital deformity had its inception in the practitioner's office after Gregg had seen three babies with congenital cataract within a relatively short period of time. The three mothers had suffered from rubella in early pregnancy and Gregg's hypothesis that this supposedly trivial disease of childhood was responsible for the ocular defects was explored and confirmed by epidemiologic observations made in the field on women who had been pregnant and at risk when rubella swept through Australia around 1940.

The third method of studying disease is to take the problem into the laboratory in order to construct or extend an hypothesis, which then must be tested back in the field by experience with human populations. The methods of science are not new, nor is the field of experimental teratology. Nearly a century ago the French scientist Dareste, experimenting with embryonating eggs, occupied himself with the broad biologic problem of determining principles governing the occurrence of congenital defects. "Let us not forget," wrote Dareste,[9] "that hypothesis, however ingenious, however reasonable it may be, is not science . . . Where, then, shall we find the elements of teratology? Since direct observation cannot procure them, it is necessary to seek them by experiment."

Assuredly, one of the high points among experimental studies was the discovery by Stockard[28] in 1910 that cyclopia in fish may be induced by exposure of the embryonating egg to an environmental insult. Using eggs of *Fundulus heteroclitus*, a saltwater fish, Stockard found that when the embryo is subjected to the action of a solution of magnesium chloride at a critical moment of development, between the thirteenth and fifteenth hours of life, cyclopia of the embryo usually develops. Further, he demonstrated that multiple agents, chloretone, alcohol, chloroform, and ether, when acting in appropriate dilutions likewise caused ocular defects and anomalous development of the central nervous system. A clue to the mechanism involved may lie in Quastel's findings, presented at this symposium, that magnesium ions and narcotics inhibit respiratory and enzyme functions of nerve tissue cells isolated in the Warburg apparatus.[25]

The importance of Stockard's work lies first in the biologic demonstration that a particular defect can be induced in the animal embryo by diverse agents; that similar diseases result from dissimilar causes. It follows that in the study of naturally occurring cyclopia in fish, a reasonable approach is to search for a variety of agents and to abandon preconceived notions that in all instances there must be a single cause or that the causative agent is uniformly the same. Secondly, this work showed that, in fish at least, there are characteristic and specific defects directly related to a particular moment in ontogenic development, and occurring at that moment only.

During the past fifteen years, appropriate laboratory experiments by a number of investigators have made it clear that similar principles operate in the production of acquired congenital anomalies in higher animals. Thus, Hale[13] working with pigs and Warkany[30, 31] with rats have demonstrated that congenital defects of the skeleton and soft tissues may develop in the mammalian fetus as manifestations of a prenatal nutritional deficiency. Diets lacking adequate amounts of vitamin A or of riboflavin, prosthetic groups in enzyme systems playing vital roles in oxidation-reduction processes, result in a type of cleft palate indistinguishable from genetic forms. Similar malformations have been produced by Gillman, Gilbert, and Gillman[10] using Trypan blue repeatedly injected into pregnant rats, and in the laboratory of the Department of Epidemiology at the Harvard School of Public Health where systemic anoxia was the method of administering an environmental insult to the mouse fetus in utero.[18]

An abbreviated description of this latter method and of experiments made on some 300 pregnancies involving about 2500 embryos is introduced because the developmental defects have included gross cerebral anomalies. The results appear germane to a discussion of mongolism, although that particular syndrome has never been produced in animals. Indeed, it is pertinent to speculate whether the counterpart of mongolism could be recognized in the mouse, should it exist.

Within a plastic high-altitude chamber, pregnant mice were subjected to rarefied atmosphere deficient in oxygen. Each mouse was introduced into the chamber on a single occasion during gestation for a period of five hours. In this manner twenty litters were subjected to intrauterine anoxia on each of the first seventeen days of pregnancy. On the eighteenth day the young were delivered by surgical section in order that the mother should not devour defective offspring naturally born. All fetuses, together with suitable controls, were observed for results of anoxic anoxia as manifested by gross congenital defects. The quantitative aspect of the method is its important feature. One fires bullets, so to speak, at the embryo during selected stages of its development rather than subjecting it to continuous bombardment by a dietary or metabolic agent. Not only is it possible to quantitate multiple factors of cause and effect at the cell, organ, and

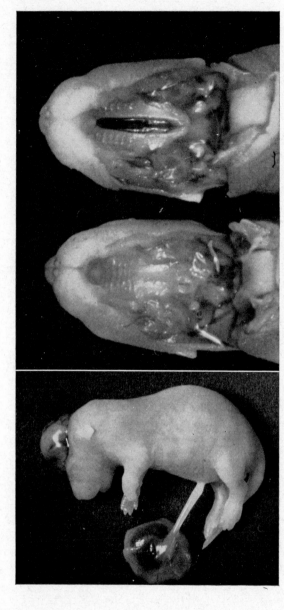

FIG. 143. Congenital anomalies experimentally produced in the mouse fetus: anencephaly following anoxic anoxia for five hours on the eighth day of gestation; and cleft palate (compared with normal palate of littermate) resulting from anoxic insult on the fourteenth day. *New England J. Med.* 243: 67, 1950.

humoral levels of the pathologist, physiologist, and biochemist but at population levels of the epidemiologist and geneticist.

After exposure of the animals to simulated altitudes of approximately 25,000 to 27,000 feet for a period of five hours, an ontogenetic series of deformities is observed with the particular result determined by the intensity, duration, and timing of anoxia. Thus, anencephaly and other gross malformations of the skeleton are found in nearly a third of litters after anoxia on the eighth day of development. Cleft palate (Fig. 143) results from anoxia on the fourteenth day; and so-called "open eye" from an insult delivered on the sixteenth day of intrauterine existence. Not the least challenging feature of the method by which these results were obtained is the opportunity provided for measuring the contribution to defective growth of both the causative agent (anoxia) and the changing fetus. The degree of anoxia and duration of exposure (dosage factor) are easily regulated. With the critical conditions for the development of a particular defect stabilized, the mechanism of pathogenesis can be explored biochemically and histologically. An evaluation of the further effects of litter size, maternal aging, and genetic properties of the strain of mice used is also favored.

The principal gain from these experiments in relation to mongolism is a rather clear indication of why the eighty-five-year long search for a single cause has been fruitless, and why it will continue to produce little. There is no more reason to believe that a single cause operates in the genesis of mongolism in nature than in the genesis of cleft palate experimentally produced. The investigator focusing his attention on one factor has as limited a perspective as the three blind men holding an elephant. One found it all foot, another all trunk, and a third had hold of the tail. Exponents of a single causation for mongolism have variously concluded that it is due to "advanced maternal age,"[5] "uterine exhaustion,"[12] "diminished viability of the ovum,"[20] and "scars marking the sites of old ovulation."[26] Most of the endocrine glands have been assigned the decisive role, and it has been variously asserted that "mongolism is the congenital type of hypopituitarism,"[3] is caused by "fetal hyperthyroidism ceasing at birth,"[8] and is "associated with only one constant locus of anomaly, a hypoplastic adrenal cortex."[7] An ingenious genetic interpretation ascribes the disease "to the simultaneous presence in the germ cell of five pairs of recessive factors or two dominant and four pairs of recessive factors carried in as many different chromosomes."[23] The investigators cited have contributed facts describing the foot, the trunk, or the tail of mongolism, but none has undertaken to reconstruct the elephant. The modern trend toward teamwork by specialists, such as are gathered here, should insure a larger perspective in future research.

A group of scientists approaching the problem of mongolism immediately recognizes that concern is with the biology of congenital anomalies. To describe the clinical features of the skull, or the brain, or the little finger is not enough. The challenge is to interpret the meaning of these anomalies, define the field of investigation, and work out a program of prevention. The interpretation advanced here is that the mongoloid child has survived a period of intrauterine stress, just as the mouse with cleft palate has survived a period of anoxic distress. The permanent impress of a critical insult

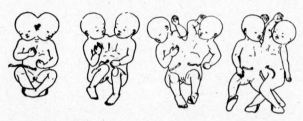

FIG. 144.   Biologic gradient of arrests between single individual and identical twins. Source: Wilder, illustrated after Patten, *New England J. Med.* 243: 67, 1950.

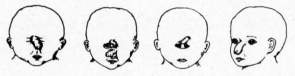

FIG. 145.   Biologic gradient of arrests between vestigial eye and cyclopia and between cyclopia and duplicate eyes. Source: Wilder, illustrated after Patten, *New England J. Med.* 243: 67, 1950.

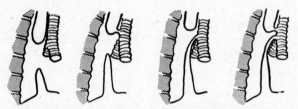

FIG. 146.   Biologic gradient between different types of tracheo-esophageal fistula. *New England J. Med.* 243: 67, 1950.

is registered on multiple budding tissues, the most fragile parts of the host. If this conclusion is correct, the problem is of concern not only to clinicians, geneticists, and public health workers but to those engaged in the fields of embryology, cerebral circulation, brain tissue respiration, oxidation-reduction mechanisms, and enzyme chemistry. Not only is the study of multiple causative factors indicated, but their multiple effects. The universe under investigation should be enlarged to orient mongolism within a framework of related anomalies. Conjoined twins (Fig. 144), cyclopean (Fig. 145), and anencephalic monsters and infants with lesser defects, such as tracheo-esophageal fistula (Fig. 146), cleft palate with or without harelip, give every suggestion of being naturally related as members of an ontogenetic series. The anomalous individual is only an isolated unit of a larger dynamic process, like a single "still" removed from a moving picture strip, or like one person with congenital syphilis.

Summary

The biologic implication of mongolism is that of postrubella cataract in human beings and of congenital anomalies in mice, rats, and pigs produced by metabolic insults to the mother during pregnancy. Stockard's one-eyed fish hatched after exposure to anesthetic solutions, Dareste's freak chick embryos incubated under adverse environmental conditions, and Saint Hilaire's observation made one hundred and twenty-five years ago on the natural history of anomalies have lost none of their importance as intimations that the biologic laws governing the occurrence of monstrosities and lesser anomalies can be formulated. Contemporary research has clearly demonstrated that environmental factors account for a substantial fraction of all congenital anomalies and crippling defects. The pendulum which started a century and a half ago to swing towards a belief wholly in environmental causes seems later to have turned too far in the opposite direction of genetic causes through the impetus of the classical discoveries of Abbé Mendel.

Until recently, clear distinction was not commonly made between the inherited defect and the defect acquired in utero. With increasing knowledge of the importance of acquired factors, much genetic material will need critical review. This is not to resurrect the hoary dispute between Mendelianism and Lamarckism or to smuggle out the Lysenko controversy from behind the iron curtain. Both influences, genetic and acquired, are of consequence in determining man's deformities, and Hogben has interpreted the genetic background of mongolism in a manner completely in harmony with the conclusion of this study. "Whatever gene differences are involved in the appearance of this condition appear to require a special pre-natal environment to make them recognizable." The important consideration, however, is the prenatal environment. It is man's environment that is susceptible to manipulation, not his genes and chromosomes.

Present knowledge suggests that coordinated and energetic study of the causes of congenital defects will result in a significant contribution to the public health. Present knowledge allows hope that acquired anomalies of the embryo, fetus, and premature infant may be prevented by an increased knowledge of their pathogenesis and epidemiology. The objective is an improved quality, rather than quantity, of the human race—the kind of thing we might hope for were the application of eugenics as practicable among mankind as it is among pets and beasts of burden.

REFERENCES

1. BARDEEN, C. R., and LEWIS, W. H.: *American Journal of Anatomy,* 1901, 1, p. 1.
2. BEIDLEMAN, B.: *American Journal of Mental Deficiency,* 1945, 50, p. 35.
3. BENDA, C. E.: Mongolism and Cretinism, 310 pp. New York, Grune & Stratton, 1946.
4. BLEYER, A.: *American Journal of Diseases of Children,* 1934, 47, p. 342.
5. BLEYER, A.: *American Journal of Diseases of Children,* 1938, 55, p. 79.
6. BOOK, J. A., and REED, S. C.: *Journal of the American Medical Association,* 1950, 143, p. 730.
7. BROWN, E. E.: *Northwest Medicine,* 1947, 46, p. 288.
8. CLARK, R. M.: *Journal of Mental Science,* 1929, 75, p. 261.
9. DARESTE, C.: Recherches sur la production artificielle des monstruosités ou essais de tératogénie expérimentale, p. 39. Paris, C. Reinwald & Cie., 1877.
10. GILLMAN, J.; GILBERT, C.; and GILLMAN, T.: *South African Journal of Medical Sciences,* 1948, 13, p. 47.
11. GREGG, N. M.: *Transactions of the Opthalmological Society of Australia,* 1942, 3, p. 35.
12. HALBERSMA, T.: *Nederlandsch tijdschrift voor geneeskunde,* 1922, 2, p. 22.
13. HALE, F.: *American Journal of Opthalmology,* 1935, 18, p. 1087.
14. INGALLS, T. H.: *American Journal of Diseases of Children,* 1947, 73, p. 279.
15. INGALLS, T. H.: *American Journal of Diseases of Children,* 1947, 74, p. 147.
16. INGALLS, T. H.: *New England Journal of Medicine,* 1950, 243, p. 67.
17. INGALLS, T. H., and BUTLER, R. L.: The Teeth in Mongolism. In preparation.
18. INGALLS, T. H.; CURLEY, F. J.; and PRINDLE, R. A.: *American Journal of Diseases of Children,* 1950, 80, p. 34.
19. INGALLS, T. H., and DAVIES, J. A. V.: *New England Journal of Medicine,* 1947, 236, p. 437.
20. JENKINS, R. L.: *American Journal of Diseases of Children,* 1933, 45, p. 506.
21. LOWE, R. F.: *British Journal of Ophthalmology,* 1949, 33, p. 131.
22. MACKINTOSH, J. M.: *British Medical Journal,* 1928, 2, p. 129.
23. MACKLIN, M. T.: *American Journal of the Medical Sciences,* 1929, 178, p. 315.
24. PARKER, G. J.: *The Journal of Pediatrics,* 1950, 36, p. 493.
25. QUASTEL, J. H.: in The Biology of Mental Health and Disease, p. 360. New York, Paul B. Hoeber, Inc., 1952.
26. ROSANOFF, A. J., and HANDY, L. M.: *American Journal of Diseases of Children,* 1934, 48, p. 764.
27. RUSSELL, P. M. G.: *Lancet,* 1933, 1, p. 802.
28. STOCKARD, C. R.: *Journal of Experimental Zoology,* 1909, 6, p. 285.
29. SWANN, C.; TOSTEVIN, A. L.; MOORE, B.; MAYO, H.; and BLACK, G. H. B.: *Medical Journal of Australia,* 1943, 2, p. 201.
30. WARKANY, J., and NELSON, R. C.: *Anatomical Record,* 1941, 79, p. 83.
31. WARKANY, J.; NELSON, R. C.; and SCHRAFFENBERGER, E.: *American Journal of Diseases of Children,* 1943, 65, p. 882.

Acromicria Congenita or the Mongoloid Deficiency

CLEMENS E. BENDA, M.D.

Although mongolism has been known for eighty-four years and many outstanding scientists have contributed to its knowledge, it is still much less well understood than are some of the conditions which have been discovered later, such as the amaurotic idiocies. Even the morbid entities that have been added most recently to the group of "dysmetabolic oligophreniae," such as phenylpyruvic oligophrenia and gargoylism, are much better known in many respects. One of the reasons that mongolism proves so resistant to research is the fact that it is a prenatal disorder and, thus, is present at birth. It has not yet been possible to produce mongolism experimentally in animals, nor can the condition of mongolism develop after birth. Advances in the knowledge of cretinism have been made through the study of postoperative myxedema and states of postnatal thyroid deficiency. Gargoylism, a congenital genetic metabolic error, develops to its full extent after birth and a study of the pathologic process offers an opportunity to determine accurately the character of the metabolic disorder.

The stalemate between geneticists,[15] who claim that the whimsical occurrence of mongolism can only be explained by the postulation of a number of recessive genes (five recessive or two dominant and four recessive pairs of factors), and the clinicians, who claim that mongolism develops out of the influence of noxious factors which interfere with the normal development of the germ cells, cannot be overcome without approaching the fundamental question: What is mongolism? Is mongolism a "monstrosity" or a "malformation" in the sense that it represents a structural deviation from the norm by arrest of development, like cleft formations such as open foramen ovale of the heart or spina bifida, or is mongolism a growth deficiency? Mongolism is associated frequently with true malformations like septum defects in the heart, occasionally with syndactylism, atresia ani, and ear anomalies; but the fact that a mongoloid child may have several malformations does not necessarily mean that the condition which we call mongolism is a malformation. There are probably very few people today who, like Langdon Down and Cruikshank, consider mongolism a regression into another race.

Most people will agree that the appearance of mongolism is produced by a specific configuration of the head, with an abnormal setting of the eyes, the face, and the mouth, typically mongoloid features. The anomalies in the hands, feet, and sex organs are significant, but the mongoloid shares similar anomalies with many other mentally defective children and some normal children, and the diagnosis of mongolism could never be based on any of these anomalies except those of the head. In order to understand mongolism, an analysis of the anomalies of the head appears most revealing.

Analysis of Cranial Anomalies in Mongolism

The mongoloid appearance is produced by a specific configuration of the skull and skeleton. Greig,[10] to whom we owe a very thorough anatomic analysis of three mongoloid skulls, came to the conclusion that these "skulls have certain features in common, and several indicating a delay in the completion of the development, delay which Dr. John Fraser's skull shows to persist throughout life." The ages of his patients were 16, 14, and 5 years, respectively. His observations indicated that "it is the nasal bones and the maxillae that are particularly affected, and this affection must begin early in intrauterine life. . . . The nasal bones, maxillae and pre-maxillae, show restriction in development. . . ." He offered the conclusion: "Even from the skull alone there seems evidence that *development normally begun* has mapped out all structures and features in the embryo but has failed to lead them to perfection during foetal growth, using the terms embryonic and foetal as understood by Ballantyne to indicate in the former a period of evolution, in the latter a period of *growth*." Observations on the mongoloid skull have also been presented by Van der Scheer.[22]

My own studies have been based on clinical observations, x-ray studies, and autopsies performed on patients of different age groups: a premature stillborn baby, newborn babies, infants, children, and adults including one patient as old as 60 years. This material offers the opportunity to compare different stages of the morbid process.

Autopsies on mongoloid babies revealed anomalies on the skull basis which consist of an abnormally set sphenoid body, a steep ascending anterior skull cavity, short nasal bones and maxillae, and an abnormally shaped and compressed brain.[3] Analysis of the orbits showed that they are egg-shaped and in a slanting position. At the same time, the skull sutures are unusually wide, and poorly joined and ossified. The frontal suture, normally almost closed at birth and not palpable, is very frequently open down to the nasion. All these anomalies, first observed in autopsy material, could be confirmed and demonstrated in x-ray examinations. Thus, the main question which arose was: What happened to the fetus before it was born, to become a mongoloid? Are these anomalies, as mentioned, true malformations or the result of a deceleration of fetal or neofetal growth? If mongolism at birth is a kind of "fetalism," a name which some authors have suggested, why does not every premature baby look "mongoloid," at least in one phase of fetal development?

An answer to these questions was sought through a study of fetal development, for which four fetuses were available representing different stages, from the beginning to the end of the fourth fetal month.

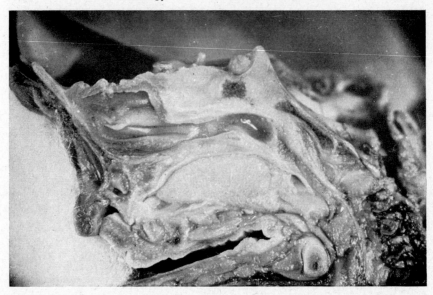

Fig. 147. Sagittal section through 19-week-old embryo skull. Note the development of the sphenoid body with the primary bone marrow formation beneath the pituitary body, and bone marrow in the clivus. Note the angulation between the clivus and anterior skull cavity. The palate is large and well ossified. The tongue lies completely retracted within the oral cavity.

Fetus 47/674 was, according to determination from the last menstruation of the mother and the size of the fetus, about one hundred and twelve days old. The roof of the mouth was well ossified, and the distance to the anterior alveolar ridge measured more than 2.5 cm. The tongue was well inside the mouth. The nasal septum, from the sella to the tip, measured almost 3 cm. The cribriform plate was in a horizontal position and measured 1.5 cm. from the anterior clinoid process to the frontal bone. The sphenoid body was partly calcified, and showed a bony cavity beneath the pituitary, with osteoplastic and osteoclastic activity. Most of the other cartilaginous blastemata were still cartilaginous. It was obvious that the angulation between the clivus and the anterior cavity was about 145 degrees.

In an embryo (47/706) determined to be nineteen weeks (end of fourth month), the development of the skull basis had greatly advanced. In this embryo (Fig. 147), the bony roof of the mouth measured 2.5 cm., and the anterior cavity from the clinoid to the frontal bone, 2 cm. The sphenoid body alone measured 1.5 cm. in length. Beneath the sella, there was an ossification center with bone marrow formation measuring 4 mm. The cartilage between clivus and sphenoid was large and consisted of a disk running up to the posterior clinoid process, measuring 5 mm. The anterior edge between sphenoid and ethmoid consisted of a large, fibrous band. The nasal tube and its appendixes were well ossified. The anterior cavity

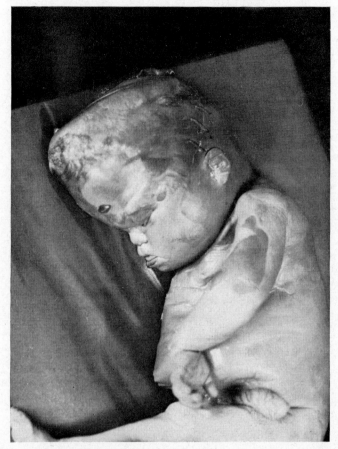

Fig. 148. Stillborn mongoloid, left lateral view. Note the high forehead, the retracted nose bridge, the short nose, and the protruding tongue. The neck is also shortened.

and the anterior part of the sphenoid body formed a straight flat plate on which the frontal lobes rested. The ossified clivus (Blumenbachi) of the occiput measured about 14 mm. and showed a "diplococcus" shape.

As has been mentioned, autopsies and radiographs of newborn mongoloids indicated that the configuration of the skull base in mongolism is abnormal. It was, however, not possible to arrive at definite conclusions until, through the cooperation of a physician—whose name I naturally wish to withhold, but to whom Science is much indebted—it was possible to study a prematurely stillborn mongoloid of the ninth month of gestation. The diagnosis of the cause of death was prematurity, and the diagnosis of mongolism was not made. But, since the parents had the misfortune of having had one mongoloid child, they contacted me and I was given the opportunity to study the premature stillborn. The child showed conspicuous evidence of mongolism (Fig. 148), with a retracted and abnormally shaped nose and maxillae, and unusually high forehead and striking brachycephaly. A sagittal section through skull and body (Fig. 149) revealed that the anterior part of the sphenoid formed a straight continuation of the clivus. The angle between clivus and sphenoid at its basis was 180 degrees. The clivus was short, measuring only 1 cm. in length. There was a cartilage disk between clivus and sphenoid, measuring 2 mm., and the sphenoid body was a straight bone with a well-formed sella and pituitary body. The bone was ossified, but the cartilage in the center of the sphenoid was degenerated and reduced to a thin fragment. There was no angulation of the anterior part of the sphenoid. The anterior part of the sella was divided in two sections at the junction of the sphenoid wings and the main body, and the anterior cavity measured 1.5 cm. from the anterior clinoid to the frontal bone. The orbit roofs sloped upwards steeply. The roof of the mouth was short, and measured 27 mm. The nasal septum was poorly ossified and extremely short. The tongue was much too big for the undersized mouth, and protruded for 1.5 cm. between the alveolar ridges.

To understand what had happened in this mongoloid child, one has to go deeper into normal fetal development. Virchow, who made his famous studies on the human skull basis exactly one hundred years ago, thought that the anterior cavity makes a turn downward until the final normal angulation in the basilaris cranii is obtained. Why does the mongoloid skull fail to make this postulated turn?* An analysis of fetal development reveals some surprising facts which have not found sufficient recognition in the general appreciation of developmental disorders of the skull.

When a fetus of seven weeks is compared with that of seven and a half weeks, it is seen that within three and a half days the shape of the fetus has entirely changed; fingers and toes are differentiated; eyes and ears have taken different sites, and the neofetus has changed from an animal to the specific human configuration. It is hardly believable that such a rapid change could take place within three and a half days, and one may easily recognize how each hour counts during those decisive days. Fetal develop-

---

* The observation of a basilar lordosis which is so consistent in the newborn mongoloid offers the opportunity to compare briefly the conditions seen in mongolism with another condition associated with basilar lordosis, that of acrocephaly and scaphocephaly. Park and Powers[17] published a thorough investigation of acrocephaly and scaphocephaly in 1920, and reviewed the many theories which had been developed since Virchow's well-known publication of 1851. Park and Powers demonstrate that in acrocephaly the fundamental pathologic change does not rest upon abnormal conditions in the skull base. They provide evidence that the basilar lordosis and certain peculiarities of the anomaly of the head "can be explained on the ground of the peculiar relation of the cranium to the growing brain. Because the brain is bound to fulfill its inherent demand for growth, a factor is introduced into the production of the cranial deformity for which no counterpart exists in the case of the extremity, namely, intercranial pressure."

According to Park and Powers, acrocephaly is due to premature synostosis of cranial sutures which, in its course, is due to genetically determined defective factors in the "blastemal cranial vault."

Fig. 149. Sagittal section through the skull of a stillborn mongoloid. Note the lack of angulation between the clivus and sphenoid body. The ventral surface of the sphenoid body continues in a straight line, the direction of the clivus, while in normal subjects there is an angulation of about 145 degrees. The clivus and sphenoid body contain some bone marrow, but the synchondrosis spheno-occipitalis is thin and irregular, and the cartilage in the sphenoid body is almost absent. The anterior cavity of the skull is extremely short. The frontal bone is bulging; the skull cavity is brachycephalic, almost rounded and "balloon shaped." Note the extreme shortness of the palate and lower jaw with the tongue protruding between the alveolar crests.

ment of the head proceeds according to a strange timetable. Nature is primarily interested in developing a central nervous system, for which much time is taken. To prepare the fetus for birth, emphasis is placed entirely on development of the mouth and nose, and there may be seen two different lines of development which proceed fairly independently for a long time, at least as far as one can talk of independence in biologic development at all. The maxilla is the earliest bone to show ossification, starting in a 15-mm. fetus, which corresponds to the sixth week. In quick succession, other bony structures connected with the formation of the nose and mouth are developing and showing the most conspicuous developmental rate, which forms a fairly well ossified and cemented facial scaffolding by the end of the tenth week. This development does not depend on central regulation or brain development, as can be clearly demonstrated in anencephalic and microcephalic children. At the same time, but at a much slower rate, Nature provides a basis for the developing brain, which rests on the supporting structures like a specimen on a plate. It is significant that the basi occipital (clivus) starts ossification on the sixty-fifth day, while the sphenoid starts eighteen days later, on the eighty-third day. The sphenoid is composed of not less than fourteen different ossification centers, which proceed independently and are still connected by loose, cartilaginous and fibrous joints, capable of changes according to shape. Nature is slow to provide the bony envelope for the central nervous system, leaving ample space for its growth and extension, and providing only a firm basis for its resting place, while ossification of the convexity proceeds in a patchy manner, with plenty of flexible joints between.

From these studies, it is evident that the skull base does not make a turn by its own power but is attached to the firm and well-established facial portion in a relatively late stage of neofetal development, when the size of the skull basis is large enough to support the growing brain and provide a resting place for the frontal lobes. At the same time, the cerebrum is still in an entirely undifferentiated condition. It is a fast-increasing mass of soft tissue, flexible and without definite shape, and the particular shape of the human brain is determined through the schedule of growth of the facial bones and the skull base, which are firm long in advance of other areas.

In mongolism we see that the areas of facial scaffolding and skull basis have failed to grow adequately in the neofetal period (Fig. 150). Having to deal with the same amount of brain tissue as in normal development, the skull envelope of the brain can only be joined on the basis by a flattening of the angulation and a huge extension of the skull cavity in a vertical direction, producing apparent brachycephaly and extension of the bitemporal diameter, which is frequently almost equal to the sagittal diameter of the skull, sometimes even exceeding it in length. That the mongoloid brain has about the same weight as the normal brain has been shown by me in a study of twenty-four brains during the first two years of life. In the youngest of these subjects, a two days' prematurely born mongoloid, the brain weighed 218 Gm., corresponding to normal weight at the eighth fetal month. All the other brains of infants in the first two years of life had weights corresponding to the brains of infants between two weeks and twelve months after birth. However, in a study of a corresponding group of brains in subjects over 2 years of age, practically every one showed

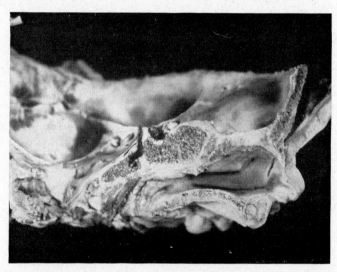

Fig. 150.   Sagittal section through the skull of a 5-month-old mongoloid. Note that the ventral surface of the sphenoid and clivus again forms an angulation of almost 180 degrees, instead of the angulation of 145 to 155 degrees. The clivus is very short, the sphenoid body is fairly well developed in this case, and there is some cartilage present within the sphenoid body. Note the extreme shortness of the floor of the anterior cavity and the shortness of the bony palate. The nasal cavity is narrow.

an arrest of further growth and the brain weights corresponded, in the majority of cases, to the weight of infantile brains of children not older than 3 years of age.

Effect of Mongolism on Development of Other Portions of Body

As far as the development of the nervous system is concerned, we see that the deceleration of neofetal development affects the spinal cord, which runs through a stage of decisive differentiation during those critical days. Spinal dysraphism is not rare in mongolism and the anomalies in the differentiation of the spinal cord add another item to the table of synchronisms of maldevelopment. The cerebrum, however, is at that time still in an undifferentiated condition. As the gradient concept in biology indicates, interference with development always hits most severely areas of greatest

susceptibility which are the center of most intensive growth at that particular moment. It is no surprise that the cerebrum in mongolism appears
less affected at that time, and the pathologic change producing mental
deficiency is caused partly by other factors which will be discussed later.

These observations provide evidence in several respects: (1) The mongoloid deformity is primarily not a developmental arrest, but a deceleration
of neofetal growth. (2) The mongoloid anomaly is primarily not caused
by cerebral anomalies, but, on the contrary, the cerebral anomalies are
caused by the neofetal growth disorder.[2]

If the mongoloid deficiency were restricted to cranial anomalies depending upon brain development, one should postulate that the development
of the remaining parts of the skeleton is not involved.

Having established the character of the cranial anomaly in mongolism,
the next question was whether, at the time of birth and in early infancy,
the degeneration of the cartilaginous synchondroses and the fibrillary
synchondroses have proceeded to a point beyond repair, or whether the
cartilaginous and fibrous sutures still show some degree of activity. A
histologic study of the synchondroses,[2] published in 1940, indicates that in
a young mongoloid infant of less than three months, the synchondrosis
spheno-occipitalis still showed preparatory cartilaginous cell columns,
although the disk was somewhat smaller than normal. In a seven-months
mongoloid, the disk measured 1.5 mm. in thickness and 7 mm. in height,
instead of the normal measures of 3 to 3.5 mm. in thickness and about 10
mm. in height for that age (measurements given by Stoccada[21] in 1916).
In mongoloid children of 8 years, 9 years, and 14 years, synchondroses
appeared much smaller than normally seen, and growth of cartilage was
arrested. There was heavy ossification of the bone, with formation of
primary and secondary bone ridges which prevented the cartilage cells
from further activity.

These observations were not restricted to the skull basis, but can be
demonstrated in the vertebrae, the ribs, and the distal epiphyses of the
bones, as has been shown by Lauche[13] in a study of metatarsal and meta-
carpal bones in 1924. Lauche came to the conclusion that the growth disorder in mongolism is a reverse of acromegaly.

These observations on the skeleton indicate that we are dealing with a
true congenital acromicria, due to a deficiency in central growth regulation
which we may tentatively call a pituitary-like factor. I would like to
emphasize that the concept of "acromicria" is not based on observations
of the finished condition but rather on a comparative study of the skull
and skeleton throughout the growth period. These studies indicate a
specific behavior of the growth process, with an inadequacy of growth at
the periphery, while the central and proximal fields of growth gain more
adequately.

It has been most satisfactory to discover that other investigators, independently of each other, have come to a similar conclusion. As early as 1907, Schüller[20] wrote in an article on "infantilism": "The growth disorder which characterizes this type (mongolism) forms the opposite of the one found in acromegaly. The facial bones and the end parts (acra) of the extremities are strikingly shortened so that one may speak of 'acromicria.' "*

Clift[6] reported roentgenologic findings in 1922. He found a "disproportionate developmental deficiency" of the nose, maxilla, and other bony structures, whose development is "in opposition to acromegaly."

If the claim that the mongoloid growth deficiency represents the opposite of acromegaly is true, one has to postulate that the growth disorder is not restricted to skull and skeleton, but involves also the different body organs, especially all endocrine glands.

The Gonads: It is significant, and needs to be stressed, that the gonads of the newborn mongoloid child appear normal and are not different from the gonads of other newborns, with the exception that undescended testes are more frequent in mongolism and that ovaries occasionally show less advanced development than in control subjects. The important observation is that the gonads, which are within normal range in mongoloid infants who die in the first year after birth, show severe lack of maturation and progressive degeneration and fibrosis in all mongoloids who have died in their adolescent or adult years.† This evidence suggests a deficiency of gonadotropic hormones; the gonads which have an apparently normal anlage fail to progress toward complete maturation. Moreover, as in other hormonal deficiency diseases, the degree of involvement varies from case to case. From a complete immaturity to almost but not complete maturation, all transitional stages have been observed.

The Adrenal Glands: The adrenal glands exhibit a comparable history. Hirning and Farber[11] made a study of the adrenals in mongoloid babies and came to these conclusions:

"1. The width of the permanent cortex of mongols in the first year of life does not differ essentially from that of controls of the same age.

"2. There is a definite lack in the growth of the permanent cortex in the older mongols, as compared with the control group."

My own studies on thirty-eight cases confirmed fully Hirning's and Farber's observations, and added new observations in older children and adults. The adrenal glands of the mongoloid appear normal in infancy but fail to mature at a normal rate and the older the mongoloid, the more striking the pathologic change. Moreover, the anomalies suggest lack of

* "Die für diesen Typus charakteristische Wachstums-anomalie bildet gewissermassen einen Gegensatz zur acromegalen. Die Gesichtsknochen und die Endteile der Extremitäten sind nämlich auffallend verkürzt, sodass man von einer Acromicrie sprechen kann."

† Recently, there has been reported the first well-controlled case of a mongoloid woman who had given birth to a perfectly normal child with an I.Q. of 110, who had been observed over a period of ten years.[19]

adreno-corticotropic hormones, which is suggested by a specific structural under-development of the three outer layers of the cortex[4] while the juxta-medullary layer appears large.

The Liver: The liver was studied in cooperation with Roosen-Runge.[18] He showed that the liver of the mongoloid child is normal in an early period of life but shows an increased tendency to fatty degeneration, and in older mongoloid children and young adults, fatty degeneration may be found to an extreme degree.

The Thyroid Gland: The structure of the thyroid gland deserves special attention. In comparing the thyroid of the mongoloid with that of normal control subjects, it was found that the thyroid of the mongoloid shows two main types of anomalies. In the neonatal stage, the thyroid is either normal or shows a retardation in development, as seen in inability of the embryonic thyroid epithelium to differentiate and to form follicles with colloid. The thyroid shows in these cases the presence of large embryonic nests, consisting of immature cells which may persist throughout life. In the majority of children, however, it was noticed that the thyroid showed a tendency to a stagnant colloid goiter. I say "goiter" to point to the accumulation of colloid and the enlargement of the follicles. It does not mean, however, that the whole thyroid is enlarged. The thyroid remains small and its weight is far below normal. The picture of the thyroid of the mongoloid resembles that seen in hypophysectomized animals.

Different investigators have compared the thyroid of the mongoloid with the thyroid of the cretin, and have concluded that the thyroid of the mongoloid is "normal." In the cretin, the gland is either missing (congenital aplasia), or shows a fundamental inability to form colloid, though parts of it may form a colloid goiter as a compensatory measure; the thyroid of the mongoloid is generally able to form colloid, but the colloid is stagnant.[4] The stagnation of colloid, easily demonstrated by its brittle nature, by the color differences and the enlargement of the follicles with compression of the epithelium and lack of vascularization, seems to indicate that the thyroid of the mongoloid lacks the stimulation which is necessary for proper function and which is generally supposed to come via the thyrotropic hormones of the pituitary.

All this circumstantial evidence points toward a functional disorder of the pituitary body as a cornerstone in the faulty developments that characterize mongolism. I may repeat that the behavior of the "target" glands is different from that seen in other congenital anomalies, for which study there was a wealth of material available. The apparently normal state of the adrenals, gonads, and thyroid at the time of birth and shortly afterward, succeeded by lack of further development and even regression, indicates a deficient stimulation of these organs such as is produced experimentally by hypophysectomy. The characteristics of the cartilage-bone border and the behavior of the thyroid, adrenals, and gonads, indicate lack of hormones which normally influence these organs, making it necessary to focus attention on the pituitary.

The Pituitary Body: The observations on the pituitary body in mongolism are not only confusing, but disappointing, if one expects simple pathologic findings falling into well-established patterns.

For over ten years, the writer has been engaged in a study of the pituitary body of children, with the purpose of investigating whether or not the eosinophilic cells in the infant and child can be credited with producing the tremendous growth rate seen at that time. These investigations have not yet been concluded because material of over 300 cases is to be covered.* The conclusions thus far arrived at can, however, be summarized: The child has a relatively small amount of eosinophilic cells in infancy and childhood, which increase greatly after puberty when the growth period has closed. At that time the number of eosinophilic cells reaches the adult level of 50 to 60 per cent of all pituitary cells. It appears unlikely that the child having such a tremendous growth rate in infancy and in the period from 8 to 12 years of age, derives his growth hormones from the relatively small amount of eosinophilic cells. Some investigators suspect now that the second growth phase is produced through the medium of gonadal hormones, and not through direct pituitary action.

The absence of normal chromophobic cells in mongolism suggests that the pituitary is not able to produce a sufficient amount of tropic hormones for the production of adequate growth. The accumulation of eosinophilic cells and/or the presence of degenerated chromophobic cells suggest that the pituitary is in a stagnant, inactive state. It fails to enter into proper function after birth, when high demands are made on pituitary function. Of course, pituitary dwarfism developing after birth cannot produce a mongoloid-like appearance because the abnormal configuration of mongolism can develop only in fetal life.

While these observations point toward a basic deficiency in the function of the pituitary body, resulting in a lack of chondrotropic, adrenotropic, thyrotropic, and gonadotropic hormones, the conclusion that a pituitary disorder is the "cause" of mongolism is a misinterpretation of the observations at hand. My observations on the pituitary indicate lack of function but the histologic findings point rather to a stagnant, resting pituitary than to a primary defect or malformation. As I have pointed out before:

"Pituitary function on its part depends on the brain, which receives the stimuli from the outside world and primes the organism as a whole for proper responses. Extensive studies of the nervous system reveal that the nervous system is immature at birth and develops at a much slower rate than necessary. The vicious circle between brain and endocrine system

* The study is aided by a fund of the Ella Sachs Plotz Foundation, for which I wish to express my gratitude.

keeps the mongoloid child constantly out of tune with normal development and, if left to its own resources, the mongoloid child falls consistently further back in its mental and physical growth."[4]

Comments

Various investigators have contributed to the knowledge that the disorder leading to mongolism (neofetal acromicria) is produced by interference with growth during the sixth to twelfth week of fetal development, a period which is obviously not controlled by the endocrine glands or the brain of the embryo. The factors which interfere with its progress are, therefore, either noxious nutritional factors which impair the development of the fetus at this critical point, or genetic factors as claimed by some geneticists (Macklin, Reed, and others).

In analyzing the data which indicate an interference with neofetal development, we have evidence that the damage occurred to the embryo as a whole, meaning that all organ systems of ectodermal, mesodermal, and entodermal origin which undergo specific development during that phase are impaired. This simultaneous concurrence of several developmental faults at various places has been called "synchronism" by Ingalls,[12] who adopted the term which Ibsen introduced into medicine. The synchronism of developmental errors involves, to mention only a few, the following items: (1) Anomaly of angulation in basilar-sphenoid junction and inhibition of nasion, premaxilla, maxilla: forty-second to fifty-seventh day of gestation.[2, 10] (2) Influence on differentiation of dermatoglyphic patterns: before fourth month.[7, 8] (3) Inhibition of differentiation of spinal cord: third month.[4] (4) Inhibition of laying out of second phalanx of little finger and other digital anomalies: sixth to ninth week.[12] (5) Inhibition of development of heart septum: seventh to eighth week. (6) Hypoplasia of iris stroma and arcuate lens opacities: seventh to eighth week.[14] (7) Arrested upward slope of orbital axis, and anomalies in palpebral aperture: before fourth month.[2, 14]

These anomalies, involving distinctly separate areas and tissue elements of the body, point toward the operation of factors which have made themselves felt at a distinctly circumscribed period of development. The pathogenic factors are neither regional nor tissue specific. Such an interference cannot be explained through local factors, nor is it likely that they are of a genetic nature on account of the fact that the variety of anomalies would make it necessary to postulate such a great number of genes involved that an individual who is genetically defective in such a number is not likely to develop to the general perfection which many mongoloids attain after all, in spite of being "mongoloids."

It will be noted that the synchronism of mongoloid anomalies points distinctly to that circumscribed period during fetal life which Ballantyne[1] has called "the neofetal period." While according to him the first period, the embryonic, lasts for six weeks, the neofetal period is a period of transition between the second half of the second lunar month and the end of the third month, when the so-called fetal period commences. Few clinicians and biologists have realized that the neofetal period represents a distinct developmental period, the importance of which cannot be overestimated. Ballantyne[1] has emphasized this situation with a remarkable insight into the developmental aspects of prenatal life:

"Just as postnatal life begins with a period of transition or readjustment to suit new environmental conditions, a period named the neonatal; so the passage from embryonic to foetal life is marked by a transition time of adaptation (Natura non facit saltus—Nature makes no leaps) which we may call the neofoetal, during which, among other notable phenomena, the placental economy is being established. The neofoetal period coincides roughly with the second half of second (lunar) month of intrauterine life. Its commencement is on or about the fortieth day (end of sixth week), when the new organism takes on a form which can be recognised as distinctly human. . . .

"The great changes seen in the environment of the foetus at this epoch are the replacement of the vitelline by the allantoic or umbilical circulation, and the progressive growth in importance of the placental over the general chorionic circulation. The end of the neofoetal period (therefore) coincides with the beginning of the placental connections. There is thus a sort of birth before birth, a transition not so sharp as that which occurs at the tenth month of intrauterine life, but nevertheless definite enough and of great importance.

"By the end of the third month, as will be seen, the new-born foetus is fairly established under the placental régime, its yolk-sac (vitelline) connections can be dispensed with and all its circulatory activities can be concentrated in the allantoidal union with the decidua serotina. The transition thus accomplished is not without its element of danger; and just as the neonatal period is commonly one of danger to the new-born infant, so the neofoetal is full of risk to the 'new-born foetus.' It is, at any rate, a fact well known that intrauterine life is often brought to an untimely end by abortion at the third month. The incidence of abortion so immediately after the neofoetal period suggests want of complete adaptation to the new condition of life, in other words, a defective establishment of the placental connections."

The importance of these observations cannot be overestimated in regard to mongolism. This condition seems to be connected with anomalies in the transition from the first nutritional period under the influence of corpus luteum hormones, into the second period under the domination of the placenta.

The conclusion offered in several previous publications has been that mongolism is a congenital growth deficiency which can be termed "congenital acromicria," and we may now add that circumstantial evidence points towards the fact that mongolism can more definitely be termed a "neofetal acromicria." The cause of the neofetal growth defect has been seen by me and by some other investigators in a "nutritional" deficiency of the embryo under "threshold conditions of abortion." In using the term "nutritional," I followed Franklin P. Mall.[16] This great embryologist has pointed out in a study of the causes underlying the origin of human monsters:

"It is found that . . . some tissues are more susceptible than others, and when the *nutrition* of the ovum is impaired it is these that are affected first. . . . A very large number of monsters are to be classed as total monsters. They are probably brought into existence by a large variety of circumstances, all of which interfere with the nutrition and growth of the whole embryo. . . . A monster is due to the influence of external *substances* which retard the growth of the embryo, usually one portion more than the other. . . . I think that every human ovum has within it the power to develop into a monster . . . and that it is not due to any abnormal condition of the germ but to external influences which affect the growth of the egg."

Mall stated the case of a woman who had a continuous hemorrhage for seven days before an abortion: ". . . since then I have learned that the detachment of a normal ovum for a much shorter time than seven days is sufficient to cause an embryo to become monstrous."

In three publications I have provided evidence for abnormal prenatal maternal factors.[5] These were: frequent bleeding in the first trimester of pregnancy, continuation of menstruation, increased occurrence of abortions in other pregnancies, inability to become pregnant and carry a child through pregnancy, and factors indicating an abnormal hormonal regulation of the specific gestational environment.

Critics of the hormonal deficiency theory of mongolism, especially geneticists, have emphasized that the observations on twins are against the importance of environmental factors operating during pregnancy. They argue that the nutritional conditions under which twins live are identical because they derive their nutrition from the same maternal blood. This is indeed the only set of data which has remained in the hands of the geneticists for their claim of a genetic disorder in mongolism. The facts are that dizygotic twins are, in the great majority of instances, discordant, while monozygotic twins are always concordant. If environmental circumstances in the environment of the embryos were responsible, so argue the geneticists, one should find more dizygotic concordant twins. The idea that twins live under identical environmental circumstances reveals a profound lack of knowledge of the very basic data on physiology of twin pregnancies. As has been pointed out by me on several occasions, mongolism develops in a period before the placental nutrition is established. But it may be remembered that even in the placental phase, there is no direct communication between the maternal and embryonic circulation. The chorionic villi are bathed in the placental pool but fetal circulation is entirely self-sustained and closed, and all exchange between the fetal and maternal blood takes place through the double barrier between the fetal membrane and the maternal placental membrane which surrounds the tufts. Yet it has to be remembered that it takes as much as ten days for the fertilized ovum to reach the uterine cavity, and it takes three more days to establish itself on the place of nidation. During that time, the growing ovum relies entirely on its own nutritional sources. After this first period, lasting almost a fortnight, the process of development of the amnion-chorion and the nidation of the egg takes place. The development of these membranes is entirely a function of the ovum, and nidation in the uterine mucosa represents a struggle between ovum and maternal organism in which the mucosa not only does not help its ovum to find a proper place of nidation, but the secretion of antiferments limits the fermentive capacity of the ovum to penetrate the uterine mucosa into deeper layers. It is known that the faculties of the ovum to nidate and the antifermentative forces of the mother represent a struggle with a great variety of possibilities in the balance of power. Some ova are only able to effect a very superficial nidation, while others penetrate the uterine mucosa as deep as the muscularis. During all this time, the embryonic parasite lying more or less on the surface of the uterine mucosa relies entirely on its own strength and provides for itself some maternal blood supply through surface contact. During that whole month, from the middle of the first month to the middle of the second month, the maternal nutrition of the embryo consists entirely of what the embryo is able to draw in true parasitic fashion from the maternal blood stream without any formation of a regular circulation or means of exchange between the two organisms.

It is quite obvious, and it has been shown by several investigators, that if the uterine mucosa is unprepared for pregnancy, or increased scarring and sclerosis of the endometrium are present which are physiologic manifestations of increased age, the difficulties for a proper nidation become stronger and stronger. It has also been shown that even in young women, previous abortions or regional peculiarities may make certain areas of the uterus improper nests for nidation and may inhibit the process of establishing an adequate nutritional exchange.

In the life history of the neofetus, being forty-two to seventy days, a period of two weeks of pre-nidation represents almost a quarter of its life history, and the four weeks of nidational struggle represent two-thirds of its full past.

Considering now the conditions under which twin pregnancies occur, it is obvious for any pathologist familiar with the intrauterine field of nidation that the environmental factors in twins are as different as could be imagined. Not only are the places of implantation different, and one ovum may find a place "in the sun" while the other is pushed into the opposite corners (Fig. 151), but the formation of the embryonic mantle is greatly influenced by the conditions which the other ovum has created. There is evidence that twin pregnancies occur under many different conditions. Non-identical twins may be due to two ova, released at the same time from the same ovum but two Graafian follicles, or from the same follicle, or even from two ova in the same germ center. But they may also be due to ova released from two ovaries, and may not even be fertilized at the same occasion. The arrival of the two fertilized ova in the uterine cavity may

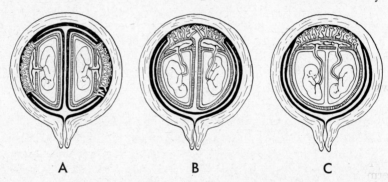

A　　　　　　　　B　　　　　　　　C

Fig. 151. Three different modes of implantation of nonidentical twins. In A, the twins have similar sites of implantation with entirely independent development of placentas. However, if one twin shows a higher growth rate the space for the other is greatly limited. In B, there are independent placentas which, however, overlap and are partially fused. In C, implantation is so close that only one placenta is developed and the circulation of the two twins is interwoven. (Drawings after O. Hoehne in Stoeckel: Lehrbuch der Geburtshilfe, Jena, 1930.)

differ by several days, and the second ovum may find a uterine mucosa in a state of reaction to the first ovum which is entirely unfavorable for a new nidation.

Macklin[15] figured the number of genes necessary for mongolism as five recessive, or two dominant and four recessive pairs of factors by using a box filled with red and white balls and mixing these balls in a proportion that simulated the frequency of mongolism. It would be much easier to divide the uterine mucosa in a field with islands of possible nidation and others unfit, and calculate the probability of hitting a feasible area if a certain percentage of the field is eliminated as unfit.

With regard to the fact that mongoloid twins are rarely dizygotic and concordant, it may be further pointed out that the two ova have not only to be impaired in their development in exactly the same manner, but at the same time the pregnancy has to be carried to full term. It is very unlikely that a pregnancy with two separate abnormal fetuses is normally terminated. The threshold of abortion is so easily reached that in the majority of cases a hemorrhage will end the struggle once and for all. Intrauterine nutrition in the preplacental phase represents such a delicate balance between the capacity of the ovum to provide its own food supply from its own sources, and nonplacental nutritional exchange between ovum and maternal blood stream, that "nutritional" deficiency cannot be conceived in such a simple term as maternal health or illness. It is not necessarily a deficiency of the maternal blood stream, but a defect in the barrier between ovum and maternal blood.

While these investigations agree with Van der Scheer's and Engler's[9] idea that the nidation of the ovum is of paramount importance, my concept of neofetal nutrition differs in that it does not necessarily look for anomalies in the uterine mucosa but considers the whole problem of embryonic nutrition, which relies as much on the ovum's own parasitic abilities as on the maternal blood supply. Thus, anomalies in fetal nutrition can be due to a great variety of factors: in the mother's general health, in her hormonal response to pregnancy, in uterine regional conditions, and in the capacity of the ovum to overcome the resistance of the maternal organism and provide sufficient nutrition for itself. The whole scale of possibilities runs from a maternal illness to a possible inability of an "over-aged" or even genetically inferior ovum to grow adequately in the neofetal period. No data as such have indicated a genetic origin of mongolism but the observations at hand leave full space for the possibility that genetically inferior ova can develop into a mongoloid fetus if the genetic deficiency results in a nutritional deficiency during the neofetal period.

Summary

1. Based on anatomic, histologic, and x-ray studies of skull and skeleton, the author presents the conclusion that the growth deficiency in mongolism represents a congenital acromicria which begins to manifest itself in the neofetal period. Attention is called to the fact that three previous investigators have come to the same conclusion (Schüller, Clift, and Lauche), that the mongoloid growth disorder represents "the opposite of acromegaly."

2. It is demonstrated that the growth deficiency of mongolism is not restricted to the skull, but involves the whole skeleton. Further evidence is presented that the growth deficiency cannot be explained by anomalies in the brain. It is necessary to postulate a disorder of central growth regulation.

3. If the postulate of a central growth deficiency of a pituitary-like factor is correct, the deficiency should not be restricted to the skull and skeleton, but should involve those endocrine glands which depend on stimulation from the pituitary body.

4. Extensive anatomic studies on the gonads, adrenals, liver, and thyroid in mongolism have shown that all these glands have a normal anlage and, though sometimes hypoplastic, are within normal range at the time of birth and shortly after. Comparison with later stages of development shows that

these organs fall increasingly below normal, and remain immature and underdeveloped.

5. Observations on the mongoloid pituitary body indicate that the pituitary is in an inactive, stagnant condition with an accumulation of eosinophilic granules and, often, increased amounts of "colloid" in the residual lumen and interalveolar spaces.

6. The congenital acromicria and pituitary deficiency which manifests itself after birth is not the cause of mongolism, but the result of factors which have interfered with neofetal development and have decelerated the growth and maturation of the fetus.

7. The noxious factors which lead to the production of congenital acromicria are still a matter of argument. Several investigators (Geyer, Engler, the author, and others) have produced a wealth of evidence as to the operation of prenatal maternal factors which account, to the satisfaction of these authors, for the deceleration of fetal growth. The geneticists maintain that the whimsical occurrence of mongolism can be explained only by postulating genetic factors.

8. An analysis of the prenatal growth deficiency of mongolism has led to the exact determination of the time in which the congenital acromicria develops. Through the coordinated findings of several investigators (Greig, Cummins-Platou, Ingalls, Lowe, Benda), the synchronism of mongoloid symptoms points to a neofetal deficiency developing between the sixth and twelfth week of fetal life. An analysis of the conditions during the neofetal period indicates that this is the period of transition before placental nutrition is established. It is demonstrated that the period is especially critical for the occurrence of abortions and a "threshold condition" for nutritional defects. It is demonstrated that the "environment" of dissimilar twins during that period is so different that the observations offer a satisfactory explanation for the fact that dissimilar twins are discordant in the great majority of instances.

The concept of mongolism as a congenital acromicria offers a biologic interpretation of this morbid entity, and a workable hypothesis which may help to improve the condition even if it is impossible to cure it or correct the prenatal anomalies. The data at hand may make it possible to outline a program of preventive measures against mongolism, and of a more successful treatment immediately after birth. It has been demonstrated that the failure of treatment is frequently due to the fact that treatment is not begun until many years after birth, when degenerative changes in brain and body are marked and irreversible.

REFERENCES

1. BALLANTYNE, J. W.: Antenatal Pathology and Hygiene. Edinburgh, Wm. Green & Sons, 1902.
2. BENDA, C. E.: *American Journal of Pathology*, 1940, 16, p. 71.
3. BENDA, C. E.: *Journal of Pediatrics*, 1941, 19, p. 800.
4. BENDA, C. E.: Mongolism and Cretinism. New York, Grune & Stratton, second edition, 1949.
5. BENDA, C. E.: *Journal of the American Medical Association*, 1949, 139, p. 979.
6. CLIFT, W.: *American Journal of Roentgenology and Radium Therapy*, 1922, 9, p. 420.
7. CUMMINS, H., and PLATOU, R. V.: *Southern Medical Journal*, 1946, 39, p. 925.
8. CUMMINS, H., and PLATOU, R. V.: *Pediatrics*, February, 1950.
9. ENGLER, M.: Mongolism. Baltimore, Williams & Wilkins Co., 1949.
10. GREIG, DAVID M.: *Edinburgh Medical Journal*, 1927, 34, p. 253.
11. HIRNING, L. C., and FARBER, S.: *American Journal of Pathology*, 1934, 10, p. 435.
12. INGALLS, T. H.: *American Journal of Diseases of Children*, 1947, 74, p. 147.
13. LAUCHE, A.: *Virchows Archiv für pathologische Anatomie und für klinische Medizin*, 1924, 249, pp. 315-334.
14. LOWE, R. F.: *British Journal of Ophthalmology*, March, 1949.
15. MACKLIN, M. T.: *American Journal of Mental Sciences*, 1929, 178, p. 315.
16. MALL, F. P.: *Journal of Morphology*, 1908, 19, p. 3.
17. PARK, E. A., and POWERS, G. F.: *American Journal of Diseases of Children*, 1920, 20, p. 235.
18. ROOSEN-RUNGE, E. C.: *American Journal of Pathology*, 1947, 33, p. 79.
19. SAWYER, G. M.: *American Journal of Mental Deficiency*, 1949, 54, p. 204.
20. SCHÜLLER, ARTHUR: *Wiener medizinische Wochenschrift*, 1907, 57, p. 629.
21. STOCCADA, FABIO: *Beiträge zur pathologischen Anatomie und zur allgemeinen Pathologie*, 1916, 61, pp. 450-513.
22. VAN DER SCHEER, W. M.: *Abhandlungen aus der Neurologie und Psychiatrie*, Heft 41, 1927.

CHAPTER 25

Mental Deficiency and Aberrant Metabolism

GEORGE A. JERVIS, M.D.

THE DISTINCTIVE GROUP of diseases characterized by mental defect and aberrant metabolism is of interest to many investigators. The geneticist sees in these conditions some of the most striking illustrations of Mendelian inheritance. The biochemist is here confronted with true experiments of Nature and is in the position to better evaluate normal paths of metabolism from the investigation of metabolic aberration. The neuropsychiatrist may find in these diseases a fertile field for investigating relationships of metabolic processes to mental functions.

The purpose of this presentation is to outline very briefly the main clinical, biochemical, and genetic data and to indicate some of the numerous problems which still await clarification.

One may conveniently divide these conditions into three groups: (1) types of mental deficiency associated with disorders of lipid metabolism; (2) types of mental deficiency associated with abnormal metabolism of amino acids; (3) types of mental deficiency associated with aberrant metabolism of carbohydrates.

Cerebral Lipoidosis

The first group includes the so-called cerebral lipoidoses. Table 38 shows the various forms. Each form possesses distinctive clinical features. Congenital amaurotic idiocy is present at birth and appears to be rapidly fatal.[29] Infantile amaurotic idiocy (Tay-Sachs disease) begins at about 6 months of age, is characterized by rapid mental deterioration, blindness, and motor impairment. Death occurs usually before the third year of life.[12] In the late infantile form (Bielschowsky disease), onset is between the second and third year and the course is somewhat more protracted than in the infantile form.[15] Juvenile amaurotic idiocy (Spielmeyer-Vogt disease) shows slow progressive mental deterioration extending from the age of 5 to 6 years to the age of 16 to 18 years when death usually occurs; there are blindness and pigmentary degeneration of the retina.[16] The onset of late amaurotic idiocy (Kufs disease) is after adolescence, the progression is slow extending over a period of ten to twenty years, and terminal profound dementia is observed.[18] Niemann-Pick disease is similar in its mental manifestations to Tay-Sachs disease but there is in addition conspicuous hepatosplenomegaly.[12] Gargoylism is characterized by mental defect, dystrophic changes of bones, and enlargement of liver and spleen.[19] The rare infantile form of Gaucher's disease shows rapid fatal course, idiocy, and various neurologic changes in addition to enlargement of spleen and liver.[33] In cerebral cholesterinosis, a condition first described by Bogaert and associates,[3] the clinical picture is that of mental defect with cerebellar symptoms. Mental symptoms and neurologic signs are seen only occasionally in the course of the well-known Schüller-Christian disease when the xanthomatous process invades the central nervous system.

TABLE 38.   LIPID INVOLVED IN VARIOUS FORMS OF LIPOIDOSIS

Disease	Lipid Involved
Congenital amaurotic idiocy	Unknown
Infantile amaurotic idiocy	Ganglioside
Late infantile amaurotic idiocy	Unknown
Juvenile amaurotic idiocy	Unknown
Late amaurotic idiocy	Unknown
Niemann-Pick disease	Sphingomyelin
Gargoylism	Unknown
Gaucher's disease (infantile form)	Kerasin
Cerebral cholesterinosis	Cholesterol ester
Schüller-Christian disease	Cholesterol

With the exception of the last two conditions, all forms of cerebral lipoidosis possess a common basic pathologic feature. The neuron cells throughout the entire nervous system are replete with, and more or less distended by, lipid material. There is some evidence, based on staining and solubility properties as well as on direct chemical examination, which suggests that the infiltrating lipid is different in each form of cerebral lipoidosis. In Tay-Sachs disease the lipid is ganglioside, a galactoside containing neuraminic acid;[23] in Niemann-Pick disease, sphingomyelin;[22] in Gaucher's disease, kerasin.[36]

Since in the various forms of cerebral lipoidosis no changes of blood lipids have been demonstrated, the process may be interpreted as a local abnormality of lipid metabolism within the neuron cells. It is possible that the stored lipid represents some normal metabolite which is not utilized because of faulty biochemical mechanism. The ganglioside found in Tay-Sachs disease, for instance, is apparently a normal component of cerebral cortex. However, in other conditions there is some evidence suggesting that the lipid involved is an abnormal metabolite. The sphingomyelin of Niemann-Pick disease is abnormal inasmuch as it contains only one fatty acid, stearic acid.[21] In the kerasin of Gaucher's disease the normally found galactose is replaced by glucose,[24] an extraordinary example of misdirected synthesis.

While the biochemical mechanism underlying the metabolic aberration of lipids is entirely unknown, the genetical basis of the main forms of cerebral lipoidoses is fairly well understood. Conditions of this type exhibit a strong family incidence with two or more sibs often affected. When statistical methods are applied in the calculation of the number of affected

TABLE 39.   INFANTILE AMAUROTIC IDIOCY*

s	ns	xs	xns	ts	m^2	m^2ns
1	19	1.000	19.000	19	0.000	0.000
2	21	1.143	24.003	26	0.122	2.562
3	13	1.297	16.861	21	0.263	3.419
4	7	1.463	10.231	8	0.420	2.540
5	10	1.639	16.390	20	0.592	5.920
6	9	1.825	16.425	14	0.776	6.984
7	2	2.020	4.040	3	0.970	1.940
8	1	2.223	2.223	4	1.172	1.172
9	1	2.443	2.433	1	1.380	1.380
10	3	2.649	7.947	7	1.592	4.776
11	1	2.870	2.870	1	1.805	1.805
12	1	3.098	3.098	6	2.180	2.180
Total	88		125.521	130		34.678

* The figures are obtained from Slome's[35] data and arrangement is according to Bernstein's method.

s=the size of the sibship; n=the number of sibships; x=the expected number of affected sibs on the basis of the hypothesis of recessivity; t=the observed number of affected sibs, and m^2=the quadratic error; $x=\dfrac{sp}{1-q^s}$ and $m^2=x_s(q-xsq^s)$; p=0.25 and q=(1-p).

sibs, observation agrees fairly well with expectation on the basis of the Mendelian hypothesis of a single recessive autosomal gene. This may be seen for infantile amaurotic idiocy in Table 39 (from Slome's data[35]), for juvenile amaurotic idiocy in Table 40 (Sjögren's material[34]), and for gargoylism in Table 41. It may be added that, as shown in Table 42, the percentage of parental consanguinity is much higher than normal in the families of affected individuals. These findings indicate that the cerebral lipoidoses are due to rare recessive genes.

Mental Deficiency Associated with Abnormal Metabolism of Amino Acids

The second group of diseases consists of types of mental deficiency associated with abnormalities in the metabolism of amino acids. The most important is phenylpyruvic oligophrenia or phenylketonuria (Fölling's disease).[10] Clinically, the disease is characterized by inborn mental defect.

TABLE 40. JUVENILE AMAUROTIC IDIOCY*

s	ns	xs	xns	ts	m^2	m^2ns
1	7	1.000	7.000	6	0.000	0.000
2	5	1.143	5.715	8	0.122	0.610
3	9	1.297	11.673	11	0.263	2.367
4	6	1.463	8.778	10	0.420	2.520
5	7	1.639	11.473	10	0.592	4.144
6	5	1.825	9.125	10	0.776	3.880
7	6	2.020	12.120	15	0.970	5.820
8	4	2.223	8.892	12	1.172	4.688
10	1	2.649	2.649	3	1.542	1.592
11	1	2.871	2.871	4	1.805	1.805
Total	51		80.296	89		27.426

* The figures are obtained from Sjögren's[34] data, and arrangement is according to Bernstein's method (as in Table 39).

TABLE 41. GARGOYLISM*

s	ns	xs	xns	ts	m^2	m^2ns
1	15	1.000	15.000	15	0.000	0.000
2	26	1.143	29.718	32	0.122	3.172
3	18	1.297	23.346	26	0.263	4.734
4	11	1.463	16.093	15	0.420	4.620
5	3	1.639	4.917	3	0.592	1.776
6	4	1.825	7.300	7	0.776	3.104
7	3	2.020	6.060	10	0.970	2.910
8	2	2.223	4.446	4	1.172	2.344
9	1	2.433	2.433	6	1.380	1.380
11	1	2.870	2.870	4	1.805	1.805
Total	84		112.183	122		25.835

* The figures are obtained from Jervis'[19] data, and arrangement is according to Bernstein's method (as in Table 39).

TABLE 42. PERCENTAGE OF PARENTAL CONSANGUINITY

Disease	Observed	Expected
Infantile amaurotic idiocy[35]	15.0	0.5–1.0
Juvenile amaurotic idiocy[34]	15.0	0.5–1.0
Gargoylism[19]	11.0	0.5–1.0

usually severe in degree, not infrequently accompanied by epileptic attacks and occasionally by psychotic episodes. The pathologic lesions consist essentially of a retardation of the normal process of myelinogenesis.[1] Biochemically, the disease is characterized by urinary excretion of phenylpyruvic acid, phenylalanine, and phenyllactic acid.[20] In the blood, phenylalanine is present in abnormally high amounts, from twenty to thirty times its normal quantity.[4] The blood concentration of phenylpyruvic acid is so low as to be almost unmeasurable.

The nature of the metabolic error is not yet clearly understood. The hypothesis that the condition is due to the patient's inability to break down the benzene ring of phenylpyruvic acid[30] would not explain the abnormal amount of phenylalanine in the blood. Another hypothesis that the error consists of an abnormal racemization of phenylalanine, the naturally occurring L form being converted into the D form which is deaminated in the kidneys and excreted as the keto acid,[10] is not supported by experimental evidence.[31] It is probable that the error consists in the inability to hydroxylate phenylalanine to tyrosine, the first stage in the oxidation of the amino acid.[17] Abnormal amounts of unmetabolized phenylalanine are therefore circulating in the body fluids and partly excreted as the amino acid and partly as the keto or the hydroxy acid. It is interesting to note that the patients excrete large amounts of phenylpyruvic acid, while the concentration in the blood is very low. The keto acid probably is formed in the kidneys from phenylalanine and thus excreted in the urine. An alternative hypothesis is that phenylpyruvic acid has a clearance volume comparable to the blood flow. The keto acid formed in various tissues of the body would then be eliminated because of the kidneys' inability to retain the acid by reabsorption. A mechanism of this type has been recently suggested in alkaptonuria.[28]

From a genetic point of view, phenylpyruvic oligophrenia behaves as a character relating to a single autosomal recessive gene.[14] In fact, as seen in Table 43, where the data from various sources[10, 14, 25, 26] are presented, observed and expected figures agree on the basis of this hypothesis.

A second type of mental deficiency associated with abnormal metabolism of amino acid is hepatolenticular degeneration (Wilson's disease) which is characterized clinically by progressive intellectual deterioration, dystonic movements, and rigidity. Pathologically there is extensive degeneration of the lenticular bodies and cirrhosis of the liver. Genetically, there is sufficient evidence indicating that the disease is a recessive condition. It has been recently shown that these patients excrete in the urine an abnormally high amount of free amino acids, the total alpha amino acid being almost three times the average excretion of the normal individual.[6] Several amino acids have been identified—threonine, histidine, valine, phenylalanine, lysine, leucine, and others. Threonine is present in more than twelve times its normal amount. However, the plasma amino acid concentrations are only slightly above the normal. The biochemical significance of these findings is still obscure. There seems to be no correlation between the extent of the amino-aciduria and the severity of the liver involvement. A defect in the intermediary amino acid metabolism seems excluded. Perhaps the best explanation is a lowered renal threshold for amino acid, the tubular reabsorption of amino acid being defective. The mechanism would be similar to that found in Franconi's syndrome.[8]

It seems, in conclusion, that in these two diseases accompanied by aberration in the metabolism of amino acids the biochemical mechanisms are entirely distinct—a failure of a metabolic step in phenylpyruvic idiocy, an abnormality of renal excretion in hepatolenticular degeneration.

TABLE 43.   PHENYLPYRUVIC OLIGOPHRENIA*

s	ns	xs	xns	ts	m^2	m^2ns
1	24	1.000	24.000	24	0.000	0.000
2	37	1.143	42.291	44	0.122	4.514
3	40	1.297	51.880	57	0.263	10.520
4	34	1.463	49.742	50	0.420	14.280
5	23	1.639	37.697	43	0.592	13.616
6	21	1.825	38.325	44	0.776	16.296
7	9	2.020	18.180	20	0.970	8.730
8	7	2.223	15.561	17	1.172	8.204
9	4	2.433	9.732	9	1.380	5.520
10	5	2.649	13.245	16	1.592	7.960
11	2	2.870	5.740	3	1.805	3.610
12	2	3.120	6.240	7	2.020	4.040
13	1	3.330	3.330	4	2.230	2.230
Total	209		325.963	338		99.520

* The data are arranged as in Table 39.

Mental Deficiency Associated with Aberrant Metabolism of Carbohydrates

The third group, consisting of types of mental deficiency associated with aberrant metabolism of carbohydrates, is only briefly mentioned, since the author has no personal experience with these conditions. One is galactosuria, a disease occurring in infants, in which galactose is not normally metabolized.[5] Abnormal amounts of this carbohydrate are found in the body fluids and the affected children show impairment of physical and mental growth. Another disease is glycogenosis (Gierke's disease), a condition characterized by a failure in the mechanism of breaking down of glycogen with consequent storage of the carbohydrate in many organs[7] including occasionally the central nervous system. In the last event, a pathologic picture resembling somewhat a cerebral lipoidosis results, the infiltrating substance being, however, glycogen instead of lipid.[13]

Some evidence exists indicating that both galactosuria and glycogenosis are genetically determined by recessive genes.

These are, briefly summarized, the main clinical, pathologic biochemical, and genetic data on these diseases.

Comments

Many problems await clarification. Some biochemical unknowns have been already mentioned; and in the discussion Dr. Waelsch will add his comments on the chemical aspects. From a genetic point of view much work remains to be done. Although all these conditions behave as recessive traits, occasionally in a family the condition manifests itself as a dominant character. Recently, for instance, the author has observed two pedigrees of phenylpyruvic idiocy which would fit better the dominant rather than the recessive hypothesis. The reason for this change of genetic behavior is not understood. The fact that males are more often affected than females, a phenomenon clearly seen in gargoylism for instance, remains unexplained genetically. Perhaps, still unknown differences between male and female normal metabolism might explain this effect. The study of linkage between the recessive genes responsible for these diseases and some known hereditary characters still remains to be done. Finally, the important genetic problem of detection of carriers[27] awaits investigation. It would appear that intensive biochemical study of the heterozygous state might be fruitful in this respect.

In a more general field, the problem of the relationship of the metabolic abnormality to the mental defect should be considered. This relationship seems to be one of cause and effect in the cerebral lipoidoses. It appears probable that the striking morphologic alteration of the neurons due to fatty infiltration causes impairment of function and consequent mental defect. A similar mechanism must be assumed for glycogenosis. In galactosuria toxic factors may be responsible for the mental defect. The toxic effect of galactose is well known experimentally.[9] It is interesting to note that fructosuria, a disease biochemically very close to galactosuria, is entirely harmless. In Wilson's disease the relationship, if any, of metabolic error to the brain lesions is not understood. In phenylketonuria several hypotheses present themselves for consideration. Phenylalanine, an essential amino acid, may not be available at some critical stage of development of the brain, for instance, during myelinization. This would explain the defect in the myelin formation which is observed on pathologic examination. Another hypothesis is that the high concentration of phenylalanine in the body fluid may have a toxic effect on the development of the nervous tissue possibly interfering with the absorption or utilization of other amino acids by nerve cells.[32] It is possible, however, that there exists no direct relation of metabolic error to mental defect, the two manifestations being simply pleiotropic effects of the same gene.

It is a singular fact that in spite of the diversity of biochemical mechanisms involved, the genetic behavior is the same in all conditions here considered.

It is tempting to attribute the common genetic behavior to a genetically determined lack of a specific normal enzyme responsible for the faulty metabolic step. In each disease, then, a gene change determines the absence of an enzyme and as a consequence there is a failure in the corresponding step in the chain of normal enzymatic reactions. This hypothesis would follow the classical conception of Garrod,[11] and new support would be found in the recent work on the genetics of a microorganism[2] indicating a one to one qualitative relation between units of inheritance, the genes, and units of biochemical activity, the enzymes. It may be an adequate explanation for phenylpyruvic idiocy in which the defective hydroxylation of phenylalanine might well be the failure of a normal enzymatic reaction genetically controlled. However, it would be difficult to explain in this simple manner the lipoidoses in which an abnormal metabolite accumulates in the nerve cells. Some much broader explanation than Garrod's would be required.

REFERENCES

1. ALVORD, E. C.; STEVENSON, L.; VOGEL, F. S.; and ENGEL, R. L.: *Journal of Neuropathology and Experimental Neurology*, 1950, 9, p. 298.
2. BEADLE, G. W.: *Chemical Reviews*, 1945, 37, p. 15.
3. BOGAERT, L.; SCHERER, H. J.; and EPSTEIN, E.: Une forme cerebrale de choléstérinose généralisée. Paris, Masson & Cie, 1937.
4. BOREK, E.; BRECHER, A.; JERVIS, G. A.; and WAELSCH, H.: *Proceedings of the Society for Experimental Biology and Medicine*, 1950, 75, p. 86.
5. BRUCK, E., and RAPOPORT, S.: *American Journal of Diseases of Children*, 1945, 70, p. 267.
6. COOPER, A. M.; ECKHARDT, R. D.; FALOON, W. W.; and DAVIDSON, G. S.: *Journal of Clinical Investigation*, 1950, 29, p. 265.
7. CRAWFORD, T.: *Quarterly Journal of Medicine*, 1946, 15, p. 285.
8. DENT, C. E.: *Quarterly Journal of Medicine*, 1947, 16, p. 275.
9. DEUEL, H. J.: *Physiological Reviews*, 1936, 16, p. 173.
10. FÖLLING, A.; MOHR, O. L.; and RUND, L.: Oligophrenia phenylpyrouvica. Oslo, Dybwad, 1945.
11. GARROD, A. E.: Inborn Errors of Metabolism. London, Oxford University Press, 1923.
12. GLOBUS, J.: *New York Mount Sinai Hospital Bulletin*, 1942, 9, p. 451.
13. GUNTHER, R.: *Virchows Archiv für pathologische Anatomie und Physiologie und für klinische Medizin*, 1939, 304, p. 87.
14. JERVIS, G. A.: *Journal of Mental Science*, 1939, 85, p. 719.
15. JERVIS, G. A.: *American Journal of Diseases of Children*, 1940, 60, p. 88.
16. JERVIS, G. A.: *American Journal of Diseases of Children*, 1941, 61, p. 327.
17. JERVIS, G. A.: *Journal of Biological Chemistry*, 1947, 169, p. 651.
18. JERVIS, G. A.: *The American Journal of Psychiatry*, 1950, 107, p. 409.
19. JERVIS, G. A.: *Archives of Neurology and Psychiatry*, 1950, 63, p. 681.
20. JERVIS, G. A.: *Proceedings of the Society for Experimental Biology and Medicine*, 1950, 75, p. 83.
21. KLENK, E.: *Zeitschrift für physiologische Chemie*, 1934, 229, p. 151.
22. KLENK, E.: *Zeitschrift für physiologische Chemie*, 1939, 262, p. 128.

23. KLENK, E.: *Zeitschrift für physiologische Chemie,* 1941, 268, p. 50.

24. KLENK, E., and SCHUMANN, E.: *Zeitschrift für physiologische Chemie,* 1940, 267, p. 130.

25. LARSON, C. A.: *Hereditas,* 1950, 36, p. 110.

26. MUNRO, T. A.: *Annals of Eugenics,* 1947, 14, p. 60.

27. NEEL, J. V.: *American Journal of Human Genetics,* 1949, 1, p. 19.

28. NEUBERGER, A.; RIMINGTON, C.; and WILSON, J. M. G.: *Biochemical Journal,* 1947, 41, p. 438.

29. NORMAN, R. M., and WOOD, N.: *Journal of Neurology and Psychiatry,* 1941, 4, p. 175.

30. PENROSE, L. S., and QUASTEL, J. H.: *Biochemical Journal,* 1937, 31, p. 226.

31. PRESCOTT, B. A.; BOREK, E.; BRECHER, A.; and WAELSCH, H.: *Journal of Biological Chemistry,* 1949, 181, p. 273.

32. RIMINGTON, C.: *Biochemical Society Symposia,* 1950, 4, p. 16.

33. SCHAIRER, E.: *Virchows Archiv für pathologische Anatomie und Physiologie und für klinische Medizin,* 1948, 315, p. 395.

34. SJÖGREN, T.: *Hereditas,* 1931, 14, p. 197.

35. SLOME, D.: *Journal of Genetics,* 1934, 27, p. 363.

36. THANNHAUSER, S. J., and SCHMIDT, G.: *Physiological Reviews,* 1946, 26, p. 275.

DR. ASBJÖRN FÖLLING: I appreciate the invitation to speak at this time, but I have nothing to add to what Dr. Jervis has said. He has covered those points which I had in mind. I would like to say that I am happy that so many outstanding men in this country have taken up work on this subject, and I hope that in the future its questions will be solved.

Quantitative Aspects of the Metabolic Error in Oligophrenia Phenylpyruvica

HEINRICH B. WAELSCH, M.D.

In his comprehensive and clear review, Dr. Jervis has discussed types of mental deficiency which are not only of great interest to the pathologist and geneticist but also of particular fascination to the biochemist.

I should like to add a few remarks on the biochemistry of phenylketonuria or oligophrenia phenylpyruvica. Some of the biochemical aspects of this disease have been studied in our laboratory during the recent years and I am particularly happy to report on this investigation today in the presence of Dr. Fölling, the discoverer of this experiment of nature.

As Dr. Jervis has pointed out, phenylketonuria is characterized by the excretion of abnormally high concentrations of phenylalanine, phenyllactic acid, and phenylpyruvic acid in the urine and by an abnormally high phenylalanine level in blood. This metabolic error in phenylalanine metabolism is accompanied by mental deficiency. It is assumed, and rightly so, that the abnormally high excretion of phenylalanine and its metabolic derivatives in the urine is the result of the high blood concentration of the amino acid. When the blood circulates through the kidneys part of the phenylalanine is excreted as such, part of it is oxidatively deaminated to phenylpyruvic acid which is partly reduced to phenyllactic acid.

We felt at the time when we became interested in the biochemistry of phenylketonuria that the first thing to do was to design reliable methods for the determination in body fluids of phenylalanine and its metabolic derivatives, particularly phenyllactic acid. The growth response of *Lactobacillus arabinosus* to phenylalanine, phenyllactic acid, and phenylpyruvic acid was investigated, and a microbiologic assay method was evolved on the basis of this study.[2]

The most plausible explanation for the abnormal metabolism of phenylalanine in phenylketonuria is found in the suggestion of Jervis that these subjects are unable to hydroxylate phenylalanine to tyrosine. It is not known whether the inability to hydroxylate is only restricted to the para-hydroxylation of phenylalanine nor is it known whether the block in para-hydroxylation is complete, i.e., that no tyrosine whatsoever is formed from the dietary phenylalanine. If the block in hydroxylation is complete, which seems likely on the basis of preliminary balance studies, tyrosine becomes an essential amino acid for the mental defectives suffering from phenylketonuria.

With the microbiologic assay method the level of L-phenylalanine in the blood plasma ultrafiltrates of eighteen phenylketonurics was determined (Table 44).[1] The values varied from 18 to 38 mg. per 100 ml. of plasma, and repeated analyses at different times indicated that the variation among individuals was significantly greater than in one individual from day to day. The phenylalanine concentration in the blood plasma of phenylketonurics is, therefore, approximately twenty times higher than that found in normal subjects. The increase of phenylalanine over the normal values of spinal fluid was of an order of magnitude similar to that observed in blood plasma.

It is important to compare the level of the intelligence quotient (I.Q.) with the concentration of phenylalanine in blood plasma (Table 44). It may be seen that no correlation whatsoever exists between these two values. This becomes understandable if one considers the mechanisms by which the high phenylalanine level in blood is maintained. Small amounts of an amino acid excreted with the glomerular filtrate are reabsorbed by the kidney tubuli and do not appear in the urine. It has to be assumed that in phenylketonurics the inability to metabolize phenylalanine causes a level of the amino acid in blood, and consequently in the glomerular filtrate, to be established which overwhelms the tubular reabsorption. Although the cause of the increased phenylalanine level in blood plasma is undoubtedly the metabolic error, its quantitative expression seems to be determined by the reabsorptive power of the tubuli. Since the block in phenylalanine metabolism appears to be complete, the relative constancy of the plasma level of phenylalanine as well as the lack of correlation between this value and the I.Q. can be understood.

The analysis of the quantitative aspects of the metabolic error in phenylketonuria suggested the possibility of the occurrence of an elevated phenylalanine level in blood—not as high as in phenylketonurics—without excre-

TABLE 44. CONCENTRATION OF L-PHENYLALANINE (PA) AND PHENYLLACTIC ACID (PL) IN SERUM AND SPINAL FLUID OF PATIENTS WITH PHENYLPYRUVIC OLIGOPHRENIA

Patient	Age	I.Q.	Sample I		Sample II		Sample III		Sample IV		Spinal Fluid PA mg. %
			PA+PL mg. %	PA mg. %	PA+PL mg. %	PA mg. %	PA+PL mg. %	PA mg. %	PA+PL mg. %	PA mg. %	
1	28	5	32	31	39	38	33	33	33	34	7.7
2	42	46	29	29	33	32	31	28	33	30	7.6
3	41	11	27	27		34					
4	32	7	33	32	31	29					
5	29	47	33	35	38	36	34	32			7.8
6	26	7	27	27	33	31					
7	15	35	31	31							7.5
8	17	12	33	33							
9	23	7	30	29	34	34	33	33			7.9
10	30	38	27	27							
11	26	10	26	26							
12	6	14	29	27							
13	5	24	27	26							
14	19	9	24	26	29	31	32	31			8.2
15	29	5	33	29							
16	5	24	25	24							
17	27	40	24	22							6.2
18	8	10	21	19							
19	22	6									6.1
20	20	7									6.3

From Borek, Brecher, Jervis, and Waelsch.[1]

tion of the amino acid and its metabolic derivatives in the urine. Such a finding would indicate a partial block of phenylalanine utilization. We have analyzed the blood plasma of ten pairs of parents of phenylketonurics. Since the disease behaves as a recessive Mendelian character, these parents are heterozygous for phenylketonuria. In all twenty blood plasma samples, normal phenylalanine values were found.

It seems to me that the quantitative description of phenylketonuria has come to a preliminary conclusion, and that we may expect further information by the study of the intermediary amino acid metabolism in this metabolic error.

REFERENCES

1. BOREK, E.; BRECHER, A.; JERVIS, G. A.; and WAELSCH, H.: *Proceedings of the Society for Experimental Biology and Medicine,* 1950, 75, p. 86.
2. PRESCOTT, B. A.; BOREK, E.; BRECHER, A.; and WAELSCH, H.: *Journal of Biological Chemistry,* 1949, 181, p. 273.

CHAPTER 26

Metabolic and Physiologic Disturbances in the Psychoses

HUDSON HOAGLAND, PH.D.

THE STATEMENT that all human behavior is a function of the activity of the nervous system and of other body processes is a hardly debatable premise. This is as true of the behavior of normal man as it is of the mentally ill. The so-called functional disorders of psychiatry of which schizophrenia is an example presumably are those involving disturbances of brain function, since behavior of a disembodied psyche is a meaningless concept. Such disturbances evidently occur at a molecular level, too subtle to yield directly to present-day analysis by neuroanatomists and neurophysiologists. Schizophrenia, whether it be a unitary disease process or a complex syndrome involving a multiplicity of factors, is certainly no less an "organic" disease than is any other, but science is not as yet sufficiently advanced to analyze the brain mechanisms involved in either normal or abnormal behavior at the level necessary for understanding so complex a problem as that presented by schizophrenia.

To the physiologist interested in these problems an indirect and necessarily crude approach may be had by studies of metabolic events as reflected in body fluids such as blood and urine. By such studies we have found differences of steroid metabolism between psychotic and nonpsychotic persons. For the remainder of this paper I would like to discuss these differences and the possible light they may shed on the physiology of psychosis.

Stress Responses of the Adrenal Cortex in Normal Persons

Our investigations of adrenal physiology have been shared by a number of workers at the Worcester Foundation. Dr. Gregory Pincus has been a principal collaborator and other participants have been Harry Freeman, Fred Elmadjian, David Stone, John Bergen, Louise Romanoff, and James

From the Worcester Foundation for Experimental Biology and the National Institute of Mental Health Cooperative Research Station at the Worcester Foundation, Public Health Service, Federal Security Agency.

The work reviewed here has been aided by grants or contracts from the Office of Naval Research, The Dementia Praecox Research Committee of the Scottish Rite, The Williams Waterman Fund of the Research Corporation, the F.C.B. Foundation and the G. D. Searle Company.

Carlo. Associated with us in work with patients at the Worcester State Hospital have been William Malamud, R. G. Hoskins, Charles Kaufman, Sidney Sands, Eliot Rodnick, David Shakow, Enoch Calloway, and Austin Berkeley.

Since 1941 we have been engaged in the study of adrenal responses to a wide variety of work-a-day stresses in normal men and women and in those

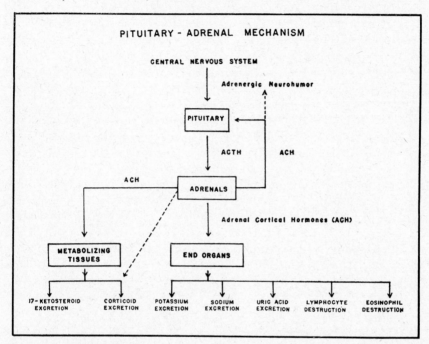

FIG. 152. Schema showing pituitary-adrenal response system. Adrenocorticotrophin (ACTH) stimulates the adrenal cortex to synthesize and release adrenal cortical hormones (ACH). Cortical steroid hormones exert negative feed-back to control the ACTH release. ACH are metabolized and act upon target organs to modify the amounts of excreted urinary substances and blood cell levels listed at the bottom of the figure. End-organs are tissues of the body, the metabolism of which is affected by adrenal steroids. These include the lymphatic system, kidney, muscle, and brain. (From *American Journal of Psychiatry*, 1950, 106.)

hospitalized for severe personality disorders. In the early period of this work, changes in the excretion of 17-ketosteroids was the only practical index of adrenocortical function. Later, changes in the number of circulating lymphocytes became available, and in the last two years relative changes in seven urinary and blood indices have been used by us in our adrenal studies. Figure 152 shows schematically how increases in urinary 17-ketosteroids, corticoids (neutral reducing lipids), potassium, sodium, and uric acid together with lymphocyte and eosinophil destruction reflect enhanced activity of the adrenal cortex. In this figure, "end-organs" correspond to lymphoid tissue and other protein reservoirs acted upon by the 11-oxysteroids which convert protein to sugar which is stored in the liver. Uric acid and lymphopenia reflect aspects of this conversion. Changes in the rates of potassium and sodium excretion are affected by several adrenal steroids by modification of kidney thresholds and changes in tissue electrolyte balance.

The adrenal cortex, unlike the adrenal medulla, has no innervation and its hormones are released solely in response to adrenocorticotrophin (ACTH), a protein from the anterior lobe of the pituitary body. While there have been isolated twenty-eight different steroid substances from the adrenal little can be said on the basis of isolation work alone about the hormonal role of these substances since many are metabolic intermediates and some may be artefact substances resulting from the extraction. Of the twenty-eight steroids only six have been recognized as specific hormones. Two of these, Compound E (cortisone) and Compound F have oxygen or hydroxyl functions at both the number 11 and number 17 carbon atoms of the steroid skeleton and two, Compounds A and B, have oxygen or hydroxyl at the number 11 carbon but not at the 17 position. Desoxycorticosterone, without oxygen at either the 11 or 17 positions, has been recognized as a fifth adrenal cortical hormone and is active primarily as an electrolyte regulator causing retention of sodium and loss of potassium in the adrenalectomized animal and in Addisonian patients. The amorphous fraction, a mixture of unknown steroids, has also been recognized as functionally important. Thus far only Compounds E and F have been shown to be active against the collagen diseases although Compounds A, B, E, and F affect protein and sugar metabolism and have some action in maintaining electrolyte homeostasis. Recent experiments reported by a group at the Worcester Foundation[6] involving perfusion of the beef adrenal gland have demonstrated, in addition to the five specific hormones just described, that there are ten other steroids released in response to ACTH. Thus ACTH produces, by synthesis and release in varying quantities, fifteen steroid substances.

We have studied adrenal stress responses in approximately 200 normal persons and analyzed our data statistically. Our stresses have included: exposure to cold[15] and to heat and high humidity,[16] the prolonged operation of an airplane-type pursuit meter which quantitatively measures fatigability,[17] 208 test flights of twenty-three professional airplane pilots,[17] the taking of examinations and interviews and of an especially designed frustration test (target-ball test).[22, 26] We have examined extensively the pituitary-adrenal response to the chemical stress of ingesting large quantities of sugar.[1, 3, 4, 5, 20] In most of these tests urine and usually blood samples have been taken before each stress, fifteen minutes after the end of the stress (usually lasting an hour), and again two hours later. The stresses, while varying in effectiveness, enhanced the adrenal activity of our normal population as reflected in post-stress percentage changes from pre-test levels of the various urinary and blood indices, and we were able to correlate measured aspects of psychomotor fatigability with levels of adrenocortical response to the same stress in different individuals. These results were especially striking with subjects performing on the pursuit meter.[17, 20]

As a result of these findings we attempted to improve prolonged psychomotor performance by the administration of certain steroid substances and found that the synthetic steroid Δ5-pregnenolone taken by mouth in 50- to 100-mg. doses significantly improved fatiguing psychomotor performance compared to that when taking placebos.[18, 19, 23] This substance does not produce untoward side effects. Our perfusion studies of the beef adrenal have shown that pregnenolone is converted by the adrenal to a number of true adrenal cortical hormones.[6]

Stress Responses of the Adrenal Cortex in Psychotic and in Normal Persons

Schizophrenic patients as a group have failed to meet the daily stresses of living and have developed bizarre forms of behavior necessitating hospitalization. We were interested to find that these patients, in general, displayed abnormal and inadequate adrenal stress responses as compared to controls. We have studied approximately 100 male schizophrenic patients in many of the same stressful tests we used with our control group.[1, 3, 4, 5, 15, 16, 20, 21, 22, 24]

Chronic schizophrenic patients, not subjected to special stresses, give evidence of adrenal cortical secretion differing relatively little from that of normal controls. It is in response to stress that more marked group differences appear. Thus we have found that the excretion of 17-ketosteroids, potassium, and uric acid in thirty-four patients and thirty-six controls fasted overnight is not significantly different, although a significantly smaller excretion of neutral reducing lipids (corticoids) was observed in the patient group. The patients also excrete significantly more sodium and urine, but water intake was not adequately controlled and these last results are difficult to evaluate.[20]

Table 45 shows data for the resting output of variables useful in adrenal assay from two sets of determinations on the same groups of patients and controls. The patients at rest show some hypoadrenalism as judged by their low corticoid and high sodium output but otherwise they are not like Addisonian patients. They appear to excrete at rest more 17-ketosteroids than do the normals and this might suggest that their adrenals are overactive but the difference is not statistically significant ($P > 0.05$), and the view that they are hyperactive is contradicted by the sodium and corticoid data of the table. As will be seen later in this paper, enhanced 17-ketosteroid excretion in response to stress and to injected ACTH is less in the patients than in the normal group and we have suggested[20, 21] that this may be because the patients' adrenals are secreting maximally most of the time and have little reserve to meet stress. As will be seen the patients secrete qualitatively different types of steroids from the controls, and the resting levels of the values recorded in Table 45 of themselves tell us nothing about what happens to these variables in response to stress.

Resting lymphocyte and eosinophil values are not included in the table since they depend upon such a multiplicity of factors that their inclusion as an index of adrenal function would be irrelevant. Relative (percentage) changes of these variables on stress will be discussed later. The normal fasting values of 17-ketosteroids and uric acid indicate that the patients are in a satisfactory nutritional state and are not at all like undernourished ill persons who show low fasting outputs of these substances.

TABLE 45.   MEAN BASAL VALUES AFTER FOURTEEN HOURS FASTING FOR
CONTROL SUBJECTS AND SCHIZOPHRENIC PATIENTS

(Two sets of determinations on each group. Bold face numbers in the control group are different from those of the patient group to a one per cent level of confidence by Fisher's t test)

	Urine Volume cc./hr.	17-Keto-steroids mg./hr.	Neutral Reducing Lipids mg./24 hrs.	Uric Acid mg./min.	Potas-sium mg./min.	Sodium mg./hr.	Urinary PO₄ mg./min.	Creati-nine gm./24 hr.
36 controls	**66.4**	0.50	**3.02**	0.48	191	**231**	**0.59**	1.80
34 patients	156.2	0.68	1.77	0.55	199	361	0.32	1.69
36 controls	**61.2**	0.38	**3.00**	0.50	157	**193**	**0.55**	1.68
34 patients	132.9	0.61	1.57	0.50	193	322	0.24	1.60

From Pincus and Hoagland.[20]

When the patients are put through our series of stress tests, differences of a more marked kind appear to separate them from the normal group. Patient and normal control groups were subjected to a purely chemical stress (the ingestion of sugar by the Exton-Rose technic), to a psychomotor fatiguing test (the operation of a pursuit meter), and to a psychologic frustration test (target-ball test). Timed urine and blood samples were collected just before each test which lasts one hour, fifteen minutes after the test, and again at two hours and fifteen minutes post-test. The urinary samples were analyzed for 17-ketosteroids, corticoids (neutral reducing lipids), sodium, potassium, and uric acid. Lymphocyte counts were made on the blood samples and eosinophils were counted in many of the samples.

Not all the subjects were put through all of the tests and studied by all the indices, but our findings have been evaluated statistically and may be summarized by saying that the patient group (schizophrenics hospitalized on an average of two and one-half years) failed markedly to enhance adrenal cortical output with stress as compared to the control group. Figure 153 shows group differences in responses to an hour of operation of a pursuit meter by forty-six controls and thirty-six patients. The first rectangle of each

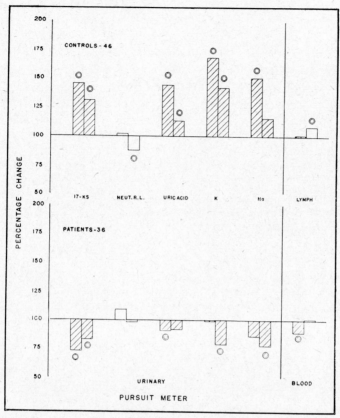

Fig. 153. Comparison of six adrenal cortical stress-response indices in pursuit meter tests lasting one hour for forty-six fasting normal controls and thirty-six fasting schizophrenic patients. The first of each pair of rectangles is from timed urine and blood samples taken within fifteen minutes of the termination of the stress. The second rectangle of each pair corresponds to samples taken two and a quarter hours post stress. Analysis of timed pre-stress samples taken just before the test furnish the base for the relative per cent changes. Cross-hatching indicates statistically significant differences to better than the 5 per cent level of confidence between patients and controls; circles above the rectangles indicate this same level of confidence for changes from the pre-stress (100 per cent) values. (From *American Journal of Psychiatry*, 1950, 106.)

pair represents per cent changes from pre-test levels at fifteen minutes post-test, and the second rectangle shows changes at two and one-quarter hours post-test. Circles above the rectangles represent changes from resting levels at better than the 5 per cent level of confidence, and cross-hatching indicates differences between patients and controls at this same level of confidence. Control urine and blood samples were collected over the first two hours after rising, and the post-test samples were late morning samples. We have demonstrated a diurnal rhythm of adrenal secretion which is

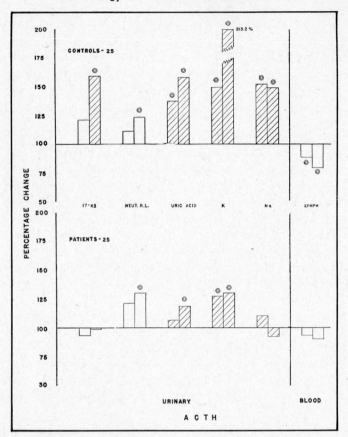

Fig. 154. Mean per cent changes in six adrenal response indices following injection of 25 mg. of ACTH. Data on twenty-five normal controls above, and on twenty-five schizophrenic patients below. Symbols as in Figure 153. (From *American Journal of Psychiatry*, 1950, 106.)

maximal after rising and which falls during the day.[14, 17, 24] If the stress does not enhance adrenal output, the values of the urinary variables should fall below the resting early morning samples, and this they do in the patient group. The normal subjects responding to the stress show enhancement of the urinary indices of adrenal cortical function. It is interesting to note that the drop in lymphocytes is greater in the patients than it is in the controls where there is a tendency for the lymphocytes to rise in the second post-stress sample. This result taken alone would suggest that the patients are more responsive to the stress than are the controls. This is clearly contradicted by all our urine data in this experiment. For a discussion of these lymphocyte changes the reader is referred to Pincus and Hoagland.[20]

Plots similar to those of Figure 153 have been made for the stress of our target-ball frustration test and for the stress of the ingestion of sugar.[5, 15, 22]

The target organs responding to adrenal steroids are normally responsive in our patients as has been demonstrated in control and patient groups by the injection of standard doses of Upjohn's lipo-adrenal extract.[20]

Thus the lowered responsivity of the patient group must be due to a failure to release adequate amounts and/or types of adrenal hormones in response to stress. This could result from an inadequate release of ACTH from the pituitary body or from the inability of the adrenal cortex to respond adequately to ACTH.

That the latter is generally the case is indicated by the fact that the injection of ACTH produces a subnormal response in the patient group in comparison to the control group.[20] This may be seen in Figure 154 which is plotted in the same way as is Figure 153. Here we see as in Figure 153 that there is no difference between the effect of stress in the patient and control groups on the per cent change in corticoids, and only small and insignificant group differences appear in the lymphocyte changes. Marked group differences appear in per cent changes in 17-ketosteroid, potassium, sodium, and uric acid excretion following ACTH injection. It is thus clear from Table 45 that although at rest the corticoid output is only about 60 per cent as much in the patient group as in the controls, its relative (percentage) change with stress is the same in the two groups. The lymphocyte changes with stress are, next to the cortins, the poorest of our indices in demonstrating group differences with the stresses under consideration. They are significantly lowered in the controls but there is no statistically significant difference (absence of cross-hatching) between the patient and control groups with respect to this variable and this is in sharp contrast to most of the urinary data. Thus the measures of adrenal stress response in these particular tests which show clear group differences are 17-ketosteroids, potassium, sodium, and uric acid changes.

In severe stress tests such as pursuit meter operation combined with anoxia[10] and exposure for an hour to 100° F. and 94 per cent humidity the per cent lymphocyte changes have shown striking group differences, but these are not delineative with the milder stresses used in the experiments under discussion (cf. Figs. 153 and 154).

A total response index (abbreviated TRI) has been devised[20, 22] as a measure of over-all adrenal responsivity to our stresses and to hormone injections. This consists of a mean of the sum of the per cent changes from prestress or preinjection levels of the two post-stress samples of urinary sodium, potassium, uric acid, 17-ketosteroids, and corticoids plus twice (for weighting purposes) the two post-stress percentage drops in lymphocytes added as positive numbers. For example, all of twenty-five normal control subjects showed a TRI value of 20 units or greater following 25-mg. injections of ACTH, while only twenty-eight per cent of twenty-five schizophrenic patients show a response of 20 units or greater.[20] Table 46 compares TRI values in some of our tests. Approximately this same ratio of normal responders to schizophrenic responders is also found for our various stress tests (last column of table) which suggests a common mechanism for the failure in all of the tests. This common mechanism appears to be the inability of the patients' adrenals to respond normally either to endogenous or to injected ACTH.

If we compare ratios of our various specific measures of adrenal responsivity we find evidence of qualitative differences in the stress and ACTH responses of our normal and patient populations. One typical example of this is shown in Table 47.

Further evidence of qualitative abnormalities of adrenal function may be seen in the schizophrenic group who gave quantitatively normal TRI re-

TABLE 46. THE TOTAL RESPONSE INDEX OF VARIOUS SUBJECTS IN THE STRESS TESTS

Test	Subjects	Mean TRI	Subjects with Score of 20 or Greater	Ratio of Normal Responders to Schizophrenic Responders
			per cent	
ACTH	Normal (25)	46.2	100.0	3.6
ACTH	Schizophrenic (25)	12.0	28.0	
Pursuit meter	Normal (46)	22.1	47.8	3.0
Pursuit meter	Schizophrenic (36)	−2.7	15.8	
Target-ball (frustration test)	Normal (36)	11.5	32.5	3.3
Target-ball (frustration test)	Schizophrenic (20)	−6.7	10.0	
Glucose tolerance	Normal (47)	22.1	48.6	3.2
Glucose tolerance	Schizophrenic (38)	5.7	15.0	

From Pincus and Hoagland.[20]

sponses (i.e., TRI values > 20) to the stress tests (approximately one-third of the total). As we have pointed out we found no group difference in increased corticoid excretion on stress and we have compared our other indices of adrenal function which differ in the two groups, using corticoid percentage increases of excretion as a standard. In Table 48 we express the ratio of mean corticoid changes to mean changes in the other variables. The urinary variables in normal men show ratios of 1.30 to 1.38, but the ratios are lower in the patient group and these differences are highly significant. Thus the chronic schizophrenic displays both quantitative and qualitative abnormalities of adrenal stress responses which appear to lie specifically at the level of the inability of his adrenal cortex to respond to ACTH by release of normal amounts and normal ratios of steroid hormones.

During the past year Mittleman (unpublished) in our laboratory has discovered further evidence of qualitative abnormalities of adrenal physiology in schizophrenic patients. In a study of twenty-three patients and fifteen normal controls he has found that the twenty-four-hour excretion of adrenal steroid metabolites in the form of alpha and beta ketones is significantly different in the two groups. The patients excrete over twice as much beta ketones as do the controls and the difference is significant at the 1 per cent level of confidence. This indicates a difference in the production of steroid metabolites perhaps due to enzyme differences in the patient and normal groups.

The subnormal stress responses of the psychotic patients are not corrected by a vitamin- and protein-rich diet.[20, 25] They are not found in psy-

TABLE 47.

Ratio =	$\dfrac{\text{Stress Change Uric Acid}}{\text{Stress Change Lymphocytes}}$		
	Target-Ball Test	Pursuit Meter Test	ACTH Injection Test
Normal subjects	1.2	1.4	1.8
Patients	1.0	1.05	1.1

TABLE 48.   THE RATIO OF MEAN PERCENTAGE CHANGES IN VARIOUS SPECIFIC INDICES TO THE MEAN PERCENTAGE CHANGE IN NEUTRAL REDUCING LIPIDS

Response Index	Ratio	
	Schizophrenic Men	Normal Men
17-ketosteroid output	1.12	1.35
Uric acid output	0.80	1.38
Potassium output	0.87	1.31
Sodium output	0.94	1.30
Lymphocyte number	0.61	0.82

The data are those of the fourteen schizophrenic men classified as positive responders (TRI > 20) to the three stress tests and a similar group of normal subjects (see text).

From Pincus and Hoagland.[20]

choneurotic patients whom we have found to give normal responses to 25-mg. injections of ACTH.[20, 21] Figure 155 shows data obtained by us on normal males and females, contrasted to psychoneurotic male and female patients at the Massachusetts General Hospital.

The refractoriness of the adrenals to ACTH in the psychotic patients displaying abnormal responses is clearly, according to our data, not absolute. This is further shown by the fact that larger quantities of ACTH (75 to

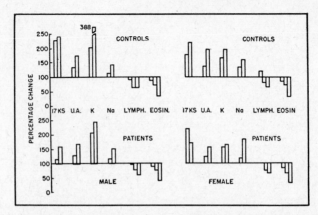

Fig. 155. Mean per cent changes in six adrenal response indices in six urinary and blood constituents after the administration of 25 mg. of ACTH to groups of normal men (eight subjects), psychoneurotic men (nine subjects), normal women (nine subjects), and psychoneurotic women (eleven subjects). Rectangles as in Figures 153 and 154. The normal individuals and the patients show no significant group differences. Note contrast to Figure 154. (From *The American Journal of Psychiatry*, 1950, 106.)

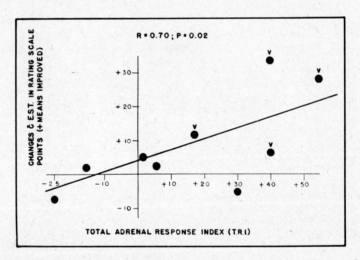

Fig. 156. Individual adrenal cortical pre-therapy responses (TRI values) to 25-mg. injections of ACTH of nine schizophrenic patients are plotted as ordinates against the psychiatric improvement of each patient as measured by the Malamud rating scale after a standardized course of electroshock therapy. The four patients indicated by a V mark recovered sufficiently to go out on visit. All four had pre-treatment TRI values > 15. With only one exception the remaining patients (with TRI values of < 15) showed little improvement on EST. (From *Psychosomatic Medicine*, 1945, 7.)

100 mg.) produce TRI responses more nearly approaching those of the controls given 25-mg. doses, but qualitative differences in the patient and control groups are more in evidence with these larger doses.[20]

We have reported that normal persons show an increase of 50 ± 14 per cent in output of 17-ketosteroids in the first two hours after rising after a night's sleep.[14, 17, 24] This may reflect a special form of adrenal stress response associated with waking and starting the day's activities. In general, schizophrenic patients display, as a group, a somewhat lower diurnal rhythm of excretion than do normal controls.[2, 15]

In ten female patients suffering from involutional depression we also found evidence of adrenal cortical unresponsivity.[11] These patients averaged an insignificant (3 per cent) morning increase in 17-ketosteroid excretion over the night level before they were given a course of electroshock treatments. During the treatment course the morning increase in output rose to an average 32 per cent over the night level, and it was 25 per cent over the night level a month after the treatments had ended. Eight of the ten women showed good social remission resulting from the treatments. Thus we see that indications of adrenal unresponsivity to stress may be found in psychotics other than schizophrenics and that the condition improves with therapy.

We have found[9] that favorable prognosis in electroshock therapy of schizophrenic patients is correlated with the degree of responsivity of the adrenal cortex to a pre-treatment test dose of 25 mg. of ACTH ($r = 0.7$, $P = 0.02$). Figure 156 is a plot of the TRI (horizontally) against the total number of units of improvement on the Malamud rating scale[12, 13] resulting from a course of electroshock therapy. Patients indicated by a V were out on visit two months post-treatment. Four out of five patients with pretreatment TRI's of greater than 15 were well enough after treatment to leave the hospital on a visit. The four patients with pre-treatment TRI values of <15 did not improve. From these data it would appear that the more normally responsive a patient's adrenal cortex the better is the chance of reversing his schizophrenia with electroshock therapy.

Comments

In our studies we have used percentage changes from pre-stress resting levels of a number of measures of adrenal action as indications of adrenal stress responses. This has been useful because of the wide variations in resting levels of some of these measures from person to person which are independent of adrenal function. We have, for example, found resting eosinophil counts in normal persons to range all the way from 30 to 1100 per cubic millimeter. We have observed no correlation between the absolute pre-stress levels and the percentage changes with stress.

The following unpublished observations in this connection may be of interest. Eosinophil counts on thirty-five normal persons (age 40 to 60 years) gave a mean value of 236; counts on thirty-one schizophrenic patients (same age range) gave a mean value of 105 and the difference is significant (P<0.01). Following injection of 25 mg. of ACTH the normals showed greater percentage decreases than the patients at the one and one quarter- and three and one quarter-hour periods, P<0.01. It is clear from this that one cannot infer that the lower resting counts of the patients are an index of greater adrenal cortical responsivity.

The resting eosinophil counts are determined by their rate of formation and rate of destruction and by themselves give no relevant information about adrenal function. Nutrition may play a role here. Two of our schizophrenic patients showed resting counts of 94 and 122. After two weeks of a protein- and vitamin-rich dietary regimen these values were 277 and 373 respectively. The percentage drop in their eosinophils with injection of 25 mg. of ACTH (i.e., their adrenal responsivity) was not changed by the diet.

Adrenal steroids are known to modify brain function including several aspects of its metabolism[8, 27] and it is natural to inquire about the relation of our findings to the etiologic basis of schizophrenia. Parenthetically it may be pointed out that Hemphill and Reiss[7] have confirmed our finding that psychotic patients, in general, display subnormal adrenal cortical responsivity to stress.

Our data do not indicate whether the adrenal abnormalities precede the psychoses or are developed as a by-product of it. Kallmann's genetic studies indicate an expectancy of schizophrenia of approximately 1 per cent in the population and it is tempting to consider that some people may have a genetically determined aberration of adrenal steroid synthesis through disturbances in enzyme balance that may make them, on the average, more vulnerable to psychosis in the face of life's stresses. Psychologic and social as well as purely physiologic stresses excite enhanced pituitary-adrenal activity and since adrenal steroids have far-reaching metabolic repercussions on tissue metabolism including that of the brain there are many possible mechanisms that might modify brain function to produce distortions of affect and association processes in relation to aberrant adrenal physiology. There is no direct evidence in support of this hypothesis but it might be tested by a study of schizophrenia in twins in combination with our ACTH test procedures.

We do not think that the adrenal abnormality is "the cause" of schizophrenia, but that it may be one of several factors involved is possible especially in view of our finding that the better a patient's adrenal responsivity the better is his prognosis with electroshock therapy. Our study of involutional psychosis[12] and work of Hemphill and Reiss[7] indicate that subnormal adrenal responsivity occurs in psychoses other than schizophrenia. If adrenal abnormality is one of several factors involved it is quite possible that schizophrenia may occur in persons with entirely normal adrenal glands. A third of our patients fall within the normal quantitative range of responsivity when the TRI is used as a measure (i.e., their TRI values are >20 units which in normal persons is a statistically significant stress increase). If one used only eosinophil or lymphocyte or urinary corticoid (neutral-reducing lipid) stress responses, relatively little in the way of group differences would appear in response to the stresses (including 25-mg. injections of ACTH) described in this paper. At present the indirect measures of adrenal assay and their variability do not permit us to say with assurance that some patients may not be entirely normal responders. It should be remembered however, that the third of the patients who are quantitatively normal responders, as a group display qualitative abnormalities, and with improved technics of direct analysis of adrenal steroids it may prove to be the rule for each psychotic patient. Methods developed[6] in conjunction with our adrenal perfusion studies, previously referred to, now make possible a highly specific delineation of just what steroids an individual's adrenals produce. We hope that our future work will clarify this matter.

We have used ACTH and cortisone therapeutically but without beneficial results. Cortisone is only one of fifteen adrenal steroids produced by the beef adrenal in response to ACTH. We believe it desirable to learn more specifically what the patients' adrenals produce in comparison to normal persons before doing much more along therapeutic lines. Since aberrant responses tend to be increased with large injections of ACTH, we would expect this hormone to produce still more abnormal adrenal action and thus not act as a therapeutic agent if aberrant adrenal physiology is a determinative factor in psychoses. In this connection the occasional development of psychotic episodes in arthritic patients subjected to prolonged ACTH therapy is of interest.

Summary

Evidence is reviewed indicating that approximately two-thirds of a group of schizophrenic paients are quantitatively subnormal in their adrenal stress responses and in their responses to injected ACTH in comparison to a group of normal controls.

Our results further indicate that, on the average, our schizophrenic population, including the one-third who give quantitatively normal stress responses, show qualitatively abnormal adrenal stress responses.

It is emphasized that these results are meaningful only in terms of the analytic procedures we have used. Several measures of adrenal responsivity useful in other connections cannot alone delineate differences between the patient and control groups.

Possible relations of the findings to the etiologic bases of psychoses are discussed.

REFERENCES

1. ELMADJIAN, F.; FREEMAN, H.; and PINCUS, G.; *Endocrinology*, 1946, 39, pp. 293-299.

2. ELMADJIAN, F., and PINCUS, G.: *The Journal of Clinical Endocrinology*, 1946, 6, pp. 287-294.

3. FREEMAN, H., and ELMADJIAN, F.: *The Journal of Clinical Endocrinology*, 1946, 6, pp. 668-674.

4. FREEMAN, H., and ELMADJIAN, F.: *Psychosomatic Medicine*, 1947, 9, pp. 226-232.

5. FREEMAN, H., and ELMADJIAN, F.: *The American Journal of Psychiatry*, 1950, 106, pp. 660-667.

6. HECHTER, O.; ZAFFARONI, A.; JACOBSEN, R. P.; LEVY, H.; JEANLOZ, R. W.; SCHENKER, V.; and PINCUS, G.: *Recent Progress in Hormone Research*, 6, Academic Press, Inc., New York. In press.

7. HEMPHILL, R. E., and REISS, M.: Paper given at the Paris, 1950, International Congress of Psychiatrists.

8. HOAGLAND, H.: Steroid Hormones and Events in the Nervous System. Neurochemistry. The chemical dynamics of brain and nerve. (Thudicum Memorial Volume). In press.

9. HOAGLAND, H.; CALLAWAY, E.; ELMADJIAN, F.; and PINCUS, G.: *Psychosomatic Medicine*, 1950, 12, pp. 73-77.

10. HOAGLAND, H.; ELMADJIAN, F.; and PINCUS, G.: *The Journal of Clinical Endocrinology*, 1946, 6, pp. 301-311.

11. HOAGLAND, H.; MALAMUD, W.; KAUFMAN, I. C.; and PINCUS, G.: *Psychosomatic Medicine*, 1946, 8, pp. 246-251.

12. MALAMUD, W.; HOAGLAND, H.; and KAUFMAN, I. C.: *Psychosomatic Medicine*, 1946, 8, pp. 243-245.

13. MALAMUD, W., and SANDS, S. D.: *The American Journal of Psychiatry*, 1947, 104, pp. 231-237.

14. PINCUS, G.: *The Journal of Clinical Endocrinology*, 1943, 3, pp. 195-199.

15. PINCUS, G.: *Recent Progress in Hormone Research*, 1947, 1, pp. 123-145. Academic Press, Inc., New York.

16. PINCUS, G., and ELMADJIAN, F.: *The Journal of Clinical Endocrinology*, 1946, 6, pp. 295-300.

17. PINCUS, G., and HOAGLAND, H.: *The Journal of Aviation Medicine*, 1943, 14, pp. 173-193.

18. PINCUS, G., and HOAGLAND, H.: *The Journal of Aviation Medicine*, 1944, 15, pp. 98-117.

19. PINCUS, G., and HOAGLAND, H.: *Psychosomatic Medicine*, 1945, 7, pp. 342-346.

20. PINCUS, G., and HOAGLAND, H.: *The American Journal of Psychiatry*, 1950, 106, pp. 641-659.

21. PINCUS, G.; HOAGLAND, H.; FREEMAN, H.; and ELMADJIAN, F.: *Recent Progress in Hormone Research*, 1949, 4, pp. 291-322.

22. PINCUS, G.; HOAGLAND, H.; and FREEMAN, H.; ELMADJIAN, F.; and ROMANOFF, L.: *Psychosomatic Medicine*, 1949, 11, pp. 74-101.

23. PINCUS, G.; HOAGLAND, H.; WILSON, C. H.; and FAY, N. J.: *Psychosomatic Medicine*, 1945, 7, pp. 347-352.

24. PINCUS, G.; ROMANOFF, L. P.; and CARLO, J.: *The Journal of Clinical Endocrinology*, 1948, 8, pp. 221-226.

25. PINCUS, G.; SCHENKER, V.; ELMADJIAN, F.; and HOAGLAND, H.: *Psychosomatic Medicine,* 1949, 11, pp. 146-150.
26. ROTTER, J. B., and RODNICK, E. H.: *Psychological Bulletin,* 1940, 37, p. 577.
27. SELYE, H., and FORTIER, C.: *Psychosomatic Medicine,* 1950, 12 pp. 149-157.

Discussion

MARK D. ALTSCHULE, M.D.

Dr. Hoagland has discussed in great detail the physiology of the adrenal cortex in schizophrenics. This is appropriate because experience in the last two or three years in a number of general hospitals has shown that some persons, previously mentally normal, became manic or depressed even to the point of suicide when given ACTH or cortisone in large amounts; in occasional instances they may become hallucinated, paranoid, or catatonic. It is important, therefore, to know accurately what the status of the adrenal cortex is in spontaneously occurring psychosis.

We are all aware of the fact that differences in geographic location give rise to important differences in diseases. In view of the fact that Worcester and Waverley are separated by 35 miles by road, and possibly a little more as the average crow flies in Massachusetts, it is not surprising that schizophrenia as seen in Waverley differs from the physiologic description of that disease as it was found in Worcester.

There have been many studies of the metabolism in schizophrenia, manic-depressive psychosis, and involutional psychosis over the past half century which, taken together, suggest chronic hyperactivity of the adrenal cortex. Also, it was first pointed out almost half a century ago that in patients with schizophrenia, manic-depressive psychoses, and involutional psychoses, the blood eosinophil count is characteristically low on admission to the hospital. In fact, one author had trouble finding eosinophils in the blood except in a group of patients in whom the number seemed to be rather high; experience told that physician that this was a sign of impending recovery. That observation has been ignored, largely, I suppose, because it has no psychodynamic implications, but I am happy to say that we, as well as others, have been able to corroborate it.

Table 49 shows eosinophil counts in 147 psychotic patients. All counts were made on venous blood, since counts made on peripheral blood are likely to be in error. In our series no normal subject had a count below 100 per cubic millimeter, and only half below 200. In all categories of mental disease there was an excessive number of low counts. I might say that our patients with neuroses are sick enough to have to be locked in, and therefore probably differ from the ordinary common garden-variety of neurotic that seems to constitute the population of this City.

Table 50 presents the change in eosinophil counts in 61 patients after treatment. The counts were made before the start of all forms of shock therapy, including fever, insulin therapy, electroshock, and psychotherapy. We considered that a change in the eosinophil count of less than 85 per cent may not be significant, and made that the dividing line. It may be seen that thirty-one patients showed a rise of 85 per cent or more, and all but one improved; nineteen patients showed a rise of less than 85 per cent, and four did not improve while fifteen did. As patients get better it is evident that they tend to show a rise in the eosinophil count.

In addition, we recently published a work on 17-ketosteroids, which might be taken as favoring the concept that untreated patients with schizophrenia,

TABLE 49. BLOOD EOSINOPHILIC CELL COUNTS

	No. of Cases	Per Cent Below 100	Per Cent Below 200
Normal		0	50
Neurosis	32	38	69
Manic-depressive psychosis	32	53	69
Involutional psychosis	19	53	84
Schizophrenia	64	39	78

TABLE 50. CHANGE IN EOSINOPHIL COUNTS IN SIXTY-ONE PATIENTS AFTER TREATMENT

	Improved	Not Improved
Significant rise	30	1
Insignificant rise	15	4
Insignificant fall	5	4
Significant fall	1	1

and manic-depressive and involutional psychoses show mild or moderate hyperactivity of the adrenal cortex; there appears to be depression of the adrenal cortex with recovery.

In regard to the activity of the adrenal cortex in relation to stress in schizophrenia, we, and others, showed that insulin, electroshock, and psychiatric interviews—all cause good changes in the physiologic indices of adrenal activity in patients with all types of mental disease. We studied also the response to ACTH and here too found no diminution in responsiveness in psychosis, including schizophrenia, irrespective of whether the patients had been sick for thirty days or thirty years. In order to standardize procedure, studies were made using a dose of 25 mg. of carefully standardized preparations of ACTH.

Figure 157 shows the effect of ACTH on eosinophil counts in several mental disorders. The patients were chosen in order to get a wide range of eosinophil count. Patients with chronic severe neuroses, untreated schizophrenia, and untreated manic-depressive psychoses all showed a

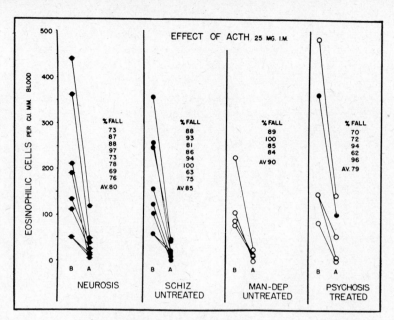

FIG. 157. Effect of ACTH on eosinophil counts in mental disorders.

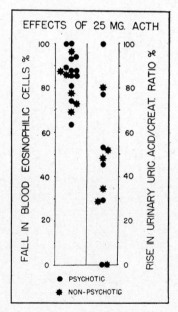

FIG. 158. Increase in uric acid excretion after ACTH administration in psychotic patients (ordinary dots), and in nonpsychotic, neurotic, or normal subjects (crenated dots).

striking fall in eosinophil count, and irrespective of the initial level, the percentage fall was about the same. After treatment, the change in this respect seemed to be about the same as before treatment.

Figure 158 shows the increase in uric acid excretion after ACTH administration in psychotic patients (ordinary dots), and in nonpsychotic, neurotic, or normal subjects (crenated dots); there is no difference in the distribution. It may be observed that some patients, psychotic or nonpsychotic, do show a subnormal increase in the excretion of uric acid

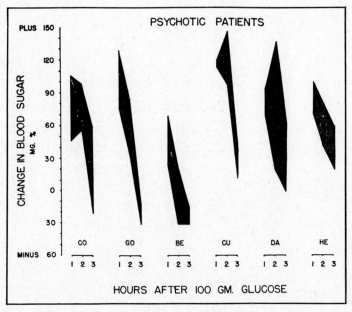

FIG. 159.   Changes in glucose tolerance of psychotic patients under the influence of ACTH. The black area indicates elevation of the curve after ACTH as compared to the curve obtained before.

after ACTH, but that is common in patients chronically ill with almost anything, and so has no specific significance with regard to mental disease.

Having studied blood for a number of years, we have turned our attention to sweat; I suppose the tears will come later. The amount of lowering of the sweat sodium concentration which occurs with administration of ACTH has been studied, and in our patients with schizophrenia, one sick for thirty-one years, it was found that the fall was at least as large as normal, and possibly a little greater.

Figure 159 shows certain changes in glucose tolerance under the influence of ACTH. These are the first few patients so studied. The patient was given 100 grams of glucose by mouth, and the usual glucose tolerance curve shown by the lower part of the black area was plotted. Then a day or two later the test was repeated, but before the glucose was given, 25 mg. of ACTH was injected intramuscularly. In normal subjects there is no significant difference between the two curves, but in patients with psychoses it is clear that the curve for glucose tolerance on the same day that 25 milligrams of ACTH had been injected was much higher. It does not depend on an initially high glucose tolerance curve because Figure 159 shows one subject whose initial curve was normal and he showed the same change. Accordingly we must conclude that patients with schizophrenia, as well as the other psychoses studied, show changes in sugar metabolism after ACTH administration which are certainly normal, and probably greater than normal.

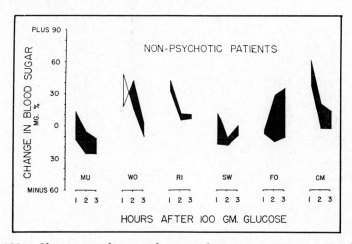

Fig. 160.   Changes in glucose tolerance of neurotic patients under the influence of ACTH. The black area indicates elevation of the curve after ACTH as compared to the curve obtained before it.

Figure 160 shows the glucose tolerance curves of neurotic patients. Some gave a normal response, while others of the neurotic patients merged over into psychotic, at least in regard to this test. We are not suggesting this would be a useful test for any form of mental disease but are merely using it as an indicator of a change in carbohydrate metabolism. The full significance of these figures is not entirely clear, even after study by a Rorschach expert; but I think that we must conclude that, at least in Waverley, the adrenal cortex in patients who have been hospitalized for schizophrenia, manic-depressive, or involutional psychoses from periods ranging from three days to thirty-one years tends to be chronically hyperactive, and that when given ACTH, these patients, irrespective of the type of psychosis and of the duration of hospitalization, show responses in at least four of the categories of adrenal cortical function which are within the normal range, or possibly greater.

Discussion

EDWIN F. GILDEA, M.D.

I dislike adding to the controversy by saying that the majority of our patients in St. Louis, to take up the geographic point of view, react to chemical stress tests in a manner similar to normal control subjects, that is, their reactions were somewhere between the Worcester and Waverly subjects.

With regard to the eosinophils, Dr. Hoagland has pointed out how extraordinarily sensitive that kind of test is for the effect of stress on the adrenal cortex, and certainly in animals it has been equally sensitive. We are puzzled to find that in our psychotic patients the eosinophils vary only slightly more than they do in our normal subjects. If you follow a psychotic patient, it makes no difference whether it is through a panic state in a schizophrenic, or a depressed state into an agitated or manic state in a manic patient, there is a very poor correlation between circulating eosinophils and evidence of extreme emotional turmoil, which in a normal person would mean a tremendous change in eosinophils. In these patients we find variations that are only slightly greater than those in normal subjects. Statistically, the results are nothing like what Dr. Altschule seems to have been obtaining in Waverley.

In the schizophrenics in St. Louis, adrenal cortical function, when tested by physical stresses, heat, epinephrine, or other means, appears to be normal. The only function in which they seem to be defective is in capacity to react to psychologic stresses. This is true of all observed psychologic disturbances whether as a result of the change in the mental condition of the patient, or induced by work stress situations. Schizophrenic patients in those situations do not show changes in eosinophils or display any marked reactions to other tests of the adrenal cortical function.

Psychiatric Disorder in Temporal Lobe Epilepsy*

FREDERIC A. GIBBS, M.D.

As Dr. Hoagland has emphasized in his own work and writings, the electrical activity of the brain has a metabolic basis, for it is closely related to the oxidation of glucose by the nerve cells of the brain. Epilepsy is characterized by disorders of the electrical activity of the brain, and the investigator finds in this condition an opportunity to see in full array the symptoms that result from certain types of chemical disorder in the cerebral neurons. The electroencephalograph reveals the time-course of some of the underlying chemical disturbances and their location. The symptoms which result from an epileptic type of disorder in the anterior portion of

* Read by Dr. L. J. Meduna.

the temporal lobe clearly reveal the closeness of the linkage between the physiology of the cerebral neurons and mental health.

Psychomotor epilepsy is characterized clinically by trancelike states and confusional episodes, and electroencephalographically by a focus of spike seizure discharges in the anterior-temporal region.[1] The motor components take the form of coordinated, apparently purposeful activity; the patient is usually amnesic and not unconscious. When subsequently able to report on his subjective sensations during an attack the patient usually explains that he felt worried, afraid, or angry, and his behavior was appropriate to these moods. Convulsions may occur in association with or independent of the psychomotor seizure, but they are not usually as frequent as the psychomotor attacks. Psychiatric disorder which takes the form of personality disturbances and even psychoses is a common associated complication. Though such disorder is more or less constant for a given patient, no single specific psychiatric syndrome is encountered. Patients with apparently identical anterior temporal foci of seizure activity and closely comparable brief confusional states may have quite different psychiatric symptoms. For example, the patient may be paranoid, depressed, catatonic, or hysterical. These psychiatric symptoms are a real and important part of the clinical disorder and may overshadow the epileptic manifestations to such a degree that the diagnosis of schizophrenia or depression is made on a symptomatic basis.

Studies with phenurone (phenacetylurea),[4] a new anti-epileptic substance which has proved more effective against psychomotor seizures than has any previously available substance, indicate that if the psychomotor seizure is blocked the psychiatric disorder is likely to be intensified. In fact, the chief limiting side effect of phenurone in psychomotor cases is the exacerbation of psychiatric symptomatology. However, in patients without pre-existing personality disorder, this complication does not occur. For purposes of discussion, it is convenient to refer to the psychomotor seizure as the epileptic or ictal component, and to the personality disturbances, paranoid trends, and the like, as non-ictal psychiatric disorder. These two components are independent, and, to some extent, antithetic. This antithesis is also evident from the effects of older anti-epileptic substances; for example, phenobarbital, dilantin, and mesantoin, all of which, in certain cases, block the psychomotor seizures and produce an exacerbation of psychiatric symptomatology, even to the point of precipitating a psychosis. With these drugs, and also with phenurone, elimination of the drug usually results in the prompt reappearance of seizures and subsidence of psychotic manifestations. Thus, normalization of the electroencephalogram and elimination of the purely epileptic component, by medication, can relieve the epileptic symptomatology while greatly intensifying the psychiatric symptomatology. This is in sharp contrast to what happens when the discharging temporal lobe is removed surgically: the psychomotor epilepsy is usually eliminated and the psychiatric disorder reduced, suggesting that both types of symptomatology rest on a more or less common anatomic base.

The question arises as to whether or not spike foci localized to other parts of the brain give symptoms which might be confused with those of psychomotor epilepsy. On going over several thousand cases of epilepsy it was discovered that anterior temporal foci are much commoner than any other type. Out of a total of 2080 patients with sharply localized spike foci, 59 per cent of the foci were in the anterior temporal lobe. Next in point of commonness as a site for focal spike activity was the mid-temporal region (13 per cent). The occipital was next with 11 per cent, then the parietal and frontal areas with 10 and 7 per cent, respectively. There was a 95 per cent incidence of trancelike episodes and confusional attacks in patients with anterior temporal spike foci, whereas these occurred in 11 per cent or less in patients with foci in other regions.

The highest incidence of psychiatric disorder occurred among patients in whom the spike focus occurred in the anterior temporal area. Approximately half (49 per cent) of the patients with an anterior temporal focus had psychiatric disorder. Only 13 per cent of those with a spike focus in the mid-temporal area and 12 per cent with a focus in the occipital area had psychiatric symptoms. On the other hand, only 5 per cent of patients with a spike focus in the frontal area had psychiatric disorder.

The association of antithetic disorders, namely non-ictal psychiatric manifestations and psychomotor seizures in psychomotor epilepsy, may seem difficult to comprehend. However, another example of such an antithetic association is found in grand mal and petit mal epilepsy. Although these two types of seizures often occur in the same patient, they tend to be temporally separated and to substitute for each other. They are associated with opposite types of displacement of acid-base balance,[2] and drugs that make one better commonly make the other worse.[3] However, there is an outstanding difference between the brain disorder which underlies the non-ictal symptoms of psychomotor epilepsy and that underlying all types of epileptic seizures including the psychomotor. Non-ictal psychiatric symptoms of psychomotor epilepsy are not temporally associated with or immediately evidenced by electroencephalographic abnormalities.

It seems reasonable to suppose that the temporal lobe is the locus of the disorders that give rise to both the epileptic and the non-ictal psychiatric symptomatology of psychomotor epilepsy, and that, although spatially associated, the two types of disorder are physiologically antithetic.

REFERENCES

1. GIBBS, ERNA L.; FUSTER, BARTOLOME; and GIBBS, FREDERIC A.: *Archives of Neurology and Psychiatry*, 1948, 60, pp. 331-339.
2. GIBBS, FREDERIC A.: *Journal of Pediatrics*, Dec., 1939, 15, pp. 749-762.
3. GIBBS, FREDERIC A.: *Annals of Internal Medicine*, 1947, 27, pp. 548-554.
4. GIBBS, FREDERIC A.; EVERETT, GUY M.; and RICHARDS, R. K.: *Diseases of the Nervous System*, 1949, 10, pp. 47-49.

CHAPTER 27

Enzymatic Changes in Mental Diseases

ALFRED POPE, M.D.

DISCUSSION OF the role of enzymology in relation to the mental disease problem is necessarily more hypothetic than factual because of the paucity of studies in this field. In introducing this subject, I shall first discuss the theoretic considerations that prompt investigation of enzymes in the mentally ill and review such studies as have been reported. I shall finish by describing the nature, outcome, and possible meaning of a pilot experiment carried out in our laboratory on the quantitative enzymatic histochemistry of cerebral cortical biopsies obtained from patients with various forms of mental disease.

The biologic importance of enzymes has been repeatedly emphasized during this symposium. These biocatalysts govern and direct the metabolic events that yield and utilize energy in every living cell. Their significance is not exceeded by any other chemical constituents of protoplasm. This is as true for the cells, conducting structures, and supportive elements of the central nervous system as for any other tissue. The activities of intracellular enzymes are important determinants for the chemical events constituting the resting metabolism and accompanying the facilitation, discharge, and inhibition both of single neurons and of neuronal aggregates. In this way enzyme activities are causally linked to those synchronous, and spatially and temporally dispersed, electrochemical events within the brain that are the physical equivalents of behavior, both normal and abnormal.

That disturbances in behavior may result from interference with the integrity of certain cerebral enzymes is shown by such entities as the psychosis of pellagra with its depletion of brain pyridine nucleotide codehydrogenases, or the psychotic symptoms that accompany partial inactivation of brain cholinesterase by DFP. Psychotic manifestations occurring during the course of various specific diseases of the brain or accompanying intoxications, febrile illnesses, or other disturbances in cerebral homeostasis may well be on the same basis. Enzymatic changes in brain tissue have been demonstrated for some of these.

The comparative study of enzymes that are constituents of chemical systems of known importance in the metabolism of the nervous system should be one suitable neurochemical approach to answering the question as to whether or not chronic alterations in cellular metabolism underlie or accompany schizophrenia and manic-depressive psychosis. Such studies are based on the assumption that enzyme activities are an index of the rate of turnover of the particular metabolic system of which each is a part and, therefore, a means of sampling the states of activity and integrity of such systems and of comparing them from individual to individual. The possibility exists that some disturbance in cerebral tissue metabolism is a factor of significance in patients exhibiting abnormal behavior. If so, it should be demonstrable by suitable comparative studies upon enzymes of critical importance in the metabolic pathways that yield and utilize energy in the various histologic constituents that contribute to cerebral function. Conversely, if all such enzymes as may be examined are found to be within normal ranges of activity, it would render unlikely important changes in cerebral cellular metabolism in the major psychoses. Even though changes of this sort were to be demonstrated, however, it should be recognized that they could well represent the result of chronic mental illness rather than having necessarily any relationship to its genesis. To attribute etiologic significance to any such findings would be hazardous indeed.

Previous Investigations

Most of the published material on enzymes in psychiatric conditions has been reports of studies on blood or cerebrospinal fluid, and these unfortunately afford little insight into the state of affairs in the cerebral tissue itself.

Such enzymes as have been thus studied have usually been found to be within normal limits. This was the case for blood glyoxylase in patients with schizophrenia, manic-depressive insanity, and organic psychoses according to the work of Franks and Proctor.[8] More recently Spiegel-Adolph, Wilcox, and Spiegel[25] have found great variability in amounts of ribo and desoxyribonucleases in the spinal fluids of schizophrenics with an increase in activity following electric shock. Lipase and esterase activities were negligible before treatment but increased somewhat subsequent to it. During the current year Schou[24] has reported essentially normal values for blood pyridine nucleotides in psychotic subjects.

A number of authors have studied the activity of cholinesterase in the blood and spinal fluid in patients with different psychiatric syndromes. The most complete study is that of Mutrux and Glasson[18] in France who found widely variable amounts of the specific and nonspecific enzymes in red cells, serum, and CSF without any discernible correlations with the clinical disorders. The more recent work in England of Early and co-workers[7] and of Rowntree, Nevin, and Wilson[23] is essentially confirmatory as is that of Tower and McEachern[26] in Montreal who found normal spinal fluid cholinesterase values in a number of untreated psychotic subjects. In 1937 Jones and Tod[14] reported high serum cholinesterase values in psychotic or psychoneurotic subjects showing evidence of autonomic hyperactivity and the reverse in stuporous or inert patients. The serum cholinesterase has also been reported as elevated in anxiety neurosis by Richter[12] and following insulin therapy of schizophrenics by Randall and Jellinek[22] irrespective of the clinical result. Such reports are difficult to evaluate since the cholinesterase of serum is, of course, the nonspecific enzyme presumably unrelated to acetylcholine metabolism and not correlatable with the specific enzyme in brain. This has been clearly shown by Mendel, Hawkins, and Nishikawara.[17]

The study of enzymes in the brains of those with mental illness has been limited to a few pioneer investigations. There are a number of reasons for this, the principal one probably being that except for study of a few especially stable enzymes that are resistant to autolytic processes, autopsy material is not suitable for work of this sort. Only with the advent of the various forms of psychosurgery has it become possible to obtain brain tissue in the form of biopsies from such patients under relatively standardized and biochemically sound conditions.

The pioneer quantitative work on brain enzymes in the mentally ill has been that of Dr. Winifred Ashby upon carbonic anhydrase.[4] The exact role of this enzyme in the nervous system is unknown, but her work has indicated that embryologically its appearance coincides with the onset of function, and it is to be supposed that it has an important role in the hydration and dehydration of carbon dioxide and hence in the maintenance of tissue acid-base balance. Ashby and Weickhardt[5] found striking irregularities in distribution of carbonic anhydrase in the hemispheres of patients dying of paretic neurosyphilis as well as of those dying of other organic brain diseases. Dr. Ashby[3, 4] also has reported abnormalities in its distribution in the brains of schizophrenics, with decreases in some cortical areas relative to the rest. She feels that this might be of significance in relation to hypothetic changes in relative rates of discharge of the neurons in the affected areas.

A few studies have been made utilizing qualitative histochemical technics for cytologic localization of enzymes. In 1930, Dr. Walter Freeman[9] reported a quantitative and cytochemical reduction in iron content in the frontal pole cortex, especially in the large ganglion cells, in autopsy material from schizophrenics. This, of course, might be construed as evidence of a depletion of the cytochrome-cytochrome oxidase system in these specimens. Drs. Wolf and Cowan will, I am sure, speak of their negative findings with respect to the phosphatases in the prefrontal cortex of patients subjected to topectomy in their discussion of the neuropathology of mental illness.

Quantitative Histochemical Studies

In our laboratory, study is being made of the quantitative histochemical distribution of enzymes within the cytoarchitectonic layers of the cerebral cortex both in animals and in man. The objectives are two-fold. The first is to correlate chemical composition with histologic structure in the case of the cerebral cortex which, having a laminated architecture, is technically suitable for this type of study. Such correlation is of course a general frontier in biology which does have a special importance in the case of the nervous system because of the close inherent interdependence of structure and function. The second objective is to proceed with the search for enzymatic evidence of chronic changes in cortical cell metabolism in mental disease according to the rationale previously discussed. For such clinical study the use of micro-analytic methods is of great advantage since it permits accurate neuropathologic control of all observations, furnishes maximal information from small biopsy specimens, and presumably affords an optimum chance for discerning relatively subtle changes in cortical enzyme activities.

For these studies use is being made of the technics for alternate frozen section sampling and ultra micro quantitative analysis for enzymes due principally to the ingenuity of Linderstrøm-Lang and his associates.[15] An effort is made to interpret the resulting architectonic distribution pattern of each enzyme in terms of the histologic fine structure of the cortex. In this way it has been possible to show in the somatosensory sector of rat cortex, that peptidase activity and diphosphopyridine nucleotide are concentrated in layers II, IV, and VIa which are those cortical levels richest in nerve cell bodies, whereas cholinesterase and adenosinetriphosphatase are most active in layers I, the II-IIIa junction, IIIb, Va and Vc, levels at which the axonal and dendritic plexuses have their greatest development.[20] Thus far, only cholinesterase has been studied to any extent in human material, and I shall conclude my remarks by describing a pilot study upon its activity and histochemical distribution in biopsy specimens from the human cortex. This study was made during the year 1948 with the clinical collaboration of Drs. William Caveness and Kenneth Livingston, and has already been given preliminary presentation.[19] The biopsy specimens were obtained during the course of prefrontal lobotomy upon patients at the Boston Psychopathic Hospital through the kindness of Dr. Harry Solomon and Dr. James Poppen.

Patients were selected for study according to these criteria: (1) that clinically they be relatively classical examples of the principal formal diagnostic entities of psychiatry; (2) that they be between 20 and 50 years of age; (3) that they be free of objective evidence of somatic disease of the nervous system; and (4) that they have had as little convulsive therapy as possible.

Most of the patients fell into two principal clinical categories. The first was comprised of nonpsychotic individuals, either persons lobotomized for intractable pain, or psychoneurotics, most of them operated upon because of crippling obsessive states. None of these patients had ever shown truly psychotic manifestations or required protracted previous hospitalization, and all were in good contact at the time of operation. The second group consisted of profoundly psychotic patients having a diagnosis of schizophrenia—hebephrenic, catatonic, or other types. All were individuals with a history of onset of their illness at an early age, continuous preoperative hospitalization for periods of eight to seventeen years, and intractable progression of the schizophrenic process towards severe dilapidation and withdrawal at the time of operation.

Standard preoperative medication and anesthesia were employed. Lobotomy was according to the technic of Poppen.[21] Following exposure of the cortex a biopsy specimen including most of the presenting gyrus was excised without the use of electrocautery, placed immediately in a refrigerated container, and removed to our laboratory for enzymatic and neuropathologic study. The architectonic area in each case was 9 of Brodmann (FD in von Economo's nomenclature).

For cholinesterase assay a portion of each biopsy specimen was frozen, and from it a 2-mm. in diameter cylinder of cortex was punched out, the long axis of which was perpendicular to the plane of the pial surface. This cylinder was cut into serial, 40-micra thick, horizontal, frozen sections from pia to white matter by means of a rotary microtome maintained at $-12°C$. in a cold room. The frozen sections were used alternately for histologic preparation, for cholinesterase assay, and for desiccation and dry-weight determination by means of an ultra micro quartz balance of the sort described by Lowry.[16] Cholinesterase activity was measured by means of the ultra micro titrimetric technic of Glick.[10] In addition, vertical histologic sections were prepared from the thawed and fixed parent block whence the cylinder was derived and stained for nerve cells and neurofibrils. Direct measurements of layer thicknesses upon these, in conjunction with study of the horizontal histologic controls, made possible identification of the cytoarchitectonic layers from which the specimens used for cholinesterase assay were derived, and the quantitative distribution of the enzyme within the cortical layers was thus established. Its average activity at all levels was also calculated in order to estimate the cholinesterase content of each biopsy specimen as a whole.

Figure 161 shows a composite distribution curve of nineteen such experiments in which the averaged cholinesterase activities expressed in arbitrary units per microgram dry weight along the ordinate, are plotted against the theoretic depth of the sample beneath the pial surface and correlated with the averaged widths of the cytoarchitectonic layers. Cholinesterase shows relative peaks of activity in Layers I, the II-IIIa junction, the mid-zones of layers III and V, and in VIb. These correspond with zones in which the neuropil contributes a relatively high proportion of the tissue mass and arborization of the axonal and dendritic plexuses is greatest. The presence of numerous axonal and dendritic telodendria brings about a relative increase in surface area of conducting structures together with an increased number of synaptic end-knobs. Since cholinesterase has been shown by Boell and Nachmansohn[6] to be localized at the nerve fiber surface in the giant axon of the squid and by Anfinsen[2] to be concentrated in the bovine retina at levels rich in synapses, it is not unreasonable that

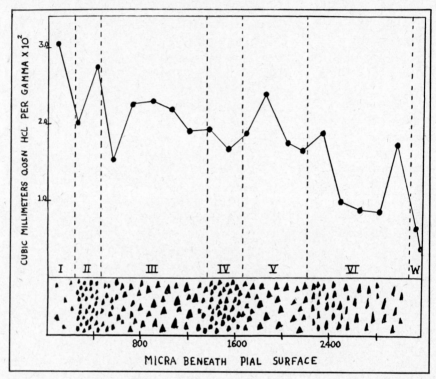

Fig. 161.   Cytoarchitectural distribution of cholinesterase in human prefrontal isocortex.

in cerebral cortex this enzyme should show maximal activity at those levels where the density of the plexuses is presumably greatest. This distribution pattern was essentially constant in all the biopsy specimens studied.

When the cholinesterase activity of each biopsy specimen as a whole was computed and compared with the clinical diagnosis in the case of those twelve patients most rigidly fulfilling the clinical criteria described, it was found that five of seven patients among the deteriorated schizophrenics exhibited an over-all cortical cholinesterase activity in excess of the range of activities found among the relatively normal pain-psychoneurosis patients (Table 51). Obviously, these are far too few observations to be more than suggestive, and even though this trend were fully established, its meaning is obscure. All that can be directly inferred is that the prefrontal cortex of some of the deeply psychotic patients hydrolyzed acetylcholine faster than usual. If cholinesterase activity is an index of the rate of turnover of the system metabolizing acetylcholine, and if the latter is a compound of critical importance in the physical chemistry of impulse initiation, propagation, and synaptic transfer, it might suggest a chronic increase in rate of neuronal discharge in the cortex in question. Such an hypothesis would not be entirely out of line with certain other reported findings. The

TABLE 51.   CHOLINESTERASE ACTIVITY IN HUMAN CORTICAL BIOPSIES

Expressed as average volume in cubic millimeters of 0.05 N HCl (equivalent to acetic acid liberated by enzymatic hydrolysis of acetylcholine bromide) per gamma dry weight per hour at $37°$ $C \times 10^2$.

Diagnosis		Patient	Age	Cholinesterase
Intractable pain:		R.L	45	1.77
		C.S.	53	1.49
Psychoneurosis:	conversion-hysteria	E.C.	47	0.76
	obsessive-compulsive	M.K.	37	1.27
		V. R.	33	1.44
Schizophrenia:	hebephrenic	D.A.	37	2.54
	catatonic	E.V.	37	2.92
		R.M.	44	2.14
		J.K.	32	1.43
		G.F.	35	1.72
	other types	H.C.	31	3.28
		R.E.	41	2.21

work of Hyden and Hartelius[13] showing protein and nucleoprotein depletion in ganglion cells from this same cortical region in psychotic patients is consistent with chronic exhaustion of the cells resulting from long-standing increased rates of discharge. Alcobar Coloma[1] in Spain has reported the presence of acetylcholine in the cerebrospinal fluid of psychotic subjects, particularly catatonics. This is, however, not in accord with the findings of Tower and McEachern.[26] Rowntree, Nevin, and Wilson[23] have reported from the Maudsley Hospital that schizophrenics are unusually resistant to the electroencephalographic changes induced by the cholinesterase inhibitor, DFP, and this finding is, of course, not inconsistent with our limited observations.

In many of these same biopsy specimens, Dr. Meath in our laboratory estimated the cortical acid phosphatase activity histochemically. This he did by means of a modification of Gomori's staining technic[11] in which vertical sections of freshly frozen cortex were used thus avoiding the partial inactivation of the enzyme consequent to fixation and embedding. The re-

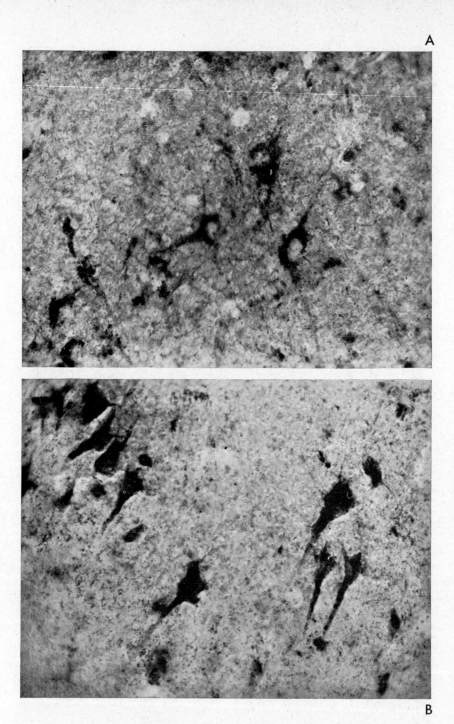

Fig. 162. Acid phosphatase reaction in human cortical ganglion cells. A, normally developed and distributed acid phosphatase reaction in pyramidal cells of layer IIIb (Patient V.R.). B, pyramids of layer IIIb showing reduced phosphatase reaction and nuclear areas devoid of activity (Patient R.M.).

sults are summarized in Table 52. In eight of twelve specimens from among the deeply psychotic patients the acid phosphatase reaction in cortical ganglion cells seemed somewhat reduced as was the case also in one of four specimens from among nonpsychotic patients. Figure 162, A is a photomicrograph of normally developed phosphatase reaction in layer III pyramids and shows the presence of an enzyme that splits glycerophosphate in all parts of the cell body and extending into the apical dendrite. In four instances from among the schizophrenic group a majority of such cells had

TABLE 52.   ACID PHOSPHATASE ACTIVITY IN HUMAN CORTICAL BIOPSY SPECIMENS

Diagnosis		Patient		Age	Acid Phosphatase
Intractable pain:		C.S.		53	Reduced
Psychoneurosis: obsessive-compulsive	{	M.K.		37	Normal
		V.R.		33	Normal
		J.C.		39	Normal
Schizophrenia: hebephrenic	{	E.R.		26	Reduced
		T.G.		27	*Reduced
	{	D.C.		35	Normal
		E.C.		33	Normal
catatonic		E.W.		18	*Normal
		R.M.		44	*Reduced
		A.T.		20	Reduced
	{	H.C.		31	Reduced
		R.E.	Right—	41	Normal
other types			Left —		*Reduced
		L.P.		24	Reduced
		A.M.		20	Reduced

* In these specimens a high proportion of the nerve cell bodies exhibited the unusually pale central regions described in the text and shown in Figure 162, B.

the appearance shown in Figure 162, B with large central regions apparently including the nucleus, but sometimes more than just the nucleus, which were virtually devoid of phosphatase activity. The significance of this observation, if any, is obscure. It is possible that it does not lie beyond the normal range of variability of the staining reaction. It may represent the result of intracellular accumulations of lipochrome pigment.

These enzyme experiments were accompanied in all cases by neuropathologic study using the usual battery of chromatic stains and metallic impregnations for neurons, neuroglia, and their processes. Many of the specimens revealed minor, and probably not important, pathologic changes of the sort so often described in material of this type. We were unable to correlate the discrepancies in cholinesterase or phosphatase activity either with each other or with such neuropathologic changes as were observed.

In closing, may I re-emphasize how provisional these findings are and re-state how important when considering data of this sort to distinguish between what may have etiologic significance and what is far more likely the result of long-standing mental illness and hospitalization. Nevertheless, it seems probable that the study of cerebral enzymes can be one pertinent way of attacking the manifold problems related to the physical substratum of behavior, and that the use of quantitative histochemical technics not only has special advantages for such study but also may be counted on to furnish considerable insight into the finer chemical anatomy of the nervous system.

REFERENCES

1. ALCOBER, COLOMA, T.; Medicina española, 1943-1944, 3, p. 359.
2. ANFINSEN, C. B.: Journal of Biological Chemistry, 1944, 152, p. 267.
3. ASHBY, W. R.: Journal of Nervous and Mental Disease, 1947, 105, p. 107.
4. ASHBY, W. R.: The American Journal of Psychiatry, 1950, 106, p. 48.
5. ASHBY, W. R., and WEICKHARDT, G. D.: Journal of Nervous and Mental Disease, 1947, 106, p. 107.
6. BOELL, E. J., and NACHMANSOHN, D.: Science, 1940, 92, p. 513.
7. EARLY, D. F.; HEMPHILL, R. E.; REISS, M.; and BRUMMEL, E.: Biochemical Journal, 1949, 45, p. 552.
8. FRANKS, W. R., and PROCTOR, L. D.: The American Journal of Psychiatry, 1941, 97, p. 1403.
9. FREEMAN, W.: Archives of Neurology and Psychiatry, 1930, 24, p. 300.
10. GLICK, D.: Journal of General Physiology, 1938, 21, p. 289.
11. GOMORI, G.: Proceedings of the Society for Experimental Biology and Medicine, 1939, 42, p. 23.
12. GREVILLE, G. D.; RICHTER, D.; QUASTEL, J. H.; and BENESCH, R.: Proceedings of the Royal Society of Medicine, 1945, 38, p. 671.
13. HYDEN, H., and HARTELIUS, H.: Acta psychiatrica et neurologica Supplement, 1948, 48, p. 1.
14. JONES, M. S., and TOD, H.: Journal of Mental Science, 1937, 83, p. 202.
15. LINDERSTRØM-LANG, K.: Harvey Lectures, Series XXXIV, 1939, p. 214.
16. LOWRY, O. H.: Journal of Biological Chemistry, 1944, 152, p. 293.
17. MENDEL, B.; HAWKINS, R. D.; and NISHIKAWARA, M.: American Journal of Physiology, 1948, 154, p. 489.
18. MUTRUX, S., and GLASSON, B.: Monatsschrift für Psychiatrie und Neurologie, 1947, 114, p. 20.
19. POPE, A.; MEATH, J. A.; CAVENESS, W. C.; LIVINGSTON, K. E.; and THOMSON, R. H.: Transactions of the American Neurological Association, 1949, 74, p. 147.
20. POPE, A.; WARE, J. R.; and THOMSON, R. H.: Federation Proceedings, 1950, 9, p. 215.
21. POPPEN, J. L.: Journal of Neurosurgery, 1948, 5, p. 514.
22. RANDALL, L. O., and JELLINEK, E. M.: Endocrinology, 1939, 25, p. 278.
23. ROWNTREE, D. W.; NEVIN, S.; and WILSON, A.: Journal of Neurology, Neurosurgery and Psychiatry, 1950, 13, p. 47.
24. SCHOU, M.: Biochimica et Biophysica Acta, 1950, 4, p. 422.
25. SPIEGEL-ADOLPH, M.; WILCOX, P. H.; and SPIEGEL, E. A.: The American Journal of Psychiatry, 1948, 104, p. 697.
26. TOWER, D. B., and McEACHERN, D.: Canadian Journal of Research, E, 1949, 27, p. 105.

Discussion

WINIFRED M. ASHBY, PH.D.

We are only at the threshold of the studies necessary for an understanding of the part that brain enzymes must play in mental disease. Practically all is in the future.

A piece of work which has interested me greatly was one by Dr. Pope. Adjacent to scar tissue causing epileptic attacks he found an excess of choline esterase. Since the metabolism of the brain and its consequent tendency to react depends upon its enzyme content, we will have to look for such disturbances in the pattern of quantitative distribution in addition to considering over-all levels.

Certain enzymes have well-defined patterns of quantitative distribution in the brain. Choline esterase has the well-marked pattern which has been found to occur through several species. Carbonic anhydrase also has a well-defined pattern, quite different, however, from that of choline esterase. This enzyme even shows an evolutionary trend as there is a distinct difference in its pattern in primates and lower mammals. Acetyl phosphate, on the other hand, is quite evenly distributed throughout the central nervous system.

It would seem probable that those enzymes with a definite pattern are minimal enzymes and constitute the limiting factor in the metabolic process to which they contribute; while the enzymes which are more evenly distributed are present in excess and will not be important in offering a background for the integration of the central nervous system.

It is the enzymes with a well-defined pattern of quantitative distribution which are probable factors in determining functional integration and which will be more interesting to study in relation to the functional disintegration which takes place in the so-called functional mental diseases.

In the so-called organic diseases in which cytologic changes can be seen, such as Alzheimer's disease or the cellular deterioration of age, I think it would be more interesting to consider more especially those enzymes which contribute to the cytoplasmic structure, e.g., enzymes of the cyclophorase system which centrifuge down with the mitochondria.

Of course, when we have discovered which are the aberrant enzymes involved in any particular mental abnormality, we will be in a position to study the effect of different hormones, trace elements, vitamins, and the like, upon their quantitative control and use of them therapeutically.

I have made a rather extensive study of the enzyme, carbonic anhydrase. I have found it interesting because, in the first place, the uncontrolled use of its inhibitor, sulfanilamide, has led to mental disturbances; and secondly, because its distribution pattern closely parallels oxygen uptake, as has been reported by Elliott, Dixon and others. Also its content in the brain of the infant rat bears an inverse relationship to the time necessary for death by anoxia; and this in turn has, according to Dr. Himwich, a relationship to the increase of aerobic metabolism. There is a close correlation between the presence of carbonic anhydrase in the cerebrum at birth and the maturity of the newborn. The carbonic anhydrase first appears in the cerebrum with evident function. In the human newborn there is no carbonic anhydrase in the cerebrum at birth, although there is a considerable amount in lower centers. The alpha waves, as reported in the human infant, the fetal guinea pig, and the newborn rabbit, make their appearance with carbonic anhydrase.

I have found a low content of this enzyme in the brains of patients who have been subjected to conditions likely to be generally injurious to the brain: acute alcoholism with sclerosis of the liver and kidney; uremia with prolonged coma; juvenile paresis; chronic epidemic encephalitis. With the lowered content I found that some of the normal gradients of distribution had flattened out.

On the other hand, in arteriosclerosis and recent cases of taboparesis, the enzyme level was not necessarily low but there were focal irregularities.

The majority of patients with dementia praecox had brains with a low content. This was true of the brain of a young soldier recently admitted. But there was an appreciable number of brains from patients with a diagnosis of dementia praecox that showed a high carbonic anhydrase content, approaching that found in normal subjects. For an explanation of this, more work will have to be done on the relative distribution. I am planning to compare the carbonic anhydrase content of the thalamic nuclei with that of the cortical areas to which they project.

I am convinced that the pattern of quantitative distribution must be considered as well as the level of content.

CHAPTER 28

Histopathology of Schizophrenia and Other Psychoses of Unknown Origin

ABNER WOLF, M.D., AND DAVID COWEN, M.D.

THIS PRESENTATION is limited to those psychoses which have no generally accepted specific pathologic picture; in particular, to dementia praecox. In discussing the possibility of a morphologic basis for schizophrenia, one must consider those cases in which a schizophrenic syndrome is associated with unquestionable organic disease of the brain. Ferraro[23] recorded three patients, in whom the diagnosis of schizophrenia was made during life. Postmortem examination revealed diffuse demyelination of the white matter of the cerebral hemispheres, involving the frontal lobes most severely. Holt and Tedeschi[32] described the findings in a patient supposedly suffering from catatonic dementia praecox, in whom there was a demyelinating process in the brain marked by sharply outlined lesions, limited to the white matter. The cortex and arcuate fibers were intact. Roizin and his associates[62] reported a schizophrenic reaction syndrome in a patient who at autopsy was found to have acute demyelinating disease of the central nervous system.

In view of the great rarity of demyelinating lesions in patients presenting a schizophrenic syndrome, the probability that there is an accidental coincidence of two diseases must be considered. The possibility that the demyelinating disease precipitated the schizophrenic episode is also to be entertained. A patient with Pick's disease described by the Vogts[70] manifested a schizophrenic syndrome during life. The concurrence of such organic disorders associated with a schizophrenic syndrome in isolated cases has been considered by some as evidence that the morphologic changes in the brain are responsible for the psychosis and, by implication, that abnormal histologic changes in the brain must be present in schizophrenia in general. However, in the great majority of subjects in whom the diagnosis of dementia praecox is made, no obvious morphologic changes in the brain have been encountered. In these the changes described are of a more subtle and debatable nature; it is to this type of case that we now turn.

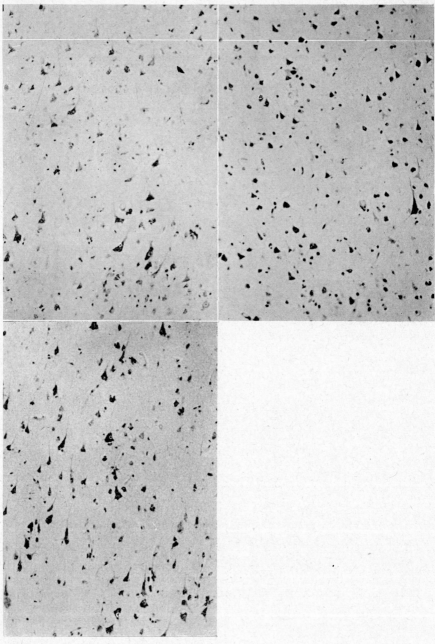

Fig. 163.   A, "focal nerve cell losses" in frontal cerebral cortex of a male of 46 years. Schizophrenia: hebephrenic. Nissl stain. x 50. B, "focal nerve cell losses" in frontal cerebral cortex of a female of 45 years. Nonpsychotic. Nissl stain. x 50. Fig. 164.   Nerve cell "shrinkage and sclerosis" in frontal cerebral cortex of a male of 32 years. Schizophrenia: hebephrenic. Nissl stain. x 50.

Central Nervous System in Schizophrenia

Over the past half century a series of investigators has studied tissues from patients suffering from the so-called functional psychoses in an attempt to determine whether the tissues are marked by any characteristic histopathologic abnormalities. Most of the brain specimens studied have been from autopsy material, but more recently biopsy specimens of the cerebral cortex and white matter have been examined in the course of lobotomies, topectomies, or similar procedures. The majority of investigators have found abnormalities in the cerebral cortex.

Cerebral Cortex: Alzheimer[2] reported a localized disappearance of ganglion cells in foci in the outer layers of the cerebral cortex in patients with schizophrenia. Such losses, both focal and diffuse, in various cortical layers, were recorded by Sioli,[64] Zingerle,[80] Wada,[71] Goldstein,[29] Zimmerman,[79] the Vogts,[69] Klarfeld,[37] Naito,[51] Schuster,[63] Fünfgeld,[27] Boumann,[7] Josephy,[35] Hechst,[30] Meyer,[46] Watanabe,[73] Miskolczy,[48] Hiresaki,[31] Jakob and Pedace,[34] Winkelman and Book,[75] and others (Fig. 163,A).

Involvement of Cerebral Cortex by Lobes: Naito[51] and Josephy[35] found the greatest changes in the frontal lobes of schizophrenic patients. Josephy claimed that there was less frequent involvement of the temporal and parietal lobes and the fewest changes in the occipital region. Boumann[7] concluded that the frontal and temporal lobes were most often affected. Hechst[30] reported the most severe lesions in the prefrontal area, supramarginal and angular gyri, regio parietalis basalis, and superior temporal gyrus, while the areas that were least affected were the area striata, pre- and post-central gyri and the gyri of Heschl. The two hemispheres were not always symmetrically affected. Miskolczy[48] recorded abnormal findings in the frontal, parietal, and temporal lobes. Hiresaki[31] described a preponderance of abnormalities in the frontal, temporal, and parietal lobes. Jakob and Pedace[34] saw changes chiefly in the frontal lobes, but also in the temporal and parietal regions of the cerebrum. Kirschbaum and Heilbrunn[36] and Polatin and co-workers[58] reported nerve cell losses in biopsy specimens of the frontal lobe. Winkelman and Book[75] found cortical cell losses in the anterior half of the cerebrum. They stated that the frontal cortex was not always most markedly affected; the temporal and parietal lobes were at times more severely involved.

Involvement of Cerebral Cortex by Areas: Naito[51] was not impressed with any regularity of involvement of specific cortical areas, noting that one area might be affected in a given case and not in another. He did report regular but moderate changes in area 4. Fünfgeld's[27] findings were in consonance with Naito's in that he discovered no regularity of involvement of particular cortical areas. For instance, areas 38, 46, 8, and 11 were severely changed in one subject and showed little if any alteration in another. In contrast, however, he found area 17 always free of lesions and areas 4 and 7 almost

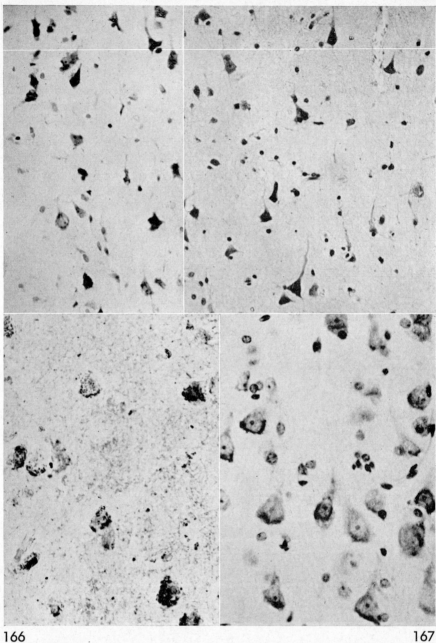

Fig. 165.   A, nerve cell "shrinkage and sclerosis" in frontal cerebral cortex of a male of 46 years. Schizophrenia: hebephrenic. Nissl stain. x 125. B, nerve cell "shrinkage and sclerosis" in frontal cerebral cortex of a woman of 40 years. Nonpsychotic. Nissl stain. x 125.   Fig. 166. Scarlet red stainable lipid in nerve cells in a male of 53 years. Schizophrenia. Scarlet red stain. x 250.   Fig. 167. Normal nerve cells in frontal cerebral cortex of a male of 32 years. Schizophrenia: hebephrenic. Nissl stain. x 250.

always clear. Josephy[35] confirmed Fünfgeld's observations but the latter disagreed with Naito's report of the constant involvement of area 4.

Involvement of Cerebral Cortex by Laminae: As referred to above, Alzheimer,[2] Sioli,[64] and others found pathologic changes in the upper layers of the cerebral cortex. Klarfeld[37] noted that all of the laminae could be affected. Fünfgeld[27] confirmed the findings of Alzheimer. Boumann[7] observed that all layers of the cerebral cortex could be involved and that this occurred in the following order of frequency: third, second, fifth, sixth, and fourth. Josephy[35] reported that the cortical layers involved in the order of their frequency, were the third, fifth, fourth, and second. Hechst[30] concurred in Boumann's findings that all layers were implicated, but in a different order: third, fifth, second, sixth, and fourth. Winkelman and Book[75] described the third cortical layer as that most often affected.

Pathologic Changes in Nerve Cells of the Cerebral Cortex: Pathologic changes in the nerve cells of the cerebral cortex were described by all of those who reported a loss of such cells in schizophrenia. These were noted by Alzheimer[2] and confirmed by others including Josephy[35] who summarized them as being of two main types: cell sclerosis (Figs. 164 and 165,A) and fatty degeneration (Fig. 166) (Cotton[14]). Josephy stated that normal nerve cells persisted among the abnormal and that the cortical layers in which large cells predominated were more involved than those which were composed of small cells. Fünfgeld[27] and later Hechst[30] recorded a thinning out of the cytoplasm of the nerve cells and intense staining of the nucleus which might proceed to cell sclerosis or to shadow-cell formation. Josephy[35] repeated this observation but denied that it was specific. Jakob and Pedace[34] described a series of pathologic changes in ganglion cells and called particular attention to a process of lysis of the cytoplasm with vacuolization which they termed "plasmocytolysis." Kirschbaum and Heilbrunn[36] examined small biopsy specimens of the frontal cortex prior to lobotomy. They reported nerve cell changes consisting of fatty degeneration, swelling and vacuolization, cell shrinkage and pyknosis, and cell shadows. Polatin, Eisenstein and Barrera[58] recorded biopsy findings on material from the frontal lobes of two patients considered to have dementia praecox. Many cortical nerve cells were described as shrunken, elongated and deeply staining with nuclear pyknosis or as showing shadow-cell formation and fatty changes. Winkelman and Book[75] studied ten cases of schizophrenia postmortem and reported that numerous cerebral cortical nerve cells showed shrinkage, vacuolization of their cytoplasm, "ghost-cell" formation, loss of polarity, and fatty infiltration.

Dunlap,[18] Spielmeyer,[65] Peters,[55] Wohlfahrt,[77] Roeder-Kutsch,[61] and Ferrero,[25] studying autopsy material, and Wolf and Cowen[78] surveying biopsy material, contended that such apparent deviations from the normal can be encountered in nonpsychotic control individuals (Figs. 163,B and 165,B) and thus are probably of no etiologic significance. Dunlap[18] stressed the errors introduced by fixation and technical defects, and those which arose from erroneous conceptions of what was normal. In his own work, he attempted to reduce the sources of error by using material only from young patients, whose course was uncomplicated and of reasonably short duration, and comparing this with tissues from the best available nonpsychotic subjects of the same age range. He reported that under these conditions, the findings in the brains of the schizophrenic patients were indistinguishable from those in the normal controls. Peters[55] and Roeder-Kutsch[61] were able to confirm Dunlap's findings, comparing their observations on schizophrenic patients with those on nonpsychotic individuals. Spielmeyer[65] and Peters[55] examined the promptly fixed brains of executed individuals. Dunlap[18] and Roeder-Kutsch[61] studied material from hospital patients who had died suddenly or had suffered only a short illness. The control brain sections revealed apparent loss of ganglion cells in the cerebral cortex and abnormalities in the nerve cells indistinguishable from those described as cell sclerosis, fatty degeneration, and shadow-cell formation as noted in schizophrenic patients. Indeed, Dunlap shuffled sections of brain from schizophrenic and nonpsychotic individuals and could not distinguish between them and thus identify their source. Even those who have contended that there are nerve cell losses in the cortex and degenerative changes in the remaining nerve cells, particularly in the frontal lobes, have admitted that such changes were absent in some clear-cut instances of schizophrenia (Fig. 167). Josephy,[35] for instance, pointed out that in a long-standing case of his own, and in another described by Rosental (cited by Josephy[35]), no abnormalities were encountered in the brain in spite of the chronicity of the disease.

While it was thought that the use of biopsy material might overcome some of the artefacts encountered in postmortem material, it seems not to have done so. The common appearance of nerve cell shrinkage and pyknosis is seen even more frequently in biopsy material (Wolf and Cowen[78]). It was striking that this was present more often near the surface of the biopsy specimen, both superficial and deep, and near tears, cuts, and other injuries to the parenchyma (as it is in postmortem material). It was most frequent in small blocks of tissue with their relatively greater surfaces. It would appear that this type of nerve cell change is often an artefact, since it seems to be related to adventitious factors, such as nearness of neurons to surfaces of the tissue, trauma to the tissue, and size of the tissue block. This type of cell shrinkage and hyperchromatism has been repeatedly noted in surgical biopsy specimens of cerebral tissue from nonpsychotic individuals which proved to be free of tumor or other lesions (Wolf and Cowen[78]). Its frequency seemed to be inversely proportional to the size of the specimen and directly proportional to the degree of trauma it had sustained.

The extensive use of shock therapy in the treatment of schizophrenia in recent years introduces another possible source of error since any or all of the neuronal changes may be the consequence of such treatment. Kob-

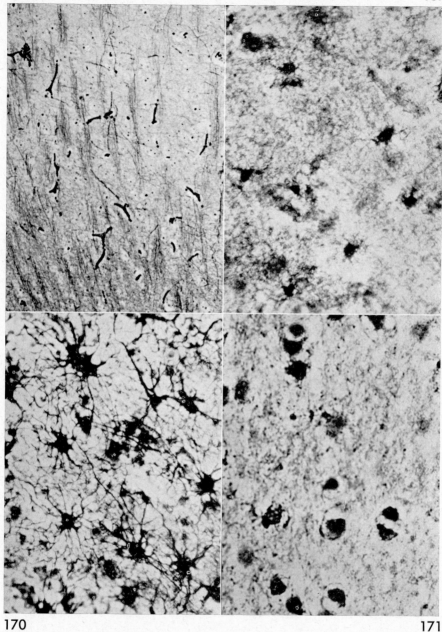

FIG. 168. Normal myelin sheaths in frontal cerebral cortex of a male of 46 years. Schizophrenia: hebephrenic. Mahon stain. x 50. FIG. 169. Normal protoplasmic astrocytes in frontal cerebral cortex of a male of 44 years. Schizophrenia: paranoid. Cajal's gold chloride sublimate stain. x 250. FIG. 170. Focal astrocytosis in subcortical white matter of a male of 44 years. Schizophrenia; paranoid. Cajal's gold chloride sublimate stain. x 250. FIG. 171. Swollen oligodendroglia in subcortical white matter of frontal lobe of a male of 40 years. Schizophrenia: paranoid. Hortega's silver carbonate stain. x 450.

ler,[39] Leppien and Peters,[40] Cammermeyer,[12] Ferraro and Jervis,[24] and many others have reported ganglion cell diminution in the cortex of the cerebrum and abnormalities of persisting nerve cells in patients with dementia praecox treated with insulin. Metrazol shock treatment was considered responsible for pathologic changes of varying degree in the cerebral cortex of psychotic individuals by Petersen[56] and Weil and Liebert.[74] Ebaugh, Barnacle, and Neuberger[19] noted mild changes in the cortex of psychotic patients receiving electroshock therapy. Wolf and Cowen[78] and Peyton, Haavik, and Schiele[57] found no differences between their patients with schizophrenia who had received shock therapy and those who had not.

Myelin Sheaths and Axons: The tangential myelin sheaths in the upper layers of the cerebral cortex were reported to be diminished in schizophrenic patients by Naito,[51] Marburg,[43] and Fünfgeld.[27] Alzheimer,[2] Wada,[71] and Goldstein[29] described a diminution in myelin sheaths in the tangential layer, in the radiating fibers, and in the supraradial network in chronic cases. Focal areas of demyelination, chiefly in the basal ganglia and in the white matter and cortex of the frontal and temporal lobes, were recorded by Marcus.[45] Winkelman and Book[75] referred to a diffuse, mild, subcortical demyelination usually in the anterior half of the brain. Jakob and Pedace[34] stated that the radial and tangential fibers were never altered and Rosental (quoted by Klarfeld[37]) found the myelin sheaths normal in early cases. Klarfeld[37] reported that observations comparable to those in the myelin sheath stain could be made in fiber stains, implying that there was a loss of axons. Wolf and Cowen[78] found the myelin sheaths and axons intact in their biopsy material of the frontal lobe (Fig. 168).

Astrocytes: Abnormal changes in the astrocytes have been reported as absent, mild, or moderate in the brains of schizophrenic patients. Alzheimer[1, 2] described small, focal zones of proliferation of astrocytes in the deeper layers of the cerebral cortex. Similar observations were made by Eisath,[20] Goldstein,[29] Walter,[72] and Josephy.[35] The last two investigators also recorded similar foci of astrocytosis in the subcortical white matter and thought these were of particular significance. Alzheimer,[1] and before him Eisath,[20] referred to so-called regressive (degenerative) changes in the astrocytes of the type which he termed "amoeboid glia." Rosental (quoted by Klarfeld[37]) and Walter,[72] as well as others, confirmed these findings. Watanabe[73] described moderate astrocytic proliferation in acute cases of schizophrenia and a marginal astrocytosis in old cases. Hiresaki[31] recorded an astrocytosis in acute cases and in chronic catatonic excitement. Miskolczy[48] refers to a mild glial proliferation in instances of dementia praecox. Winkelman and Book[75] found a diffuse astrocytosis proportionate to the amount of nerve damage and loss. The biopsies of Elvidge and Reed[21] revealed a mild astrocytosis in the subcortical white matter, while Kirschbaum and Heilbrunn[36] reported hypertrophy of protoplasmic astrocytes in biopsy specimens from all their patients with schizophrenia and multipli-

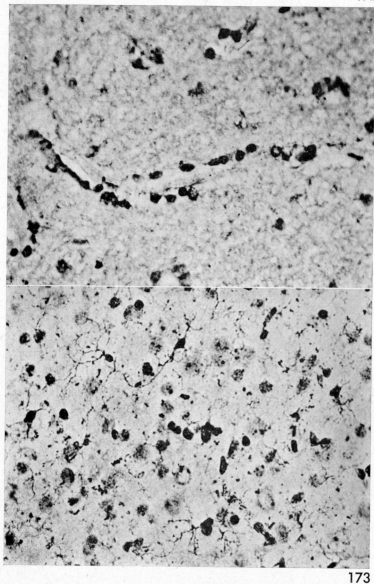

173

Fig. 172. Normal oligodendroglia in subcortical white matter of frontal lobe of a male of 46 years. Schizophrenia: hebephrenic. Hortega's silver carbonate stain. x 250. Fig. 173. Normal microglia in frontal cerebral cortex of a male of 29 years. Schizophrenia: paranoid. Hortega's silver carbonate stain. x 250.

cation of these cells in some. There was a lesser reaction of the fibrillary astrocytes. Kirschbaum and Heilbrunn attributed the severer grades of astrocytosis to shock therapy.

Steiner[66] took exception to the claim of Josephy that focal areas of astrocytosis were typical of schizophrenia, pointing out their occurrence in chronic infections. Peters,[55] Jakob and Pedace,[34] and Roeder-Kutsch[61] noted no reaction of the neuroglia in schizophrenia. Ferrero,[25] who attempted to quantitate the ratio of neural to glial cells in the cortex of schizophrenic patients and studied his subjects by age groups, found the usual increase in astrocytes proportional to increasing age and concluded that there was no astrocytosis. Wolf and Cowen[78] reported no significant astrocytosis (Fig. 169) in their biopsy material from schizophrenic patients. Rare focal astrocytosis was considered to be insignificant and probably similar to the focal gliosis referred to above (Fig. 170).

Oligodendroglia: Cardona[13] noted a moderate degree of swelling of the oligodendroglia in autopsy material from schizophrenic patients. Buscaino[9] had described "grape-like" areas of degeneration in the white matter in individuals with schizophrenia. Penfield[54] stated that the substance in such lesions is identical with the mucinoid material that has been described in acutely swollen oligodendroglia. "Grape-like areas of degeneration" in the white matter have been seen occasionally in routine autopsy material and there is a strong suspicion that they may be artefacts. Freeman[26] has pointed out that they are produced by the action of alcohol upon the tissue and have no diagnostic significance. Elvidge and Reed[21] confirmed Cardona's finding of swelling of the oligodendroglia in the subcortical white matter in biopsy material and suggested that the same process which produces oligodendroglial changes may adversely affect conduction in the axons of the cerebral white matter and thus interfere with the passage of associative impulses from one portion of the brain to another, disrupting thought processes. Kirschbaum and Heilbrunn[36] noted a minor degree of similar swelling of the oligodendroglia in biopsy specimens from the frontal lobe. Wolf and Cowen[78] reported some degree of swelling of the oligodendroglia in the subcortical white matter and less in the lower layers of the cortex in most of their frontal lobe specimens from schizophrenic patients (Fig. 171). Often the oligodendroglia were normal (Fig. 172). Pope and his co-workers[59] also encountered oligodendroglial swelling in one-quarter of their biopsy specimens of the brain but no more frequently in psychotic than in nonpsychotic patients. The ease with which the oligodendroglia swell makes one loath to draw too many conclusions from this phenomenon, since the possibility that it might be nonspecific is so strong.

Microglia: Roberti[60] described microglial activation in a single instance of schizophrenia and felt that this was parallel to the nerve cell changes. Josephy[35] has referred to the finding of rare "glial rosettes," presumably a focal proliferation of microglia. Kirschbaum and Heilbrunn[36] refer to mild satellitosis and neuronophagia in the cortex in their biopsy specimens. Wolf and Cowen,[78] using Hortega's silver carbonate stain on biopsy specimens of the frontal lobes, found no evidence of microglial activation (Fig. 173).

Central Nervous System Other than Cerebral Cortex: Portions of the brain other than the cerebral cortex and white matter have been studied much less frequently. As has been pointed out by Steiner[66] the areas of degeneration in the gray matter and the tract degeneration in the white matter, described in the basal ganglia, pons, cerebellum, and spinal cord in schizophrenic patients by Klippel and Lhermitte,[38] Urechia,[68] and Stocker,[67] are very difficult to interpret. This is true, as well, of the changes in the spinal cord reported by Goldstein,[29] those described in the basal ganglia by Cahane and Cahane,[10] those observed in the medulla by Dawson and Latham,[15] and the appearance of abnormal amounts of lipid in the nerve cells of the thalamus and globus pallidus described by Freeman.[26] Fünfgeld[27] found similar changes in the thalamus associated with gliosis and considered them to be secondary to cortical degeneration. The Vogts[70] studied a series of cases of catatonia and observed degeneration of nerve cells in the thalamus, chiefly in the medial nucleus. They described vacuolization of the cytoplasm and dendrites, swelling of the nucleus, and pallor of the nuclear membrane. Although not often present, they noted some astrocytosis in the protracted cases. The Vogts were inclined to attribute specific significance to their findings in the thalamus although they could not be certain whether the changes were the cause or the result of the catatonic state. They also pointed out that they had not examined other portions of the brain or the brains of nonschizophrenic patients as controls. They referred to as yet unpublished work by K. v. Buttlar in their laboratory, who found ganglion cell abnormalities in hypothalamic structures such as the basal, tuberal, mammillary, supraoptic, and paraventricular nuclei. There is no way in which we can logically associate some of the noncortical lesions described in schizophrenic patients with the schizophrenic syndrome, in particular the tract degeneration in the spinal cord described by Klippel and Lhermitte[38] and by Goldstein.[29] It would seem that these were coincidental or that the clinical diagnoses may have been mistaken. Wohlfahrt,[77] in an examination of the corpus striatum, thalamus, and hypothalamus in a series of schizophrenic patients and a group of normal controls, found no differences between them.

Circulatory System: Abnormalities of the blood vessels of the brain have been reported in schizophrenia by Lewis.[42] He stated that there was a consistent aplastic circulatory apparatus in catatonia and hebephrenia, the heart and blood vessels being smaller than normal. Detengof,[17] however, described premature arteriosclerotic changes in schizophrenics in the age range of 24 to 29 years and ascribed these changes to toxic factors. Bessalko[4] claimed to have found many circulatory anomalies in addition to other anomalies during autopsies on schizophrenic patients. Bruetsch[8] recorded the finding of rheumatic endarteritis in the brain in some subjects with dementia praecox. Only a few of the vessels showed the changes described and the problem arises as to whether there may have been a concurrence of two diseases. Bodechtel[5] reported similar changes in the blood vessels of the brain in individuals with verrucous endocarditis who appeared mentally healthy. The fresh areas of degeneration in the brain occasionally encountered in acute fatal catatonia have the earmarks of vascular lesions, and would seem to be an acute complication of schizophrenia rather than part of its specific pathologic picture. They are seen in a great variety of other conditions in which there are known circulatory abnormalities. Wohlfahrt's[77] ischemic foci in the globus pallidus, hypothalamus, and elsewhere appeared to be of this nature. In most reports of the findings in the brain in schizophrenics, no abnormalities of the blood vessels are described. In some reports, the blood vessels are described as normal (Wolf and Cowen[78]).

Perivascular Spaces: Cotton[14] referred to an accumulation of fat in the cells of the walls of blood vessels in schizophrenics which was associated with fatty substances present in the nerve cells and glia. Freeman[26] described fat-laden and pigment-laden phagocytes in the perivascular spaces in the thalamus and globus pallidus in such subjects. Josephy,[35] and Jakob and Pedace[34] reported similar perivascular fat and pigment-laden elements in the cortex and subcortical white matter. Kirschbaum and Heilbrunn,[36] in examining biopsy specimens from schizophrenic patients, described fat in the walls and perivascular spaces of blood vessels of the cortex. Spielmeyer[65] found similar appearances in control subjects, some being young normal individuals between the ages of 20 and 25 years. Peters[55] observed the same in the brains of recently executed relatively young individuals. Roeder-Kutsch[61] has recorded such findings in nonpsychotic individuals. Wolf and Cowen[78] reported minor degrees of such fat deposition in relation to blood vessels in biopsy material from schizophrenic patients but attributed no specific significance to it. The frequent occurrence of such changes, particularly in the subcortical white matter, in nonpsychotic individuals, makes it highly unlikely that they have any special meaning for schizophrenia.

Choroid Plexus: Monakow, Kitabayashi and Allende-Navarro (cited by Josephy[35]) described vascular lesions of the choroid plexus associated with degeneration of the choroid cells in schizophrenic individuals. They referred to highly acellular, fibrin-containing exudate in the choroidal stroma. Monakow considered these typical for schizophrenia or schizophrenic syndromes. Fünfgeld,[27] Josephy,[35] and Jakob and Pedace[34] found the choroid plexuses relatively normal in subjects with dementia praecox.

Leptomeninges: The great majority of investigators found no leptomeningeal abnormalities although an occasional one was reported such as fibrosis of the leptomeninges referred to by Goldstein.[29]

Histochemical Studies of Cerebral Cortex: Some have used histochemical methods in their investigation of the brain in schizophrenia. Wolf and Cowen,[78] using biopsy specimens of the frontal lobe, found both alkaline and acid phosphatase activity similar to that observed in the brains obtained at autopsy from nonpsychotic individuals. Pope and his co-workers[59] also used brain biopsy specimens. The material was excised from Brodmann's area 9 prior to prefrontal lobotomy in cases of schizophrenia and control cases of psychoneurosis and intractable pain. They demonstrated acid phosphatase activity and found it more frequently reduced in deteriorated schizophrenic patients than in those of the pain-neurosis group and most particularly reduced in the central cytoplasm of the large pyramidal cells. These investigators were not certain that their findings lay beyond the normal variability range of the method. They also studied the cholinesterase activity of the cortex histochemically in the same group of patients and found it significantly increased in five of seven patients in whom the diagnosis was deteriorated schizophrenia, as compared to the five nonpsychotic individuals. They suggested that this indicated an increased potential rate of acetylcholine turnover. Histochemical methods for the demonstration of enzyme activity are, as yet, little adapted for quantitative determinations and therefore caution is necessary in the interpretation of degrees of enzyme activity.

Microspectrographic Observations in the Cerebral Cortex: The investigations of Hydén and Hartelius[33] were concerned with a microspectrographic study of cerebral cortical nerve cells in biopsy specimens obtained during lobotomy. They found a considerable decrease in the polynucleotides and the proteins in some of these ganglion cells in persons suffering from psychoses, principally schizophrenia, as contrasted with those in equivalent cells from nonpsychotic individuals. So far as we know, this work has not yet been confirmed and if it be true, its significance must be determined. It might perhaps have the same relative significance as the dissolution of Nissl substance, which has no specific meaning for a particular disease and occurs with such ease that its importance for any given pathologic process must be cautiously considered.

Acid-Fast Pigment: Wolf and Cowen[78] found that acid-fast pigment in the nerve cells of biopsy specimens of the frontal cortex of schizophrenic patients was similar in distribution and quantity to that in nonpsychotic individuals.

"Inclusion Bodies" of Papez: Papez[52, 53] studied biopsy material of the prefrontal cortex in forty-two patients with dementia praecox. Using a special staining method, he found deeply blue staining inclusion bodies in cortical nerve cells, which he believed were made up principally of ribonucleic acid. He also described progressive degeneration of the nuclei and cytoplasm of such nerve cells ending in what he called "naked nuclei." The various stages of degeneration were said to correspond to the severity of the disease. The fact that Papez[53] found his "inclusions" in the brains of

patients with manic-depressive psychosis, general paresis, multiple sclerosis, and other conditions, as well as in those with schizophrenia, proves that they have no specificity, even if their occurrence should be confirmed.

Other Organs in Schizophrenia

Some have found what they considered to be significant changes in organs other than the central nervous system. Gaupp[28] reported instances of acute fatal catatonia in which there was central degeneration of the lobules of the liver and pointed out that Penacchieti and Lingjaerde found similar changes in biopsy specimens of the liver of schizophrenic patients. De Jong[16] believed that experimental catatonia was related to abnormal changes in the liver. Gaupp observed red metaplasia of the bone marrow of the femur in subjects with acute fatal catatonia and referred to a similar finding by Jahn and Greving. Gaupp also described depletion of lipids in the adrenal cortex in such acute cases and pointed out that Witte[76] had also recorded it. Witte[76] reported no atrophy of the thyroid gland in schizophrenic patients similar to that which he had observed in other psychotics. He also[76] stated that the adrenal glands in schizophrenic patients lost their capacity to store lipids and the ovaries of some of the patients were markedly deficient in lipids. Mott[49] recorded severe changes in the ovaries and testes of patients with dementia praecox. Lewis[42] referred to histopathologic changes in the thyroid, adrenals, and gonads. Münzer[50] described what he considered to be congenital abnormalities of the testes, pituitary body, and parathyroid glands in schizophrenic individuals. Bamford and Bean[3] reported fibrosis of many of the organs, particularly the kidney and spleen, and in the internal secretory glands. Cahane and Cahane[11] recorded abnormalities in the pituitary body. A series of other investigators, Borberg,[6] Fauser and Heddaeus[22] Lewin,[41] and Josephy[35] found the internal secretory glands in schizophrenic patients to be relatively normal. As has been pointed out by Lewin and others, terminal diseases such as tuberculosis, as well as the nutritional difficulties of these individuals, may well be the cause for most of the findings in the other organs, in many cases. They are so often encountered in routine autopsies as to make their specificity doubtful. There is no good ground at present for placing any of the pathologic changes encountered in such organs in a primary etiologic position.

Psychoses Other Than Schizophrenia

The pathologic changes in manic-depressive psychosis are virtually unknown. Such postmortem studies as those of Marchand[44] and Meyer,[47] describing changes in the leptomeninges and cerebral vessels, and in Meyer's material, describing degeneration and disappearance of cortical nerve cells chiefly in the frontal and temporal lobes, are still unsubstantiated. Wolf and Cowen,[78] studying biopsy material from the frontal lobe removed in the course of topectomy in manic-depressive patients, found the changes similar to, and of the same slight and nonspecific character, as those which they had encountered in simultaneously examined material from schizophrenic individuals. Three cases of involutional psychosis investigated in the same fashion by these authors showed a similar absence of significant changes. The pathologic picture of involutional psychosis is very poorly documented.

Comment

It would appear from a review of the histopathologic findings in patients with schizophrenia that one is not dealing with obvious or even unequivocal changes in the central nervous system. The abnormal findings in other organs are even more ambiguous and ill-defined. It seems reasonable to conclude that if there are microscopic variations from the norm, they are of such a subtle nature as either not to be detectable by ordinary methods of microscopic observation or to be masked by the effects of tissue death or those due to manipulation incidental to preparation of the material for histologic study. All the reported microscopic abnormalities have been challenged as nonspecific by a group of competent histologists and have been attributed to misjudgment of the limits of normal variation, misinterpretation of artefacts, or the uncritical attribution of special significance to casual, coincidental findings. Similar conclusions may be drawn from the histologic findings in manic-depressive psychosis and involutional melancholia, although it must be stressed that the available data on these are, as yet, extremely scanty. One cannot deny that there may be an organic basis for schizophrenia and other psychoses of unknown origin but if there be, there is, at present, no reliable histologic evidence for it.

REFERENCES

1. ALZHEIMER, A.: Nissl-Alzheimer Histologische Arb. 3 (Heft 3), 1910, pp. 401-562.
2. ALZHEIMER, A.: *Monatsschrift für Psychiatrie und Neurologie,* 1897, 2, pp. 82-120; *Zeitschrift für die gesamte Neurologie und Psychiatrie,* 1913, (ref) 7, pp. 621-622.
3. BAMFORD, C. B., and BEAN, H.: *Journal of Mental Science,* 1932, 78, pp. 353-358.
4. BESSALKO, S. A.: *Sovetskaya psikhonevrologiya,* 1939, 15, pp. 75-84.
5. BODECHTEL, G.: *Zeitschrift für die gesamte Neurologie und Psychiatrie,* 1932, 140, pp. 657-709.
6. BORBERG, N. C.: *Archiv für Psychiatrie und Nervenkrankheiten,* 1921, 63, pp. 390-462.
7. BOUMANN, K. H.: *Psychiatrische en neurologische bladen,* 1928, 32, pp. 517-539.
8. BRUETSCH, W. L.: *The American Journal of Psychiatry,* 1940, 97, pp. 276-296.
9. BUSCAINO, V. M.: *Rivista di patologia nervosa,* 1921, 26, pp. 57-73.
10. CAHANE, M., and CAHANE, T.: *La Riforma medica,* 1937, 53, pp. 14-16.

11. CAHANE, M., and CAHANE, T.: *Annales médico psychologiques*, 1939, 97, pp. 214-219.
12. CAMMERMEYER, J.: *Zeitschrift für die gesamte Neurologie und Psychiatrie*, 1938, 163, pp. 617-633.
13. CARDONA, F.: *Rassegna di studi psichiatrici*, 1934, 23, pp. 271-281; *Rivista di patologia nervosa e mentale*, 1947, 68, pp. 37-42.
14. COTTON, H. A.: *Journal of Experimental Medicine*, 1915, 22, pp. 492-516.
15. DAWSON, W. S., and LATHAM, O.: *Medical Journal of Australia*, 1943, 1, pp. 245-248.
16. DE JONG, H.: Experimental Catatonia. Baltimore, Williams and Wilkins, 1935.
17. DETENGOF, F. F.: *Sovetskaya psikhonevrologiya*, 1937, 1, pp. 11-27.
18. DUNLAP, C. B.: *The American Journal of Psychiatry*, 1924, 3, pp. 403-421; Association for Research in Nervous and Mental Disease, Proceedings, Vol. V (Schizophrenia). New York, Paul B. Hoeber, 1928.
19. EBAUGH, F. G., BARNACLE, C. H., and NEUBERGER, K. T.: *Archives of Neurology and Psychiatry*, 1943, 49, pp. 107-117.
20. EISATH, G.: *Monatsschrift für Psychiatrie und Neurologie*, 1906, 20, pp. 139-165; and *ibid*, 1906, 20, pp. 240-265.
21. ELVIDGE, A. R., and REED, G.: *Archives of Neurology and Psychiatry*, 1936, 40, pp. 227-264.
22. FAUSER, H., and HEDDAEUS, E.: *Zeitschrift für die gesamte Neurologie und Psychiatrie*, 1922, 74, pp. 616-627.
23. FERRARO, A.: *The American Journal of Psychiatry*, 1934, 13, pp. 883-902; *Journal of Neuropathology and Experimental Neurology*, 1943, 2, pp. 84-94.
24. FERRARO, A., and JERVIS, G. A.: *Psychiatric Quarterly*, 1939, 13, pp. 207-228.
25. FERRERO, C.: *Archiv für Neurologie und Psychiatrie*, 1947, 49, pp. 41-70.
26. FREEMAN, W.: Association for Research in Nervous and Mental Disease, Proceedings, Vol. V (Schizophrenia), pp. 382-389, New York, Paul B. Hoeber, Inc., 1928.
27. FÜNFGELD, E.: *Monatsschrift für Psychiatrie und Neurologie*, 1927, 63, pp. 1-68.
28. GAUPP, R.: *Zeitschrift für die gesamte Neurologie und Psychiatrie*, 1943, 176, pp. 225-264.
29. GOLDSTEIN, K.: *Archiv für Psychiatrie*, 1910, 46, pp. 1062-1090.
30. HECHST, B.: *Monatsschrift für Psychiatrie und Neurologie*, 1933, 87, pp. 32-47.
31. HIRESAKI, T.: *Psychiatria et neurologie japonica*, 1937, 41, p. 95.
32. HOLT, E. K., and TEDESCHI, C.: *Journal of Neuropathology and Experimental Neurology*, 1943, 2, pp. 306-314.
33. HYDÉN, H., and HARTELIUS, H.: *Acta psychiatrica et neurologica*, 1948, Supp. XLVIII: pp. 1-117.
34. JAKOB, C., and PEDACE, E. A.: *Revista de la Asociación médica argentina*, 1938, 52, pp. 326-334.
35. JOSEPHY, H.: Dementia praecox (Schizophrenie). Handbuch der Geiteskrankheiten. (O. Bumke) Bd. XI, VII Teil: Die Anatomie der Psychosen (W. Spielmeyer), p. 763-778. Berlin, J. Springer, 1930.
36. KIRSCHBAUM, W. R., and HEILBRUNN, G.: *Archives of Neurology and Psychiatry*, 1944, 51, pp. 155-162.
37. KLARFELD, B.: *Klinische Wochenschrift*, 1923, 2, pp. 2269-2272.
38. KLIPPEL, R., and LHERMITTE, J.: *Jahresbericht Neurologie und Psychiatrie*, 1904, 8, p. 1092, and *Neurologische Zentralblatt*, 1906, p. 735.
39. KOBLER, F.: *Archiv für Psychiatrie*, 1938, 107, pp. 688-700.

40. LEPPIEN, R., and PETERS, G.: *Zeitschrift für die gesamte Neurologie und Psychiatrie*, 1937, 160, pp. 444-454.
41. LEWIN, B. D.: Association for Research in Nervous and Mental Disease, Proceedings, Vol. V (Schizophrenia), pp. 390-400. New York, Paul B. Hoeber, Inc., 1928.
42. LEWIS, N. D. C.: Nervous and Mental Disease Monographs Series, No. 35. New York and Washington, Nervous and Mental Disease Publishing Company, 1923.
43. MARBURG, O.: *Arbeiten aus dem neurologischen Institut an der Wiener Universität*, 1924, 26, pp. 245-251.
44. MARCHAND, L.: *Bulletin de la Société clinique de médecine mentale*, 1928, 16, pp. 176-179.
45. MARCUS, H.: *Acta medica Scandinavica*, 1936, 87, pp. 365-401.
46. MEYER, F.: *Monatsschrift für Psychiatrie und Neurologie*, 1934, 88, pp. 265-323.
47. MEYER, F.: *Monatsschrift für Psychiatrie und Neurologie*, 1935, 91, pp. 137-159.
48. MISKOLCZY, D.: *Zeitschrift für die gesamte Neurolgie und Psychiatrie*, 1933, 147, pp. 509-544, and *ibid.* 1937, 158, pp. 203-208.
49. MOTT, F. W.: *British Medical Journal*, 1922, 1, pp. 463-466.
50. MUNZER, F. T.: *Zentralblatt für Neurochirurgie*, 1928, 48, pp. 484-485.
51. NAITO, I.: *Arbeiten aus dem Neurologischen Institut an der Wiener Universität*, 1924, 26, pp. 1-156.
52. PAPEZ, J. W.: *Archives of Neurology and Psychiatry*, 1944, 52, pp. 217-229.
53. PAPEZ, J. W.: *Journal of Nervous and Mental Disease*, 1948, 108, pp. 431-434; PAPEZ, J. W., and BATEMAN, J. F.: *Journal of Nervous and Mental Disease*, 1949, 110, pp. 425-437.
54. PENFIELD, W.: Cytology and Cellular Pathology of the Nervous System. W. Penfield, editor, Vol. II. p. 423. New York, Paul B. Hoeber, Inc., 1932.
55. PETERS, G.: *Zeitschrift für die gesamte Neurologie und Psychiatrie*, 1937, 160, pp. 361-380.
56. PETERSEN, F.: *Allgemeine Zeitschrift für Psychiatrie und psychisch-gerichtliche Medicin*, 1939, 111, pp. 366-388.
57. PEYTON, W. T.; HAAVIK, J. E.; and SCHIELE, B. C.: *Archives of Neurology and Psychiatry*, 1949, 62, pp. 560-571.
58. POLATIN, P.; EISENSTEIN, B. W.; and BARRERA, S. E.: *Psychiatric Quarterly*, 1944, 18, pp. 391-412.
59. POPE, A.; MEATH, J. A.; CAVENESS, W. F.; LIVINGSTON, H. E.; and THOMPSON, R. H.: *Transactions of the American Neurological Association*, 1949, pp. 147-153.
60. ROBERTI, C. E.: *Rivista di patologia nervosa e mentale*, 1931, 38, pp. 461-482.
61. ROEDER-KUTSCH, T.: *Allgemeine Zeitschrift für Psychiatrie und psychisch-gerichtliche Medicin*, 1939, 112, pp. 63-74.
62. ROIZIN, L.; MORIARTY, J. D.; and WEIL, A. A.: *Archives of Neurology and Psychiatry*, 1945, 54, pp. 202-211.
63. SCHUSTER, J.: *Journal für Psychologie und Neurologie*, 1924, 31, pp. 1-52.
64. SIOLI, F.: *Allgemeine Zeitschrift für Psychiatrie*, 1909, 66, pp. 195-196.
65. SPIELMEYER, W.: Association for Research in Nervous and Mental Disease, Proceedings, Vol. 10 (Schizophrenia). Baltimore, Williams and Wilkins, 1931.
66. STEINER, G.: Handbuch der Geiteskrankheiten. Oswald Bumke. Bd. IV. Spez. Teil pp. 606-611. Berlin, J. Springer, 1932.
67. STOCKER, A.: *Zeitschrift für die gesamte Neurologie und Psychiatrie*, 1922, 75, pp. 47-55.

68. URECHIA, C.: *Revue neurologique*, 1922, 38, pp. 171-174.
69. VOGT, C., and VOGT, O.: *Journal für Psychologie und Neurologie*, 1922, 28, pp. 1-171.
70. VOGT, C., and VOGT, O.: *Ärztliche Forschung*, 1948, 7-8, pp. 101-104.
71. WADA, T.: *Arbeiten aus dem Neurologischen Institut an der Wiener Universität*, 1910, 18, pp. 313-345.
72. WALTER, F. K.: *Zeitschrift für die gesamte Neurologie und Psychiatrie*, 1919, 47, pp. 112-127.
73. WATANABE, M.: *Japanese Journal of Medical Sciences*, VIII, Int. Med. Pediat. and Psychiat. 1934, 3, pp. 97-107.
74. WEIL, A., and LIEBERT, E.: *Archives of Neurology and Psychiatry*, 1940, 44, pp. 1031-1043.
75. WINKELMAN, N. W., and BOOK, M. H.: *The American Journal of Psychiatry*, 1949, 105, pp. 889-896.
76. WITTE, F.: *Zeitschrift für die gesamte Neurologie und Psychiatrie*, 1921, 72, pp. 308-319, and *ibid.* 1922, 80, pp. 190-199.
77. WOHLFAHRT, S.: *Acta psychiatrica et neurologica*, 1937, 11, pp. 687-707.
78. WOLF, A., and COWEN, D.: Pathology, Chap. 27, in Selective Partial Ablation of the Frontal Cortex. Columbia-Greystone Associates, Fred A. Mettler, Editor. New York, Paul B. Hoeber, Inc., 1949.
79. ZIMMERMAN, R.: *Zeitschrift für die gesamte Neurologie und Psychiatrie*, 1915, 30, pp. 354-378.
80. ZINGERLE, H.: *Monatsschrift für Psychiatrie und Neurologie*, 1910, 27, pp. 285-321.

Histopathology of Mental Disease

N. W. WINKELMAN, M.D.

Doctors Wolf and Cowen have given us a broad picture of the different viewpoints held by two widely divergent schools of thought regarding the histopathologic findings in schizophrenia. They themselves subscribe to the view that there is nothing in the schizophrenic brain that cannot be duplicated in any nonschizophrenic state.

I, myself, belong to the opposite school, the one that believes that there must be and there are changes in the brain in schizophrenia, just as truly as there are changes in the cortex in arteriosclerotic deterioration, Pick's disease, and in paresis. My interest in psychiatric pathology dates back over twenty-five years and I have had occasion to examine many patients with all sorts of mental conditions in which the relationship between cortical change and psychiatric problems has been fairly obvious. No one today would claim that the changes in the cortex, e.g., in paresis, would have nothing to do with the clinical picture. It is possible to duplicate the different clinical divisions in paresis that are met with in schizophrenia. We see a deteriorated type akin to the hebephrenic and simple types of schizophrenia. We speak of catatonic excitement and mutism and these can also be seen in paresis. The paranoid form can also be found in both diseases although I want to eliminate this subdivision from our present discussion

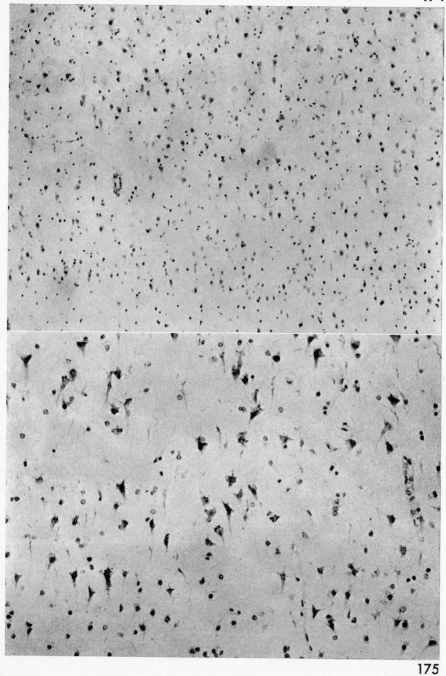

FIG. 174.   Diffuse nerve cell loss with degenerative changes in nerve elements.
Tol. blue. x 150.   FIG. 175.   Focal and general cell loss as well as degenerative
changes in nerve cells shown. Tol. blue. x 340.

since I am not prepared to describe the changes that may be found. We shall eventually describe this problem in a separate presentation.

Let me first enumerate two interesting gross findings in schizophrenia. It has been known for a long time (Nolan Lewis[7]) that in schizophrenia an hypoplasia of the cardiovascular system is a fairly consistent finding. We have also known from the work of Moore and his associates[8] that the pneumoencephalogram depicts a fairly severe convolutional atrophy, especially over the anterior half of the brain.

From the microscopic side there is frequently noted a mild generalized demyelination in the subcortex, especially in the anterior half of the brain.

The most common feature of the schizophrenic brain is not only a general decrease in the number of nerve cells in the cortex of the anterior half of the brain (Fig. 174) but also numerous areas are found in which the ganglion cells have either completely disappeared (Verödungsherde) or the nerve cells are in the process of disintegration (shadow or ghost cells) (Figs. 175 and 176).

There is no associated inflammatory reaction in or around these foci, but there is a general glial proliferation in proportion to the severity of the nerve cell degeneration and loss (Fig. 177). The frontal, temporal, and parietal lobes are usually most markedly affected and in them the third cortical layer is the most vulnerable.

Different types of cell disease have been noted in schizophrenia. We have encountered a variety of cell changes; the most constant has been the so-called chronic cell disease, including cell shrinkage and ghost cells and at times loss of polarity (Fig. 176).

The amount of fat in the nerve cells has usually been greater than one would expect from the age of the patient. This is in agreement with the studies of Cotton[1] and Josephy.[5]

The microscopic picture is not a startling one, a fact which cannot be too strongly emphasized. When, however, all the above changes are found in the brain of a comparatively young psychotic individual (below 40 years of age and in the absence of arteriosclerosis or severe infections or toxemias) they are extremely suggestive of schizophrenia.

It is universally agreed that there is a definite predisposition to the development of schizophrenia. It usually attacks those who are biologically vulnerable, known clinically as a "schizoid personality." One can quote an analogous situation in physical medicine in which tuberculosis attacks individuals with the so-called asthenic habitus. In schizophrenia, it can probably be boiled down to saying that the "schizoid brain" is vulnerable.

Additional evidence in favor of the organic nature of schizophrenia has been reported by reliable investigators in related fields. The electroencephalogram has been abnormal in many schizophrenic patients. Gibbs, Gibbs and Lennox[3] concluded that the electroencephalographic record of patients with schizophrenia is similar to that of individuals with psycho-

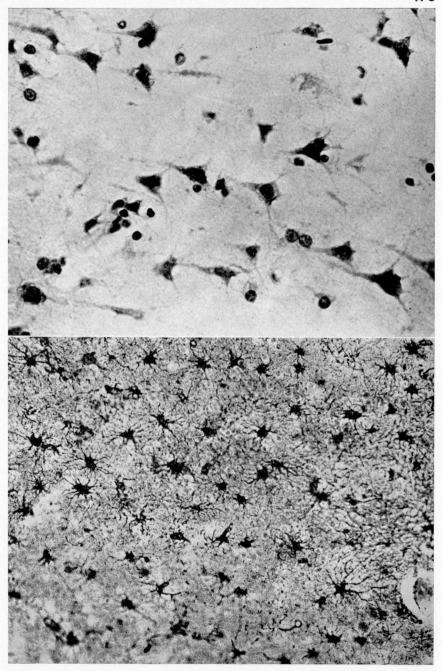

176

Fig. 176.   Nerve cell changes including pyknosis, vacuolization of cytoplasm, cell shrinkage, shadow cells, shown in greater detail in Figures 174 and 175. Tol. blue. x 700.   Fig. 177. General glial hyperplasia and hypertrophy in frontal cortex. Cajal stain. x 320.

motor epilepsy. They speak of schizophrenia as a form of "cerebral dysrhythmia."

Biopsy studies have been reported by two groups of investigators (Elvidge and Reed,[2] and Kirschbaum and Heilbrunn[6]). The former noted swelling of the oligoglia in the subcortex. The latter described degenerative changes in the ganglion cells and progressive and regressive reactions of the glia and blood vessels, such as are commonly seen in subjects with chronic intoxication and metabolic disorders.

The work of Caspersson and his associates[4] in Stockholm has revealed for the first time important chemical differences between the nerve cells in the frontal lobes of normal human beings and those in persons suffering from various mental diseases. These investigators showed that the poly-nucleotide content of the cytoplasm of the nerve cells was "very low" compared to that in the normal individual.

The fact that the schizophrenic patient can be restored to normal for hours or even days by amytal administration, inhalations of oxygen and carbon dioxide mixtures, and similar means is not proof against the organic nature of schizophrenia. We can quote an analogous condition the organic nature of which is undisputed. I refer to myasthenia gravis in which the patient can be restored to normal or near normal for a period of hours by the subcutaneous injection of neostigmine in sufficient amounts. When the effect of this drug wears off the subject regains his myasthenic symptoms.

Summary

1. The gross findings of cortical atrophy plus a hypoplastic arterial system in the brain are frequently found in schizophrenia.

2. The main microscopic findings are: focal and general loss of nerve cells, especially in the anterior half of the brain; the presence of numerous nerve cells showing degenerative changes, such as shrinkage, vacuolization of cytoplasm, "ghost cells," loss of polarity, and fatty infiltration. A fairly uniform hyperplasia and hypertrophy of macroglia was noted. A diffuse mild subcortical demyelination was present.

3. There was no involvement of the mesodermal components of the brain.

4. An increasing array of evidence in many related fields is accumulating to bolster the contention that schizophrenia should be included among the "organic" psychoses.

REFERENCES

1. COTTON, H. A.: *Journal of Experimental Medicine*, 1915, 22, p. 492.
2. ELVIDGE, A. R., and REED, G. E.: *Archives of Neurology and Psychiatry*, 1938, 40, p. 227.
3. GIBBS, F. A.; GIBBS, E. L.; and LENNOX, W. G.: *The American Journal of Psychiatry*, 1938, 95, p. 255.

4. HYDEN, H., and HARTELIUS, H.: *Acta psychiatrica et neurologica*, 1948, 58, p. 1.
5. JOSEPHY, H.: *Ztschr. f. d. ges. Neurol u. Psychiat.*, 1923, 86, p. 391.
6. KIRSCHBAUM, W. R., and HEILBRUNN, G.: *Archives of Neurology and Psychiatry*, 1944, 51, p. 155.
7. LEWIS, NOLAN D. C.: *The American Journal of Psychiatry*, 1929, 9, p. 543.
8. MOORE, M. T.; NATHAN, D.; ELLIOTT, A. R.; and LAUBACH, C.: *The American Journal of Psychiatry*, 1933, 89, p. 801.

Combined Use of Soft X-Rays and Monochromatic Ultraviolet Light for Microabsorption Measurements of Nerve Cell Components

JOHN I. NURNBERGER, M.D.

I wish to describe two microabsorption technics which make possible quantitative estimation of certain chemical constituents of the nerve cell. The first of these, developed by Arne Engström and Bo Lindström[2] of Stockholm, utilizes soft x-rays.

The central element in Engström's instrument is a vacuum x-ray tube (Fig. 178). The water-cooled anode shown in this diagram is bombarded by radiation from a hot filament cathode. X-radiation thus generated is filtered through a 9-micron aluminum foil to give continuous x-rays of wave length 8 to 11 Ångstrom units, which strike the tissue mounted in the line of the beam. The mounting technic is shown in the lower diagram of Figure 178. A microtome section is floated over the slit in a thin copper disk and is supported by a 0.3-micron collodion membrane. The section is then deparaffinized. A step wedge reference system of superimposed collodion foils of known mass and composition is mounted close to the tissue section over the slit. Filtered radiation passes through the exposed section and reference system and unabsorbed radiation falls upon a fine-grained Lippmann emulsion clamped in immediate apposition to the tissue and reference. An x-ray image of the exposed tissue and wedge is recorded on the photographic emulsion. The optical density of any portion of this image is directly proportional to the amount of energy absorbed by the constituent atomic C, N, and O of the wedge or tissue. Since the mass per unit area of the absorbing foils is determined by previously weighing unit areas of the foil material, the optical density in the image corresponding to this mass or any multiple of it, serves as a direct reference for determining the mass of any resolvable component of the tissue studied. Appropriate corrections and acceptable ranges for elements other than C, N, and O absorbing in this region have been made by Engström and Lindström.[2] Likewise they have shown that extremely large deviations from the usual proportions of C, N, and O encountered in representative tissue proteins do not affect appreciably the mass as determined by this technic. Further chemical measurements made on the same cells (since this technic neither destroys nor specifically alters the section) can then be referred to unit mass of the studied constituent.

To specify further the chemical components contributing in largest measure to total mass I have used a simple photographic modification of Caspersson's ultraviolet microspectrography, described by him in 1936.[1]

A spark, generated by the rotating metallic spark gap, diagrammed in Figure 179, is collimated through a quartz telescope lens, then separated into its monochromatic spectral components by a quartz, water-filled double-

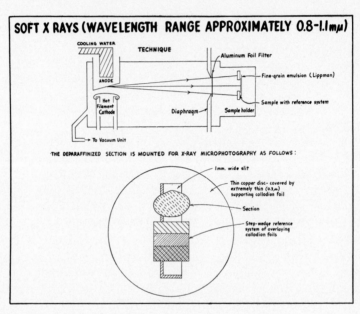

SOFT X RAYS (WAVELENGTH RANGE APPROXIMATELY 0.8-1.1mμ)

Fig. 178.   The basic instrumental tools for microradiography. (Diagram modified from Engström and Lindström: *Biochimica et Biophysica Acta*, 1950, 4.)

prism monochromator. This beam, properly filtered, serves as the illuminating ray for the usual fused quartz optical microscope system. Several factors decrease the amount of light transmitted by the microscopic preparation. A portion of the light is chemicophysically absorbed by materials within the cell. If this factor alone were operative, calculated extinctions by this technic would be fully as reliable as those obtained by, for example, the Beckman for solutions. In biologic tissues, however, some of the incident light is scattered by submicroscopic particles (ray #2, Fig 179) and additional light is lost by reflection (ray #3, Fig. 179). Our studies indicate that factors 2 and 3 are negligible in frozen-dried nervous tissue, deparaffinized with xylol, and suspended in glycerin; that ray #1 is, in fact, here a reliable measure of specific chemicophysical absorption. These same studies likewise demonstrate that formalin or Carnoy fixation markedly increases non-

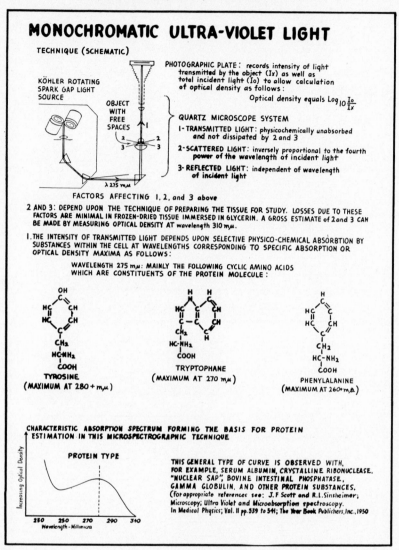

FIG. 179. The tools and basic principles of the photographic ultraviolet microabsorption technic.

specific light losses but does not preclude semi-quantitative estimation of relative concentration ratios of certain substances.

Two classes of substances have been studied by this technic. A protein component is measured in terms of its contained tyrosine, tryptophane, and phenylalanine at an observed maximum of 275 to 280 mu (Fig. 179). Protein fraction A of lobster nerve extract, and squid axoplasm, as recently reported by Schmitt,[5] are among many animal protein substances displaying this absorption maximum at 275 to 280 mu.

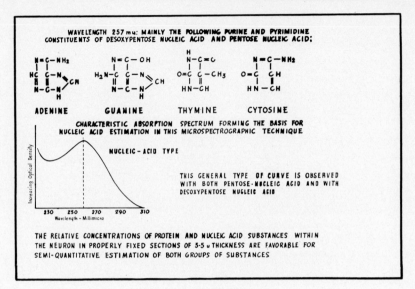

FIG. 179.   (Continued)

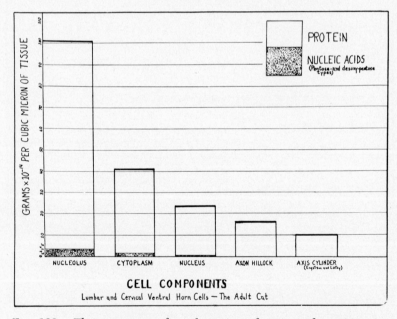

FIG. 180.   The percentage dry-substance and estimated partition into protein and nucleic acids in ventral horn cells of the adult cat.

At wave length 257 mu, purine and pyrimidine components of nucleic acids absorb maximally to give the typical nucleic acid maximum indicated in Figure 179, lower curve. The nerve cell because of its relatively low concentration of nucleic acid and high concentration of protein is particularly well adapted to simultaneous estimation of both these absorbing classes.

An application of these technics to a practical problem is illustrated in Figure 180.

The values represented here are the means of somewhat over 20,000 separate determinations on 100 formalin and Carnoy fixed and frozen-dried ventral horn cells of the adult cat made by Drs. Engström, Lindström, and myself[4] in Stockholm. The heights of the vertical columns represent not only mean mass values in the units noted but also, by design, direct percentage dry substance as determined by historadiography. It is probable that the value of 102 for nucleolar mass reflects more the effect of fixation contraction in this remarkably compact body than that this tissue has a specific density greater than one. Measurements of nucleoli fixed by freezing-drying indicate that the more probable value is about 75 per cent dry substance. Ultraviolet measurements of the same nucleoli indicate that 3.5 per cent of the dry substance is nucleic acid, the remainder of protein nature. In the cytoplasm, by contrast, there is about 40 per cent dry substance (60 per cent water) of which approximately 1.5 per cent is nucleic acid. Frozen-dried cells show 31 per cent cytoplasmic dry substance, thus displaying minimal fixation contraction. The proportion of dry substance has decreased to somewhat over 15 per cent in the axon hillock and to 10 per cent in the axis cylinder (if we may borrow the data of Engström and Lüthy[3] from measurements of fresh single sciatic nerve fibers in the amphibian). No measurable nucleic acid was encountered in the axon hillock region. There thus appears to be an impressive water gradient from central to peripheral nerve substance (with the exception of the nucleus) as likewise a strict topical localization of nucleic acid (almost exclusively of pentose type). I have presented this fragment of material to illustrate the type of data obtainable by these two technics in combination.

REFERENCES

1. CASPERSSON, TORBJÖRN: Skandinavisches Archiv für Physiologie, Suppl. 8. 1936, 73.
2. ENGSTRÖM, ARNE, and LINDSTRÖM, BO: Biochemica et Biophysica Acta, 1950, 4, 351-373.
3. ENGSTRÖM, ARNE, and LÜTHY, H.: Experientia, June 15, 1949, 5, p. 244.
4. NURNBERGER, J. I.; ENGSTRÖM, ARNE, and LINDSTRÖM, BO: A study of the Ventral Horn Cells of the Adult Cat by Two Independent Cytochemical Microabsorption Technics. In preparation.
5. SCHMITT, F. O.: Personal communication to author.

Discussion

CHAIRMAN STANLEY COBB: Thank you very much, Dr. Nurnberger. It is work using new methods like this that is the hope of the future. I hope you will go on with this laboratory work at Hartford.

I don't want to harp on my old hobby, semantics, but I must speak about the semantic troubles that we have in a discussion like this. You have shown us in these slides that a change in the chemistry of the brain is a structural change. I just wanted to add to that, as we heard earlier this morning, mind is a function of the brain. As biologists, we know that if there are changes in function, there must be changes in structure. Then we go on from that to say that if there is a change in structure whenever there is function, that is an "organic" change. Therefore this talking about "functional change" and "organic change" is nonsense. It is only by work like yours in which you show events of this sort happening, that we are able to begin to realize that the habit of thought of a hundred years, of thinking of the microscope as the only arbiter, is pernicious. To say that there is no "organic" change because you cannot see it with a microscope is silly.

The speakers earlier this morning were, on the whole, rather careful to say "histologic change" and not "organic change." But you have shown tissue changes that one cannot see with the microscope.

I wonder if I can add for the record that in my opinion a psychologic process is necessarily an "organic" process. I would rather specify "cerebral process" because the organ happens to be the brain.

It is obvious that the three main speakers who have discussed psychoneurosis have used the word to designate a special group of observed symptoms. They have shown that similar syndromes may originate from the varied etiologic sources. I think that is one of the main lessons. As we move ahead and obtain etiologic explanations, we can separate the syndromes on a more useful basis.

DR. WALTER L. BRUETSCH: I enjoyed the paper of Drs. Wolf and Cowen and also the peppery logic of Dr. Winkelman.

In the beginning of Drs. Wolf and Cowen's presentation it was emphasized how difficult it is at times to determine whether a histologic brain preparation is normal or pathologic. A slide was shown from the brain cortex of a patient with dementia praecox with areas in which some ganglion cells had apparently disappeared. Dr. Percival Bailey, who was sitting next to me, said: "I can show you half a dozen similar preparations from normal people. All this is still within normal limits." I said, "I agree with you."

In recent years, I have been using an approach to this important histopathologic problem from which I derived useful information. I am fortunate to have in my neuropathologic material records of patients with general paresis who had malariotherapy twenty and twenty-five years ago and who continued to live for many years. Prior to death they showed marked mental deterioration. The blood and spinal fluid had reverted to complete negativity many years before death. Histologic examination showed that the patients had been cured of the syphilitic meningoencephalitis. In fact, the brain sections looked quite normal, with the exception of absence of a few ganglion cells and slight changes in some of the remaining ones. If such a preparation is interchanged with one from a subject with dementia praecox, one cannot see a difference. In other words, with our present methods of staining we are not able to say in all instances whether a preparation comes from the brain with an organic process or from a patient with a "psychogenic" psychosis.

Now, a few words as to rheumatic brain disease. It has been said that in some patients with rheumatic endocarditis there were lesions in the brain, i.e., there was rheumatic brain disease, but the patient did not exhibit mental symptoms. In my earlier discussion I mentioned that in some individuals with cerebral arteriosclerosis, associated with areas of softening, there is no psychosis. But this does not deter us from making a diagnosis of cerebral arteriosclerosis. And the same situation exists relative to rheumatic encephalopathy.

In my classes I show the medical students a patient with rheumatic brain disease. This patient, a woman 54 years of age, has had rheumatic heart disease for many years, and had a stroke, a year prior to admission, involving mainly the left arm. Several months later she became violent; she kicked in door panels and tore pictures from the wall. This was followed by a period with delusions of persecution. Today all the psychotic manifestations have disappeared, and the patient makes a normal impression. If this patient would suddenly die at home, and an autopsy would be made, someone would say: "Here it is. A lesion in the brain and nothing wrong with her mentally."

CHAIRMAN STANLEY COBB: I believe that in your laboratory, Dr. Pope, you were not able to substantiate Dr. Elvidge's observations on the oligodendroglia cells.

DR. ALFRED POPE: We examined the oligodendroglia in the same series of patients that I previously described as studied from the point of view of their enzymatic histochemistry and also the oligodendroglia in a good many other cortical biopsy specimens that were acquired at the same time. We did make a special effort to repeat the work of Elvidge and Reed. We found exactly what Dr. Wolf reported. There was acute swelling of the oligodendroglia in our Hortega preparation in quite a few of the specimens—I believe in about a third of those studied (there were some fifty-odd altogether).

When we examined the results, however, we found exactly the same proportion of patients showing swelling of oligodendroglia who were in a nonpsychotic category as among the deeply psychotic patients were very deteriorated schizophrenics. Therefore, we could not see any sign of specificity of this change in the schizophrenic group.

DR. WINIFRED ASHBY: In the majority of brains from dementia praecox subjects which I have studied there was a low content of carbonic anhydrase, which ranged from 18 to 22 units per gram (as measured by our technic) as against a range of 28 to 35 units found in brains from supposedly mental normals. In patients with general paresis in whom treatment had produced a reversal of the spinal fluid findings but in whom clinically there was deterioration, there was also a generalized low content of this enzyme.

This enzyme is readily extracted from a ground mush and, as it is almost as active in the supernatant fluid as in the sediment, it is not an integral part of the formed elements of the cell. Its deterioration would not necessarily be evident histologically.

CHAPTER 29

Experimental Induction of Psychoneuroses by Conditioned Reflex with Stress

HOWARD S. LIDDELL, PH.D.

CANNON'S CLASSICAL conception of emergency function has catalyzed medical research contributing to our understanding of the biologic basis of mental stress and disease. In fact, research on the endocrinology of reaction to stress has made team mates of biochemist and psychiatrist in the laboratory investigation of specific problems of mental disorder.

Pavlov's long-continued study of conditioned reflexes and experimental neuroses has, by contrast, fared ill. To those of us continuing in this field of research it has seemed until quite recently that the conditioned reflex was a closed chapter—a subject for formal instruction in medical physiology similar to the nerve-muscle preparation before Lucas, Adrian, and Gasser brought a realization of its fundamental significance for neurophysiology.

The relative unimportance of Pavlov's notion of conditioned reflex action in comparison with Cannon's emergency reaction in contemporary experimental medicine is due, I believe, to a misunderstanding of the significance of the conditioned reflex method and of its relation to the so-called experimental neurosis. Pavlov's reflex theory of behavior, like Freud's instinct theory, is the conceptual product of a bygone epoch in medical thinking. Both of these teleologic formulations, stressing the opposition of nature and nurture, have outlived their usefulness.

Another conception of pavlovian conditioning will, I believe, increase its usefulness and importance for experimental medicine. Through modifications of Pavlov's classical conditioning method it is possible to arrange standard stress situations of graded severity. One can then precipitate at will "neurotic" breakdown which affects all aspects of the animal's total behavioral performance in laboratory and living quarters, and such an experimental neurosis may persist for life.

It is erroneous, then, to think of the conditioned reflex method as just another method for the study of animal intelligence or learning similar to the maze, discrimination box, or multiple choice device. I have come to believe that it is fundamentally a procedure for the experimental analysis of basic mammalian emotional reactions as modified by the long-continued repetition of a few standardized emergency situations.

Although Cannon discussed the conditioning of the emergency reaction neither he nor Pavlov realized, as I think we now must, that all conditioned reflexes established by Pavlov's method, whether the reinforcement or unconditioned stimulus be food, weak acid in the mouth, or electric shock to a limb, are actually conditioned emergency reactions to controlled stresses.

The experimental interview situation so successfully exploited by Harold Wolff and his associates differs in no fundamental respect from the conditioning situation in which our sheep or goat, confined for an hour in the Pavlov restraining harness, is plied by the experimenter with carefully predetermined conditioned and unconditioned stimuli.

Describing the method of the experimental interview, Wolff says: "The changes in form and function occurring in various membranes during stress in humans have been studied. Stress in these instances involved emotional conflict characterized by such feelings as anxiety, resentment, anger, fear, and frustration. . . . While readings of mucous-membrane functions, including colorimetric and photographic readings and collection of secretions for chemical analysis, were being made each minute, relevant conflicts gleaned from the life history and from the day-to-day observations in the laboratory were abruptly introduced and discussed. Thus the relevance of the conflict situation as a stimulus productive of bodily change could be assessed experimentally."[5]

A parallel situation in the conditioned reflex laboratory is intriguingly similar. One of our neurotic subjects—a goat—is brought to the laboratory for an "interview." It is placed in the Pavlov frame and the experimenter retires to the adjoining room to carry out the routine examination. The experimenter starts a telegraph sounder clicking once a second for the four thousand two hundred and eighty-sixth time (Fig. 181, A). At the first click the animal flinches and assumes a strikingly rigid posture staring straight ahead. Then at the sixth click it slowly raises the rigidly extended left foreleg from the shoulder. With the eleventh click the noise ceases but the goat seems unable to return the foot to the platform and the foreleg remains rigidly extended, slowly sinking downward. Two minutes later the experimenter starts the clicking again for ten seconds with the same result. But now a mild, brief electric shock is applied to the foreleg and this brings immediate relief. After a brisk but awkward flexion the animal is able to replace the forefoot on the platform. Sometimes at the first try the foot skids forward as if on a roller skate and must be placed a second time.

If the examiner now proceeds to give the ten-second clicking signal every two minutes, terminating each signal with shock (which in every case serves to relax the animal's muscular tension and to bring relief) until twenty tests have been given the goat will almost exactly duplicate the marionette-

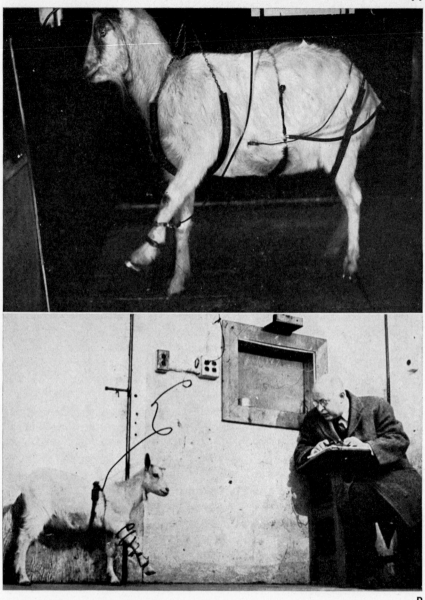

A

B

Fig. 181. A, an "experimentally neurotic" goat exhibiting behavior of the type characterized as tonic immobility. Note the awkward lifting of the rigidly extended left foreleg in response to the signal for shock. B, a goat 3 months of age exhibiting the characteristic neurotic reactions of tonic immobility. The lights have gone out for ten seconds as a signal for shock and this flash-bulb photograph shows the same awkward lifting of the rigidly extended foreleg as seen in the adult goat pictured in A. Here the goat has complete freedom of locomotion but has relinquished this freedom and become "neurotic" in conse-quence of a rigid time schedule of twenty "darkness" signals per day separated by two-minute intervals. This picture shows the reaction to the last signal of the twenty-third day of training.

like behavior just described in response to each signal. Moreover, it will maintain rigid immobility during the two-minute intervals of waiting.

The significance of this extensor rigidity can be further explored during the usual test hour. If the experimenter enters the room and, standing near the goat's head, suddenly claps his hands the animal's left foreleg stiffens and is thrust forward in rigid extension. Or if a revolver is fired near the goat's head the same foreleg is stiffly extended with the forefoot seemingly glued to the platform while the animal struggles violently for some seconds before the limb can be freed from its fixed position.

The behavior as described thus far suggests a freezing of the animal's normal startle pattern. If one approaches goats in pasture they suddenly raise their heads and prick up the ears with extended forelegs close together.

When, at the end of the examination, our neurotic subject is released from the restraining harness it may limp on the stiffened left foreleg to the exit, but on leaving the building it instantly loses the limp.

A visitor to the laboratory observing the goat's behavior during the daily examination period at once notices its immobility during the two-minute waiting period between signals and its extremely stereotyped and laborious reaction to the clicking of the telegraph sounder. He also invariably notices the further gradual tensing of the animal's already rigid posture as the time for the next signal approaches. He may also have the opportunity for observing that the goat remains mute throughout the hour even when the loudly bleating flock passes by the laboratory door. In such cases the animal does not even look toward the door. Our neurotic goat has become habituated to a situation in which it, like the asthma patient described by Thomas French, "must suppress his emotion or in which he finds himself completely helpless to give adequate expression to it."[1]

In the experimental interview situation where the patient's conflicts are abruptly introduced and discussed, their potency as stimuli productive of bodily change can, we assume from Wolff's account, be at least roughly quantified. Even the most casual observation of our neurotic goat's behavior when the telegraph clicking is abruptly introduced shows that this innocuous series of sounds is most disturbing to the animal and arouses muscular reactions that are obviously abnormal.

The stresses of emotional conflict in the patient's past must be most elusive to identify and clearly characterize since they involve such intricate patterns of interpersonal relations. Therefore, the attempt to identify these conflicts individually as stimuli productive of specific bodily changes offers an almost irresistible temptation to explain the simple in terms of the complex.

Because of his therapeutic responsibility we cannot expect the physician always to be rigidly scientific in his appraisal of the emotional context of the patient's behavior. He must employ common sense psychology, i.e. intuition. But in the relatively simple animal-conditioning situation under discussion we ourselves are responsible for the perturbations of bodily function which the clicking noise precipitates in our neurotic goat. Why then need we go out of the biologic frame of reference to invoke such concepts as reward, punishment, conflict, needs, and need-reductions in order to arrive at a scientific formulation of the nature and origin of our goat's neurotic-like behavior? Many investigators (and theorists) of animal behavior do this and in so doing yield to the temptation just mentioned of explaining the simple in terms of the complex.

Returning to the case of our neurotic goat, other specific bodily changes can be demonstrated during the examination. There is obvious disturbance of respiration. Long apneic pauses give place to irregular inspiratory gasps and labored expirations beginning ten minutes before the first signal and continuing for at least ten minutes following the twentieth signal of the day. Unlike normal goats in the laboratory our neurotic animal does not urinate or defecate during the experimental hour. Instead, when the experimenter comes to the barn to get him he hides and when caught immediately urinates and defecates before being led to the laboratory. Outside of the laboratory his behavior appears to be secretive and lonely, i.e., his gregariousness has been impaired. Finally the heart rate in the laboratory continues low (around 60 per minute) and increases little, if at all, during the signal for shock.

How did our goat arrive at his present neurotic state? The regimen of training which led to the experimental neurosis is exceedingly simple and we have employed it in precipitating almost identical neurotic manifestations in other goats, in the sheep, and in the dog. The animal began his training at 3 months of age and every day, five days a week, he was brought to the laboratory and placed in the restraining harness. During each of the ensuing hours he was given twenty signals (the telegraph sounder clicking once a second for ten seconds), each signal followed by shock to the left foreleg. The signals were spaced two minutes apart. After about 100 signals the positive conditioned reflex was well established. At the sound of the clicking the goat executed a precise flexion of the forelimb. From the thousandth signal, however, a stiffening of the limb in response to the signal imparted an increasing awkwardness and appearance of effort to the former precise and skilled response. Finally the abnormal and stereotyped extensor reaction already described supervened and remained until death at 7 years. In another goat trained at the same time the neurotic pattern persisted until the animal was subjected to a brain operation at 8 years of age. Along with the extensor freezing of the reacting limb a progressive change in respiratory pattern was observed from the normal rhythm of respiration during intervals between signals to a stage of fading respiration with long apneic pauses and finally to the irregular, gasping respiration mentioned earlier.

To gain further understanding of the essential etiologic factors in this simple training routine which leads inevitably to the experimental neurosis just described we have recently employed a still simpler procedure. A mother goat and her twin kids of the same sex, 3 weeks of age, are selected for the following experiment. The mother and one twin are confined to a room 10 feet by 10 feet. The mother is completely free but her twin by means of a web strap around its chest is connected by a flexible cable to a lever system on the ceiling and electrodes run from the cable to its right foreleg. The little goat's locomotion is not interfered with. It may run, jump, or even fall over backward without becoming entangled in the suspended cable. Its movements around the room during the test hour are recorded on a paper tape in a distant room. An observer sits in one corner recording the animals' behavior.

Every two minutes the overhead lights are turned off leaving just enough illumination to see the animal anywhere in the room. After ten seconds the lights come on again and a brief shock is applied to the little goat's foreleg. Twenty darkness signals are given each day and the sequence of signals and shocks is automatically administered by a clocking device.

The other twin is confined alone in the adjoining room and subjected to exactly the same regimen.

The observer always sits in the same corner of the room and in order to stabilize this necessary experimenter-animal relationship we have made each observer solely responsible for conducting the training sessions with a particular animal. With the young animals (either kids or lambs) completely free to move about the laboratory room the progressive changes in behavior resulting from this monotonous regimen of training are practically identical. The little animal in the room with its mother develops a stereotyped response to the conditioned stimulus (darkness) although it maintains relative freedom of locomotion during the two-minute intervals between signals. The twin isolated in the adjoining room behaves quite differently. It soon avoids the center of the room and moves cautiously along the walls. Later it limits its locomotion to one wall and finally assumes a position against the wall near the observer and about three feet from his chair (Figs. 181, B; 182, A-D). Moreover, it develops the characteristic neurotic pattern exhibited by our goat trained in the conventional Pavlov restraining harness. Somehow the mother's presence protects her baby goat from the traumatic influence of the monotonously rigid temporal patterning of tensions to which its twin in the adjoining room succumbs.

Perhaps the most instructive result of the experiments just reviewed* in which the isolated young animal is permitted freedom of locomotion in the laboratory during its conditioning routine is the following: In spite of the fact that the animal is not physically restrained by the Pavlov harness it nevertheless finds itself eventually confined by the psychic strait-jacket imposed by the monotonous regularity of the ten-second periods of darkness, each intimating mild electric shock to follow. If one arrives at the rail-

* This investigation was supported (in part) by a research grant from the National Institute of Health, United States Public Health Service.

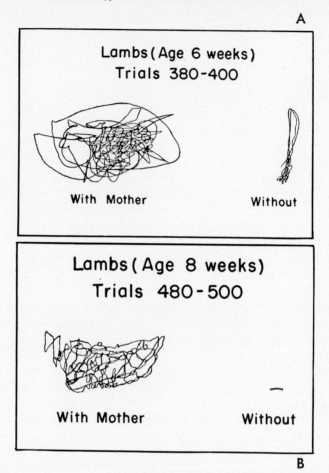

A

FIG. 182. A-D are tracings of twin lambs in separate, adjoining laboratory rooms during the test hour described in the text in which twenty signals separated by two-minute intervals are given. The total locomotion is traced in each figure. A, B, C, and D depict different stages in the training. Trials 80-100 mean that twenty ten-second "darkness" signals are given during one test period. Notice that in each tracing the lamb in the presence of its mother shows much greater freedom of locomotion than does its twin tested alone in the adjoining laboratory room.

road station a little early he does not wander far but usually stands on the platform looking for the train to come.

If we think of the conditioned reflex as a stimulus-bound episode of emergency behavior it is possible to reduce all of the various procedures employed by Pavlov and others in precipitating experimental neurosis to the basis of stimulus load. Neurosis-producing stimulus loads would include: first, excessive conditioned stimulation (intensity, duration, or number of stimuli per test period); secondly, confusion or inconsistency of conditioned stimuli (e.g., where Pavlov's dog confused circle and oval when the circle

C

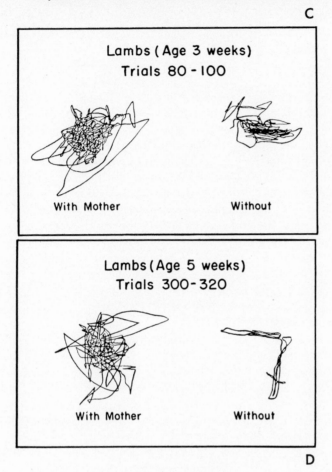

D

FIG. 182 (*Continued*)

was the signal for food and the no-food oval was almost circular, or where without warning all positive conditioned stimuli are made negative and *vice versa*); and thirdly, monotonous repetition of conditioned stimuli according to a rigid temporal pattern (as in the case of our neurotic goats).

More than a decade ago John Whitehorn was employing the experimental interview situation much as Harold Wolff is doing at present. From his study he derived the notion of the acute emotional experience.[4] This fruitful concept, neglected at the time, will, I believe, completely alter current conceptions of Pavlov's conditioned reflex and bring both conditioning and experimental neurosis into effective operational relations with Cannon's emergency hypothesis.

Whitehorn says: "The primary focus of attention in this discussion of emotion is 'the acute emotional experience,' by which I mean to designate a biological condition, characterized subjectively as an excited, tense feeling with considerable tendency to act, but with some uncertainty as to what to do, and characterized objectively by motor restlessness or activity not smoothly patterned, with indications of excess effort as shown in the facial and respiratory musculature, tremor of voice and of skeleto-muscular action. . . .

"The acute emotional experience has, as its biological function, the precipitation of an internal crisis, in which habit is interrupted and the more raw or primitive facilities for biological adjustment are summoned up—not merely sugar for energy production and hastened circulation for increased oxygen use, but also the neural capacities of the organism for forming new associations between reaction and situation and for reorganizing behavior. These latter are the resources which we recognize as intelligence—the capacity for modifying reaction by experience—a capacity which might lie latent and unused if not activated by an emotional experience.

"This idea represents, essentially, an extension of Cannon's emergency hypothesis, somewhat broadened to emphasize the disruptive and the subsequently re-integrative aspects of the emotional event.

"In postulating such a function for the acute emotional experience, one must admit that, in life, its purpose is not always successfully achieved. Inhibitory influences may block the activation of potential resources. By rigid conditions, it is possible, experimentally, to produce predicaments which elicit acute emotional experiences whose resolution is blocked by inhibitory training, and thus to reduce the functional value of emotion, transforming it, so to speak, into the condition of disability and distress which we call *anxiety*, chronic or recurrent."

For purposes of the present discussion I wish to broaden still further Whitehorn's conception to embrace the organism's general alerting function at all intensities and to characterize this sentinel activity of the nervous system as vigilance, borrowing the term from Henry Head.[2]

In our experiments, if a well-conditioned sheep or goat is brought to the laboratory, placed in the restraining harness, and allowed to stand for an hour, even though no signals or shocks are given, its steadily maintained watchfulness or vigilance increases in intensity during the customary period, as shown in one test of a 3-year old "highly educated" ram by a gradual increase in respiratory rate from 41 per minute at the end of five minutes to 135 per minute at the end of the hour.

In addition to the gradual rising of the vigilance level in the absence of the usual signals, each positive or negative conditioned stimulus contributes its own sharp spike of sudden alertness and this we may think of as stimulus-vigilance. Such spikes of stimulus-vigilance we may imagine to decay more and more slowly as the experimental session progresses. Thus the stimulus residues will increase the general intensity level of the background vigilance. When an animal undergoing a regimen of difficult conditioning succumbs to an experimental neurosis we may suppose that its final traumatic reaction to the repeated stress situations of the conditioning laboratory was due to a gradual heightening of the vigilance level from day to day in consequence of the summation of the after-effects of stimulus-vigilance enduring for days, weeks, or months. Finally, an end point or breaking point is reached beyond which the animal's management of its emergency function becomes faulty as indicated by its neurotic manifestations. The intensity of the vigilance level of the day depends then not only upon the total stimulus load, i.e., upon the number, intensity, duration, and temporal spacing of the specific vigilance reactions aroused by the positive and negative conditioned stimuli of the experimental day, but also upon the lingering traces of stimulus-vigilance from previous conditioning sessions.

In conclusion, let us cautiously speculate concerning the relevance of all this for mental health and disease. If, as we have argued here, pavlovian conditioning is primarily concerned with the emotional context of behavior rather than with learning or intelligence, we may define a conditioned reflex as an emotionally charged episode of behavior bracketed between two primitive, stereotyped, forced reactions, viz., the vigilance reaction or what-is-it reflex of Pavlov and the unconditioned reaction to the reinforcement by food or acid in the mouth, or electric shock to a limb. This conditioned reflex is a special case of the emergency reaction of Cannon's cat when barked at by the dog and represents an episode of emergency behavior in response to a stress stimulus in a stressful situation—a situation which arouses a persisting quiet watchfulness on the animal's part.

Does the study of the animal's emotional reaction help us better to understand the intricate patterning of human feeling and emotion in its social setting? If Lashley's view of human and animal emotion is accepted we may answer our question in the affirmative.

Lashley says: "Fundamental patterns of emotional reaction and temperamental types seem to have undergone little change in mammalian evolution. The major changes are rather the result of development of intelligent foresight and the inhibition of action in anticipation of more remote prospects. . . . The changes in the integrative network are most probably quantitative; indeed the difference in behavioral capacity between man and chimpanzee may be no more than the addition of one cell generation in the segmentation of the neuroblasts which form the cerebral network."[3]

REFERENCES

1. FRENCH, T. M., and ALEXANDER, F.: Psychosomatic Medicine Monograph IV, 1941.
2. HEAD, H.: *British Journal of Medical Psychology*, 1923, 14, p. 126.
3. LASHLEY, K. S.: *Quarterly Review of Biology*, 1949, 24, p. 28.
4. WHITEHORN, J. C.: Association for Research in Nervous and Mental Disease, 1939, 19, p. 236.
5. WOLFF, H. G.: In: Feelings and Emotions (ed. M. L. Reymert), p. 284. New York, McGraw-Hill Book Company, 1950.

Postscript to Experimental Induction of Psychoneuroses by Conditioned Reflex
with Stress

W. HORSLEY GANTT, M.D.

In this postscript to the paper of Dr. Liddell (one of the American pioneers in the study of experimental neuroses), I shall add two points: (1) even in the field of higher mental phenomena, behavior can better be explained by laws rather than by anthropomorphism; (2) maladaptation is as inherent in the physiology of the organism as is adaptation, and like adaptation it has its basis on physiologic structures, which are revealed to us by the responses in a given situation.

As an example of the operation of laws, let us take the observation (Liddell, Gantt, Beritov) that the animal is quieter after the shock than after its "negative expectancy" created by giving the positive conditional stimulus without shock. The restlessness that follows non-reenforcement is based upon a general law[1,2] governing the relation between the conditional reflex and the unconditional stimulus from which it is formed. The mechanism involved is, as I have shown, inhibition of the conditional reflex by the unconditional stimulus. Without the reenforcement of the shock or food, the animal is kept agitated and restless for a long time—"in suspense" as we say subjectively. The unconditional stimulus cuts short the conditional reflex activity, initiating a period of quiescence. The reference of this phenomenon to a law gives us a much clearer understanding of what happens than the fruitless attempt to explain the behavior in this situation subjectively—by how we conjecture we would feel and act in such a situation.

The explanation is not related to the nature of the stimulus—whether the unconditional stimulus represents the cessation of a pleasant act (eating) or of a disagreeable sensation (pain of an electric shock),[6] i.e., opposite subjective feelings; in both cases the law is operative; either shock or food inhibits previous conditional reflexes and initiates a quiescent phase during which the animal is free from further excitation—an anabolic, recuperative phase. This may be looked upon as a useful protective mechanism, limiting and even abruptly terminating excitation.

On the other hand, agitation and anxiety may result when the appropriate unconditional stimulus does not follow its conditional reflex. The same law seems to be operative on a higher level, e.g., with goals. The attainment of the goal, from the insects up to man, checks and inhibits all the antecedent related activity, and, as with the following of the conditional reflex by an unconditional stimulus, initiates a period of quiescence. And even though the goal may no longer serve any purpose or may actually be injurious to the interests of the organism, the individual persists almost mechanically (as in a fight against odds) to exhaustion or to inhibition through attainment. The simple prototype of this often noxious activity exists in the relation between conditional reflex and unconditional stimulus—where even a

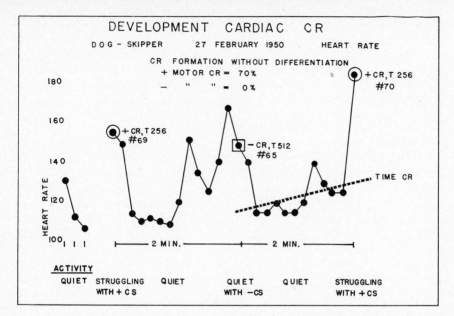

Fig. 183. Early formation of the cardiac conditional reflex without differentiation between the two tones T256+ and T512−.

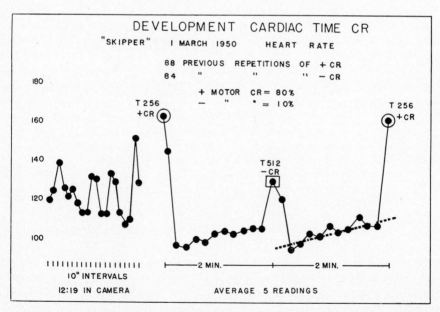

Fig. 184. Control readings of heart rate and beginning differentiation between T256+ and T512−. There is as yet no cardiac time reflex (indicated by the slant of the dotted line).

much more intense conditional reflex than the unconditional stimulus can
be inhibited by the latter.

In the "expectancy reaction" there may also be a time factor. As the dog
becomes conditioned to a regular routine there is first the development of
the conditional reflex to the individual stimulus. Then there gradually
appears what may be described as an "expectancy" reaction, or in more
mechanical terms, a time conditioning.[3] If we follow this through the

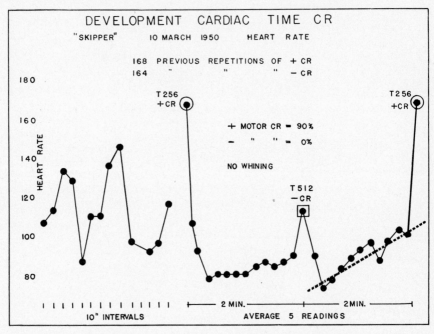

FIG. 185.   Although the control heart rate before any stimulation is marked by
irregularity, there is now, after 168 and 164 repetitions respectively of the two
tones, fairly good differentiation, and a beginning time reflex, indicated by the rise
of the heart rate in the interval *preceding* the excitatory T256+.

cardiac conditional reflex we find that the heart rate goes up at first to the
actual signal for the shock, but that after some scores of repetitions the
heart rate increases not only to the signal but a few seconds before the
conditional signal is accustomed to appear—an anticipatory reaction
expressed in the visceral general responses much more definitely than in
the external movements. Even when there is no rigid time sequence, but
instead a pattern of stimulation, such as that of alternating positive and
negative stimulations, the dog's system becomes set, prepared by previous
stimulation for the one which is to follow.

The following example from the experiments of Dr. Gakenheimer illustrates the development of the cardiac time conditional reflex. The dog

"Skipper" was given two tones, one T256 for three seconds followed by an instantaneous foradic shock to the forepaw, and two minutes later another tone an octave higher (T512) not accompanied by shock; in another two minutes the first tone T256 with shock, then in another two minutes T512 without shock; this routine was repeated daily for ten repetitions of each tone. The animal at first reacts to both tones alike—raising the forepaw, whining, or similar reaction (Fig. 183). Then after about fifty trials he

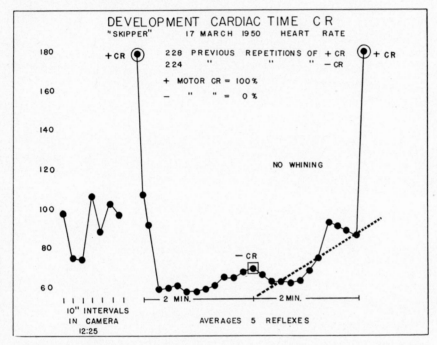

FIG. 186. The differentiation between the two tones, measured both by the heart rate and by the motor conditioned reflexes, is excellent, after 228 repetitions of reinforced T256+. In spite of the developing cardiac time reflex, there are no movements indicative of a time reflex.

begins to show the differentiation between the two tones, lifting his foot to T256 70 per cent of the trials and 0 per cent to T512. On March 1, 1950, "Skipper" shows a beginning differentiation in the heart rate to the two tones, although there is still a rise to T512 which is never accompanied by a shock (Fig. 184). The direction of the dotted line in the figures shows the slight rise in heart rate during the interval between the inhibitory T512 and the excitatory T256. After 168 repetitions of T256 with shock, differentiation between the two tones is improved (90 per cent lifting of paw with T256 and 0 per cent with T512), and there is a beginning of a time reflex, shown by the steady rise in heart rate in the intervals between T512 and T256 (Fig. 185). On March 17, 1950, after 228 repetitions of

T256 and shock, alternated regularly with T512 at two-minute intervals, there is perfect motor differentiation (100 per cent and 0 per cent) as well as cardiac differentiation (180 heart rate to T256 and 65 heart rate to T512); the heart rate in the interval now rises more sharply (Fig. 186), i.e., there is a definite developing time conditional reflex. In Figures 187 and 188, after 298 and 464 repetitions, respectively, of T256 alternated with T512, the cardiac time reflex becomes well established, and there is in addition to

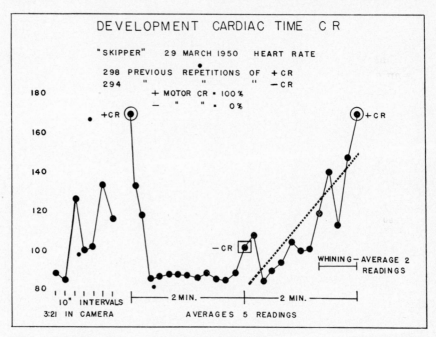

FIG. 187. The time reflex is more marked, shown in the cardiac rise *before* T256+ as well as in the cardiac deceleration *after* T256+. Motor symptoms of anxiety now accompany the rise in heart rate shown by whining and some restlessness a few seconds before T256+.

the rise in heart rate, anticipatory behavior (whining, barking, lifting of the forepaw) in the dog beginning about fifty seconds before each T256.

The above is an example of fine adaptation, inherent in the organism. But there is an opposite maladaptive function also inherent in the physiologic structure. This maladaptation of dysfunction rests upon (1) the rigidity of the organism for unlearning as the environment changes, and (2) a special split between two functions—between the less evident visceral reactions and the more obvious external movements; the former are usually hidden from observation, the latter are open to conscious inspection.

First let us look at the function of retention of learned responses.[5] These are made as adaptations to the environment—the organism conserves energy; it does not have to relearn each time the situation recurs. From conditional reflex studies in puppies and in children we know that the young learn much quicker but also forget quicker, but that with increasing age the adult learns more slowly while retaining more stably the already formed conditional reflexes and that as age increases learning tends to be replaced almost entirely by the retention of past, often inappropriate responses. The retention becomes maladaptive and pernicious, converting

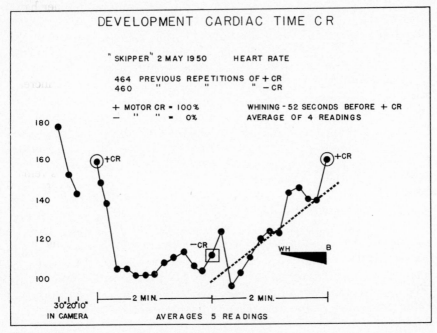

Fig. 188.   The same as Fig. 187 except that the motor and anxiety movements are more marked and accompanied by barking. The time reflex is now evident in the cardiac rate, the specific leg lifting and in the "anxiety-like" "anticipatory" reactions.

an adult from a once plastic organism into a rigid structure housing a museum of antiquities, containing the antique reactions to past stimulations no longer operative. (As I myself advance in this adult category, I console myself that in our culture a good museum is highly prized!)

For the luxury of these fine, adaptive, acquired, cortical responses we pay heavily—through the function of retention of the unuseful as well as the useful. In psychiatry we attempt to relieve our patients of this cortical rigidity through shock therapy and modern operative technics of varying degrees of decerebration.

Besides the rigidity through cortical retention of once adaptive responses there is another maladaptation based on an inherent split between the general visceral emotional and the specific responses. The visceral reactions are especially rigid; they persist long after the external adaptation for conforming to the changed environment has dropped out; this split represents an inner maladaptation. There is evidence in my work that these general visceral reactions are never good adaptations, that the most efficient adaptations take place without this preparatory state—and most probably without the "emergency" reaction of Cannon. The visceral responses react excessively to the needs of the situation; the mobilization of energy is not required for the act, which is usually performed better without the emotional response.[4]

The following example will illustrate this difference between the emotional (less adaptive) and the specific (better adaptive) responses. In the conditional reflex training, the cardiac and respiratory reactions often appear long before the more specific movement (withdrawal of the foot to the pain signal) or secretion (salivation to the food signal). On the other hand, these emotional components, increased heart rate and respiration in the presence of the signal, are difficult to eliminate. In one dog, whose motor and secretory components of the reflex to the food signal were destroyed after a day or two of repeating the signal without food, the cardiac increase to a signal persisted even for a year after the specific component had dropped out. Thus the animal was in good adaptation judging by the external aspects of the behavior (movement and secretion), but maladaptive in the emotional components, measured by the heart rate. There is much other evidence from the clinic that the emotional components remain or even increase (as they did in my neurotic dog Nick[2]) long after the situation has passed, and perhaps when it has long been forgotten.

The understanding of our *schizokinesis* * (split function) is as important as the recognition of our marvelous adaptive capacity in helping us to cope more successfully with our changing environment.

REFERENCES

1. GANTT, W. HORSLEY: *American Journal of Physiology*, 1941, 133, p. 286.
2. GANTT, W. HORSLEY: Experimental Basis for Neurotic Behavior, p. 212. New York, Paul B. Hoeber, Inc., 1944.
3. GANTT, W. HORSLEY: *Transactions of the American Neurological Association*, 1946, p. 166.
4. GANTT, W. HORSLEY: *Bulletin of the Johns Hopkins Hospital*, 1948, 82, p. 416.
5. GANTT, W. HORSLEY, and TRAUGOTT, URSULA: *American Journal of Physiology*, 1949, 159, p. 569.
6. MUNCIE, WENDELL, and GANTT, W. HORSLEY: *American Journal of Physiology*, 1938, 123, p. 152.

* *Schizokinesis* has been suggested to me by my collaborator Dr. John E. Peters as a more accurate term than the general one *dysfunction* which I formerly used for this phenomenon.

CHAPTER 30

Experimental Induction of Psychoneuroses by Starvation

ANCEL KEYS, PH.D.

A DISCUSSION of the induction of psychoneurosis by starvation might properly begin with definitions of both starvation and psychoneurosis.

The classification of abnormal mental states and of patients with mental disease tends to bewilder the neophyte and to exasperate the expert. It is difficult to define and to recognize the precise boundaries between normality and psychoneurosis and between psychoneurosis and psychosis. Others must judge as to what label is most appropriate for the behavior and mental characteristics to be discussed presently.

The classification of psychiatrists is, perhaps, simpler than that of their patients. Since there are basic differences in the prevailing general viewpoints in psychiatry, and since observations on starving men may have some relevance to these viewpoints, it may be useful to examine the doctors before the patients.

Professional workers who deal with mental disease may be placed generally into two categories. The majority of practicing psychiatrists appear to regard the body as merely a vehicle or residence in which the mind pursues its own way to health or disease with relative independence from the state or history of the body. With the exception of gross trauma to the brain itself, they are inclined to recognize no physical factor as important in the etiology or in the treatment of the major psychoses and psychoneuroses. These psychodynamicists point to the long succession of failures to explain or to cure their patients on a physical basis and to their own occasional remarkable success with a purely psychologic approach.

On the other hand, there are the organicists, those experts who see or suspect, mostly the latter, an important physical aspect in mental disease— as cause or at least as a major influence. If nothing else, the organicist, without differentiating cause and effect, is unremitting in his search for physical peculiarities which may accompany mental disease.

As I see it, the present Symposium is devoted to an examination of the evidence for the organicist without necessarily espousing the exclusive validity of the organic concept. In the general medical world there is lately much interest in psychosomatics and this is enthusiastically aided and abetted by all psychiatrists. And I think most medical scientists agree that it is valuable to recognize the influence of mind on body. But here the opposite direction of interrelationship, the influence of body on the mind, is more properly under scrutiny. Somatopsychics must not be neglected. I propose to discuss as an example of somatopsychics the effects on the mental state of alteration in the calorie nutritional state of the body.

Constitutional Types

A statistical correlation between mental and bodily characteristics does not necessarily mean or imply any direct causal relation between them in either direction. Throughout the centuries the "constitutionalists" have said that both mental and bodily characteristics depend on the basic constitution.

W. H. Sheldon explicitly states two premises: (1) structure is fixed and immutable, and (2) "behavior is a function of structure." His latest book is entitled: "*Varieties of Delinquent Youth, an Introduction to Constitutional Psychiatry.*" In his writings there is very little if any suggestion of a functional interplay between mind and body. One looks in vain for physiologic mechanisms. Sheldon and similar constitutionalists are neither organicists nor psychodynamicists, as I see it.

Calorie Status and Personality

Popular belief, powerfully reinforced by the stereotypes repeatedly portrayed in creative literature, contrasts the fat with the thin person in regard to all aspects of the personality—behavior, attitude, and tendency to disease. There is actually not much scientific evidence at hand, but I suppose we should all agree as to the general truth of the popular differentiation between the fat and the lean. We may concede, with George Bernard Shaw, that some facts are known before they are discovered "scientifically."

In any case, for the "explanation" of a fat man, there are three possibilities corresponding to the schools of thought already mentioned. From the standpoint of psychosomatics, and probably that of most psychiatrists, the physical state of fatness would be ascribed to eating habits which reflect the emotional state. The constitutionalist, perhaps, would say that the man in question has a "fat and jolly constitution." And the organicist, speaking for the viewpoint of somatopsychics, would explain the personality of the fat man as a reflection of the accumulated effects of overeating. The lean and emaciated person would provoke a similar set of answers.

Now the first two of these three "explanations" assume that man is a completely free agent in regard to his calorie intake and balance. This assumption is unwarranted for a large portion of the world's population at all times and is manifestly absurd whenever there are general food shortages. The pressure of social custom may operate in the direction opposite to that of food shortage; I suspect that many a fat man is a victim of his social milieu though he may not struggle much for release. The art of cookery consists, in large part, in deceiving and titillating the palate so that more food is eaten than is either needed or actually wanted. Finally, allowance must be made for the tendency of the body to adjust and to stabilize itself to prevent change. Let us say that a protracted period of illness or of remarkable cookery and food supplies have made a person lean or fat, as the case may be; there is a tendency thereafter for the person to stay that way—the appetite tends to become adjusted to the prevailing calorie level of habit unless this is too far from metabolic balance.

The position of the organicist, on the other hand, is that psychic alteration follows physical change and the major problem becomes that of discovering the nature and extent of psychic alterations which proceed from definite physical situations.

Starvation, Undernutrition, and Habitual Emaciation

The physical situation of starvation and undernutrition is, unhappily, one of widespread occurrence. Famine, poverty, and many illnesses provoke the situation in which the bodily stores of fat and glycogen are depleted and the body consumes itself. The physical consequences of this are numerous and far-reaching; their description and discussion constitutes the major part of our recent treatise, "*The Biology of Human Starvation.*"

It is a striking fact that whatever may be the cause of inadequate calorie intake, the physical consequences are much the same. But here we must differentiate between the active state of starving and the maintained state of undernutrition. Two very thin persons, one having become that way recently and the other being habitually thin, may have identical body compositions but physiologically (and psychologically) there are great differences. The starving man has a low basal metabolic rate, bradycardia, arterial and venous hypotension, polyuria, hypothermia, great muscular weakness, and anemia. The equally thin man whose starvation is long past and who is now habitually in calorie balance, apparently presents none of these characteristics in any marked degree.

The transition between active starvation and maintained emaciation deserves special study and our knowledge of the physiology of persons who differ in regard to the habitual level of emaciation-obesity is most inadequate, but it is clear enough that calorie imbalance is very different from maintenance of balance at high or low levels.

Our evidence from the Minnesota Experiment on the personality in relation to nutritional status is confined to active starvation and to active repletion in rehabilitation. The situation in different habitual states of calorie nutrition may be more important but is beyond our present province and knowledge. Here it is enough to say that just as the physiology of active starvation differs from chronically maintained undernutrition, so may we expect psychologic differences, differences in behavior and emotion, in these different nutritional situations.

The Minnesota Experiment

The Minnesota Experiment consisted primarily of a detailed study of thirty-six "normal" young men during three months of control on a good diet, six months of semistarvation on a diet of the European famine type, and in subsequent months of nutritional rehabilitation. In the semistarvation period the men lost about one fourth of their previous body weight and developed all the classical signs of severe semistarvation.

There were no other abnormal physical stresses besides those imposed by the nutritional level. The men were comfortably housed and clothed, had a fixed program of moderate physical activity, were under constant medical supervision, and were provided with a friendly social environment. They were substantially free of apprehension about permanent injury from the experiment. All of them had the satisfaction of participation in work which they believed would be of general value to mankind. Their voluntary continuation in the experiment presumably met their avowed desire to make personal sacrifices for the common good and to match, in a way, the contribution of their classmates in the military services.

Purely psychologic stresses, however, were not absent from the experiment. There was, firstly, the separation from home and family; in most cases this did not seem to be very important. Secondly, there was the continuing problem of the position of the conscientious objector; this was mitigated by their sense of contribution by way of the Minnesota Experiment and did not seem to be of much consequence for most of the men. Finally, there was the strain of continuous self-discipline and control in the experiment itself.

Although the men were under close supervision, their acceptance of the entire experiment was voluntary and each man could at any time escape from the rigors of the diet and its attendant bodily sensations. They could, so to speak, "walk out" of the experiment with no consequence other than being returned to their former activities in Civilian Public Service camps. In this fact there was created a conflict between mind and body which was unquestionably troublesome to some of the men. But the outcome is significant; with the exception of two men who were withdrawn from the experiment at an early stage, the group came through with remarkably well-maintained cooperation and fidelity to the program.

Tests in the Minnesota Experiment

The tests and measurements applied to these young men were very numerous and only those items of relevance to the present discussion can be mentioned here. It will help to indicate, firstly, some important items of the total personality and functional capacity which did not change.

Rather elaborate efforts to appraise the intellective functions, as represented by various speed, power, and information tests of "intelligence," disclosed no change in intellective capacity at any time. However, ordinary intellective performance in day-to-day life was markedly affected. Voluntary intellective effort in non-test situations was progressively diminished in starvation. It was "too much bother" to think or to engage in reading, conversation, or writing which demanded mental concentration and effort.

There was, likewise, no loss in the capacity of the special senses. Visual acuity, color discrimination, and other visual functions were unimpaired. Auditory acuity actually improved slightly during semistarvation and returned to the control value in rehabilitation.

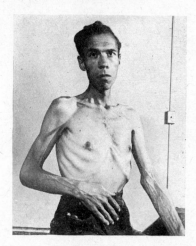

FIG. 189.

The results of several tests widely used in psychiatry and psychology were negative. Nothing of significance emerged at any time from the Rorschach test or from the Rosenzweig frustration test.

In contrast to these negative findings were the majority of the physical tests and measurements, the personality inventories such as the Minnesota Multiphasic Personality Inventory, the results of the analysis of personal diaries and interviews, and the observed behavior.

The results of the physical tests and measurements, which covered morphology, biochemistry, physiology, and physical responses to physical stresses such as exercise, showed great homogeneity in the responses of the individual subjects to the alterations in nutritional status. Moreover, these findings appeared to be closely similar to the results of "natural" semistarvation as seen in famine areas and in prison camps.

There were, likewise, marked tendencies for behavioral changes to follow uniform patterns resembling those reported from natural starvation. There was, however, considerable individual variation in the behavior and emotional changes and the differences between individuals in these respects were accentuated as the stress of semistarvation progressed. This fact was attested to by the scores of the Minnesota Multiphasic Personality Inventory as well as by simple observation of behavior.

Some Findings in the Minnesota Experiment

A reduction of the calorie intake to somewhat less than half that normally required for balance produced a progressive loss of weight which proceeded at a diminishing rate as time went on. At the end of twenty-four weeks there was little further weight change and a new metabolic balance point

TABLE 53. SELF RATINGS OF THE SUBJECTS IN THE MINNESOTA EXPERIMENT
Mean values for thirty-two men for the pre-starvation control (C), for twelve and for twenty-four weeks of semistarvation (S12 and S24)

Symptom	C	S12	S24
Depression	0	.69	1.38
Moodiness	0	.84	1.50
Irritability	0	1.31	1.81
Apprehension	−.03	.34	.41
Apathy	0	1.09	1.81
Sensitivity to noise	0	1.31	1.81
Ambition	0	−1.19	−1.75
Self-discipline	0	−.56	−1.72
Mental alertness	0	−.84	−1.53
Concentration	0	−.91	−1.66
Comprehension	0	−.44	−1.03

Ratings: Normal 0, and deviations from normal:
More 1, some more 2, much more 3, very much more 4, extremely much more 5.
Less−1, some less−2, much less−3, very much less−4, extremely much less−5.

was being approximated. The explanation of this adjustment is interesting but is beside the present inquiry.

During this time the men became not only progressively emaciated, but increasingly quiet, somber, apathetic, and slow in motion. Thinness alone does not account for the characteristic facies. Many others have agreed with us that all starved men look alike and that the uniformity of expression accounts for this more than anything else. The appearance of the face alone suggests depression and world-weariness even more than it does emaciation and tissue atrophy (Fig. 189). Famine victims everywhere exhibit much the same facial appearance and this is not to be confused with the expressions of pain, of anger, of fear, or of confusion.

If we attempt to probe into the starved person's evaluation of himself, either by questionnaire or by psychiatric interview, we find alterations which are, on the whole, consonant with his appearance. The starved man states that he is depressed, moody, apathetic, that he is not alert mentally and has lost ambition (Table 53). His self-judgment of inability to concentrate and to comprehend is explained by his assertion that he finds nothing interesting except questions of food and eating.

One somewhat surprising point is the recognition of increased irritability by the starved man. This is surprising because there is little or no indication of this in the overt behavior. But the explanation is forthcoming from the

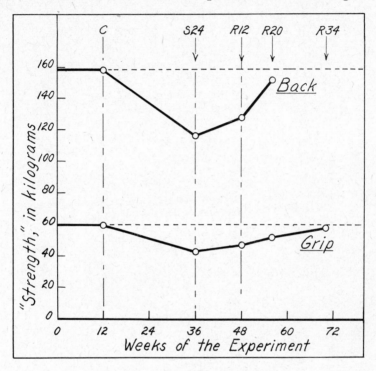

Fig. 190.

starved man himself. He explains that he is frequently moved to inward rage, for example, but neither says nor does anything about it because "it is too much trouble."

The starving man conserves energy in every possible way, both consciously and unconsciously. His own sense of diminishing strength, and particularly of diminishing physical endurance, is a constant reminder to avoid effort, and a conditioned reflex is soon established, much as a sore foot produces a limp.

In the Minnesota Experiment the loss of strength for a single brief effort was roughly proportional to the estimated changed muscle mass. Simple strength in hand grip and in back lift decreased 25 to 35 per cent in semistarvation (Fig. 190). The decline in the capacity for continued effort was much more extreme. Depending on the method of estimation and of calculation, the loss in muscular endurance was from 70 to 90 per cent (Fig. 191). These changes in strength and endurance were clearly reflected in the behavior. The reluctance to make even the most trivial movement becomes, in effect, a delay and lack of vigor in all responses. This could well explain the slowness in responding to questions which conveys an impression of mental dullness, although purely mental apathy probably also plays a role.

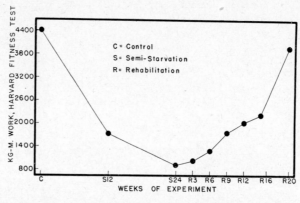

FIG. 191.

Evidence for Neurosis

Nothing said so far would justify the label of neurosis for these men. Evidence for neurosis was afforded from two sources: (1) Results in the Minnesota Multiphasic Personality Inventory (MMPI) and (2) the details of behavior and the findings in psychiatric interviews.

The mean profile in the MMPI showed entirely normal T scores on all scales before starvation, a marked rise during starvation in the neurosis triad of hysteria, depression, and hypochondriasis, and these changes were roughly proportional to the extent of weight loss as the experiment continued (Fig. 192). There was a full return to normal on nutritional rehabilitation. On the average the starvation T scores for depression and for hypochondriasis were above 70, that is, more than two standard deviations beyond the normal mean. But the scores for the scales of psychosis, those on the right-hand side of the MMPI profile, showed essentially no real change at any time.

The individual profiles in the MMPI tell much the same story. Almost without exception the greatest change in starvation was in the depression score where values of 70 to 80 were common. Scores above 60 in the "psychosis" scales were infrequent and scores above 70 in these scales were very rare.

Time does not permit a discussion of the findings in the individuals. Case

records of nine of the men who most clearly developed neurotic behavior
and ideas have been summarized elsewhere by Schiele and Brozek.[8]

Four men showed a character neurosis, which included inability to maintain their former standards of morals and honesty. One man had sensory
and motor disturbances of an hysterical nature. One man twice indulged
in self-mutilation. Many of the men increasingly engaged in daydreaming,
with fanciful ideas mainly about or related to food. Many of the men began

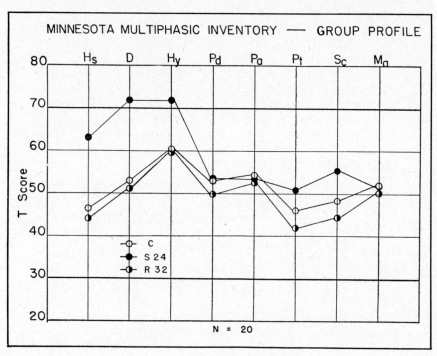

Fig. 192.

to collect and to hoard any items at hand, and some of the men were disturbed that they could not resist acquiring useless "junk."

Bizarre behavior in connection with food was almost universal and often
took the form of compulsive action or of ritual. Some of this behavior was
obviously motivated by desire to increase food satisfaction—plate licking,
"souping" everything with water, eating extremely slowly and arranging
the food in fantastic ways. Other peculiar behavior and ideas were likewise
indicative of obsessions about food—resentment of fat people, compulsions
to look in garbage cans, refusal to talk at meals, and the like. All of these
attitudes about food may be considered relatively reasonable under the
circumstances, though the casual onlooker would be mystified, for example.
by the expression of anger provoked by a simple joke about food.

All of the peculiarities of idea and behavior observed in the Minnesota

Experiment are represented in observations made on victims of "natural" starvation in famine areas and in prison camps. In the main, the personality and psychologic tendencies in semistarvation present a pattern common to famine victims and to the subjects in the Minnesota Experiment. Besides obsession with food, the outstanding features are depression, apathy, progressive narrowing of interests and of the area of social consciousness, and increasing irritability without physical expression.

Rehabilitation

During rehabilitation there was a general return toward normality which was, however, not simply a reversal of the changes in starvation. Perhaps the most interesting feature was the outward manifestation of irritability previously well concealed. It appeared as though the beginning of a return of strength and of well-being released the inhibitions to overt action. The Minnesota subjects were far more troublesome to the staff and to each other in the first weeks of rehabilitation than at any time in actual starvation. Again, there are striking parallels to observations made in natural starvation. Eventually, however, the neurotic tendencies regressed and at the end of a year there were few traces left. Some of the men had considerable persistent difficulty in achieving a normal attitude toward food and compulsive overeating was common for many months or even years in some of the men.

We have placed much reliance on the Minnesota Multiphasic Personality Inventory in our analysis. The question can be raised, however, whether the scores in the MMPI have the same meaning with physically abnormal as with physically normal people. To answer this question, an analysis was made of the items in the MMPI scales for hysteria, depression, and hypochondriasis. The items on these scales were separated into four categories— somatic, psychic, corrective, and subtle. Analysis was then made to determine whether the items contributing to the observed elevated scores in the semistarved subjects were the same items which contribute to the high scores of neurotic patients without physical abnormality. The percentage frequencies of the several categories were strikingly similar in the two groups (see Brozek and Erickson[2]). There were no fundamental differences between the kind of answers given by the semistarved subjects and those given by patients with a clinical diagnosis of psychoneurosis.

Conclusion

The general conclusion from all of the foregoing is that simple semistarvation, without unusual psychic stress, can produce changes in personality which correspond to mild to moderate psychoneurosis as customarily defined. The extent of this change varied from individual to individual in the Minnesota Experiment and these individual differences were not predicted from detailed psychologic and psychiatric analysis of the individuals before starvation. *Ex post facto*, explanations of some of the differences in the responses of the individuals could be advanced but such rationalization is not useful.

REFERENCES

1. BROZEK, J.: *Scientific Monthly*, 1950, 70, pp. 270-274.
2. BROZEK, J., and ERICKSON, N. K.: *Journal of Consulting Psychology*, 1948, 12, pp. 403-411.
3. BROZEK, J., and SCHIELE, B. C.: *American Journal of Psychiatry*, 1948, 105, pp. 259-266.
4. FRANKLIN, J. C., and BROZEK, J.: *Journal of Consulting Psychology*, 1949, 13, pp. 293-301.
5. FRANKLIN, J. C., SCHIELE, B. C., BROZEK, J., and KEYS, A.: *Journal of Clinical Psychology*, 1948, 4, pp. 28-45.
6. KEYS, A.: *Science*, 1950, 112, pp. 371-373.
7. KEYS, A.; BROZEK, J.; HENSCHEL, A.; MICKELSEN, O.; and TAYLOR, H. L.: The Biology of Human Starvation, 2 vols., 1426 pp. Minneapolis, Univ. Minnesota Press, 1950.
8. SCHIELE, B. C., and BROZEK, J.: *Psychosomatic Medicine*, 1948, 10, pp. 31-50.
9. SHELDON, W. H.: Varieties of Delinquent Youth, an Introduction to Constitutional Psychiatry. New York, Harper & Brothers, 1949.

Observations in German Concentration Camps

LLOYD J. THOMPSON, M.D.

Two German concentration camps were visited soon after they were liberated by Allied Armies. One was a Polish slave camp at Ohrdruf near Gotha and the other was the notorious camp at Dachau.

The Ohrdruf camp was visited about the middle of April, 1945, on the day after it was liberated. Unfortunately, very little information could be obtained from the remaining inhabitants because of language difficulties and because very few prisoners remained. Near the entrance to the camp were about twenty bodies lying as if they had fallen after standing in line. It was observed that each body had a bullet hole in the back of the head. Not far away in a wooden shed were approximately fifty extremely emaciated bodies piled up like cordwood. They had not been dead over two or three days. The emaciation was quite extreme.

On May 13, 1945, five days after V-E Day, the concentration camp at Dachau was visited. Permission was obtained to enter the inner prison camp and visit the prison hospital. This camp, originally built for 6000 people, contained between 30,000 and 40,000 prisoners at the time of the visit. It was learned that as the Allies advanced from both sides in Germany, Himmler would order prisoners from other camps sent to this area. A copy of the final order written by Himmler and dated April 14, 1945 was seen. Among other things it stated that no prisoners would be allowed to fall into enemy hands alive. The crematory with its four ovens still in use and the gas chamber were seen, and there was no doubt about the function of either.

In the inner prison hospital there were two doctors who had carried on valuable medical service during several years of confinement in this camp. One of these men, from Yugoslavia, spoke English very well and at one time had studied preventive medicine in the United States. It was observed that in the entire camp only the doctors and other hospital workers retained an interest in work and were active in a constructive way.

At the time of the visit there were about 800 cases of typhus and about 1000 cases of tuberculosis in the hospital. Malnutrition was a very serious problem, deaths from this cause being frequent, according to the attending doctors. In the preceding weeks there had been many cases of peripheral neuritis which the doctors attributed to vitamin deficiency. However, pellagra was rare and central nervous system involvement such as occurs in pellagra had not been noted. Also, no instances of Korsakoff's psychosis or other syndromes which might be related to vitamin deficiency affecting the central nervous system could be remembered. Careful inquiry into the existence of true prison psychoses brought only negative answers. Suicides or attempts to commit suicide had not been frequent and the doctors thought that the incidence of mental disease had been about what might be expected in a similar group living as ordinary citizens.

The outstanding thing the doctors had noted long before was the increasing inertia which overtook almost all prisoners in time. (Hospital workers seemed to be the exception to this.) New prisoners would attempt to keep up interest and activities but before long the inertia would overtake them. It was practically impossible to arouse interest and prisoners were of very little help about the camp, outside of the hospital. The inertia was evident at the time of the visit. At noon time on a pleasant day men were lying prone on the ground everywhere and practically none were moving about. Perhaps the state of nutrition contributed a large share in this state. The serving of one meal to the hospital patients was observed but the contents of the one course could not be adequately ascertained. It appeared to be a rather thick gruel in which there were some objects that certainly were not made of meat. The doctors themselves did not know exactly what the meal consisted of, and they expressed the opinion that outside of the hospital the diet might not be so good, although they were not certain about this.

Upon leaving this inner prison hospital, observation was made of two large wagons hauling very emaciated bodies toward the crematory. Apparently these bodies came from outside of the hospital. Bodies were observed stacked high near the crematory furnaces and these bodies were extremely emaciated and somewhat discolored.

It was reported by the hospital doctors that with the coming of the liberating army before V-E Day the camp seemed to come to life rather suddenly and there was considerable elation and activity for a very short time. This was followed by a letdown in spirits with increasing suspicion and anxiety for personal safety. Frequently when attempts were made to remove seriously ill patients from the prison hospital to our Army evacuation hospitals nearby there would be terror and struggling because the patients thought that they might be taken away to be tortured to death as they claimed had happened to friends in the past.

The foregoing report was presented at the Inner-Allied Conference on War Medicine in London in June, 1945. At that conference others gave experience in some of the other concentration camps.

For example, Professor Richet of France who was a prisoner in the Buchenwald Camp for about two years, gave some pertinent points. He stated that in 1944 the diet for the prisoners consisted of 1750 calories per day, and these prisoners were supposed to work. Later this caloric content was lowered to 1050 calories per day. The diet usually consisted of 1 liter of soup, 500 Gm. of bread, and 25 Gm. of margarine. On this most prisoners lost from 20 to 40 kilograms. General weakness developed and the blood pressure became lower. Professor Richet, who apparently had access to autopsy materials, stated that myocarditis was always found. However, he made no mention of central nervous system involvement.

Colonel F. M. Lipscomb of the Royal Army Medical Corps told about his experiences at the Belsen Camp. He found definite evidence about the diet from January, 1945, to April, 1945. This consisted of 300 Gm. of bread and vegetable soup with some kind of root vegetables. The total amounted to 800 calories per day. There was meat brought in occasionally, but it went to the kitchen help and their special friends. There was no food for five days before the camp was liberated, and then when food was brought in they found that the prisoners were being overfed. The outstanding diseases found among the prisoners were (1) deficiency diseases, (2) typhus, and (3) pulmonary tuberculosis. The deficiency diseases were the major problem and were found in at least 60 per cent of all patients admitted to a hospital, or roughly 8000 cases.

Colonel Lipscomb divided the deficiency diseases into two groups. The first showed extreme emaciation with lowering of bodily and mental processes resulting in prostration, apathy, and grossly impaired digestive function. The majority of these were definitely dehydrated. The second group showed edema in addition to some of the above symptoms. The edema often became more pronounced when fluid was given to relieve dehydration.

Diarrhea was common and was aggravating to the dehydration. Anemia was a secondary feature of the starvation. The effect of heat was noted. On two hot days many who were improving collapsed.

No clear-cut specific vitamin deficiency syndromes such as beriberi or scurvy could be definitely found. In certain persons with diarrhea, a raw red tongue, skin pigmentation, and mental changes suggested nicotinic acid deficiency, but no cases of classical pellagra were encountered.

Cases of actual psychosis, excluding the infective toxic cases and well-developed cases of psychoneurosis, were less common than one would expect in an average community of the same size, probably because the subjects had not survived the conditions in the camp.

Loss of normal moral standards and sense of responsibility for the welfare of others was widespread; evidently the instinct to survive alone remained even to the extent of eating human flesh. These psychologic changes were proportional to the degree of starvation. Recovery of normal behavior ran parallel with improvement of bodily health and was often surprisingly rapid, leaving only a feeling akin to that of having had a bad dream.

Discussion

A. FERRARO, M.D. AND LEON ROIZIN, M.D.

In experimental total inanition in cats[1] as well as partial chronic inanition in rats subjected to essential amino acid deficiencies,[2, 3] we have observed some reversible and irreversible structural alterations of the cerebrospinal and neurovegetative systems and of some endocrine glands. Similar morphologic changes of the nervous system were observed also in experimental B_1 avitaminosis.

In the light of experimental and clinical evidence concerning the close correlation between some morphologic changes and functional disorders of the nervous system, and in view of the fact that psychoneurotic symptoms are considered expression of a functional disorder though associated at times with neurovegetative imbalance and metabolic changes of endocrine origin, one might speculate upon the following considerations:

1. That the psychoneurotic manifestations reported by the authors following nutritional deficiencies might have resulted from primary psychogenic conflicts and that the somatic changes induced by starvation or avitaminosis may have merely complicated the original situation.

2. That the psychoneurotic manifestations might have been facilitated or precipitated by organic changes in the course of inanition or vitamin deficiency. The somatic changes of the central nervous system, of the autonomic nervous system, and of the endocrine glands might constitute the primary dysfunction followed by psychoneurotic manifestations.

In support of this view we present illustrations of morphologic changes of the nervous system and endocrine glands in experimental starvation and in amino acid deficiencies. Figure 193 illustrates the histologic appearance of the normal glandular structure in a normal control rat. Note the presence

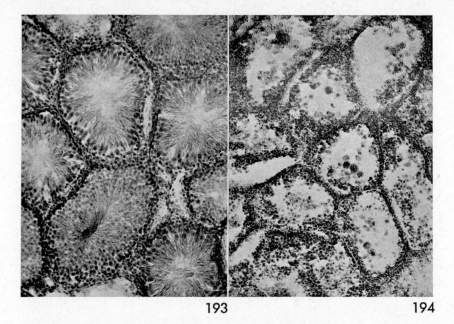

193   194

Fig. 193. Testicular tissue from a normal control rat. Fig. 194. Severe degeneration of testicular organization in a rat maintained on tryptophane-deficient diet. Hematoxylin and eosin stain. High-power magnification.

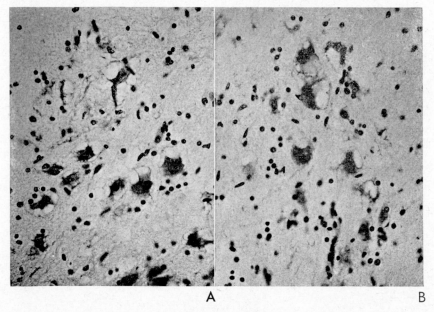

A   B

Fig. 195. Severe changes in cytoplasm of the nerve cells in a rat maintained on a valine-deficient diet. A and B were taken from different levels of the spinal cord. Nissl stain. High-power magnification.

of a large number of spermatozoa. Figure 194 shows severe degeneration of the testicular organization with complete absence of spermatozoa in a rat maintained on a prolonged tryptophane-deficient diet. Figure 195 illustrates severe changes and vacuolization of the cytoplasm of the nerve cells, marked satellitosis and neuronophagia (lumbar enlargement of spinal cord) in a rat maintained on prolonged valine-deficient diet.

3. That the psychoneurotic manifestations may be the expression of the interplay and interdependence between structure and function in the sense of somatopsychic integrations. Consequently the organic changes could not be considered either a cause or a complication of the psychoneurosis but the expression of the ever-present interplay between function and structure, i.e., a part and parcel of the physiodynamics of every function. Excessive functioning or insufficient functioning may lead to pathologic manifestations (somatic and mental).

REFERENCES

1. FERRARO, A., and ROIZIN, L.: *Journal of Neuropathology and Experimental Neurology,* 1942, 1, p. 81.
2. FERRARO, A., and ROIZIN, L.: *Archives of Ophthalmology,* 1947, 38, p. 31.
3. FERRARO, A., and ROIZIN, L.: *Journal of Neuropathology and Experimental Neurology,* 1947, 6, p. 383.

CHAPTER 31

Experimental Induction of Psychoneuroses Through Restriction of Intake of Thiamine

RUSSELL M. WILDER, M.D.

THE EARLY abnormalities from insufficiency of thiamine are changes in attitude and behavior, notably depression, anxiety, irritability, and uncertainty of memory. Disturbances of sensation such as formication, paresthesia, and increased sensitivity to noise and to painful stimuli follow, and appearing after these, are loss of tendon reflexes and paralysis.

Such were the observations made in Rochester, Minnesota, between 1939 and 1942[16-19] in an investigation of patients deprived of this vitamin. The subjects were women, young to middle-aged inmates of the Rochester State Hospital, whom the psychiatric staff regarded as "recovered" from the acute phases of their mental illnesses. The subjects all possessed fair intelligence and were cooperative. The complication introduced by their psychiatric abnormalities was minimized by plans which made each subject her own control. The long period of deficiency of thiamine was preceded in each instance by a long period of observation and followed by an after-period of sufficient length to permit complete recovery from the abnormalities developing in the period during which intake of thiamine was restricted. Rigid control of the environment was maintained in a locked-off section of the hospital with continuous attendance of nurses and dietitians. The diet was analyzed for its content of thiamine and was arranged to be adequate with respect to calories and to all micronutrients except thiamine. In one series of observations the allowance of thiamine approximated 450 micrograms a day. The ten subjects in the preliminary period were asymptomatic, well-adjusted, congenial, industrious, efficient, and vigorous. Some weeks after the thiamine was restricted to 450 micrograms they were neglecting their work and followed instructions poorly. They became forgetful, irritable, quarrelsome, apathetic, confused, depressed, restless, and anxious. In the end, but not until after many weeks, symptoms and minimal signs of peripheral neuropathy developed in some but not in all subjects. These disappeared gradually as did the mental symptoms when the allowance of thiamine was increased.

In these early Rochester investigations measurement of psychologic abnormality was not attempted. However, in 1942, O'Shea, Elsom, and Higbe[10] reported on such measurements on four middle-aged nonpsychotic women in a ward of the Philadelphia General Hospital. As controls four other women were equated with them with respect to age, intelligence, and socioeconomic levels. The latter were employees of the hospital and consumed the hospital diet to which they were accustomed. The diet of the four patients under investigation was deficient not only in thiamine but in other vitamins of the vitamin B complex. The psychologic testing was done at the conclusion of the period of deficiency, at the end of a period of supplementation with thiamine alone, and again after a period of supplementation with the vitamin B complex as a whole. One test only gave significant results. This was the Porteus Maze Scale. According to it performance was impaired during the period of deficient intake of vitamin B complex and improved after treatment with thiamine. The subsequent addition of the whole vitamin B complex was without additional effect.

In 1941, Guetzkow and Brozek[6] restricted the intake of thiamine of eight normal young men and measured their psychomotor skills, mental efficiency, and personality. No abnormalities of significance were found until the allowance of thiamine per 1000 calories of the diet was more rigidly restricted than had been necessary to provoke effects in Rochester. The difference was explained by the larger intake of calories. However, with more severe restriction marked deterioration was observed affecting psychomotor functions but not mental efficiency.

In the meantime a more prolonged and very elaborate study of thiamine was carried out in the Elgin State Hospital at Elgin, Illinois, by Horwitt, Liebert, Kreisler, and Wittman.[7] Support and supervision of their project was provided by a committee of the Food and Nutrition Board of the National Research Council, of which committee I was chairman at the time. The primary interest was in the biochemical effects of the deficiency induced, but psychologic measurements were also obtained.

In this investigation at Elgin which extended from June, 1943, to August, 1946, a period longer than that of any previous study of the kind, twelve male patients, five young and seven aged, selected from the inmates of the hospital, were continuously maintained on a diet which provided 400 micrograms of thiamine and 800 micrograms of riboflavin a day. The allowance of thiamine was estimated to be something less but nevertheless approaching the requirement for this vitamin, and biochemical evidence of insufficiency with respect to thiamine developed in the course of the study. Neurologic abnormalities, such as loss of tendon reflexes and changed vibration sense, also were observed as time went on. Additional persons, five young and eight old men, received the same diet as the others but it was supplemented with yeast, thereby providing an adequate supply of thiamine. Fifteen other subjects who subsisted on the hospital diet were used as additional controls.

At the end of the second year of this study at Elgin some of the members of the committee noted abnormalities in the experimental patients whose intake of thiamine and riboflavin was restricted. These they attributed to deficiency of thiamine. However, the committee as a whole was not convinced, and so the group of men who up to then had been receiving yeast were deprived of yeast and given a diet which provided only 200 micrograms of thiamine a day. Striking abnormalities, both clinical and biochemical, developed in these subjects fairly promptly, thereby substantiating the validity of the less striking changes observed in a group receiving 400 micrograms of thiamine. Likewise the favorable response of both groups of subjects to later treatment, either with thiamine or with yeast, provided confirmation of the validity of the earlier observations.

For psychologic testing three batteries of tests were used at monthly intervals. The first of these was designed to measure mental levels, the second to measure psychomotor skill, the third to measure efficiency and attitude. The psychologist who made the tests had no knowledge of the patient's diet so that the results obtained were unbiased by subjective correlations. On the other hand, the patients who had been selected with biochemical testing in mind differed greatly in ability as well as in attitude and behavior, so that the several groups were not equated properly. However, each subject served as his own control and the results obtained were these:

1. With moderate restriction of thiamine (400 micrograms per day) attitude and behavior declined. However, a similar trend was noted in the group of men to whom the supplement of yeast was given, which suggested that boredom and ennui, dependent on the long-continued regimentation, played some part in the decline observed.

2. With moderate restriction both young and old declined in those tests of performance which stressed speed and manual dexterity. The decline was greater in the older subjects, but this difference was thought to be in part explained by the deteriorative processes of additional aging of the old men in the three-year period of the study.

3. Impairment of mental efficiency was variable and unequal. In some subjects there was none at all. The decline was marked in two of the old men, but again deterioration from aging may have contributed to this since some of the old patients who received yeast also showed mental deterioration.

4. With more severe restriction of thiamine (200 micrograms per day) the decline of both old and young was rapid and involved mental efficiency in the majority of old men and in one of the young men.

Despite the difficulty encountered in quantitation of these psychologic effects of restriction of thiamine and despite individual variations, it was evident to all observers that mental changes had developed. It often happened that individuals would make an effort under stimulation to overcome their disability when confronted with a given task and score higher intellectually than could have been anticipated from their general behavior; later they would relapse into apathy. With moderate restriction of thiamine the abnormalities came on slowly, so gradually in fact as to escape attention for a year or more. In time, however, faculties involving attention, interest, ambition, and sociability were unmistakably affected; as a result there was much less talking and much less activity. With more severe restriction of thiamine mental changes appeared more rapidly and were unmistakable; in some instances explosive episodes, tantrums, furors, and even rages occurred. These more extreme disturbances were thought to be related to underlying earlier psychotic trends and patterns which were reinforced or reawakened by the chemical effects of lack of thiamine.

The fact that the old subjects, with few exceptions, were more affected than the young supported in a way the observations of Stephenson, Penton, and Korenchevsky[15] who had studied effects of vitamin therapy in an old people's home in England. They used psychologic technics and although the findings by their tests were not reported in detail they concluded that by treating aged people with vitamins it was possible to prevent or improve, in some cases to a striking degree, certain of those senile features which could be considered as pathologic because they appeared prematurely or in an extreme degree (for example, muscular, cardiovascular and mental deterioration), or which did not seem to be inevitable in normal physiologic senility (for example, dementia, insomnia, skin rashes, itching, and constipation). However, it was felt at Elgin that continued aging over the period of three years had itself effected a degree of deterioration in the older subjects, who were only moderately restricted as to thiamine and that this might well explain the difference between the behavior of the older men and that of the younger group. With more severe restriction both the young and the old men were affected almost equally. This could mean that the biochemical disorder induced by the severe restriction was the same in all or that the severity of the deficiency led to a reaction which was severe enough to obscure the effects of age. The later response of young and old to treatment with thiamine or yeast occurred so promptly, in each instance, that proof was not obtainable for the impression generally held by the observers that recuperation in the aged was slower than in the young.

The diet in the study at Elgin was deficient not only in thiamine (400 micrograms daily for one group, 200 micrograms for another) but also in riboflavin (800 micrograms daily). One patient developed skin rashes characteristic of ariboflavinosis. However, in a subsequent investigation at Elgin in which the diet was restricted only with respect to riboflavin and was adequate in thiamine the mental condition of the patients was unaffected. Therefore it is highly probable that the mental changes which occurred in the so-called B complex experiment at Elgin were due primarily at least to lack of thiamine. The conclusion is supported by the fact that the changes noted were the same as those which previously had occurred in the Rochester study when thiamine alone was restricted.

Isolated vitamin deficiencies such as those produced in Rochester and Elgin are rarely if ever seen in clinical practice. Sebrell[11] and others have noted that the peripheral neuritis so common in pellagra is alleviated not by niacin but by thiamine, much as certain of the lesions of the skin in pellagra are corrected not with niacin but with riboflavin. Spies and his co-workers[14] chose a group of 115 patients who were subsisting on deficient diets and lived in a community where pellagra was endemic. These people had had no frank pellagra and no frank beriberi. They suffered from disturbances in emotional behavior. They were depressed, hypersensitive, anxious, and inattentive with loss of comprehension and occasionally with loss of memory. They all were markedly benefited by treatment with thiamine.

McLester[9] called attention to the similarity of the so-called prepellagrous state and what he called "neurasthenia." He noted that a considerable number of pellagrous patients in the Hillman Hospital in Birmingham had been admitted and discharged a year or more before with the diagnosis of neurasthenia.

In 1944, a group of physicians[1] with experience in nutrition examined a sample of the population of St. John's and several coastal villages of Newfoundland. The incidence of surface lesions attributable to deficiency of niacin or riboflavin was high, and with that evidence of malnutrition there occurred a remarkably high incidence of unsolicited complaints of heart consciousness, fatigue, and nervousness. In that same year (1944), the thiamine allowance of the average diet was appreciably increased by a government order requiring that all imported flour be enriched. Enriching was with thiamine, riboflavin, niacin, and iron according to the standards for enriched flour established by the Food and Drug Administration of the United States. Four years later (1948), essentially the same group of physicians[2] examined a comparable sample of the population of Newfoundland and observed improvement in the incidence of signs attributed to deficiency of riboflavin and niacin, likewise striking improvement in the attitude and behavior of the people. I quote from the report: "The people we encountered in 1948 were better dressed than they were in 1944 and their homes looked better tended. This was true not only of St. John's but for the most part also in the outports. Of more significance was the evident increased alertness of the persons we examined. Gone to a great extent was the apathy so noticeable in 1944. The children no longer waited patiently for their examinations. They clustered around the tables of the examiners unless they were shooed away. More monitoring was required. They were interested and curious as children ought to be. . . . Also they engaged in games and play, whereas absence of play had been remarked upon before." This improvement in the attitude and behavior of the population of Newfoundland can be credited, in my opinion, to the increased intake of thiamine, some 1300 micrograms of thiamine per average diet per day contributed by the flour.

It is noteworthy furthermore that among patients of charity hospitals in the United States the frequency of abnormalities attributable to athiaminosis has declined. Attention first was directed to this by Jolliffe.[8] Among alcoholics admitted to the Bellevue Hospital of New York City a Wernicke type of syndrome had been encountered not infrequently. The syndrome was characterized by paresis of ocular muscles, clouding of consciousness, and ataxia with or without an accompanying peripheral neuropathy. This syndrome almost disappeared after 1942. Jolliffe[8] ascribed the disappearance to the thiamine of the bread. Enrichment of bread and flour began in the United States in 1941. Jolliffe also called attention to a comparable decline in the incidence of cases of what he called "acute nicotinic acid deficiency encephalopathy," a syndrome characterized by delirium, sucking, and grasping reflexes; cogwheel rigidities; and irregular jerking movement of the extremities, which was effectively treated with niacin. Observations similar to those of Jolliffe have been made by Spies[13] in the Birmingham area, Darby[3] in Nashville, Goldsmith[5] in New Orleans, and Sebrell.[12] Most recently Figueroa[4] and his associates of the Medical Nutrition Laboratory of the Army commented on the low postwar incidence of avitaminosis in a population notoriously subject to nutritional disturbances. Prewar and postwar comparisons had been made among alcoholics in Chicago's Cook County Hospital and the Boston City Hospital. Field observations also had been made in the "Skid Row" area of Chicago. The results indicated no significant change in eating habits, economic status, or alcoholic consumption. In the opinion of Figueroa[4] and his associates vitamin pills and nutrition education had passed these people by and the only innovation since 1938 which bore on the alcoholic's nutriture had been vitamin-enriched bread, started in Chicago in 1941.

In closing, mention also should be made of the precipitous decline of the Wernicke type of syndrome, which formerly was encountered not infrequently in cases of pernicious vomiting of pregnancy or after abdominal or pelvic operations, when solutions of glucose were administered in considerable amounts. This improvement is most probably related to giving thiamine with the glucose, a practice which in recent years has become almost a routine procedure.

Summary

What I have told you can be summarized briefly. I have pointed out that deficiency of thiamine, when moderate, leads to disturbances of attitudes and behavior and, when severe, to serious disorders of the central nervous system; that these disturbances may or may not be accompanied by peripheral neuropathy like that which is observed in fullblown beriberi. I have mentioned the apathy and symptoms like those of anxiety neuroses, so common in malnourished populations, and the favorable response of these to an increased allowance of thiamine in the diet. Finally I again have called attention to the syndrome which simulates Wernicke's disease and is observed with or without polyneuropathy in alcoholics, in pregnant women with pernicious vomiting, and sometimes after major surgical operations when glucose is administered. It is a grave mental complication preventable by giving thiamine.

REFERENCES

1. ADAMSON, J. D.; JOLLIFFE, N.; KRUSE, H. D.; LOWRY, O. H.; MOORE, P. E.; PLATT, B. S.; SEBRELL, W. H.; TICE, J. W.; TISDALL, F. F.; and WILDER, R. M.: *Canadian Medical Association Journal*, March, 1945, 52, pp. 227-250.
2. AYKROYD, W. R.; JOLLIFFE, N.; LOWRY, O. H.; MOORE, P. E.; SEBRELL, W. H.; SHANK, R. E.; TISDALL, F. F.; WILDER, R. M.; and ZAMECNIK, P. C.: *Canadian Medical Association Journal*, April, 1949, 60, pp. 329-352.
3. DARBY, W. J.: Cited by Committee on Cereals, Food and Nutrition Board: Flour and Bread Enrichment, Washington, D. C., National Research Council, 1950.
4. FIGUEROA: Cited by Committee on Cereals, Food and Nutrition Board: Flour and Bread Enrichment, Washington, D. C., National Research Council, 1950.
5. GOLDSMITH, GRACE: Cited by Committee on Cereals, Food and Nutrition Board: Flour and Bread Enrichment, Washington, D. C. National Research Council, 1950.
6. GUETZKOW, HAROLD, and BROZEK, JOSEF: *American Journal of Psychology*, July, 1946, 59, pp. 358-381.
7. HORWITT, M. K.; LIEBERT, ERICH; KREISLER, OSCAR; and WITTMAN, PHYLLIS: *Bulletin of the National Research Council*, No. 116, June 1948, 106 pp.
8. JOLLIFFE, N.: Cited by Committee on Cereals, Food and Nutrition Board: Flour and Bread Enrichment. Washington, D. C., National Research Council, 1950.
9. McLESTER, J. S.: *Journal of the American Medical Association*, May 27, 1939, 112, pp. 2110-2214.
10. O'SHEA, HARRIET E.; ELSOM, K. O.; and HIGBE, RUTH O.: *American Journal of the Medical Sciences*, March, 1942, 203, pp. 388-397.
11. SEBRELL, W. H., JR.: *Association for Research in Nervous and Mental Disease Proceedings*, 1943, 22, pp. 113-121.
12. SEBRELL, W. H., JR.: Cited by Committee on Cereal, Food and Nutrition Board: Flour and Bread Enrichment, Washington, D. C., National Research Council, 1950.
13. SPIES, T. D.: Cited by Committee on Cereals, Food and Nutrition Board: Flour and Bread Enrichment, Washington, D. C., National Research Council, 1950.
14. SPIES, T. D.; BRADLEY, JOHN; ROSENBAUM, MILTON; and KNOTT, J. R.: *Association for Research in Nervous and Mental Disease, Proceedings*, 1943, 22, pp. 122-140.
15. STEPHENSON, W.: PENTON, C.; and KORENCHEVSKY, V.: *British Medical Journal*, December 13, 1941, 2, pp. 839-844.

16. WILDER, R. M.: *Association for Research in Nervous and Mental Disease, Proceedings,* 1943, 22, pp. 101-112.
17. WILLIAMS, R. D.; MASON, H. L.; POWER, M. H.; and WILDER, R. M.: *Archives of Internal Medicine,* January, 1943, 71, pp. 38-53.
18. WILLIAMS, R. D.; MASON, H. L.; SMITH, B. F.; and WILDER, R. M.: *Archives of Internal Medicine,* May, 1942, 69, pp. 721-738.
19. WILLIAMS, R. D.; MASON, H. L.; WILDER, R. M.; and SMITH, B. F.: *Archives of Internal Medicine,* October, 1940, 66, pp. 785-799.

CHAPTER 32

Experimental Induction of Psychoses

PAUL H. HOCH, M.D.

THAT CERTAIN drugs affect human beings has been known from time immemorial. The number of such substances is legion. Descriptively, we know the action of many of them and we also have some explanation as to how they act on the psyche. A great deal has been written on the use of alcohol, morphine, cocaine, hashish, marihuana, and similar substances, but we have very few experimental data regarding their administration to different groups of people—normals and abnormals—under controlled conditions. The use and abuse of these substances would be better known if experiments could have been carried out simultaneously from a bio-chemical, neurophysiologic, and psychiatric point of view on the same case material.

Actually many basic questions remain unsolved. For instance, from a psychiatric point of view we do not know whether an individual responds in the same way all of the time to these drugs or reacts differently at different times; whether normal and abnormal persons respond in the same manner or differently; whether normal individuals can be made psychotic under the influence of these drugs or if psychotic behavior is induced only in predisposed individuals. Furthermore, studies utilizing different substances in the same person have hardly begun. It would be of great importance to determine whether or not a person behaves in the same way under the in-fluence of different chemical agents. We would also have to ask: Are the different mental pictures seen under the different drugs due to the person's constitution expressed in his personal metabolism or are they due to his psychologic organization, inherited or acquired? All the above uncertainties indicate the scarcity of our knowledge in this field.

Alcohol, hashish, and many other drugs are unsatisfactory for experi-mental purposes in that they usually affect the sensorium in a typical "organic" manner. The consciousness is usually altered, a confusion sets in, memory impairment is present, and the person is unreliable in reporting experiences while in the intoxicated state. Because the mental alterations produced by these drugs do not occur in a clear setting, these agents have rarely been used to elucidate mental mechanisms as seen in the functional psychosis, e.g., schizophrenia.

At the present time there are available drugs which produce abnormal states phenomenologically resembling the functional psychoses, even though these agents also possess components which induce organic reactions. These drugs include mescaline, lysergic acid, DFP (di-isopropyl fluorophosphate), ACTH (adrenocorticotropic hormone), pervitin, sodium amytal, and a few others.

The observations to be discussed in the following pages were mainly obtained with the use of mescaline.

Mescal was discovered in the nineteenth century in a Mexican cactus, *Anhalonium lewini*, commonly known as peyot. It was used by Mexican Indians for religious purposes. Today, mescal, or mescaline, is produced synthetically, the chemical formula being 3,4,5,-trimethoxy phenyl ethylamine. It is water-soluble and can be given orally or by injection. We have applied it intravenously, the dosage being 0.4 to 0.6 Gm. The first symptoms appear half an hour after taking the drug and usually last ten to twelve hours. Mescaline is a stimulant and not a narcotic. It is not a habit-forming drug and the mental states produced are harmless because after a few hours complete reintegration takes place. After administration of the drug, physical signs such as paleness or flushing, insomnia, anorexia, and restlessness appear; the pupils are dilated, the deep reflexes are increased; there is some tremor; incoordination is noticed, and muscle weakness or rigidity is present. There is also a dulling of pain sensation, alterations in the sense of weight and temperature occur, and spatial discrimination and body orientation are impaired. Hyperpnea, nausea, and rising blood pressure are manifest. It was also found that an exaggeration and prolongation of visual after-images were present.

Psychotic Manifestations of Mescaline in Normal Subjects

The psychotic manifestations of mescaline have been described by Beringer,[1] Zucker,[9-11] Klüver,[4, 5] Stockings,[8] and Guttmann.[2] The most important observation is that the psychotic phenomena, especially the hallucinatory experiences, occur in a state of clear consciousness and without any formal impairment of intelligence. Each subject, however, is altered in many of his partial functions. Most conspicuous are the hallucinations. Visual hallucinations are the most common, next come auditory, and then somatic. Hallucinations of taste and smell are rare. The visual hallucinations consist of complex and fantastically beautiful kaleidoscopic patterns of every shape and color, brilliantly colored birds, flowers, and monsters. The pictures are constantly changing. At times only beautifully illuminated or colored geometric formations are seen; at other times, however, whole reels are witnessed. The visual hallucinations are filled with condensations and symbolizations. It is also interesting, according to Stockings,[8] that these hallucinations are in line with the subject's past experiences. They are usually wish-fulfilling fantasies, and very often fantasies of childhood are reactivated. Stockings also claims that, depending upon the individual's emotional organization, the fantasies show introversion or extroversion. For instance, a schizothymic individual who in his childhood was interested in ancient mythologies sees mythical personages and monsters. An extroverted air pilot sees visions of fantastic machinery and engines. The influence of personality make-up on mescaline experiences has not yet been reliably confirmed. Under mescaline there is a marked increase of mental imagery. The images are very vivid; a hypertrophy of imagination is present. In some subjects illusions first set in, then pseudohallucinations, and finally hallucinations. The optic imagery can be followed through vivid pictures, vivid fantasies, and then full hallucinations. While under the influence of mescaline, the individual is dominated, similarly as a psychotic person is, by these hallucinatory experiences. He becomes preoccupied with them and it is difficult for him to divide his attention between the hallucinations and the environment. In contrast to the visual hallucinations of delirium tremens, these visual images are usually not influenced by suggestion or hypnosis. The auditory hallucinations are usually those of sound and music. Some subjects hear voices similar to those experienced by schizophrenic patients. The hallucinations usually start as an idea and then the concept is projected and heard from the outside. The disassociation of a thought and the perception that it comes from the outside are strikingly similar in both mescalinized individuals and in persons suffering from schizophrenia. With the somatic delusions, the subject has all kinds of sensations such as the feeling that part of his body has been altered or removed. He feels as if he had been turned into rubber, he has no heart or bowels, he feels electricity in his body. Quite a number of subjects under mescaline express delusions which are paranoid, grandiose, or hypochondriacal. Suspiciousness and ideas of reference are common in that the subjects believe that people around them are mocking them, talking about them, and plotting against them. They often misinterpret situations around them, such as believing that conversation is concerned with them—people are plotting against them, the radio is talking directly to them, and the broadcast is especially meant for them. The delusions of grandeur consist of being very tall, very beautiful, and very powerful. The hypochondriacal delusions consist of ideas of bizarre changes of the body, such as removal of arms and legs and changes in size and form of various body parts.

Depersonalization experiences are very common under the influence of mescaline and are very similar to experiences reported by schizophrenic patients. Subjects state that they feel that in some peculiar way they are altered or that the environment has changed. They express feelings that their intellect is functioning separately from their emotions (splitting) Introspection is markedly heightened. Transformation of personality is also common and feelings are expressed such as "I am living in a world of my own," or "Other people cannot understand me because I am living in a different world from them." The experiences are sometimes so peculiar that the subject is unable to express them, and must grope for new words or expressions in order to convey his feelings.

Disturbances of thought are very common. Incoherence, flight of ideas, blocking, feelings of passivity, and the feeling that thoughts are tampered with from the outside are quite often expressed. Speech disorders are frequently connected with the disorders of thought. The subject speaks in a stilted and circumstantial manner. Motor disturbances such as meaningless outbursts of restlessness or complete catatonic rigidity are also common during periods in which the subject appears to be preoccupied with hallucinations and delusions. Inability to make a decision to move or not to move is reported. This ambivalence is quite schizophrenic. Negativism and refusal of food or action is common. Stockings believes that this phenomenon occurs only in persons of a certain constitutional type, similar to that of schizophrenia. Intellectual disturbances are common in persons under the influence of mescaline. The formal intelligence is not impaired, but partial intellectual functions, if tested, show a falling-off performance. The most conspicuous impairment is divorcement of the intellect from other functions of the psyche such as that often seen in schizophrenic patients. Perceptions in general are distorted and altered, especially time perception in which the patient feels that the time passes either very slowly or very quickly, although, however, he has some realization that this is not so and remains approximately oriented for time. Spatial orientation is also impaired. The space is narrower, enlarged, altered, distorted, or displaced. Persons under the influence of mescaline have no insight into their mental condition and often have an amnesia regarding their experiences. However, this is not true all of the time. Affective disturbances are common. Depression or euphoria is very often noted. Frequently depression ushers in the first symptoms and sometimes feelings of anxiety, fear, and hopelessness are expressed. Sometimes experiences are very weird and the subjects become quite upset and concerned about their depressive feelings.

Reactions of Schizophrenics to Mescaline Administration

We tried comparing the reactions of schizophrenic patients under the influence of mescaline with the clinical pictures observed in the so-called "normals." Our schizophrenic case material was subdivided into overt schizophrenics in whom no deterioration was present, chronic deteriorated schizophrenics, and the so-called pseudoneurotic or attenuated schizophrenic patients.

These three different groups of schizophrenic patients revealed the following: In the overt nondeteriorated schizophrenic patients, with few exceptions, marked accentuation of their schizophrenic symptomatology occurred in the emotional and intellectual sphere. The disorganization of these patients was more marked than in the so-called "normal" controls. The drug underscored the existing schizophrenic symptomatology of the patient and at times brought out dynamic material not previously revealed by the patient. After two or three injections of mescaline, if given in quick succession, an adaptation to the drug takes place which has to be overcome by giving higher doses in subsequent injections. If that is taken into consideration, however, the response of the patient is generally the same with each injection of mescaline. In some patients, however, variations occur in the clinical picture.

In the second group—the chronic deteriorated schizophrenics—some patients showed an underscoring of their symptoms but many remained bland under the influence of mescaline, unproductive, and burned out; they appeared unchanged as compared with their previous state. This nonproductive response to mescaline was especially interesting because a number of these patients complained of physical symptoms and had visual hallucinations or disturbances of the body image but responded less, however, to these experiences than did the normal individuals, and much less than did the overt acute schizophrenic patients.

Interesting observations were made in pseudoneurotic schizophrenics. These patients usually complained about tension and anxiety and had obsessive-compulsive or phobic manifestations. In them the drug produced typical schizophrenic reactions. These effects differed from the schizophrenic-like reactions seen in the normal controls in that they displayed a much more marked intellectual disorganization and less awareness of reality. There was a marked underscoring of emotional patterns present. The subjects suffered intensely from their experiences and were much less detached in relationship to them than were the normal controls. They had less reality control than did the normal subjects. They often released new psychodynamic material in the form of hallucinations and delusions or depersonalization which had not been noted prior to the drug studies. We feel that in this group of patients the drug actually precipitated a short-lived schizophrenic episode ordinarily seen in these individuals only in stress situations.

Studies were made which are not yet completed concerning the relationship of emotional alterations in these patients to perceptual distortions. It appears that perceptual alterations are quite often connected with emotional changes in the patient. The perceptual changes are connected with feelings of anxiety, uncertainty, and, at times, rage. Seemingly the perceptual alterations lead to a lowering of control of reality, thence to tension manifestations and anxiety, which in turn lead to depressive, aggressive, and paranoid manifestations.

Losing control over reality is perceived by these patients as a threat to their ego which then leads to tension and anxiety. It would appear that the more complex emotional reactions like depression and paranoid reactions are secondary elaborations of anxiety and tension states, and that their relationship to the individual should be studied in more detail.

A great deal of additional material will have to be gathered in order to determine whether or not mescaline produces a schizophrenic picture only in individuals who have a schizothymic temperament. Stockings[8] is of the opinion that only schizoid individuals develop these schizophrenic-like reactions to mescaline. We do not have sufficient data to prove or disprove this opinion, but our evidence to date suggests that under the drug a complete schizophrenic disorganization is much more prominent in schizophrenics and latent schizophrenics than in "normal" subjects. The experiences of the "normals" are more like organic reactions with some schizophrenic features. On the contrary, in schizophrenics and latent schizophrenics the drug is able to heighten the schizophrenic disorganization of the individual both emotionally and conceptually and, therefore, is very valuable for the study of schizophrenic structures. At present we would like to refrain from theorizing as to what is actually happening in these patients under the influence of the drug, but only point out the somewhat overlooked fact that mescaline emphasizes schizophrenia in schizophrenic individuals, especially in the so-called borderline schizophrenics.

Effect of Sodium Amytal and Pervitin

We were able to use sodium amytal and pervitin in addition to mescaline in a large group of patients. In some patients the reaction to these three drugs is dissimilar in detail. In one group, the basic manifestations were similar, but quantitatively different. In other patients, however, entirely different clinical pictures were obtained under the influence of the different drugs. The various reactions can be explained as being due to the different metabolic interferences of the drugs and also to the fact that these agents affect different parts of the central nervous system differently. Sodium amytal usually produces a state of relaxation and lowered inhibition which fosters the ability to speak, thus bringing about the establishment of a quick transference. The inhibitory mechanisms are broken down and a suggestible frame of mind is produced. Owing to lowering of these defenses the patient often releases new material. Pervitin and mescaline, on the other hand, act similarly by markedly increasing the tension of the patient and underscoring the previously existent symptomatology.

Use of Mescaline

At present there are insufficient data to warrant using mescaline for a reliable differential diagnosis. Evidence to date suggests that the drug which is able to produce schizophrenic-like reactions in normal subjects is able to underscore or precipitate schizophrenic disorganization in persons suffering from overt or latent schizophrenia. We have tried to influence the mescaline intoxication state with different methods. The mescaline intoxication is little affected by suggestion or persuasion. To some extent reassurance allays the patient's anxiety but has only a very temporary effect. Hypnosis was tried but was very difficult. It does not usually influence the patient's clinical picture, and this is especially so in the hallucinations. The patient is usually so dominated by his experiences that he does not respond to hypnosis. Electroshock treatment was also tried on patients while under mescaline intoxication but this did not influence the clinical symptoms at all. The patients continued to behave in the same way as they did prior to its trial. Electroshock, therefore, has no influence on mescaline-produced mental states. Sodium succinate was recommended as an antidote for mescaline but in our hands did not produce many positive results. We believe the easiest way to counteract the action of mescaline is to inject sodium amytal intravenously, which, before it produces any sleep reaction, eliminates the affective component of mescaline action.

We also used mescaline to study the clinical structure before and after psychosurgery. Here the interesting observations emerged that the basic structure of the psychosis and neurosis in patients after operation appeared to be the same as before the operation took place. This was especially impressive in relationship to anxiety in the pseudoneurotic group of schizophrenics in whom, after the operation was performed, the drug was able to reactivate the anxiety and obsessiveness. In overt schizophrenic patients the psychosis was reactivated indicating that qualitatively the patient remained the same. However, a difference was noted in the intensity of symptoms under the influence of mescaline before and after operation. The severity of the response in improved patients was impressively less than prior to the operation indicating that we are dealing in psychosurgery with a procedure which reduces quantitatively the emotional symptoms but does not alter their qualitative structure.

At this time we are unable to state whether or not mescaline can be used reliably for differential diagnostic purposes. A larger group of subjects has to be examined. Nevertheless, as indicated, seemingly overt schizophrenic and latent schizophrenic patients respond to the drug with a marked accentuation of their symptoms. A complete schizophrenic disorganization under the influence of the drug is more prominent in schizophrenics, latent schizophrenics, and schizothymic normals than in normal subjects with a different emotional make-up. In nonschizothymic normals the experiences are more like organic reactions. It is possible that a release occurs in schizothymic normals. This question must be further studied in detail with different drug components. The oxidation of mescaline has to be studied in animals biochemically; also the enzyme interference occurring in the nervous system must be evaluated. There is every indication that there is metabolic alteration in the enzymatic range. The drug experiments indicate that a disturbance of homeostasis physically and emotionally (which is also organic) leads to a lowering of mental integration which in turn leads to schizophrenic symptomatology. Why this occurs in a nearly clear setting in schizophrenics and in a confused state in an organic setting has to be further elucidated. The differences are probably both qualitative and quantitative. Comparative drug studies in untreated and treated patients will have to be extensively undertaken in order to assess the different treatment methods used in psychiatry today in relationship to the alterations they produce. Some basic emotional and intellectual symptoms in our patients will have to be differentiated from secondary mechanisms which today are often treated as primary phenomena. Here it is clearly indicated that tension and anxiety are at the starting point of many of the emotional disorders. Experimental psychiatry as it is undertaken today with surgical procedures and with drug studies as advocated by Schilder many years ago (pharmacopsychoanalysis) will establish psychiatry as a solid fact-finding discipline in which intra-organismic and inter-organismic knowledge and physiodynamic and psychodynamic approaches will be fused.

REFERENCES

1. BERINGER, K.: *Monographien aus dem Gesamtgebiete der Neurologie und Psychiatrie,* 1927, 49, pp. 1-315.
2. GUTTMANN, E.: *Journal of Mental Science,* 1936, 82, pp. 203-221.
3. HOCH, P.: *American Journal of Psychiatry,* 1951, 107, No. 8.
4. KLÜVER, H.: Mescal. London, Kegan Paul, 1928.
5. KLÜVER, H.: Mechanisms of Hallucinations: in Studies in Personality, pp. 175-207. New York, McGraw-Hill Book Company, 1942.
6. LEWIN, L.: Fantastica. Berlin, 1924. (English Translation, London, 1931.)
7. LINDEMANN, E., and MALAMUD, W.: *The American Journal of Psychiatry,* 1934, 13, pp. 853-879.
8. STOCKINGS, G. T.: *Journal of Mental Science,* 1940, 86, pp. 29-47.
9. ZUCKER, K.: *Zentralblatt für die gesamte Neurologie und Psychiatrie,* 1930, 56, pp. 447-448.
10. ZUCKER, K., and ZADOR, J.: *Zeitschrift für die gesamte Neurologie und Psychiatrie,* 1930, 127, pp. 15-29.
11. ZUCKER, K.: *Zeitschrift für die gesamte Neurologie und Psychiatrie,* 1930, 127, pp. 108-161.

Discussion

HARRY C. SOLOMON, M.D.

It was my intention to supplement the remarks of Dr. Hoch with a discussion of lysergic acid, which has many effects similar to synthetic mescaline, and to cause you, Mr. Chairman and audience, a considerable amount of anxiety as to whether or not I would stop; however, I shall merely call attention to certain generalities.

There is a variety of drugs available, e.g., mescaline, lysergic acid, DFP, and pervitin, that cause very curious mental changes in individuals and afford the opportunity, I believe, to study syndromes and psychologic reactions on a different basis than that previously offered. If it is necessary to produce a disease in order to understand it, as in the case of diabetes, the same is probably true in respect to psychotic states. What is needed is the collaboration of our chemical associates in order to show whether certain syndromes which result from a use of a drug are characteristic of changes in the enzyme systems that are produced by that particular drug. One of the best immediate examples is the effect of DFP on cholinesterase. If there are found other drugs that produce a similar effect on cholinesterase and also produce the same psychologic effect, then it might be assumed that it is the effect on the cholinesterase system that is responsible for the psychologic reaction.

CHAPTER 33

Effect of Shock Therapies on the Brain

HAROLD E. HIMWICH, M.D.

THE CONCEPT of pharmacologic methods in the treatment of mental disease is relatively new. We are not now employing the ancient and superseded idea that the devils of disease can be frightened out of patients by such methods. We use shock therapies with the hope of altering the underlying pathologic state, whether physiologic or morphologic, and by such a fundamental attack on the underlying processes affect directly the course of the disease. It must be admitted that in most instances the etiologic factors of these diseases are unknown. We are therefore placed in the baffling position of attacking an unknown enemy in an unknown country. We cannot at the present time adapt our attack directly to the subject at hand. We are not in a position to build up logically, step by step, a direct approach to our problem. Instead we must content ourselves with empirically obtained results.

Our methods of treatment are therefore crude at present. One means of refining our attack and giving it better direction is to analyze the effect of these treatments on the brain. By means of such studies it may be possible to determine the mechanism of therapeutic action and finally to obtain better results with less drastic procedures than are now employed.

When we mention shock therapy two chief kinds come into mind; first, insulin hypoglycemic coma[41] and second, the convulsive group.[28] It must be recognized, however, that there are combinations of the two and many variations of the convulsive form. Among the latter may be placed first, metrazol[35] and electroshock,[6] sometimes used in its severe regressive form[5] or in the milder electronarcosis.[14] The milder forms include the inhalation of gas mixtures with reduced tensions of oxygen due to the presence of other gases—nitrogen,[1] nitrous oxide,[12, 32] and carbon dioxide.[34] In the short time allotted to this discussion, however, we limit ourselves to insulin hypoglycemia, electroshock, and the injection of metrazol.

Insulin Hypoglycemia

Why is cerebral function altered in hypoglycemia? The reason for the peculiar sensitivity of the brain to lack of blood sugar lies in the fact that it is the only organ which obtains its energy from the combustion of carbohydrate alone.[24, 33] The liver, the kidneys, the heart, and voluntary muscle, for example, may oxidize either fat or carbohydrate. When the carbohydrate supply in the blood is decreased the various non-nervous organs continue to maintain their activities at the expense of the energy obtained by the oxidation of fat. The brain, however, when deprived of carbohydrate can resort to no alternate foodstuff. Its metabolism must slow down, and cerebral functions suffer. Studies of cerebral metabolism made before, during,

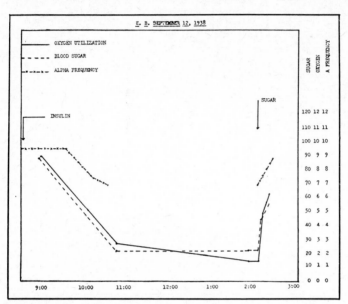

FIG. 196. The cerebral arteriovenous oxygen difference, blood sugar, and brain waves during insulin hypoglycemic treatment for schizophrenia. After insulin effect takes hold, the alpha frequency decreases, the same as cerebral arteriovenous oxygen difference and blood sugar. At the time when the alpha frequency has disappeared, the cerebral arteriovenous difference and blood sugar have fallen to a low level, and the patient is no longer in contact with the environment. During the subsequent period of hypoglycemic coma, the arteriovenous oxygen difference falls somewhat, and blood sugar remains low. When the treatment was terminated by the oral administration of sugar, the alpha waves reappeared, cerebral arteriovenous oxygen difference and blood sugar rose, and the patient aroused.

and after profound hypoglycemia reveal that the brain metabolism may be depressed below its normal rate during the treatment.[30] In Figure 196 it will be observed that following the injection of insulin as blood sugar falls from approximately 80 to 20 mg. per cent the cerebral metabolic rate also decreases as the cerebral AVO_2 difference is depressed while the cerebral blood flow remains relatively stable. At the same time the ten-per-second waves disappear from the electroencephalogram.[21] The administration of glucose, however, restores blood sugar, raises brain metabolism, and the rapid brain waves again are observed on the electroencephalogram. In Figure 197 may be seen the change which occurs as the fast waves give

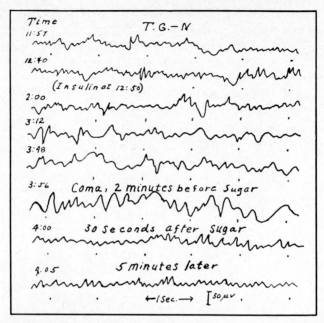

FIG. 197. Brain waves during insulin treatment. Note that the alpha waves become somewhat less rapid after the injection of insulin and are finally displaced by slow waves as the patient becomes comatose. Note also the disappearance of slow waves immediately after sugar administration, and reappearance of alpha frequency.

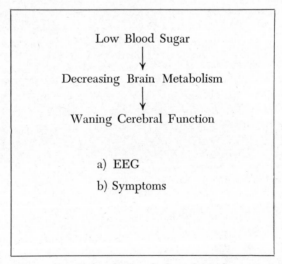

FIG. 198. The order of chemical and physiological events in the brain following administration of insulin.

way to slower ones under the influence of insulin hypoglycemia and again the restoration to the normal pattern following gavage with carbohydrate.[26] The order of events is portrayed in Figure 198: low blood sugar causes a decrease of brain metabolism, a decrease which renders the brain incapable of maintaining normal function. The waning of function is evidenced by alterations in the electroencephalogram and the production of the symptoms and signs of hypoglycemia.

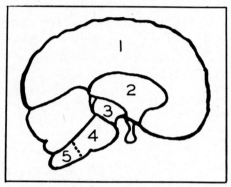

FIG. 199.   Transverse section of brain revealing the five layers to which the symptoms of hypoglycemia have been allocated. *1*, Cortex, the depression of which brings on the cortical phase in hypoglycemia; *2*, the subcortico-diencephalon, responsible for the symptoms of release in the second phase; *3*, the mesencephalon involving the symptoms of the third phase; *4*, the pons and the rostral portion of the medulla (upper) and, *5*, the caudal portion of the medulla (lower), releasing the premyelencephalic and myelencephalic symptoms, respectively. The cerebellum is left unnumbered, for it has anatomic connections with all phyletic parts of the brain, and in its function has associations especially with the spinal cord, medulla, and cerebral hemispheres. It seems logical that the many and varied symptoms of the cerebellum should be active in accordance with the metabolic state of its respective phyletic layers.

When we observe a patient injected with a shock dose of insulin we note a series of clinical changes first described by Angyal[3] and Frostig.[13] The signs and symptoms seem to show progressive allocations down the neur-axis starting with the cerebral cortex and proceeding towards the medulla oblongata (Fig. 199 and Table 54). The first constellation of signs indicates

TABLE 54.   FIVE PHYLETIC "LAYERS"

1. Depression of cerebral hemispheres and cerebellum
2. Release of subcortico-diencephalon
   a. Subcortical motor nuclei
   b. Thalamus
   c. Hypothalamus
3. Release of midbrain
4. Release of upper medulla
5. Release of lower medulla

a depression of cortical functions, for example, disturbances of vision and audition occur as the patient, drooling saliva, becomes drowsy and relaxed, and finally loses contact with the environment. Just before loss of environmental contact some patients exhibit a period of wild excitement. Once contact is lost the second stage begins as an entirely new clinical picture is exhibited. In addition to motor restlessness there are primitive movements of many kinds, grimacing, sticking out the tongue, and kissing, as well as forced grasping. At this time sensory stimuli usually evoke exaggerated responses. Release of the autonomic with sympathetic predominance over parasympathetic is marked and comes on in waves as indicated

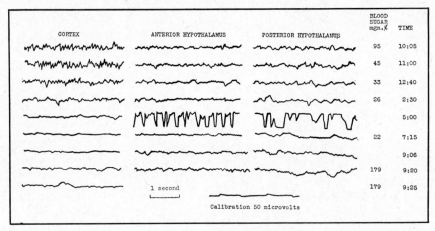

FIG. 200.   Records from cortex, posterior hypothalamus, and anterior hypothalamus during insulin hypoglycemia and recovery. At each recorded time successive records were made from the three regions about one minute apart. Note augmentation of cortical slow waves at 2:30 and flattening of record by 7:15. Thirty-seven gm. of glucose were given from 9:04 to 9:16. Note slowness of return of cortical activity after administering sugar. The hypothalamic responses are much less depressed and return more rapidly after sugar injection as seen in records taken at 9:06 and 9:20. Note the violent responses of the hypothalamus at 5:00, producing amplifier block. These surges were not accompanied by convulsions nor were they associated with changes of pulse or respiration.

by increases in blood pressure and heart rate, flushing of face, dilatation of pupils, and periodic exophthalmus. It is significant that when convulsions do occur they appear most frequently when the second phyletic layer is released from cortical control. First fine myoclonic twitchings of the facial muscles are observed and then the eyes may deviate to one side. If the larger muscles are seized by contractions which become generalized the patient undergoes grand mal-like convulsions. But in most instances these convulsive episodes do not appear and the patient gradually loses these signs and sinks to the third or mescencephalic phase. This complex tells of the release of midbrain functions reminiscent of the changes observed with high decerebration, namely, tonic spasms with flexion of the arms and extension of the legs. Sometimes the patient twists himself on his long axis in torsion spasms. With each paroxysm blood pressure and heart rate increase in order to provide visceral support for the somatic activities. Next signs of low decerebration referable to upper medulla are visible. The legs are still extended but now the arms are brought back over the head, thus in a remarkable way resembling the decerebrate rigidity produced by surgical operative intervention in lower mammals. Finally the fifth stage appears when the medullary centers are affected by the hypoglycemia. The patient is pallid, the heart rate is slow, respiration is shallow and retarded in rate, pupils are constricted, and heat loss is increased. It is best to give glucose by mouth or even better intravenously in the fourth stage. The fifth stage, however, may be allowed to proceed up to fifteen minutes with safety. Then, as a result of the administration of carbohydrate, in a comparatively short time the patient retraces his symptomatic progression proceeding in the reverse direction finally regaining contact with his environment. The recovery is, of course, a result of the increased blood sugar supplied to the brain.

Further support for the conclusion of successive syndromes is afforded by the analysis of the electrical potentials of the brain. By placing electrodes in the cortex and hypothalamus of dogs subjected to hypoglycemia Hoagland and co-workers[25] found that the cortical responses failed earlier than the hypothalamic. Again the injection of glucose restored hypothalamic activity some time before that of the cortex (Fig. 200).

The symptomatic progression due to deprivation of glucose may be duplicated to a great extent by deprivation of oxygen since both glucose and oxygen are required to support brain metabolism.[19] The signs of hypoglycemia, however, may be observed over a period of five hours while those of acute anoxia are more fleeting and must be limited to a period of as many minutes. The inhalation of undiluted nitrogen[1] is followed by a clouded consciousness of the first stage, the loss of environmental contact and the motor restlessness of the second, the tonic and torsion spasms of the third, and the extensor spasms of the fourth. The patient is permitted to respire oxygen before medullary depression occurs.[19]

TABLE 55. ACUTE ANOXIA

(Survival times for particular regions of the brain following complete cerebral anemia.)

Parts of brain	Survival Time (Seconds)
Cortex	14–15
Caudate nucleus	25–27
Thalamus	28–33
Medulla	30–40

Sugar and Gerard[45] examined the electrical changes associated with acute anoxia, and placed electrodes in different parts of the brain. In their experiments, abrupt and functionally complete anemia of the brain of cats was produced by temporary occlusion of all the vascular channels to the brain. As may be seen in Table 55, they observed that the electrical potentials of the cortex and caudate nucleus disappeared earlier then those of the thalamus and the medulla. The recovery of normal waves after release of the occlusion occurred in the reverse order. Thus we find a common denominator which seems to underlie the clinical changes whether due to

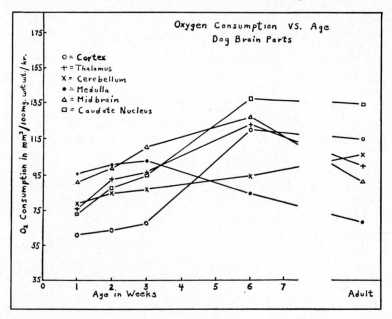

FIG. 201. The changes in oxygen consumption of the various parts of dog brain at 1, 2, 3, and 6 weeks of age and in adulthood. In general, the cerebral metabolism increases during the first six weeks and then reverses slightly.

hypoglycemia or to anoxia, namely, a deprivation of energy causing in turn a dissolution of the usual functions of the brain, a dissolution which seems to turn back that organ through the path of evolution and with recovery, due to administration of carbohydrate or inhalation of oxygen, to exhibit a rapid recapitulation of evolution, not over a period of ages but in a matter of minutes.

The next question: Why does this deprivation of energy observed with these treatments produce these clinical changes of successive syndromes? Apparently not all parts of the brain are equally susceptible to deprivation of energy. The reason for this differential susceptibility becomes apparent when the metabolic rates of the various parts of the brain are determined in the Warburg respirometer. The oxygen intake is not found to be the

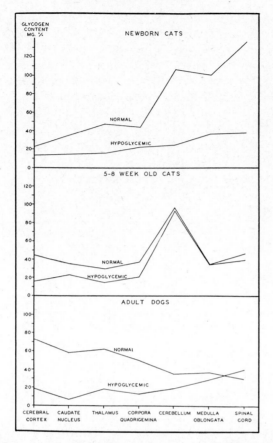

Fig. 202. These graphs show the concentrations of glycogen in the parts of the central nervous system of normal animals compared with the hypoglycemic for the three age groups. In the newborn, the curves for the normal and hypoglycemic animals become progressively farther separated from the cephalad to the caudad direction, while in the adult the reverse is true. In both of these age groups, those parts which have the higher concentrations of glycogen tend to show the greatest fall during hypoglycemia. In the adult, these are the newer parts, while in the newborn they are the phyletically older ones. In the intermediate group, the decrease in the higher areas is of less magnitude than in the adults, and, in contrast to the newborn, no significant changes occur in the lower portions.

same throughout the brain. The answer is at hand when one calls to mind that in general there is a progressive decrease in the CMR* of the various parts of the brain as one descends the neuraxis. In general the CMR is highest in the newer parts of the brain including the cerebral cortex and the basal ganglia and is lowest in the medulla oblongata. Experiments in which the various parts of the brain were studied in the Warburg apparatus reveal, in general, a decrease of oxygen intake as one proceeds from the

* Cerebral metabolic rate.

cerebral hemispheres to the medulla oblongata. Studies of the oxygen intake[22] of the various parts of the brain support this conception (Fig. 201). It seems reasonable from these experiments that the lower part with its slower metabolism will be able to retain its function longer whether in hypoglycemia or anoxia and that the medulla oblongata with its vital centers holds on the longest so that after injection of glucose or the inhalation of oxygen recovery may occur if the episode is not too prolonged.

It is not to be supposed that the function of an organ so vital as the brain is permitted to lapse without strenuous efforts to protect and to prolong its activity. Once the oxidative mechanisms are overtaxed the brain falls back on its intrinsic carbohydrate supplies and here we find a phyletic pattern of glycogen depletion of dog brain during hypoglycemia (Fig. 202).[11] In the normal brain, glycogen is in highest concentration in the cerebral hemispheres and gradually decreases as one progresses down the neuraxis. During hypoglycemia the greatest impairment is observed in the newer parts so that the cerebral hemispheres suffer the greater losses. The storage of glycogen though quantitatively small acts as an important buffer helping to extend brain function for a longer period. A significant anaerobic source of energy is found in the energy-rich phosphate bonds, the immediate origin of the energy for the function of the brain. It has been shown[36] that energy-rich compounds, adenosinetriphosphate and phosphocreatine, are depleted during the period of energy deprivation induced by hypoglycemia (Table 56). These data were obtained by Olsen and Klein working on erythroidinized cats maintained by artificial respiration.[36]

TABLE 56.   INSULIN HYPOGLYCEMIA AND BRAIN METABOLITES
(mM/1000 Gm.)

State	Brain			Plasma
	Glycogen	PC	ATP	Blood Sugar
Control	6.8	2.4	1.3	12.0
Coma	2.9	1.2	0.0	0.6

Cats, paralyzed with erythroidine and maintained with artificial respiration, received five units of crystalline zinc insulin per kilogram of body weight intramuscularly. The brain was frozen in situ by pouring liquid air on the exposed skull. The frozen brains were ground to a fine powder and assayed for metabolites.

Electroshock and Metrazol Convulsions

The symptomatic patterns observed with electroshock and metrazol injection do not yield as readily to analysis as those which accompany hypoglycemia, perhaps because the progression is such a rapid one and perhaps because of a more complex underlying mechanism. It is important, however, that in general the clinical picture produced by the convulsive treatments resembles that observed in idiopathic epilepsy[27, 44] as emphasized by Kalinowsky and Hoch[28] in their book on shock treatments.

In idiopathic epilepsy the focus of the convulsion, or to quote Hughlings Jackson the "discharging lesion," is thought to have an origin somewhere in the subcortex, and when such a focus successfully excites a motor area we are permitted to observe the dramatic effects of a grand mal fit. But whether in any particular instance the originating focus is subcortical or cortical, in addition to the signs emanating from this focus, another source for the clinical changes is operative in the acute anoxemia associated with the convulsion (Table 57). Both in electroshock and in metrazol convulsions an-

TABLE 57. EFFECT OF METRAZOL CONVULSIONS
MODIFIED BY CURARE

O_2 Content	Hb Sat.	Convulsions
17.5	95	Before
16.1	87	Early
15.1	82	Middle
7.8	42	Late

A typical instance of changes in oxygen in arterial blood of a patient with depression, before and during metrazol convulsions, is presented. If postconvulsive apnea supervenes the oxygen content and hemoglobin saturation of the arterial blood approach zero.

oxemia is produced.[23] This anoxemia, caused by a disruption of the respiratory movements inflicted by the convulsions, is not, however, the only reason why the brain suffers from anoxia. As has been calculated by Olsen and Klein[37] the energy demands become excessive during convulsions, and over a ten-second period may be eight times as large as the resting requirement. Such huge demands could not be satisfied even by normal blood supply let alone one in which oxygen is lacking. The oxygen lack of the brain is evidenced by a reduction of its oxygen tension to low levels and this phenomenon is observed even in animals paralyzed by erythroidine and artificially respired.[8, 9] It is, therefore, interesting that Yakovlev[46] suggests for epilepsy a rapid progression of signs starting with loss of consciousness and ending with tonic and clonic convulsions, conditions similar to decerebrate rigidity. Such a progression down the neuraxis may be a complicating effect, secondary to the anoxia induced by the convulsions. Thus in addition to a primary "discharging lesion," or metrazol injection, or electroshock a secondary anoxia may serve to complicate the clinical picture adding to the effects of the primary stimulation a series of syndromes like those described for acute anoxia.[1]

With the failure of the oxygen supplies to support adequately the induced convulsive activity of the brain the anaerobic sources of energy are tapped to support the enormous increase of cerebral convulsant activity. Evidence for recourse to anaerobic stores was obtained on dogs immobilized with erythroidine and maintained by artificial respiration.[43] Despite the excellent oxygenation of their arterial blood, lactate accumulated in the brain and energy-rich phosphocreatine broke down within that organ. In cats, similarly treated, the invasion of the anaerobic deposits went even further,[31] for not only were glycogen depots attenuated within the brain but lactate accrued and phosphocreatine underwent depletion while another energy-rich phosphate compound, adenosinetriphosphate, was diminished (Table 58). The psychiatric patient, however, does not receive artificial respiration with the convulsant therapy. It therefore seems probable that he may suffer from even a greater depletion of anaerobic stores than do the animals, for he is subjected to a grave decrease in arterial oxygen just at the time when his energy turnover is maximal. Even in a nonconvulsing animal a brief period of anoxemia evokes an increase of brain lactate while phosphocreatine stores are depleted.[42] The coupling of the curtailment in the oxygen available to the brain with the excessive cerebral requirements induced by the fit may make for serious inroads into the anaerobic resources of that organ. On this basis, deprivation of oxygen caused by the inhalation of nitrogen should be less taxing to the patient in general and to his anaerobic cerebral mechanisms in particular than convulsions induced by such stimulants as metrazol or an electric current.

TABLE 58. CONVULSIVE ACTIVITY OF BRAIN IN TEN-SECOND FIT
(mM/Kg. Tissue)

	Glycogen	PC	ATP
Control	6.8	2.4	1.3
Fit	4.7	1.2	0.5

Cats, paralyzed with erythroidine and maintained by artificial respiration, were subjected either to electroshock or injection of metrazol and other convulsant drugs. The brain was frozen in situ, ground to powder while frozen, and assayed for metabolites.

Effects of Shock Treatment

In this brief discussion it is impossible to review all the important effects of the shock therapies exerted on the brain but changes in the permeability of the blood-brain barrier should be mentioned. The permeability of the brain to certain inorganic substances is increased both in hypoglycemia[47] and in the convulsant therapies[7] for the cells lose their potassium and gain extracellular sodium. Such ionic shifts exert a profound influence not only because they affect the electrolyte and water patterns of the brain cells. Potassium stimulates strongly brain oxidations while enforcing other changes on carbohydrate metabolism.[4, 20] These actions may be expected to fall off as cellular potassium is lost. The entering sodium, on the other hand, interferes with so fundamental a process as phosphorylation and thus affects carbohydrate metabolism indirectly (see Racker, p. 70). In contrast to these results obtained with inorganic ions, some recent work suggests that protracted shock, sometimes called irreversible coma, is brought about by the failure of glucose to penetrate the blood-brain barrier[16] after too prolonged hypoglycemia.

We have been discussing the effects of shock treatments on the brain but it must also be remembered that the entire body may be changed by these treatments.[19] For example, during hypoglycemia the non-nervous tissues adapt themselves to the lack of blood sugar and switch over to a fat metabolism,[40] and a condition resembling diabetes is induced, assuring for the exclusive use of the brain any glucose which may happen to be present in the blood stream. Similarly in the anoxemia of convulsant treatment an adaptive rise in blood sugar occurs thus providing the brain with additional substrate for anaerobic metabolism.[18, 29] Just as the brain influences the body musculature by means of the somatic nervous system it influences the organs by the autonomic nervous system, and Gellhorn[17] and others[15] have stressed the effects on the autonomic nervous system produced by these treatments. The results of shock treatments on the endocrine balance are under investigation in several laboratories.[2, 10, 38, 39]

This analysis reveals that the convulsant therapies and hypoglycemic shock have much in common on a biochemical basis though their neurologic signs may differ widely. In all shock therapies, whether hypoglycemic or convulsive, the brain is deprived of energy, oxidative metabolism is inadequate to support cerebral function, and anaerobic breakdown of energy deposits is called upon to maintain the brain. Though these end results are similar in terms of biochemistry it must be obvious that the mechanisms differ in the two kinds of treatment. With hypoglycemia the brain is deprived of glucose and cerebral metabolic rate is depressed below normal levels. With electroshock or metrazol, brain activity is raised to such a high pitch that it cannot be sustained by the oxygen and sugar coming to the brain in the blood. Another difference between these two kinds of treatments involving their respective intensities and durations also seems to be important. Though the total effect on the brain may not be very different when one regards the biochemical result as the product of intensity and duration yet it would seem that the longer and more gradual assault made by hypoglycemia yields better results for some types of schizophrenia while the shorter and more intense convulsive attack proves better for the affective psychoses. When we are asked to explain the connection between the deprivation of energy or any other change wrought by the treatments and the mechanism of the therapeutic action we are met by many hypotheses, each more or less plausible. It is for future research to determine which mechanism of action is operative.

REFERENCES

1. ALEXANDER, F. A. D., and HIMWICH, H. E.: *The American Journal of Psychiatry*, 1939-1940, 96, pp. 643-655.
2. ALTSCHULE, M. D.; PARKHURST, B. H.; and TILLOTSON, K. J.: *The Journal of Clinical Endocrinology*, 1949, 9, pp. 440-445.
3. ANGYAL, L. v.: *Zeitschrift für die gesamte Neurologie und Psychiatrie*, 1937, 157, pp. 35-80.
4. ASHFORD, C. A., and DIXON, K. C.: *Biochemical Journal*, 1935, 29, pp. 157-168.
5. CALLAWAY, E.: *Electroencephalography and Clinical Neurophysiology*, 1950, 11, pp. 157-162.
6. CERLETTI, U., and BINI, L.: *Archivio generale di Neurologia, psichiatria e psicoanalisi*, 1938, 19, pp. 266-268.
7. COLFER, H. F.: *Association for Research in Nervous and Mental Disease, Proceedings*, 1947, 26, pp. 98-117.
8. DAVIES, P. W., and REMOND, A.: *Association for Research in Nervous and Mental Disease, Proceedings*, 1947, 26, pp. 205-217.
9. DAVIS, E. W.; MCCULLOCH, W. S.; and ROSEMAN, E.: *The American Journal of Psychiatry*, 1944, 100, pp. 825-829.
10. DURY, A.: *American Journal of Physiology*, 1950, 163, pp. 96-103.
11. FERRIS, S., and HIMWICH, H. E.: *American Journal of Physiology*, 1946, 146, pp. 389-393.
12. FOGEL, E. J., and GRAY, L. P.: *American Journal of Psychiatry*, 1940, 97, pp. 677-685.
13. FROSTIG, J. P.: *The American Journal of Psychiatry*, 1940, 96, pp. 1167-1190.
14. FROSTIG, J. P.; VAN HARREVELD, A.; REZNICK, S.; TYLER, D. B.; and WIERSMA, C. A. G.: *Archives of Neurology and Psychiatry*, 1944, 51, pp. 232-242.
15. FUNKENSTEIN, D. H.; GREENBLATT, M.; and SOLOMON, H. C.: *Journal of Nervous and Mental Disease*, 1948, 108, pp. 409-422.
16. GEIGER, A.; MAGNES, J.; TAYLOR, R.; and VERALLI, M.: The Effect of Blood Constituents on the Permeability of the Brain to Glucose in Perfusion Experiments on the Living Cat. In preparation.
17. GELLHORN, E.: Automatic Regulations, p. 54-70. New York City, Interscience Publishers.
18. HARRIS, M. M.; BLALOCK, J. R.; and HORWITZ, W. A.: *Archives of Neurology and Psychiatry*, 1938, 40, pp. 116-124.
19. HIMWICH, H. E.: Brain Metabolism and Cerebral Disorders. Williams & Wilkins Company, Baltimore, Md., 1951.
20. HIMWICH, H. E.; BERNSTEIN, A. O.; FAZEKAS, J. F.; HERRLICH, H. C.; and RICH, E.: *American Journal of Physiology*, 1942, 137, pp. 327-330.
21. HIMWICH, H. E.; BOWMAN, K. M.; DALY, C.; FAZEKAS, J. F.; WORTIS, J.; and GOLDFARB, W.: *American Journal of Physiology*, 1941, 132, pp. 640-647.
22. HIMWICH, H. E., and FAZEKAS, J. F.: *American Journal of Physiology*, 1941, 132, pp. 454-459.
23. HIMWICH, H. E., and FAZEKAS, J. F.: *Archives of Neurology and Psychiatry*, 1942, 47, pp. 800-807.
24. HIMWICH, H. E., and NAHUM, L. H.: *American Journal of Physiology*, 1929, 90, pp. 389-390; *ibid*, 1932, 101, pp. 446-453.
25. HOAGLAND, H.; HIMWICH, H. E.; CAMPBELL, E.; FAZEKAS, J. P.; and HADIDIAN, Z.; *Journal of Neurophysiology*, 1939, 2, pp. 276-288.

26. HOAGLAND, H.; RUBIN, M. A.; and CAMERON, D. E.; *American Journal of Physiology*, 1937, 120, pp. 559-570.
27. KALINOWSKY, L. B., and KENNEDY, F.: *Journal of Nervous and Mental Disease*, 1939, 90, pp. 439-452.
28. KALINOWSKY, L. D., and HOCH, P. H.: Shock Treatments. New York, Grune & Stratton, 1946.
29. KATZENELBOGEN, S.: *Psychiatry*, 1940, 3, pp. 211-228.
30. KETY, S. S.; WOODFORD, R. B.; HARMEL, M. H.; FREYHAN, F. A.; APPEL, K. E.; and SCHMIDT, C. F.: *The American Journal of Psychiatry*, 1948, 104, pp. 765-770.
31. KLEIN, J. R., and OLSEN, N. S.: *Journal of Biological Chemistry*, 1947, 168, pp. 747-756.
32. LEHMANN, H., and BOS, C.: *American Journal of Psychiatry*, 1947, 104, pp. 164-170.
33. LENNOX, W. G.: *Archives of Neurology and Psychiatry*, 1931, 26, pp. 719-724.
34. MEDUNA, L. J.: *Diseases of the Nervous System*, 1947, 8, pp. 37-40.
35. MEDUNA, L. J., and FRIEDMAN, E.: *Journal of the American Medical Association*, 1939, 112, pp. 501-509.
36. OLSEN, N. S., and KLEIN, J. R.: *Archives of Biochemistry*, 1947, 13, pp. 739-746.
37. OLSEN, N. S., and KLEIN, J. R.: *Association for Research in Nervous and Mental Disease*, 1947, 26, pp. 118-130.
38. PARSON, E. H.; GILDEA, E. F.; RONZONI, E.; and HULBERT, S. Z.: *The American Journal of Psychiatry*, 1949, 105, pp. 573-580.
39. PINCUS, G.; HOAGLAND, H.; FREEMAN, H.; ELMADJIAN, F.; ROMANOFF, L. P.: *Psychosomatic Medicine*, 1949, 11, pp. 74-101.
40. ROOT, H. F., and CARPENTER, T. M.: *American Journal of the Medical Sciences*, 1943, 206, pp. 234-243.
41. SAKEL, M.: Pharmacological Treatment of Schizophrenia. Nervous and Mental Disease, Monograph series, No. 62, New York and Washington, 1938. Authorized translation by Joseph Wortis, M. D.
42. STONE, W. E.; MARSHALL, C.; and NIMS, L. F.: *American Journal of Physiology*, 1941, 132, pp. 770-775.
43. STONE, W. E.; WEBSTER, J. E.; and GURDJIAN, E. S.: *Journal of Neurophysiology*, 1945, 8, pp. 233-240.
44. STRAUS, H.; LANDIS, C.; and HUNT, W. A.: *Journal of Nervous and Mental Disease*, 1939, 90, pp. 439-452.
45. SUGAR, O., and GERARD, R. W.: *Journal of Neurophysiology*, 1938, 1, pp. 558-572.
46. YAKOVLEV, P. I.: *Archives of Neurology and Psychiatry*, 1937, 37, pp. 523-554.
47. YANNET, H.: *Archives of Neurology and Psychiatry*, 1939, 42, pp. 237-247.

Shock Treatments in Psychiatry

LOTHAR B. KALINOWSKY, M.D.

The term "shock treatment" has no justification. The treatments in question do not resemble anything seen in surgical, anaphylactic, or other shock in a somatic sense, and they have no shocking effect on the patient in a psychologic sense. In insulin treatment, hypoglycemia is induced by injecting insulin in increasing amounts until a hypoglycemic coma is reached. Only deep comas if repeated up to forty or sixty times have therapeutic value. The amounts of insulin necessary to induce such comas vary considerably and have no meaning for the therapeutic effect. More superficial hypoglycemia has a corroborative and sedative effect but is ineffective in schizophrenia.

In the treatment of schizophrenia, insulin comas can be combined with convulsive treatment, either by injecting metrazol intravenously or by inducing convulsions electrically. Aside from such combination of the two groups of shock therapies, convulsive treatment alone, nowadays mainly in the form of electric shock, can be used in schizophrenia as well as in depressions, where it has its best results, and in some other conditions. It relieves dramatic psychotic syndromes, usually after four treatments, temporarily but must be continued in schizophrenia to twenty or more treatments if results resembling insulin treatment are to be obtained.

From a clinical standpoint the only common feature in the manifestations of insulin and convulsive therapy is a deep coma which in convulsive treatment is present during the immediate postconvulsive state from which the patient awakens spontaneously after a few minutes, while the hypoglycemic coma of insulin treatment can be maintained by the therapist at will.

Electric narcosis treatment is a milder form of electric shock treatment only in name. Actually, it is a generalized convulsion starting with a tonic phase but the clonic phase is modified. By continuing the current during the convulsion, the patient remains in tonic contraction, and only after thirty seconds, when the therapist reduces the current, do the last clonic movements become visible. The time relation shows that the total period of the convulsion amounts to the same forty or fifty seconds of other electrically induced convulsions, and that only the clonic movements become invisible during the passage of the initial current. In the second part of the electronarcosis treatment the patient is kept under a moderate amount of current leading to a state of general muscular contraction which, however, does not prevent him from regaining consciousness. In our experience this latter part is therapeutically as equally ineffective as subconvulsive petit mal, abortive or even Jacksonian seizures.

Dr. Himwich described the various stages of hypoglycemia which might reach the medullary phase in the fourth hour of hypoglycemia. In the beginning of a convulsive treatment nothing similar happens, and there is some evidence that the convulsion is elicited in some deeper part of the brain abolishing cortical function only secondarily. The various stages seen in insulin treatment can be found only in a reversed order during the awakening period after electric shock, in a less clear-cut and, as reflex changes have demonstrated to us, in a rather irregular way.

It is difficult to correlate the biochemical changes, discussed by Dr. Himwich, with clinical observations. As he pointed out, the only common denominator of the various treatments, from a biochemical viewpoint, is the anoxia. Yet, the treatment with inhalation of nitrogen did not achieve therapeutic results comparable to those of shock treatments. This might be explained by the necessity to revive the patient by means of oxygen before a sufficiently deep coma comparable to the medullary phase in insulin coma has been reached. Equally ineffective were previous attempts with inhalation of carbon dioxide made in psychiatry prior to the shock era. Carbon dioxide has been recently used again by Meduna and others in psychiatric patients but not in psychosis. None of these clinical observations supports the theory that deprivation of oxygen alone is the effective agent in shock treatments.

Another fact pointed out by Dr. Himwich is the increased permeability of the brain. He limits this permeability to substances other than glucose because of the experience in protracted insulin coma, in which glucose fails to restore brain function. It is probably not necessary to exclude glucose in a discussion on permeability because protracted coma is rather an encephalopathy with severe dysfunction of brain cells probably interfering not only with glucose metabolism but with other cell functions as well.

Dr. Himwich identified himself with the organic theories of shock treatments by saying that we alter the brain in order to improve the mind. He mentioned, however, that there are many theoretic explanations for the beneficial therapeutic results. There are psychologic theories which involve the effect of mechanisms in the patient's fear of death, his wish for punishment, and other psychologic reactions to the treatment. They can be easily disproved by such observations as, for instance, that in electric shock a generalized seizure as response to the electric stimulus is therapeutically effective in the vast majority of such favorable conditions as depressions, while the same procedure producing only a subconvulsive unconsciousness is therapeutically ineffective, although it involves the same psychologic experience for the patient.

Everything in our clinical experience points to an organic explanation for the therapeutic effectiveness of these treatments which, undoubtedly, are organic in nature. The changes which they produce in the brain and which bring about clinical improvements are still unknown. Neuropathologic changes in the brain are slight after insulin coma treatment and practically nonexistent in electric shock therapy; but there are electroencephalographic changes and organic mental changes do occur. Therefore, some disturbance of brain function due to the shock treatments has to be assumed. The approach of the physiologist to our understanding of this mode of action seems to be the only promising one. The work by Dr. Himwich and others in this direction cannot be encouraged enough because only by finding the effective agent will it be possible to replace the crude and empiric methods of today with more rational and less drastic procedures.

Some Chemical Factors in Convulsive Therapy

WILLIAM E. STONE, PH.D.

I would like to discuss two questions. The first has to do with the relation of anoxia to convulsive activity. Dr. Himwich has pointed out that the oxygen concentration within the brain tissue during a seizure decreases, presumably because the oxygen coming in is being used up more rapidly than usual. He has also brought out the fact that the changes in levels of lactate and energy-rich phosphates in the brain during a seizure resemble those occurring when oxygen is lacking, although the seizure is characterized by tremendous bursts of electrical activity while severe anoxia obliterates the cortical potentials. One would like to know whether the chemical changes noted in the cortex during the seizure are secondary to the decrease in oxygen concentration or whether they are more directly related to the seizure activity.

Dr. Gurdjian, Dr. Webster, and I[4] once attempted to answer this question. We gave the dog oxygen mixed with about 6 per cent carbon dioxide. This greatly increased the oxygen tensions of the cerebral venous blood and of the brain, but did not prevent the convulsive changes in brain lactate and phosphates after metrazol injection, suggesting that the changes are not the result of decreased oxygen tension. Experiments with an oxygen electrode of the type used by McCulloch and his co-workers showed relatively small changes in oxygen tension during the seizures, but from the work of Davies and Remond[1] with the microelectrode, it appears that greater changes must have occurred in the regions most distant from blood vessels. The larger electrode which we used does not give a true indication of the changes in such regions. I am inclined toward the view that the lactate and phosphate levels bear a distinct relation to the functional activity quite apart from their relation to the oxygen concentration, but this question cannot be regarded as settled.

Workers in several laboratories have observed that convulsive brain potentials are dependent upon a supply of oxygen and are suppressed by extreme anoxia. Potentials induced by applying convulsants to the exposed cortex are more sensitive to anoxia than are the normal potentials, disappearing more quickly when the oxygen supply is cut off, and reappearing more slowly on reoxygenation.[3]

Thus it seems unlikely that a metrazol or electroshock seizure has associated with it an extreme degree of cerebral anoxia. The changes in lactate and phosphates are generally smaller in seizures than during extreme anoxia.

It is also interesting that anoxia suppresses convulsive activity long before the store of phosphate bond energy is exhausted. The convulsive capacity must be limited by other factors than the supply of phosphate bond energy.[4]

My second point has to do with acetylcholine in the brain. Richter and Crossland[5] have studied the sequence of changes in acetylcholine of rat brain during electroshock stimulation and seizures, the brains being frozen *in vivo* with liquid air. A decrease of 56 per cent occurred during the three-second period of stimulation. The level returned to normal during the latent period between shock and seizure, then decreased again to the same low level during fifty seconds of seizure activity. Rapid recovery to the normal level followed the seizure. Thus the acetylcholine level seems to have an inverse relation to the functional activity.

The acetylcholine is thought to be stored in an inactive form, bound to some tissue constituent. Some of it is thought to be released and quickly hydrolyzed by cholinesterase during activity. Unfortunately it is not possible at present to measure separately the "free" acetylcholine, since the bound form is decomposed by freezing the brain, or more likely by the inevitable thawing process.[6]

Dr. Elliott and his co-workers have recently criticized the work of Richter and Crossland on the basis of experiments which indicate that the freezing process causes loss of acetylcholine.[2] A few experiments in our laboratory suggest that these losses do not occur if the frozen tissue is extracted with alcohol, but I hope to test this question further.

I hesitate to disagree with Dr. Elliott, and indeed, I cannot make out any reasonable explanation for this discrepancy, but for the present I still have some confidence in the liquid air technique in the study of total acetylcholine.

REFERENCES

1. DAVIES, P. W., and REDMOND, A.: *Association for Research in Nervous and Mental Disease, Proceedings,* 1947, 26, p. 205.
2. ELLIOTT, K. A. C.; SWANK, R. L.; and HENDERSON, N.: *American Journal of Physiology,* 1950, 162, p. 469.
3. GELLHORN, E., and HEYMANS, C.: *Journal of Neurophysiology,* 1948, 11, p. 261.
4. GURDJIAN, E. S.; WEBSTER, J. E.; and STONE, W. E.: *Association for Research in Nervous and Mental Disease, Proceedings,* 1947, 26, p. 184.
5. RICHTER, D., and CROSSLAND, K.: *American Journal of Physiology,* 1949, 159, p. 247.
6. STONE, W. E., and KIRSCHNER, L. B.: In preparation.

Discussion

DR. WARREN S. MCCULLOCH: The explanation of therapeutic results with any variety of shock therapy on the basis of merely pulling down the metabolism of the brain or a shift from aerobic toward anaerobic metabolism is, I believe, doomed to failure. Not only do patients drowned in nitrogen fail to show such improvement, but we have proved also, through a series of over sixty patients whom we decerebrated ten times with sodium cyanide, that sodium cyanide is without effect. It takes doses of the level of about 1 mg. per kilogram of body weight to do it. None of those patients were thrown into remission by that treatment.

There is one possibility of finding out whether a seizure, quite apart from oxygen deficiency, may be able to bring on a remission. That possibility lies in the use of oxygen as the convulsive agent.

At the present time we are engaged in a series of experiments on animals in a pressure chamber where we ventilate them with 100 per cent oxygen in an ambient atmosphere of pure nitrogen at 75 pounds gauge. The animals go into convulsions at a very high level of oxygen pressure in the animal and a very high oxygen tension as measured polarographically in the brain. We do not yet know the story of pH or blood flow in those brains, and as soon as we have that, we will start freezing them with liquid air and analyzing them. If that shows a seizure in which there is not a piling up of lactic acid, and a loss of the energetic phosphate bonds, then I think it will be worth while to try that procedure on man.

It would not be difficult as far as technic is concerned. One would simply take the subject into a pressure chamber, and allow him to breathe pure oxygen, while his accompanying physician and attendants breathe air. I think that procedure, and only that, if it is successful, may answer the question that Dr. Himwich has raised.

DR. HEINRICH B. WAELSCH: I should like to point to one substance which is a convulsive agent that has not been mentioned. This is ammonia. It has been shown that the ammonia concentrations in the brain increase in conditions of cerebral irritation and convulsions. Furthermore in insulin hypoglycemia there is a marked decrease of the glutamic acid concentration in the brain which may lead to an accumulation of toxic concentrations of ammonia.

One may speculate whether or not ammonia is actually the common denominator in different types of convulsion and that the effect of glucose in insulin hyperglycemia is in part due to the removal of the free base.

DR. SOLOMON KATZENELBOGEN: I am not going to read all of that which I have before me. Knowing Dr. Himwich's scientific work and, moreover, having had the privilege to discuss with him this very subject at a Neurological Association Meeting, I armed myself with some of the reprints of my clinical and laboratory studies of insulin, metrazol, and electrical shock treatments.

It is inconceivable to me why one chooses only one chemical reaction, in this case it is the anoxemia, to explain the effects of the shock therapies just mentioned, ignoring other chemical changes occurring at the same time. The investigators who developed the concept of anoxemia are well aware of those changes in the following chemical constituents: In blood serum: amino acids, icteric index, cholesterol, vitamin C, reducing substances, oxygen, carbon dioxide. In serum and cells: total phosphorus, organic phosphorus, acid-soluble phosphorus, chlorides, sodium, potassium, magnesium, calcium.

These definite changes, somehow, are ignored. Whether or not we are able to explain their significance is an entirely different matter, but these are facts; and if the object of science is to collect facts and try to interpret them, then, it seems to me, that not only the anoxemia but also the other chemical changes should be considered.

Electric shock treatment also provokes changes in the brain waves. In our studies we found abnormal electroencephalographic records for ten months after cessation of the treatment; the electroencephalographic changes were associated with memory defects.

REFERENCES

1. KATZENELBOGEN, S.; BAUR, A. K.; and COYNE, A. R. M.: *Archives of Neurology and Psychiatry*, 1944, 52, p. 323-326.
2. MOSOVICH, A., and KATZENELBOGEN, S.: *Journal of Nervous and Mental Disease*, June 1948, 107, p. 6.

DR. HAROLD E. HIMWICH: In reply to Dr. Katzenelbogen I wish to reiterate the remark I made in the presentation, namely, that in the brief time allowed it was impossible to review in detail all the important effects of the shock therapies exerted on the brain. I would like to make one other remark in answer to Dr. McCulloch: It may be found that one of the effects of high oxygen pressures will be to inhibit oxidations thus producing changes similar to those seen during anoxia.

CHAPTER 34

Use of Carbon Dioxide in Dementia Praecox

WILLIAM F. LORENZ, M.D.

In 1929, Loevenhart, Lorenz, and Waters[4] made a preliminary report on the effect of carbon dioxide-oxygen inhalation in certain psychotic conditions. This attempt to influence favorably the manifestations of a psychosis was suggested by our experiences with the use of sodium cyanide as a respiratory stimulant.[3] At that time our investigations were concerned with the clinical application of the work with cyanide previously carried on by Gasser, Loevenhart, and their co-workers.[2] The readily controllable respiratory stimulation induced by sodium cyanide intravenously administered was regarded by us as perhaps being useful in treating some prolonged psychotic patients in whom shallow, low-rate breathing contributes to the pulmonary complications that frequently terminate in death. Our objective was the treatment of a physical condition. We were, therefore, surprised to observe a distinct and favorable change in the mental manifestations in one of our patients. This patient had been stuporous, mute, and entirely inaccessible during several years of hospital residence. After a four- or five-minute period of continuous hyperpnea this patient was aroused and became alert, spontaneously productive, and responsive to questions. During this reaction he showed no verbal evidence of a psychosis. The alerted mental state lasted about four to five minutes. The cyanide administration was stopped shortly after this mental reaction was observed. The patient then returned, apparently, to his former state mentally and physically. After a short interval the entire phenomenon was repeated. The psychic reaction occurred only during a phase of relatively prolonged respiratory stimulation; when the latter was discontinued, the former disappeared.

Other similar psychotic patients were treated with varying results. In some the mental reactions were much less evident; in fact, none showed the same degree of alertness, awareness, and apparently complete disappearance of the psychosis that we observed in the first patient cited. We concluded at that time that a form of cerebral activity accompanies respiratory stimulation when the latter is induced by an agent, such as sodium cyanide, that interferes with oxygen utilization.

At that time this unexpected mental reaction associated with respiratory stimulation could not be studied further. Later, upon the suggestion of Loevenhart, and with the collaboration of Waters, carbon dioxide stimulation of the respiratory center was substituted for intravenous sodium cyanide.

It soon became evident to us that carbon dioxide-oxygen inhalation was more constantly effective in bringing about the cerebral activity in which we were interested. Its use permitted a wider range in respiratory stimulation which appeared necessary in order to obtain uniform results in the various psychotic conditions that were included in our series. After trying out various concentrations of carbon dioxide ranging from 10 to 60 per cent we finally adopted as a routine the following procedure.

Procedure

By means of an inhalation apparatus such as is used for surgical anesthesia, and, incidentally, observing all the usual precautions associated with gas anesthesia, a mixture of carbon dioxide and oxygen was administered. The initial ratio used was 10 per cent carbon dioxide and 90 per cent oxygen. The carbon dioxide was then increased at the rate of 5 per cent per minute until a ratio of 30 to 35 per cent of carbon dioxide and 70 to 65 per cent oxygen was reached. At that point the administration was continued for an additional four to five minutes. Higher concentrations of carbon dioxide were used in refractory cases but this was rarely necessary. We sought to avoid the rather violent muscular movements, the struggling and fear reactions, as well as the general depressant effects that were produced by the higher carbon dioxide concentrations.

The average period of treatment was approximately eight minutes. In some instances the cerebral stimulation manifested itself quite promptly, that is, during the first three or four minutes. In that event, the inhalation was discontinued. In some refractory cases, 10 minutes of treatment and higher concentrations of carbon dioxide were required.

Physical and Mental Reactions to Carbon Dioxide

Within a minute after the 10 or 15 per cent carbon dioxide mixture was inhaled the respiratory movements increased in rate and amplitude. As the carbon dioxide content increased these movements became somewhat extreme and the patient resisted more or less. Further increase in carbon dioxide usually produced a fear reaction and the patient struggled. If the carbon dioxide content was even further increased to concentrations of 35 or 40 per cent the patient manifested general muscular tension; the movements were no longer purposeful but resembled the tonic and clonic muscular movements of epilepsy and a coma-like state developed. It is to be noted that for the cerebral stimulation that we were seeking such relatively severe physical reactions to carbon dioxide were not necessary.

The mental reactions usually manifested themselves when the hyperpnea subsided. In some instances these occurred during the active phase of respiratory stimulation. In that event the inhalation of the mixture was stopped. All psychotic patients showed a mental reaction which we regarded as cerebral stimulation, but to a varying degree. The constant response observed in all subjects was mild excitement, talkativeness, and greater alertness. The more profound alterations in which psychotic manifestations seemed to be entirely absent were found only in certain patients with dementia praecox and some individuals with deep depressive reaction types of psychosis. In contrast with those in whom the psychosis seemed to disappear, we encountered patients who had been mute and uncommunicative who, as they became mildly excited and talkative, expressed delusions, admitted hallucinations, and thus revealed more psychotic thinking than had been formerly expressed. The best results were obtained in subjects with the catatonic types of dementia praecox. After five or ten minutes of respiratory stimulation these characteristically mute, inaccessible, and actively negativistic patients would relax from their fixed postures, the facial pallor disappeared, and the rigidly closed eyelids lifted. Purposeful ocular movements appeared; muscular movements were spontaneous. The former fixed expressionless facies was replaced by animation. The voice became audible, and the patient made spontaneous comments and was responsive to questions and directions. The period of cerebral stimulation was of short duration. Within two or three minutes those who merely showed volubility and mild excitement subsided into their former state. In those who showed a disappearance of psychotic symptoms and with whom a longer and more satisfactory interview could be obtained, the total duration ranged from twenty to thirty minutes. In either event the retrograde phase was relatively rapid and when started could not be halted or delayed. Within two to three minutes the return to the former state was complete and faithfully reproduced in all details as far as one could determine. In short, we were able to communicate with some patients who had been previously inaccessible. In approximately 30 per cent of our cases of dementia praecox the information obtained from the patient was used to set up a therapeutic program. The thoughts and interests revealed by some of these patients who appeared to have been completely removed from reality over a long period were surprisingly normal. Some of our profoundly depressed patients revealed past experiences and thoughts that seemed to be significant and in keeping with their deep depression.

Clinical Application and Results

As we continued with our investigations we found the therapeutic results to be negligible. No lasting benefits were observed. In evaluating our results, however, it must be held in mind that our patients had rather profound and prolonged mental disorders; also, that our therapeutic efforts were entirely in the nature of seeking to communicate with a patient in whom some barriers were created by the psychosis, and the patient appeared to be out of contact with the environment, more or less. The patient's illness could not be influenced, to any observable degree at least, by our attempts to communicate with him.

We practically ignored the usual psychiatric classifications which, incidentally, we believe may have had some clinical justification but were not helpful in any research such as we were undertaking. Our patients were selected on the basis of communicability. If this was impossible because of either stuporous states, excitement, confusion, depression, indifference, delusional thought, or any manifestation that interfered with the establishment of a measure of rapport, we sought to remove such barriers by our treatment.

Since the mental symptoms mentioned are found most frequently in the so-called functional psychoses in which the pathogenesis is still unknown, we included in our series as controls some patients with psychotic reactions of a type which is believed to be the functional projection of demonstrable organic pathologic change within the central nervous system. Favorable responses were observed only in the so-called functional group. A degree of cerebral stimulation occurred in the organic group but this was merely the mild excitement, alertness, and talkativeness previously mentioned as a common and constant phenomenon observed in practically all the patients we treated. Neither the quantity nor the quality of thinking was affected as far as could be determined.

In the nonorganic group (and this designation is being used with many reservations) the reactions ranged from a complete remission of all observable psychotic symptoms, through less pronounced alterations, to subjects in whom psychotic thinking was vigorously expressed.

As previously stated, the final results were negligible from a practical standpoint. Our therapeutic endeavors were curtailed by the limited period of contact we could make with the patients. Repeated treatments in the same patient showed, if anything, a lessened responsiveness by the patient. New information was rarely obtained at such subsequent attempts and spontaneous productiveness was diminished and fragmentary. Eventually we exhausted any available material that had been obtained and used for treatment interviews with the patient. In short, a satisfactory inquiry into mental capacity or mental functions generally was not achieved by us with carbon dioxide inhalation.

When a more prolonged reaction of a similar nature and in the same type of psychosis could be produced by other means we adopted this as more satisfactory for the therapy we were seeking to apply. Bleckwenn[1] found that the narcosis induced by short-acting barbiturates intravenously administered was followed by a phase of mental clarity in nonorganic psychotic conditions, and that this was especially pronounced in the types in which there was favorable reaction to sodium cyanide, and to a greater degree to carbon dioxide. The lengthier periods of communicability following barbiturate narcosis permitted more extensive psychologic inquiries, including the various personality projective technics, which are more time-consuming. Carbon dioxide-oxygen inhalation for this purpose was therefore discontinued. It remained for Meduna[5] to discover its therapeutic efficacy in some psychiatric disorders.

Conclusion

Our work with carbon dioxide-oxygen inhalation merely permits the conclusion that the pathogenesis in some prolonged psychotic conditions of unknown etiologic basis can be favorably influenced by a chemical means which interferes with oxygen utilization and thus alters neuronal activity.

REFERENCES

1. BLECKWENN, W. J.: *Association for Research in Nervous and Mental Disease, Proceedings*, December, 1929.
2. GASSER, H. S., and LOEVENHART, A. S.: *Journal of Pharmacology and Experimental Therapy*, 1914, 5, pp. 239-273.
3. LOEVENHART, A. S.; LORENZ, W. F.; MARTIN, H. G.; and MALONE, J. V.: *Archives of Internal Medicine*, 1918, 21, pp. 109-129.
4. LOEVENHART, A. S.; LORENZ, W. F.; and WATERS, R. M.: *Journal of the American Medical Association*, 1929, 92, pp. 880-883.
5. MEDUNA, L. J.: Carbon Dioxide Therapy. Springfield, Ill., Charles C Thomas, 1950.

The Carbon Dioxide Treatment

L. J. MEDUNA, M.D.

The carbon dioxide treatment has the unique feature of attacking directly some neurotic symptoms in spite of intentional omission of any suggestion and avoidance of catharsis and of symbolic approach to the psychoneurotic symptom. Recovery thus depends only upon the effect of the gas upon the brain tissue of the patient.

This carbon dioxide treatment consists of inducing anesthesia through repeated inhalations of a gas mixture of 30 per cent carbon dioxide and 70 per cent oxygen. During the administration of the gas the patient is lying on a bed or on a comfortably padded treatment table.

At the first treatment, it is advisable to give not more than twenty to twenty-five respirations. The patient is usually able to remember eight to sixteen, sometimes even twenty, respirations. If he does not lose consciousness with about twenty-five respirations, an increase of three to five respirations should be made on the next day. Further increase in the number of respirations should be determined by the patient's reaction to the gas during the administration and afterward, on that or on the following day.

The 30 per cent carbon dioxide produces a remarkable alteration of almost every nervous activity. It may produce simple rudimentary sensory phenomena; or complicated dreams, with or without emotional discharge; or emotional discharge without any dreams whatsoever; or complicated conditions of temporary confusion, hypnagogic hallucinations, and intricate cortical and subcortical motor discharges.

After the patient has inhaled the gas, his respiration becomes somewhat increased and forced, his pulse rate and blood pressure increase, and flushing and perspiration may appear. Some patients lose consciousness at the third or fourth respiration; some do not lose it in fifteen to twenty or more respirations. Between the tenth and the fortieth respirations, indications of psychomotor excitement may be seen. The psychomotor excitement can take almost any form, such as a struggle to escape discomfort or, in some cases, a repetition of some struggle the patient has gone through in his life.

During the first ten to forty respirations, the lower extremities are flexed at the hip and knee joints and slightly abducted. (This position, in some cases, may be of sexual context.) There is also a slight flexor hypertonus in the upper extremities and, frequently, carpal spasm of both hands.

If the administration of carbon dioxide is continued beyond this phase— let us say to between thirty and fifty respirations—adversive seizures, lasting a few seconds, may appear. During these seizures the pupils react to light. The movements of the patient during this phase resemble bicycling; sometimes they imitate quadrupedal locomotion. At fifty to sixty inhalations, plantar responses disappear, and sometimes Babinski's sign can be elicited. If, in some cases, the treatment has been prolonged beyond this phase to the next stage, say from sixty to ninety or more respirations, the pupils become rigid, and decerebrate rigidity develops.

The sensory phenomena are mostly optical in nature and consist of the appearance of a vague reddish light or small spots in the visual field. These spots, or points, or dots arrange themselves into geometric patterns, or, quite often, into elaborate figures with a straightforward or gyrating movement; or they may develop a perspective and become an actual dream. These dreams, in some cases, appear to be open to symbolic interpretation. In some other cases, they are so weird and fantastic that they may defy any description; or the patient may become the subject of an ecstatic condition such as that of some epileptic auras or of some religious experiences.

During this whole procedure the patient is free from any danger. Although I have administered more than 20,000 carbon dioxide treatments, I have seen no complications other than one tongue-biting and three or four spontaneous urinations. It must be understood, however, that before the patient is submitted to the carbon dioxide treatment a thorough physical examination should be made.

There is no set rule to determine the duration of the treatment. I usually give the treatment three times a week. Each treatment takes about six minutes: about two minutes before the administration of the gas, during which time I orient myself by asking the patient whether he has felt any kind of change since the previous treatment; about thirty to one hundred and twenty seconds for the administering of the gas; and two or three minutes in which I question the patient regarding the experiences which he has had during his inhalations of the gas.

The patient can leave the hospital or the office immediately after the treatment. The number of treatments necessary to achieve improvement in my group have varied from twenty to one hundred and fifty. If the patient does not experience considerable improvement during the first twenty or thirty treatments, there is little hope. I have found that further treatment will not be of any help to him. In many cases it is necessary to experiment with various depths of anesthesia in order to determine the dosage of gas therapeutically most useful for the individual patient. I usually experiment in the following way: On the first occasion, I administer the gas, giving the patient twenty-five respirations. On the next day, I question the patient as to any change in his condition. Two or three times on consecutive days, I repeat the treatment, with the same number of respirations. Then, if there is still no change, I increase the number of respirations to thirty. After repeating the procedure a number of times—in any case, in about ten to fifteen treatments—I am able to establish the necessary degree of saturation with carbon dioxide.

This treatment is ineffective in the anancastic reactions, such as the obsessive and compulsive neuroses and the classic form of hypochondria. And—as has been established by Loevenhart, Lorenz, and Waters,[1] who have studied the effect of carbon dioxide on psychotic patients—this treatment is of no permanent help in any psychosis. On the other hand, carbon dioxide inhalations make easily manageable a great percentage of patients with conversion symptoms, such as those patients who, without underlying organic pathologic change, create physical symptoms. Also susceptible to this treatment are two other groups of patients: those with faulty control of emergency reactions, such as anxiety neuroses with symptoms of sense of guilt or of inadequacy and irritability, and those with personality maladjustments manifested by social and unconventional behavior and by emotional instability.

Of a group of one hundred psychoneurotic patients with such personality maladjustments, sixty-eight showed a degree of improvement that can be considered practical cures. Comprising this group were patients with such varied neuroses as anxiety neuroses, spastic colitis, cardiac neuroses, female frigidity, male impotence, stuttering (thirty-five cases), character neuroses (many cases), feelings of inferiority, homosexuality (a few cases), and other more vaguely defined neurotic conditions.

The diversity of these psychoneurotic conditions helped by the carbon dioxide treatment, and the similar variety of cases influenced by an entirely different psychiatric technic—a technic utilizing ether narcosis—preclude our assuming any one of the fashionable psychodynamic explanations and force us to speculate about the common features of the pharmacologic processes involved in these different technics and different chemical agents. Our speculation, fortunately, is based on facts—facts ascertained from experimentation—at least with respect to carbon dioxide and ether; and we have every reason to believe that nitrous oxide and barbiturates work in a manner similar to that in which the first two gases work—although, perhaps, by different chemical mechanisms.

What are the known actions of carbon dioxide upon the nervous cell, and how are they related to those of ether?

Carbon dioxide, we know, produces the following effects on the nerve cells: (1) it increases the membrane potential of the nerve, which increase in the membrane potential is accompanied by a rise of the threshold of stimulation of the nerve; (2) it increases the height of the action-potential and prolongs its duration; (3) it increases the height and the duration of the negative after-potential; and (4) it decreases the fatigability of the nerve cell. Carbon dioxide, we know, increases the ability of the nerve to conduct trains of impulses, because the presence of carbon dioxide delays the appearance of the signs of fatigue.

Some of these effects must be reproducible by administration of ether; Lorente de No, indeed, found them to be so. "In general it can be said that all the changes that ether induces in the nerve fibers are a consequence of the changes in the resting membrane potential. . . . If consideration is given to the effect of ether upon the membrane potential of the nerve it becomes clear that the changes in the electrotonic potential and in the threshold of stimulation are in the main a consequence of the changes in the membrane potential. *Ether begins its action by increasing the membrane potential.*"

It is understood that an increase in membrane potential—regardless of the means by which we have achieved it—implies an increased threshold of stimulation with respect to stimuli from both within and without the system thus changed. Of what kind, then, must be the structural organization of any psychoneurotic syndrome that can be influenced by increasing the threshold of stimulation of nerve cells or of nervous circuits involved in the process?

A tentative answer to this important question can be given if we conceive our nervous system as one having an inherent tendency to restore its previous balance or to achieve a new balance after the stimulus which has upset it has ceased. This function of the brain belongs to the order of phenomena we call homeostasis. Homeostasis within the nervous system can be achieved by mobilizing various organizations. It can be achieved by mobilizing suppressive areas, which areas, by negative feed-back circuits, decrease or inhibit the function of the pertinent cortical areas even if the nociferous stimuli persist. The components of these feed-back mechanisms are fairly well known; for instance, area 4s, a typical suppressor area, receives its stimulation from corticocortical fibers of areas 4 and 6; the stimulation of area 4s is being transmitted through the nucleus caudatus to the brain stem; the ascending pathway from the brain stem reaches the cortex again through the nonspecific thalamic nuclei.

Homeostasis can be achieved also by the spreading of the stimulus through many relays to the appropriate motor cortex where adequate action is being initiated in order to arrest the stimulus and thus to allay the reverberation of the positive feed-back circuits. The components of this organization are, of necessity, complicated. They consist of afferent pathways to one or several sensory areas, of corticocortical pathways from the sensory areas to the ideomotor cortex, of the thalamic-hypothalamic-thalamic-cortical loops of each of the sensory areas, and, finally, of the corticocortical pathways to the motor cortex, with its loops through the striatum and probably to the peri-aqueductal gray matter and back to the motor cortex where, finally, the proper action is initiated.

Homeostasis can be achieved, furthermore, by mobilization of similar or identical organizations through their removing the organism as a whole from the orbit of the nociferous stimulus if the stimulus itself, for some reason, cannot be arrested.

It is easy to see that successful homeostasis, which is tantamount to successful living, is a matter of normally functioning negative and positive feed-back circuits. If the threshold of stimulation in any of these circuits is delayed by as little as a few milliseconds, homeostasis cannot be achieved, and a continuous reverberation ensues within the afflicted circuits. The continuance of this self-regenerating function, if it lasts sufficiently long, synchronizes neighboring circuits into its orbits; and when the output signals of these have spread to nonspecific effectors, perverse, wayward, interminable reactions, i.e., psychoneurosis, is produced.

Which of the nonspecific effectors will be drawn, by synchronization, into the orbit of the primarily reverberating circuits depends upon the threshold values and, thus, upon the resistance of the respective effector system; finally, this resistance, and not the original *noxa*, is responsible for the symptoms of the psychoneuroses. If the threshold of stimulation of the nonspecific ideational system is the lower, an ideomotor neurosis will develop; if the motor system is the weaker, a psychomotor neurosis will develop; if the autonomic nervous system is the most irritable, a psychosomatic or an anxiety neurosis will ensue. Thus, obsessions and phobias are symptoms of ideomotor neurosis; stuttering, tics, nailbiting, compulsive actions, and grand hysteria are symptoms of the psychomotor neurosis; spastic colitis, ulcers, and spasms are symptoms of the parasympathetic or somatic neurosis; and finally, anxiety is the classic symptom of the sympathetic neurosis. The illness will commence whenever the threshold of stimulation in the reverberating loops is lowered. A psychoneurotic condition, therefore, is a disturbance of the nervous net, a disturbance consisting of excessive prolongation of normal function and inducing originally nonaffected nervous loops into a synchronous, pathologically prolonged function. Thus, the existence of a psychoneurosis can be explained by an abnormally low threshold of stimulation with respect to normal stimuli, or by a relatively low threshold of stimulation with respect to stimuli of exceptional strength. In either case, the logical biologic treatment consists of raising the threshold of stimulation to the normal level of resistance to nociferous stimuli from within or from without.

This postulate seems to be fulfilled by the judiciously repeated administration of carbon dioxide and, to some extent, by that of the other gases.

REFERENCES

1. LOEVENHART, A. S.; LORENZ, W. P.; and WATERS, R. M.: *Journal of the American Medical Association*, 1929, 92, p. 880.
2. MEDUNA, L. J.: Carbon Dioxide Therapy. Springfield, Ill., Charles C Thomas, 1950.
3. PALMER, HAROLD: Recent Technique of Physical Treatment and Its Results. In: Modern Trends in Psychological Medicine. New York, Paul B. Hoeber, Inc., 1949.

Nitrous Oxide Inhalation as an Adjunct Therapy

H. LEHMANN, M.D.

I wish to state, at the outset, that I appreciate the privilege of having been asked to speak after these two eminent investigators have reported on their work with carbon dioxide in various psychiatric disorders. I must also say, at the outset, that I have no personal experience with carbon dioxide used as the only therapeutic procedure, and very limited experience with carbon dioxide as an adjunct to therapy.

However, during the last four years, Dr. C. Bos[2, 4] and I have used a treatment which is in many respects similar to the carbon dioxide therapy. Instead of carbon dioxide we have used nitrous oxide as the inhalant. As with carbon dioxide, unconsciousness is produced within a minute or two, dreams and automatisms may occur during this period, and complete physiologic recovery takes place rapidly.

We have, however, no precise theory as to how nitrous oxide produces its effects, and we give no statistics because, in contrast to the approach of Dr. Meduna, we have never employed nitrous oxide as the only therapeutic agent, but have been very careful to consider it only as an adjunct to the general psychiatric treatment of the patient.

That leaves us in a somewhat precarious position because, as we have been told several times during this meeting, there are the two schools of the "organicists" and the "psychodynamicists"—and where do we belong? When we give a physical treatment, the rabid psychodynamicist might call it a sadistic assault, and when we try to interpret what this treatment means to the patient, the organicist might accuse us of philosophic speculation. And the "constitutionalist" will not even look at our results because we cannot furnish him with the pedigree of the patient. Yet, no matter what we say, I think we are all practicing more or less integrated psychiatry, and, therefore, I am going to present the treatment for what it is: one of the treatments in psychiatry.

Figure 203 shows what happens to the brain during a nitrous oxide treatment administered according to our method. The patient inhales pure nitrous oxide for a period of one and a half to two and a half minutes, and during that period a state of unconsciousness (deep coma) develops.

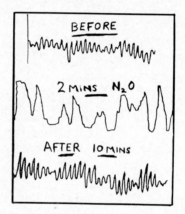

FIG. 203. Electroencephalogram before, during, and after nitrous oxide administration.

In this electroencephalogram of an experimental subject we see before the administration of nitrous oxide—in the upper row—normal alpha rhythm. After two minutes of pure nitrous oxide inhalation a very pronounced change in the pattern of brain potentials has taken place. This appears, in the middle row, in the form of large, slow waves which reflect the disturbance of brain metabolism due to cerebral anoxia. That this metabolic disturbance is completely reversible is demonstrated in the third electroencephalographic sample reproduced in the figure; it shows fully restored alpha rhythm following nitrous oxide administration, after the subject has breathed room air for ten minutes. These tracings were taken from occipital leads.

One word about the rationale that induced us to employ nitrous oxide narcosis. When Himwich[1] in 1939, did not get the therapeutic results he had hoped for with nitrogen inhalation in schizophrenic patients, we thought that the anoxia which was produced might still be useful, if not in bringing about recovery, at least in bringing about a change in the patient's mood, in the patient's mental set, in his attitude temporarily. Such a temporary change could then be used as a tool in our psychiatric follow-up work with the patient.

It is not quite clear whether nitrous oxide in addition to producing anoxia has any toxic effects. We have given nitrous oxide repeatedly, in some cases daily, over a period of weeks without ever noting any persistent untoward

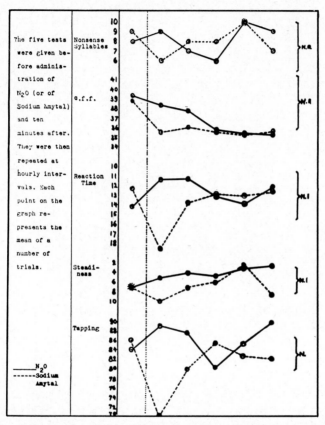

FIG. 204. Effects of nitrous oxide and sodium amytal on various psychophysiologic tests. An upward direction of the curves expresses an increase and a downward direction a decrease in functional efficiency.

effects. The action of nitrous oxide is, however, somewhat different from that of pure nitrogen so far as the speed of loss of consciousness and immediate psychologic after-effects are concerned.

Figure 204 brings out some of the psychologic changes occurring with nitrous oxide administration. The graphs represent psychophysiologic tests given before and at regular intervals after the nitrous oxide treatment. Memory was tested through the learning of nonsense syllables. Some of these tests are identical with those Dr. McFarland reported in his paper on the effects of anoxia. Tests were given for reaction time, critical flicker fusion frequency, steadiness, and tapping speed. The tests were recorded before nitrous oxide was given, and were repeated ten minutes after nitrous oxide, as well as one hour, two hours, and three and four hours later. The subject had been unconscious for sixty-five seconds. The uninterrupted line gives the test results before and after nitrous oxide. The dotted line represents the same tests with the same person, three days later, following intravenous administration of four grains of sodium amytal.

There are important differences in the test performance following nitrous oxide and sodium amytal. After nitrous oxide, there seems to be no significant change. Possibly a trend toward some temporary improvement in the learning of nonsense syllables, reaction time, hand steadiness, and tapping speed is apparent, while the critical flicker fusion frequency shows a slight drop. With sodium amytal, the test performance shows a tendency to deterioration in all five tests employed. Within ten minutes, sodium amytal produces psychomotor retardation, and nitrous oxide facilitation of various psychic and motor functions.

Then, after an hour, or more distinctly, after two hours, the curves tend to meet; in other words, the sodium amytal subject is coming out of his retardation, and the nitrous oxide-treated individual is slowly developing a mild inhibition of some psychic functions, setting in about one to two hours after the nitrous oxide treatment. At the same time, he experiences a feeling of fatigue and drowsiness.

We were hoping that we might be able to use the period of relative facilitation following nitrous oxide inhalation in psychotherapy, not only in releasing material from the patient through disinhibition but also by improving the rapport between patient and therapist and helping the patient, because of his increased confidence, to assimilate facts and mental concepts which he previously was not able to accept. We find that this is often the case.

In contrast to other workers[3, 5] who have administered nitrous oxide for the psychiatric treatment of specific conditions, we use nitrous oxide in a less restricted manner.

We use it in schizophrenia, during the rehabilitation period following shock treatments. We use it in mild depressions. We use it in depressions which threaten to relapse after electroconvulsive treatment. We use it in psychoneurotics. We have never felt that it has any specific physiologic action other than the temporary effects which we described and which can probably be explained completely on the basis of cerebral anoxia. In psychiatric treatment this alteration of brain metabolism may be a factor. In addition one has to consider the brief psychomotor facilitation produced, and the symbolic significance to the patient of his sudden loss of consciousness, and the dreams which may occur during nitrous oxide treatment.

REFERENCES

1. ALEXANDER, F. A. D., and HIMWICH, H. E.: *The American Journal of Psychiatry*, 1939, 96, p. 643.
2. BOS, C. and LEHMANN, H. E.: *Journal of Mental Science*, 1950, 96, p. 509.
3. FOGEL, E. J., and GRAY, L. P.: *The American Journal of Psychiatry*, 1940, 97, p. 677.
4. LEHMANN, H., and BOS, C.: *The American Journal of Psychiatry*, 1947, 104, p. 164.
5. ROGERSON, C. H.: *British Medical Journal*, 1944, 1, p. 811.

Discussion

DR. SEYMOUR S. KETY: I was interested in what Dr. Lorenz had to say about the ability of carbon dioxide to increase the accessibility of patients, and I recall that carbon dioxide, among its various other properties, is also a very potent narcotic. The possibility suggests itself that perhaps the mechanism and action of carbon dioxide in increasing accessibility of patients may be quite similar to that of the barbiturates in increasing the accessibility of patients as a result of its narcotic action. I am wondering if anybody has any other thoughts concerning this.

DR. L. J. MEDUNA: There is no doubt that both carbon dioxide and barbiturates increase the excitability of patients as a result of their narcotic action. This mechanism, however, does not enter into the evaluation of the results produced by carbon dioxide because in my series of one hundred patients no attempt was made to use any psychotherapy.

I believe that a salient point in the carbon dioxide treatment is an increase in the threshold of stimulation of those structures of the nervous system that were pathologically irritable. The increase of threshold of stimulation in these structures amounts to a decrease of irritability of the affected systems.

CHAPTER 35

Niacin Therapy in Psychotic States

H. LEHMANN, M.D.

I VIVIDLY remember the feeling of tragic helplessness while witnessing the slow death of a woman patient. She was suffering from full-blown clinical pellagra and was the first patient with this disease whom I had seen. That was back in 1937. We knew that pellagra was a deficiency disease but we had no effective treatment. A few months later Elvehjem and his associates[4] isolated nicotinic acid and its amide from liver and demonstrated that it was effective in curing "black tongue," a pellagra equivalent in dogs. Soon afterwards Spies and others established nicotinic acid as the specific curative agent in human pellagra.[11]

As early as 1911, Funk[5] had reported the presence of nicotinic acid in his extracts. Warburg[14] knew of its association with tissue respiratory enzymes. Let me recall to you briefly some of the essential facts concerning the chemical, metabolic, and pharmacologic properties of nicotinic acid or niacin.

Properties of Niacin

Niacin has a comparatively simple chemical structure. It is a pyridine derivative and one of the most thermostable members of the vitamin B complex.

$$
\begin{array}{c}
\text{CH} \\
\diagup\!\!\diagup \qquad \diagdown \\
\text{HC} \qquad\qquad \text{CCOOH} \\
| \qquad\qquad\quad \| \\
\text{HC} \qquad\quad \text{CH} \\
\diagdown\!\!\diagdown \qquad \diagup \\
\text{N}
\end{array}
$$

Nicotinic acid in the form of the amide is a component of the pyridine nucleotides which as important constituents of a coenzyme system play an essential role as hydrogen transporters in cellular metabolism. These coenzymes for dehydrogenases are links in the chain leading from the metabolite to the final oxidation by cytochrome oxidase.

In addition to being an indispensable factor of cellular metabolism, niacin produces pronounced and specific pharmacologic effects. Its most characteristic pharmacologic action consists in peripheral vasodilatation. After ingestion of an amount of nicotinic acid of more than 50 mg., flushing of the face and neck may occur within ten to twenty minutes. With larger doses the peripheral vasodilatation may involve the whole body. The threshold for this "flushing effect" with regard to the amount of niacin required varies not only between various individuals but also in the same individual depending on a variety of factors. Thus 50 mg. of niacin may produce flushing one day while 100 mg. may not have this effect two days later in the same subject. The amide of nicotinic acid, however, does not produce vasodilatation, and it is therefore preferred to niacin when only the metabolic vitamin action is desired, since headache and itching of the skin may accompany the flushing.

The question was raised whether the cutaneous flush produced by niacin extends into the brain with a resulting increase of cerebral blood flow. Aring and his co-workers[1] were able to demonstrate by means of a plethysmographic method that the cerebral blood flow in their subjects was increased approximately 20 per cent following the administration of niacin while the systemic blood flow was not significantly altered. Moore[9] observed increase of spinal fluid pressure in human beings and dilatation of pial vessels in the cat following intravenous administration of nicotinic acid. Recently Scheinberg[10] using an entirely different method of determining intracranial circulation came to the conclusion that nicotinic acid in doses of 300 to 800 mg. given intravenously does not increase the cerebral blood flow. The final decision in the question whether or not the facial flush produced by nicotinic acid is accompanied by a "brain flush" and an improvement of the cerebral blood supply awaits further clarification with regard to the reliability of the methods used by different workers to determine cerebral blood flow. I should like to add that most clinicians are still assuming that niacin produces cerebral vasodilatation.

Clinical Uses of Niacin

It was evident that a drug with the remarkable metabolic and pharmacologic characteristics of niacin which even in very large doses is almost nontoxic would not be allowed to gather dust on the clinician's shelves. Typical pellagra, except for the South of the United States, is a rather rare disease on the North American continent. But there are other conditions which present, if not all, at least some of the more characteristic symptoms of pellagra. Spies,[11] in 1938, had already pointed out that the mental symptoms of pellagra, which at times resemble neurotic manifestations, at other times are decidedly psychotic in nature, often precede the development of the typical dermatitis and diarrhea.

In 1939, Cleckley, Sydenstricker, and Geeslin[3] reported dramatic therapeutic results with niacin in a group of nineteen patients who though show-ing signs of malnutrition did not present the typical syndrome or history of pellagra. All patients were psychotic, either deeply stuporous or con-fused. Many of them were elderly and the diagnosis in these would ordinarily have been arteriosclerotic encephalopathy. Glossitis was present in all but two of these patients. Treatment consisted in the daily intravenous administration of 100 to 200 mg. of niacin and somewhat larger doses by mouth. The authors thought that they were dealing with atypical cases of pellagra. In 1941, however, they published an account of equally striking results with larger doses of niacin in thirty-nine psychotic patients who were almost certainly not suffering from pellagra.[12, 13] They felt that a therapeutic trial with niacin was indicated in all conditions diagnosed as toxic psychosis or exhaustion delirium and in other psychiatric conditions without clear etiologic basis particularly those associated with lethargy or stupor.

An impressive account of a series of 150 cases of a specific syndrome, which the authors called "nicotinic acid deficiency encephalopathy" was published by Jolliffe and his co-workers[6] in 1940. The clinical picture of this condition is characterized by clouding of consciousness, cogwheel rigidity of the extremities, and uncontrollable grasping and sucking reflexes. The great majority of patients presenting this syndrome had an alcoholic history but identical conditions have been described in typical and sub-clinical pellagra. The mortality of these patients if treated by hydration alone is almost 100 per cent. Hydration and thiamine chloride administra-tion did not lower the mortality rate. Addition of other factors of the vitamin B complex brought it down to about 50 per cent, but those who were treated with large doses of nicotinic acid had a mortality below 15 per cent. With sufficiently large numbers of patients in the various groups these differences furnish crucial proof that nicotinic acid in this condition has a therapeutic effect which is not equalled by any other agent tried until now. Jolliffe and his colleagues believe that there must exist a com-plete deficiency of nicotinic acid to produce this specific encephalopathy. They explain that the ordinary pellagra syndrome (dermatitis, gastro-intestinal symptoms, and mental manifestations) represents only a partial deficiency of nicotinic acid while patients showing the encephalopathic syndrome without signs of pellagra would represent a complete nicotinic acid deficiency which develops so rapidly that the structural changes in the mouth and skin have had no time to occur. Bowman and Wortis[2] pointed out that many of the patients presenting this syndrome though they remained alive, retained mental symptoms of organic brain damage since structural damage of the brain may be irreversible if the treatment is not started early enough. At the meeting at which they spoke Zimmer-man[16] drew attention to the interesting fact that there is but a scant amount of experimental evidence which indicates that uncomplicated nicotinic acid deficiency results in injury to the nervous system. Thiamine chloride and riboflavin deficiency, on the other hand, readily produce distinct lesions in animals.

Medlicott[8] summarized the conclusions of these different authors in the following manner: Psychiatric conditions may develop with niacin deficiency. They have to be considered under two headings: (1) those due to chronic deficiency, (2) those due to acute deficiency. Chronic deficiency may manifest itself as a neurasthenic syndrome or, in the more advanced stages, as typical pellagra. Acute niacin deficiency may result in a state of confusional exhaustion or profound stupor and coma or in the nicotinic acid deficiency encephalopathy with its characteristic neurological manifestations.

In the meantime another theory for the therapeutic action of nicotinic acid in certain psychotic conditions had been advanced. In discussing Sydenstricker's and Cleckley's paper in 1941, Aring[1] had pointed out that the cerebral vasodilatation and the augmented cerebral blood flow which, according to his findings, follow the administration of large doses of niacin may be responsible for the therapeutic effect of this drug regardless of its metabolic function. In his opinion, one is not justified to postulate the existence of a niacin deficiency merely because niacin has a curative action in certain conditions. Based on the cerebral vasodilator effect of niacin as a rationale, Lehmann[7] in 1944 published the report of the successful treatment of a post-traumatic confusional state with massive doses of nicotinic acid. A middle-aged man who had sustained cerebral concussion in an accident remained in a state of complete confusion for several months. A number of therapeutic procedures were tried without producing any improvement whatsoever. The patient's condition continued to deteriorate as time went on. Then large doses of nicotinic acid were administered and within a week a dramatic improvement had taken place. Within a month recovery was complete and the patient was discharged to return to his work as an accountant.

Two aspects of this case are remarkable. In the first place, special care had been taken to make certain that the patient's improvement was really due to the niacin medication and was not spontaneous and coincidental. This was done by examining the patient several times daily psychiatrically and by means of psychologic tests for some time prior to the administration of nicotinic acid and during the course of treatment. The changes in the patient's condition were so striking and almost immediate that there remained little doubt that they were due to niacin therapy, particularly in view of the fact that various other forms of treatment employed previously had failed. The second interesting aspect of this case lies in the fact that none of the predisposing conditions which had been reported in the psychotic states treated successfully with niacin until then, was present in this case. There was no history of alcoholism. The man was in the prime of life. His nutritional history and nutritional condition were excellent when the treatment with nicotinic acid was started. He had been on full diet reinforced with vitamin B complex for weeks. Surgery or exhaustion were not contributing factors. It would be difficult to postulate a deficiency state under these conditions since such a deficiency could neither be explained by an insufficient intake of niacin nor by a sudden increase of metabolic requirements nor by a failure of the liver to store and distribute niacin efficiently. The author therefore regarded the unspecific vasodilator action of niacin as the principal therapeutic factor in this case.

A new therapeutic application of niacin was described recently (1950) by Washburne.[15] Washburne has used it successfully in the treatment of functional depressive conditions of varied origin. Surveying the literature on schizophrenia, she first collected some evidence suggesting that in schizophrenia the cerebral blood flow may be diminished. Calling attention to the resemblance of certain schizophrenic symptoms to those found in depressive conditions, she formulated the theory that depressive reactions are associated with cerebral vasoconstriction. In order to produce cerebral vasodilatation she administered niacin in large doses (300 to 400 mg. intravenously or up to 900 mg. orally) to fifteen depressed patients who were also receiving psychotherapy. The results were gratifying in all but one of the cases. Improvement, that is, change in mood and increase of initiative, usually took place within a week. Some of the patients relapsed at the termination of niacin therapy, but they improved again when the treatment was resumed. The author feels that no conclusions can be drawn from the beneficial effects observed in so small a group but that the results elicited were of sufficient uniformity to suggest the desirability for further study.

In passing, some minor therapeutic applications of niacin in psychiatric practice may be mentioned. Some clinicians give niacin in doses from 300 to 600 mg. daily to patients who exhibit more than the usual amnesia following electroconvulsive therapy. Niacin given in a single dose of 100 to 150 mg. at night is often helpful in bringing about sleep in restless arteriosclerotic patients. A combination of niacin with sedatives has been recommended for the management of disturbed patients with psychiatric symptoms of organic origin.

Mechanism of Action of Niacin in Psychotic States

The mechanism by which niacin produces its beneficial effect in the psychotic states in which it has been used is not yet clear. It probably possesses more than one "modus operandi." Easily understood is its action in conditions which are known to be associated with niacin deficiency. It is, however, questionable whether one is justified to postulate a nicotinic acid deficiency merely on the basis of a successful therapeutic test with niacin. It is possible that massive doses of niacin produce their beneficial action through some kind of saturation effect which may shift the balance of coenzyme systems involved in cellular metabolism until a new compensatory equilibrium is reached. In this case, niacin would act by means of its metabolic properties without necessarily replacing a deficient factor. The role of the vasodilator action of niacin has recently been rendered uncertain by experimental work which seems to show that niacin does not alter the blood supply to the brain. There is, however, also experimental evidence that niacin does produce cerebral vasodilatation. And on the basis of an improved cerebral blood flow many of the effects of nicotinic acid could be explained. In addition to the replacement, the saturation, and the vasodilatation theories, another mode of action is suggested by its therapeutic effect in functional depressive conditions. Here it may act as a physical alterative and the repeated pronounced peripheral vasodilatation, which often makes a strong impression upon the patient, may be compared with the effects of physiotherapy which in most of its applications also produces vasodilatation.

Whether or not the vasodilator action of niacin is essential for its therapeutic effect can only be determined in a convincing manner when two matched groups of patients have been treated, one with nicotinic acid, and the other with nicotinamide. If the results are identical the vasodilator action of niacin could be considered unimportant, since the amide does not produce vasodilatation. Such a controlled experiment, however, has not yet been undertaken. In the meantime, it is probably advisable to use nicotinic acid rather than its amide in all but clear-cut deficiency states.

Summary

Summing up all the evidence available, it can be stated that niacin or its amide is the specific curative agent in pellagra. The psychotic symptoms of this disease yield promptly to the administration of niacin. There is also good evidence which has been confirmed by several investigators that niacin produces often striking therapeutic effects in psychotic states which are characterized by stupor, lethargy, coma, or confusion, conditions for which one might propose the term "total cerebral decompensation," if the etiologic basis of these conditions is not clearly defined. A trial with nicotinic acid in these conditions is always indicated, particularly in elderly patients, and if there is a history of malnutrition or suddenly increased metabolic requirements. In the specially defined syndrome which has been called nicotinic acid deficiency encephalopathy, the administration of niacin is probably a life-saving measure. The successful use of niacin therapy has also been reported but not confirmed in confusional states following head trauma. This condition may be regarded as belonging to the concept of total cerebral decompensation. Successful treatment with niacin in functional depressive conditions has recently been reported but has not yet been confirmed by other authors.

Since the treatment with niacin is simple, inexpensive, and has almost no contraindications, a therapeutic trial with niacin may be recommended in all psychiatric conditions, regardless of their nature, which occur in elderly persons or in those who have a previous history of malnutrition. If the patient responds to niacin treatment, results should appear within about a week. Recommended doses for niacin therapy range from 300 to 500 mg. given intravenously, administered slowly during several hours, or oral administration of 300 to more than 1000 mg. of niacin per day divided into several doses. Intravenous and oral administration may be combined.

We feel that niacin has established itself during the past decade as a versatile and effective physiologic agent in the treatment of certain psychotic conditions.

REFERENCES

1. ARING, CHARLES D., et al: *Archives of Neurology and Psychiatry*, 1941, 46, pp. 649-653.
2. BOWMAN, K. M., and WORTIS, H.: *Association for Research in Nervous and Mental Disease, Proceedings*, 1943, 22, pp. 168-191.
3. CLECKLEY, H. M.; SYDENSTRICKER, V. P.; and GEESLIN, L. E.: *Journal of the American Medical Association*, 1939, 112, p. 2107.
4. ELVEHJEM, C. A.; MADDEN, R. J.; et al: *Journal of Biological Chemistry*, 1938, 123, p. 137.
5. FUNK, C. J.: *Physiologist*, 1911, 43, p. 395.
6. JOLLIFFE, N.; BOWMAN, K. M.; ROSENBLUM, L. A.; and FEIN, H. D.: *Journal of the American Medical Association*, 1940, 114, p. 307.
7. LEHMANN, H. E.: *Canadian Medical Association Journal*, 1944, 51, p. 558.
8. MEDLICOTT, R. W.: *The New Zealand Medical Journal*, 1945, 44, pp. 28-33.
9. MOORE, M. T.: *Archives of Internal Medicine*, 1940, 65, pp. 1-20.
10. SCHEINBERG, PERETZ: *Circulation*, 1950, 1, p. 1148.
11. SPIES, T. D.; COOPER, C.; and BLANKENHORN, M. A.: *Journal of the American Medical Association*, 1938, 11, p. 622.
12. SYDENSTRICKER, V. P., and CLECKLEY, H. M.: *The American Journal of Psychiatry*, 1941, 98, pp. 83-92.
13. SYDENSTRICKER, V. P.: *Proceedings of the Royal Society of Medicine*, 1943, 36, pp. 169-171.
14. WARBURG, O.: *Science*, 1925, 61, p. 575.
15. WASHBURNE, A. C.: *Annals of Internal Medicine*, February, 1950, 32, p. 261.
16. ZIMMERMAN, H. M.: *Association for Research in Nervous and Mental Disease, Proceedings*, 1943, 22, pp. 49-79.

Niacin in the Treatment of Depressive States

LLOYD J. THOMPSON, M.D.

WHEN I WAS asked to discuss the paper entitled "Starvation," I saw on the program the word "niacin." I expressed some interest in this latter subject because we have just started treating some patients suffering from depression with nicotinic acid following the program laid down by Dr. A. C. Washburne.

During my summer vacation, Dr. Wingate Johnson, our Professor of Internal Medicine, proceeded to embarrass me a little by saying that he had two or three patients on this nicotinic acid regimen and he felt that he was obtaining wonderful results. I knew that Cleckley and others had used niacin in depressive states and in schizophrenia also. About the first of September, we began using it in the treatment of depression.

Dr. Wingate Johnson also has treated patients with niacin and I believe his enthusiasm is probably greater than mine concerning this type of therapy.

We both, however, believe that it is well worth pursuing and we do want to know more about it. As Dr. Lehmann suggested, we intend to run some controls with nicotinamide and also perhaps some with sugar pills, because we think there may be an element of suggestion in this method of treatment.

I have had at least a dozen patients who have had this type of treatment and Dr. Johnson probably has had an equal number. I realize that case histories may be boring, but some of these particular cases are rather dramatic in the results obtained. I should like to describe the results in one patient—a man aged 32 years, who gave a history of three attacks of typical depressions lasting from a few weeks to three months, without hospitalization. I saw this patient for the first time on September 16, 1950, about a month after the onset of his fourth attack. He had been confined to his home for three weeks and had received considerable sedation from his local doctor. He appeared very agitated. He was tearful and could not sit still. He paced the floor. He wanted a sedative while he was in the office and said he could not stay much longer if he did not have something. He gave a history of having his sleep disturbed in the early morning. He had a definite self-accusatory trend. He said that he had lost his last friend and that everything seemed to be hopeless. We could not hospitalize him that day, so I started him on the niacin regimen.

This patient came back three days later, sat quietly in the office, and did not ask for a sedative. Since he appeared more relaxed and cheerful the treatment was continued. One week after the first visit he came to the office and said that he had been downtown and was ready to resume his work. He stated that he was sleeping well and that he thought that the medicine was very fine but he saw no use in taking any more of it.

Just one month later his wife called and reported that he had had a relapse. I saw him again wringing his hands and weeping; at this time we were able to take him into the hospital. He was so agitated that he had to have intravenous sedation. He was started on niacin treatment, but after about three or four days, when there was no improvement, it was decided that electric shock therapy should be used. After five electric shock treatments in four days, he again left the hospital, against advice, but feeling quite well. Six weeks later we had not heard that he had had a relapse. (This patient was seen again December 15, 1950, and he appeared to be perfectly well. He had been working steadily for six weeks.)

I must admit that it is a little confusing to present a patient like this one in whom we obtained wonderful results with niacin therapy and then failed to do so later on. I should like to mention, in addition to this patient, two women patients who came into the office on the same afternoon with what appeared to be postpartum depressions. They both responded very nicely to the niacin therapy but one recovered more quickly than the other. I found that in the one in whom the recovery was slower, the medicine had not been taken regularly but when she did conform to the routine, she recovered in a short time. Also among the other patients treated by me was a doctor, aged 50 years, who had been in a depression for over two years. He had been in two of our better mental hospitals and had received some electric shock treatments but with very slight benefit. He was started on the niacin treatment early in September and he returned to my office within a week saying that he felt more normal than he had felt at any time since he had become ill and that he was ready to go back to his practice of medicine.

I have no theory to offer beyond what has been said here earlier. I think that Dr. Washburne's rationale for niacin therapy is somewhat shaky and I believe that we all should remain a little hesitant about using it until we can find what its rationale is. The fifteen cases reported in Dr. Washburne's article and those mentioned here are not enough to give us conclusive evidence.

In keeping with our Chairman's advice, when I return home I shall treat as many patients as quickly as possible while the cure lasts.

CHAPTER 36

Effect of Corticosteroids in Experimental Psychoneurosis

HOWARD S. LIDDELL, PH.D.

THIS BRIEF report is intended, first of all, as a tribute to the scientific insight of Frank Hartman who, about twenty years ago, developed a potent extract of adrenal cortex. He tested the effects of this extract upon a bedridden psychoneurotic woman. The injections resulted in such improvement that the patient was able to resume her household duties. He knew that in Ithaca we had a number of "experimentally neurotic" sheep and he proposed that we test the effect of his extract upon the "neurotic pattern" in these animals.

We discovered a number of years ago that the simplest procedure for precipitating an "experimental neurosis" in the sheep or goat was to employ ten-second conditioned signals separated by constant time intervals. When the interval between all signals was two minutes a type of "experimental neurosis" resulted which we have characterized as tonic immobility. At the signal the animal reacts with pronounced muscular rigidity, lifting the stiffly extended forelimb from the shoulder instead of flexing it freely in anticipation of the electric shock as the normal animal does. This neurotic pattern suggests a frozen and distorted startle pattern. It was illustrated in Chapter 29.

With a constant separation of the ten-second signals of five, six, or seven minutes the neurotic outcome was found to differ radically. Here the animal exhibits in the laboratory a pattern of diffuse nervousness, as shown by repeated movements of the head, repeated tic-like movements of the trained forelimb in the intervals between signals, and rapid, irregular respiratory movements.

Why the experimenter can at will precipitate a neurotic pattern of the frozen-vigilance type or, on the other hand, can establish the agitated pattern just described by the simple expedient of spacing the signals farther apart in this rigid temporal pattern of conditioning is a subject for future research. At present we do not know.

At the time that Hartman proposed to test the effect of his cortin on our neurotic animals we had discovered only the diffuse agitated pattern of "experimental neurosis" just described. One cubic centimeter of his extract contained the product of 50 Gm. of adrenal cortex tissue and was contaminated by epinephrine in a concentration of about 1 to 500,000. In spite of its epinephrine content, the cortin extract did exert a dramatic effect upon the agitated neurotic pattern of the three "experimentally neurotic" sheep subjected to the test.

After the administration of 5 cc. of the extract subcutaneously for eleven days the neurotic animals had become calm. Their conditioned reflexes were precise and markedly more vigorous. The spontaneous tic-like movements of the trained forelimb were almost abolished and the nervous movements of the head notably decreased. In one of the neurotic sheep the above effects of the extract persisted for twenty-four days after the last injection.

To check the effect of contamination by epinephrine it was found that 5 cc. epinephrine in a concentration of 1 to 200,000 injected daily had an effect just the opposite of the cortin. The number of nervous leg movements in the intervals between signals was sharply increased, the magnitude of the conditioned response was cut down, and the sheep became highly nervous.

The details of the investigation will be found in our original report.[1] One further fact, however, is important for our present discussion. One of the sheep employed in the cortin experiments had developed its agitated neurotic pattern in consequence of attempting a too difficult discrimination of metronome rates and had broken down when the positive rate (always followed by shock) was 120 beats per minute and the negative (or no shock) rate was 92 per minute. The animal was restored to a state of calm by the injection of cortin and its positive conditioned reflexes became vigorous and precise. But in spite of its calm deportment after three years of agitated, neurotic behavior, it was unable to discriminate between metronome rates as it had done so precisely before it became "neurotic." Cortin was unable to restore even the much easier discrimination between 120 and 50 beats per minute. Here, then, was a change in its behavior as a neurotic animal which the administration of cortin did not influence.

The failure of cortin to restore this sheep's preneurotic ability precisely to discriminate between closely similar metronome rates recalled to mind results from the twenties which I have never published. At that time I was comparing the abilities of twin sheep, one of which was thyroidectomized at three weeks of age. By the end of a year the thyroidectomized twin was a pot-bellied, stiff-legged dwarf resembling the human cretin and typically only one-third the body weight of its normal twin.

The twins were trained in an outdoor maze of three parallel alleys 72 feet long. The problem for the sheep was to run four successive times through the maze. On the first trial the animal must turn to the right of the junction of the three alleys. In trial two it must turn left, on trial three a turn to the right and on trial four to the left. Neither normal nor "cretin" sheep ever learned to alternate right, left, right, left for the four successive trials. Both twins made errors, usually on the fourth trial. The striking difference between their performances, however, was in the pauses they made in walking or running along the alleys.

The dwarf cretin twin made frequent and prolonged pauses—every few steps, in fact. Its normal twin paused briefly and only at the junction of the alleys (the choice point in the maze). On one day's tests, for example, the normal sheep in its four successive trials paused a total of seventy-three seconds while its thyroidectomized dwarfed twin paused three hundred and four seconds.

But now thyroxin was administered daily by subcutaneous injection to the dwarfed twin. Within three days its activity in the pasture, as measured by a pedometer watch attached to its foreleg, was greater than any of the other sheep in the flock and when brought to the maze for its daily test it seemed nervous enough to "jump out of its skin." In spite of its greatly increased activity and nervousness it made the usual number of long pauses in the maze and the total time spent in stops while traversing the maze was approximately the same as before the repeated injections of thyroxin.

In this case a characteristic pattern of learned behavior established in the thyroidectomized animal was not substantially modified by repeated injections of thyroxin which had a marked influence on neuromuscular function, viz., increased spontaneous activity in the pasture.

The rapid advances in the field of neuroendocrinology since the above pioneering study of the effect of cortin on experimental neurosis in animals provide a strong incentive for further investigation of the effect of corticosteroids on conditioned reflexes and on the abnormal behavior of experimentally neurotic animals.

However, I believe that we now have a better theoretic understanding both of pavlovian conditioning and of experimental neurosis and this should aid us in planning a further investigation of the effects of the corticosteroids on these manifestations of animal behavior.

The three key concepts employed by Pavlov in describing conditioned reflex action are restraint, signal, and reinforcement. If we assume that Pavlov's conditioned reflex regardless of the nature of its reinforcement (food or acid in the mouth, or electric shock to a limb) is a special case of the emergency behavior described by Cannon and Selye we can transform these pavlovian concepts into concepts appropriate to emergency function.

The restraint imposed on the animal by the Pavlov frame or its equivalent, which through habit leads to self-imposed restraint, places the experimental subject in a complex stress situation and arouses a state of quietly maintained vigilance or alertness. The signals, both positive and negative, may be thought of as specific stressors (to use Selye's term) which elicit increased vigilance—specific expectations of reinforcement or no reinforcement. Finally the unconditioned stimulus or reinforcement, whatever it may be, serves as a relaxer and suddenly drains away the tension of the animal's acute expectancy thus reducing the intensity of its emergency reaction. Paradoxically, the negative conditioned stimulus (or signal) is a greater stressor than the positive since there is no relaxer at the end to reduce the intensity of the emergency function which it arouses.

I think there is a real simplification to be obtained here by changing over to emergency concepts. First, the inhibition of restraint is replaced by the notion of vigilance level. In other words, the animal upon entering the laboratory goes on an emergency footing which it maintains. There is an attitude of general expectancy. Anything may happen. Then the signals become stressors and the reinforcing agent becomes a relaxer, lowering the intensity of the animal's emergency response. We need not think of the positive signal as arousing cerebral excitation and the negative signal, inhibition.

From this theoretic standpoint, vigilance is the prime mover in organizing new behavior. This general alerting function is channeled into a complex pattern of specific expectancies both positive and negative. Pavlov spoke of such patterns as cortical mosaics.

It is useful, I believe, to think of such a pattern of conditioned reflexes as exhibiting a dynamic stability or homeostasis of its own at a second level of complexity—beyond that of Cannon's basic homeostasis. In man we may postulate a third level of complexity in the type of pattern which some call goal structure. Here belong complex situations which are never experienced, but only thought about, fantastic imaginings and delusional systems. This third level of complexity may be assumed to have its own type of homeostatic control by which its organization is governed.

In renewing our investigation of specific endocrine substances on conditioned reflex behavior and those chronically maintained patterns of abnormal behavior which Pavlov called "experimental neurosis" we shall take into account the theoretic points made above. We shall look for direct effects of the administered endocrine substance, say cortisone, upon the intensity of the general vigilance level (maintenance of homeostasis in Cannon's sense). But we shall not expect by its use to influence either directly, or immediately, the dynamic organization of the animal's habit pattern which according to our theory operates at a second level of complexity and has its own principles of homeostasis.

REFERENCE

1. LIDDELL, H. S.; ANDERSON, O. D.; KOTYUKA E.; and HARTMAN, F. A.: *Archives of Neurology and Psychiatry*, 1935, 34, pp. 973-993.

The General Adaptation Syndrome

HANS SELYE, M.D.

We followed Dr. Liddell's work with great interest for quite some time. I thought it might be useful if, in these few minutes of discussion, I would try to give you a brief résumé of those aspects of our work on the adaptation syndrome which might be pertinent.

Observations on various species of animals showed us that the organism responds in a stereotyped manner to a variety of widely different agents, such as infections, intoxications, trauma, nervous strain, heat, cold, muscular fatigue, or x-irradiation. The specific actions of all these agents are quite different. Their only common feature is that they place the body in a state of stress. Hence, we concluded that the stereotyped response—which is superimposed upon all specific effects—represents a reaction to stress as such.

The first-noticed manifestations of this stress response were: adrenocortical enlargement with histologic signs of hyperactivity, thymicolymphatic involution with certain concomitant changes in the blood count, and gastrointestinal ulcers, often accompanied by other manifestations of damage or "shock." We were struck by the fact that, while during this reaction all the organs of the body show involutional or degenerative changes, the adrenal cortex actually seems to flourish on stress. We suspected this adrenal response to play a useful part in a nonspecific adaptive reaction, which we visualized as a "call to arms" of the body's defense forces and named the "alarm reaction."[1]

Later investigations revealed that the alarm reaction is merely the first stage of a much more prolonged general adaptation syndrome. The latter comprises three distinct stages, namely, the alarm reaction in which adaptation has not yet been acquired, the stage of resistance in which adaptation is optimal, and finally the stage of exhaustion in which the acquired adaptation is lost again.

The experimental analysis of the mechanism of this syndrome was carried out as follows:

Animals were adrenalectomized, and then exposed to stressor agents. This showed us that, in the absence of the adrenals, stress can no longer cause thymicolymphatic involution or characteristic blood count changes.

When adrenalectomized animals were treated with the impure cortical extracts available at that time, it became evident that thymicolymphatic involution and blood count changes could be produced by adrenal hormones even in the absence of the adrenals. These phenomena, therefore, were considered to be indirect results of stress mediated by corticoids

On the other hand, the gastrointestinal ulcers and other manifestations of pure damage were actually more severe in adrenalectomized than in intact animals and could be lessened by treatment with cortical extracts. It was concluded that these lesions are not mediated by the adrenal and are combated by an adequate adrenocortical response to stress.[2]

In 1937 we found that hypophysectomy prevents the adrenal response during the alarm reaction and concluded that stress stimulates the cortex through the adrenocorticotrophic hormone ACTH.[3]

Later, when pure cortical steroids became available, we could show that administration of mineralo-corticoids (such as desoxycorticosterone) produce experimental replicas of the so-called hypertensive and rheumatic diseases: notably, nephrosclerosis, hypertension, vascular lesions (especially periarteritis nodosa and hyalin necrosis of arterioles)[11] as well as arthritic changes resembling, in acute experiments, those of rheumatic fever and, after chronic treatment, those of rheumatoid arthritis.[12] Yet, even very high doses of mineralo-corticoids did not induce any noteworthy thymicolymphatic or blood count changes.

Significantly, exposure of animals to nonspecific stressor agents (e.g., cold) produced marked adrenocortical enlargement and organ changes very similar to those elicited by the administration of mineralo-corticoids.[4]

Gluco-corticoids (such as cortisone), on the other hand, were highly potent in causing thymicolymphatic involution and in eliciting the characteristic blood count changes of the alarm reaction. Furthermore, they tended to inhibit the hypertensive and rheumatic changes which can be elicited in animals by mineralo-corticoids. Thus, in many respects, the two types of corticoid hormones antagonize each other.[5, 8]

Inflammatory granulomas, especially those produced in the vicinity of joints by the local application of irritants (e.g., formalin, mustard powder), as well as certain allergic reactions are also aggravated by mineralo-corticoids and prevented by gluco-corticoids. Apparently the response of the adrenal cortex is most important not only in defense against systemic stress (affecting the whole organism), but also in the manifold topical defense reactions which occur upon exposure to local stress (e.g., bacterial or chemical irritants, responses of a "shock organ" to an allergen).[7, 8]

It was also observed that crude anterior pituitary extracts[6] or lyophilized anterior pituitary tissue (LAP)[5] duplicate the above-mentioned actions of mineralo-corticoids upon the cardiovascular system, the blood pressure, and the kidneys. The hypophyseal preparations which we used were definitely corticotrophic, in that they enlarged the adrenal cortex, but they were also rich in the so-called "growth hormone" or somatotrophic hormone (STH). As soon as we were able to obtain purified ACTH, it became evident that the above-mentioned pathogenic actions of the crude anterior pituitary preparations could not be due to their ACTH content, since even the highest tolerable doses of the latter hormone failed to duplicate these effects. On the other hand, overdosage with pure STH caused cardiovascular and renal lesions, identified with those previously observed in animals treated with mineralo-corticoids. It was concluded that the above-mentioned actions of our crude anterior pituitary preparations were due to their STH content. It remains to be seen to what extent STH acts indirectly, by stimulating the mineralo-corticoid production of the adrenal cortex, or directly by sensitizing the peripheral tissues to mineralo-corticoids. Preliminary observations suggest that both these mechanisms are implicated.[10]

We conclude that the pathogenicity of many systemic and local irritants depends largely upon the function of the hypophysis-adrenocortical system. The latter may either enhance or inhibit the body's defense reactions against stressor agents, and we think that derailments of this adaptive mechanism are the principal factor in the production of certain maladies which we therefore consider to be essentially diseases of adaptation.

Among the derailments of the general adaptation syndrome which may cause disease, the following are particularly important:

1. An absolute excess or deficiency in the amount of corticoids and STH produced during stress.

2. A disproportion in the relative secretion, during stress, of ACTH and gluco-corticoids on the one hand, and of STH and of mineralo-corticoids on the other.

3. Production by stress of metabolic derangements which abnormally alter the target organs' response to STH, ACTH, or corticoids (through the phenomenon of "conditioning").

4. Finally, we must not forget that although the hypophysis-adrenal mechanism plays a prominent role in the general adaptation syndrome, other organs which participate in the latter (e.g., nervous system, liver, kidney) may also respond abnormally and become the cause of disease during adaptation to stress.

I would not like to take up too much of your time with this review, especially since a detailed discussion of the relevant literature has been published a short time ago.[8] However, in line with Dr. Liddell's request for a brief outline of the adaptation syndrome I hope that these remarks may help to clarify the problems we face in connection with the purely endocrinologic aspects of those stress phenomena which he has so capably investigated from the psychologist's point of view.

Interrelation between Hypophysis, Adrenal Cortex, and Peripheral Target Organs during General Adaptation Syndrome

The stressor (trauma, infection, burns, and the like) acting directly upon the cells produces damage. At the same time it also mobilizes defense by evoking a stimulus, which induces the anterior pituitary to produce ACTH; under certain circumstances it may also cause a discharge of STH. The nature of this first mediator between the directly injured organ and the anterior pituitary is not yet known (humoral, nervous?). Hence, here it is indicated merely by an interrupted line, labelled with a question mark. ACTH induces the adrenal cortex to produce predominantly gluco-corticoid compounds,

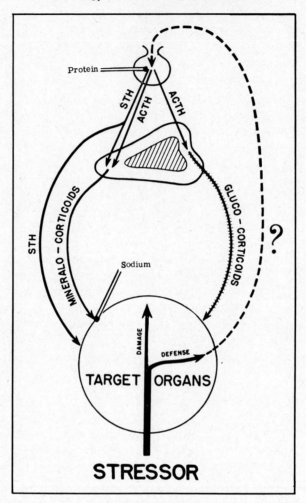

Fɪɢ. 205. Schematic diagram illustrating the principal interrelation between the hypophysis, the adrenal cortex, and the peripheral target organs during the general adaptation syndrome. (Slightly modified after Selye, H.: First Annual Report on Stress. Montreal, Acta Inc., Medical Publisher, 1951.)

whose effect upon the response of the various target organs is generally inhibitory (e.g., catabolism, diminution of granuloma formation and of allergic responses). Conversely, STH enhances a variety of defensive reactions in the target organs (e.g., anabolism, augmentation of granuloma formation and of allergic responses), primarily by stimulating the connective tissue. Part of this action is undoubtedly not mediated through the adrenal cortex, but this direct effect sensitizes the connective tissue elements to the (essentially similar) actions of the mineralo-corticoids. It is probable that STH also acts by increasing the production of mineralo-corticoids. However, in itself, it cannot maintain the cortical cells in a responsive condition, hence its "corticotrophic" effect is dependent upon the simultaneous avail-ability of ACTH. In the final analysis the physiologic and pathologic re-sponses of the target organs to stressor agents largely depend upon the balance between the mineralo-corticoids and STH on the one hand, and ACTH and the gluco-corticoids on the other.

REFERENCES

1. SELYE, HANS: *Nature*, 1936, 138, p. 32.
2. SELYE, HANS:*British Journal of Experimental Pathology*, 1936, 17, p. 234.
3. SELYE, HANS: *Endocrinology*, 1937, 21, p. 169.
4. SELYE, HANS: *Revue Canadienne de biologie*, 1943, 2, p. 501.
5. SELYE, HANS: *The Journal of Clinical Endocrinology*, 1946, 6, p. 117.
6. SELYE, HANS: *Canadian Medical Association Journal*, 1944, 50, p. 426.
7. SELYE, HANS: *British Medical Journal*, 1949, 2, p. 1129.
8. SELYE, HANS: Stress. Montreal, Acta Inc. Medical Publisher, 1950.
9. SELYE, HANS: First Annual Report on Stress. Montreal, Acta Inc., Medical Publisher, 1951.
10. SELYE, HANS: *British Medical Journal*, in press.
11. SELYE, HANS, and PENTZ, E. IRENE: *Canadian Medical Association Journal*, 1943, 49, p. 264.
12. SELYE, HANS; SYLVESTER, OCTAVIA; HALL, C. E.; and LEBLOND, C. P.: *Journal of the American Medical Association*, 1944, 124, p. 201.

CHAPTER 37

Results from the Use of ACTH and Cortisone in Psychoses

EDWIN F. GILDEA, M.D., ETHEL RONZONI, PH.D.,[*] AND
SAMUEL A. TRUFANT, M.D.[†]

It is well known to most of the group that moderate to large doses of ACTH produce changes in the behavior and subjective states of human subjects that range from psychotic excitement to no demonstrable change at all. An attempt is made in this paper to discover the kinds of patients that are particularly vulnerable or resistant to ACTH and cortisone. Also a number of components of carbohydrate, protein, steroid, and electrolyte metabolism have been measured before, during, and after treatment to discover whether the metabolic changes corresponded with variations in mental state.

Rome and Braceland[6] have summarized their observations on more than 100 patients treated with ACTH or cortisone. The diseases included rheumatoid arthritis, lupus, periarteritis nodosa, cranial arteritis, schizophrenia, involution psychoses, and allergic states.

They state that three schizophrenic patients and three with involution psychosis manifested "coincident changes of psychiatric significance," but that in none was there a true amelioration of symptoms. In the nonpsychotic patients they observed four grades of response: Grade 1—mild euphoria. Grade 2—mental excitement, increased motor activity, and sometimes elation and silly behavior. Grade 3—symptoms clearly a reactivation of previous serious psychologic disorders. Grade 4—severe psychotic reactions which subside within a few days after withdrawal of either ACTH or cortisone.

These authors conclude that the reactions observed were chiefly an exacerbation of previous personality dysfunction. In other words, a cyclothymic patient develops hypomania; a latent schizophrenic, schizophrenia;

The ACTH was generously supplied by Armour and Company Laboratories through the courtesy of John R. Mote, M.D. This work was aided by the Frank Phillips Foundation Research Grant and by the Julian Simon Fund.

[*] Assistant Professor of Biological Chemistry in Neuropsychiatry, Washington University School of Medicine.

[†] United States Public Health Service Research Fellow.

and so on. In summary, ACTH or cortisone administration constitutes a severe form of stress that tends to disrupt psychologic adaptation. About 5 per cent of all patients (over 100) have developed psychotic symptoms.

Rome and Braceland doubt that ACTH or cortisone produce positive mood changes that may have favorable effects in some patients. Sprague and associates,[8] from observation of the same patients, point to positive changes in mood, feeling of well-being, and increased mental and motor activity in more than half of those treated. It is agreed, however, that these favorable changes in behavior in most cases last only a few days, developing into marked states of irritability and excitement if treatment is continued, or reverting to pre-treatment mental condition during treatment or on cessation of administration of the drug.

Cleghorn, Cameron, and associates[2, 5] gave ACTH in doses of 100 mg. daily for five to seven days to eight patients with severe mental depressions. They observed moderate improvement within twenty-four to thirty-six hours. This consisted of increased activity, interest in surroundings, and return of ability to read and play. The last index to shift was the patients' own report. All patients regressed with cessation of treatment. No patients were made worse; the patients who had complicating symptoms of anxiety were not made worse.

Hoagland and Pincus[3] and their co-workers have treated schizophrenics with large amounts of ACTH or cortisone and have observed only moderate changes in behavior. They have not reported that patients were made worse by treatment. One patient only showed marked psychiatric improvement but relapse occurred with cessation of treatment.

The positive effects of ACTH or cortisone on mental and motor functions of alcoholic patients have been described by Smith.[7] He explains these results as due to restoration of adrenal cortical function which he states is impaired in alcoholic patients.

Hoefer and Glaser[4] in a study of fourteen patients, eight of whom had rheumatoid arthritis, observed the development of euphoria in seven of the arthritic patients—the eighth manifested a manic psychotic reaction. There were two schizophrenics who were unchanged. One patient with dermatitis became stuporous. Hoffer stressed the slowing and irregularity of the electro-encephalogram in these patients.

Bochner and Bond[1] have observed variations in response to these hormones similar to those described by the Mayo group. Bochner, however, found that normal subjects did not experience any changes in mental state following ACTH treatment. The amount of hormone given may have been too small.

We may conclude from the literature that ACTH or cortisone produces mental changes in more than half of the nonpsychotic subjects. The changes begin with a feeling of well-being; later euphoria, increased mental activity, and also motor activity are experienced. The patients recognize these as favorable changes. Approximately 25 per cent of the patients become elated, silly, and overactive. Less than 5 per cent become psychotic—usually maniacal or agitated. A few instances of schizophrenic-like reactions have been reported.

Psychotic patients respond to these drugs with increased activity, more interest in reading and play, and eventually a feeling of well-being and partial remission of symptoms. Results are temporary and in only occasional patients did favorable effects continue. A few patients, less than 5 per cent, became manic. Less frequently schizophrenic symptoms have been made worse.

Material and Methods

Group I. Seven patients with either depressive or schizophrenic psychoses have been studied intensively by metabolic and psychiatric methods. An attempt has been made to relate daily metabolic changes to mental and behavioral changes.

Group II. Nonpsychotic subjects (approximately thirty) undergoing treatment for diabetes, arthritis, and other disorders have been observed for mental changes. Only clinical description has been attempted.

Metabolic Studies (Group I): All patients were restricted to ward activities and metabolic balance studies were undertaken. The subjects lived on known measured, well-balanced diets and all urines and stools were collected.

Each patient was observed during the control period of five to nine days during which he was given saline intramuscularly every six hours and his metabolic balance established. No changes in treatment occurred except to replace saline solution with hormone at the beginning of the experiment. Treatment was terminated only by introducing saline again and balance studies were continued during recovery.

The details of the metabolic studies will be presented elsewhere.

Included here are results of measures of circulating eosinophils and lymphocytes; uric acid output in grams; and nitrogen, sodium, and potassium balances. Urinary corticoids, androgens, and ketosteroids were also studied but are not included in the charts.

Psychiatric Studies: Patients were observed by several psychiatrists and the results were compared. Activities on the ward were specially reported by the nurses and occupational therapists.

Results

The metabolic effects of the hormone are summarized in Figures 206 to 213. Key to changes in mental and motor activity shown in these figures is as follows: 0 = no change; + = some evidence of increased activity, spontaneous speech, interest in clothes, work, or play; + + = talking more, increased interaction with people; + + + = overactive, cheerful, talkative; + + + + = one case, activity increased to agitation, excitement, and panic.

It should be noted that sufficient hormone was given to reduce eosinophils practically to zero in all cases. Uric acid output was increased markedly in all but one case.

Sodium retention was present in all but one case. Nitrogen loss was marked in all cases. Potassium loss was variable.

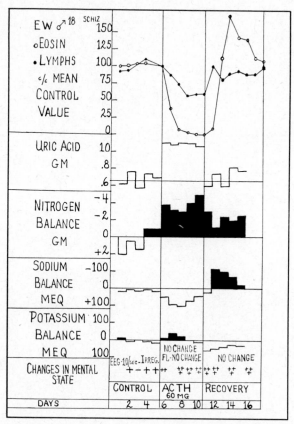

Fig. 206.   E.W. Schizophrenic male who experienced remission in symptoms. (See p. 602 for key to changes in mental and motor activity.)

Mental Changes: Within twenty-four to forty-eight hours after the beginning of treatment, four patients displayed increased interest in their surroundings, then more activity such as caring for clothing, playing, reading, and talking. This activity progressed to mild hypomanic activity and, in one case, to frantic agitation mounting to panic. No increase in schizophrenic symptoms occurred.

Consequently, it is possible to chart the variations in these patients' behavior in terms of increase or decrease in mental and motor activity.

The problem in all these studies is to determine just what exactly happened to the patient's emotional and mental status. In our experience with these patients, the chief changes that have occurred in the initial phase, which takes place in twenty-four to forty-eight hours, are this feeling of well-being and the speeding up of behavior, sometimes extending on to euphoria.

We have known a good deal about six of these patients over a number of years and have followed them since. Figure 206 presents data on a patient who is a young man 18 years of age. He was a schizophrenic with catatonic and paranoid features that fluctuated, but he had stabilized pretty well over a six-month period. We treated him with insulin (twenty periods of coma) and he changed little except that he became a little more paranoid. Then two months later we started the control period. We used saline. Probably it would have been better if we had used another hormone or cholesterol, but the patients constitute their own control. In reporting mental change, I have merely attempted to report the change in activity as measured by the interactions with other patients, by the spontaneous participation in activities such as occupational therapy, by talking, and by doing a great many different things. The one-plus can be regarded as a notable change that leads the patient to talk more or to engage in the spontaneous activities. At two-plus, he is meeting people, talking with them, and doing things almost at an ordinary recovered-patient level. At three-plus, euphoria and some abnormal overactivity are apparent.

In the middle of our control period the patient began to improve. It wasn't because he was receiving more attention, because he was a patient who had had a great deal of attention as he was a subject for a psychologic investigation—an extensive study on interrelationships of psychologic tests. Thus he had had just as many visitors in this control period as he had had over a number of months. The amount of recovery was not greater than previous variations and he was still a psychotic boy.

About twelve hours after the hormone therapy was instituted, the patient became a changed person. He said, "Do you know, I have not felt like this in years?" He was much pleased and said, "That insulin you gave me really made me feel worse. This is different." From then on he progressed to a mild euphoric state which continued after cessation of hormone therapy. Everyone who has known him (he is a doctor's son and we have many reports concerning him) says that the patient would scarcely be recognized as the same individual. This condition has now persisted for over a year and a half.

It will be noticed that the eosinophils and lymphocytes were quite stable during the control period, and the drop in the eosinophils was practically to vanishing. That is the experience of most observers with this dose of 60 mg. in twenty-four hours. I have shown these other metabolic variables in order to demonstrate the extensive degree of metabolic change. It will be noted that metabolic changes are profound and, although the patient was subjected to this treatment for five days, he experienced no change that he regarded as unfavorable.

Figure 207 gives data on a woman, aged 29 years. This patient's symptoms began when she was 12 or 14 years of age. They consisted of an increasing withdrawal from people, school, work, and all activities. She has been catatonic or hebephrenic more or less continuously for the past ten years. We brought her from another hospital because we knew a good deal about her and because she had had insulin treatment without benefit. Of special interest to me was the fact that her whole clinical history seemed to date back to infancy. She lacked interest, drive, and any evidence of an ability to meet life situations; she could be described as an individual of extremely low voltage.

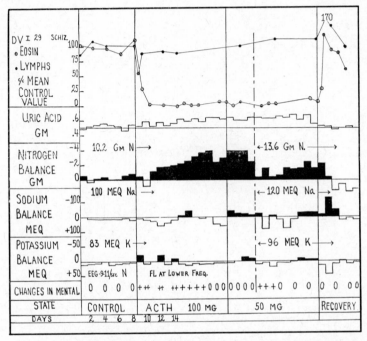

FIG. 207.   D.V. Schizophrenic female who experienced slight remission in symptoms. (See p. 602 for key to changes in mental and motor activity.)

This patient showed no change during the control period. The first noteworthy report was received about twenty-four hours after hormone therapy was instituted; the patient approached the occupational therapist asking for some work to do, and on receiving the work she undertook it readily and quite cheerfully. I talked to the patient while she was doing this work and asked her how she felt. She said, "You know, a cloud has lifted; this heavy cloud has been hanging over me for ten or more years." That cloud stayed away and the patient continued her activity but reached a plateau in improvement in six days. She was receiving 100 mg. a day, a dose sufficient to produce metabolic changes that were very marked; however, she did not retain sodium. She did not gain any weight, therefore she was not retaining any water. She lost weight. We stopped the hormone therapy for a period and then gave her more hormone to see if we could obtain another remission.

We then repeated the experiment with a larger amount of hormone and added more sodium chloride to the diet (Fig. 208). The diets routinely given were measured ones with an average intake of chlorides and other

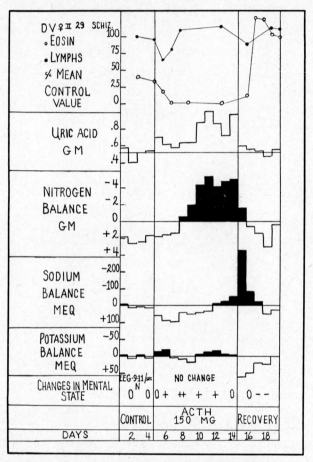

Fig. 208.   D.V. Repetition of hormone treatment in patient D.V. (See p. 602 for key to changes in mental and motor activity.)

substances. Thus hers was certainly adequate, but she wasn't able to retain much water. Even with the larger hormone dose, the sodium and the potassium changes were moderate. It is noteworthy in this second course of treatment that increase in motor and mental activity was not as great as during the first experiment, in spite of the fact that more ACTH was given and that there was retention of sodium and loss of potassium and more marked changes in other metabolites.

Our first patient had had a very marked change in his electrolyte balance, and we wondered if that had had something to do with the striking change in his mental condition.

I neglected to mention that the effects of the ACTH on eosinophils persisted for at least three weeks in the second patient, as shown in Figure 207. It was three weeks later that we tested her again with hormones. There

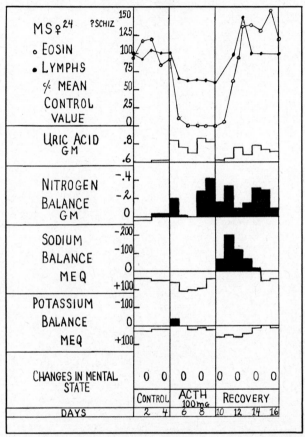

FIG. 209.   M.S. Young woman with borderline symptoms of schizophrenia. No change in symptoms. (See p. 602 for key to changes in mental and motor activity.)

were approximately half the number of eosinophils during the second course of treatment as there were before we first started the ACTH therapy.

Figure 209 presents the findings in the third patient, a young woman whose mother said that she was not like her other children because she had never been able to play much without getting tired. The patient herself fitted into the traditional pattern; she stated that she had been "in a deep depression all her life." Her symptoms consisted in feelings that she had no friends, that she couldn't make friends, and that people were down on

her. She didn't sleep well and she displayed considerable ritualistic behavior. Various psychiatrists differed as to whether she was psychoneurotic
or a latent schizophrenic. The central factors in her behavior were lack
of energy and vague depression in mood.

She received 100 mg. of ACTH daily and, as far as we could tell, nothing
happened to her subjectively: neither her mental nor motor functions
were accelerated. She did complain about being "stuck with needles."
She was unhappy when she gained weight, but her general behavior on

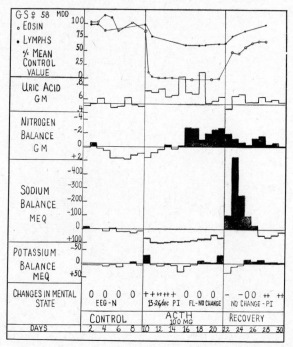

Fig. 210.   G.S. 58-year-old woman with recurrent depressions. Marked recovery after treatment with ACTH. (See p. 602 for key to changes in mental and
motor activity.)

the ward did not change significantly. Lack of mental and behavioral
change contrasted markedly with the pronounced metabolic disturbance.
The sodium was quite markedly affected; retention was followed by
marked loss of sodium after the hormone treatment was stopped. There was
no change in behavior following cessation of treatment.

Figure 210 shows the data on a patient representative of the group that
I had always believed would respond to some new drug that would give
a feeling of well-being—a patient with depression in mood. This patient,
G. S., is a 60-year-old woman who had been extremely vigorous all her
life, and, as far as physical examination was concerned, appeared younger
than her stated age. We had treated her over a number of years. Hers is

one of the rather unusual cases of agitated depression with associated evidences of metabolic disorder. She had had a number of previous depressions followed by good remissions. During depressions she has an elevated cholesterol and a low basal metabolic rate. Treatment with thyroid increases metabolism but the mental symptoms do not invariably improve. X-ray examination of the skull revealed hyperostosis frontalis interna. She

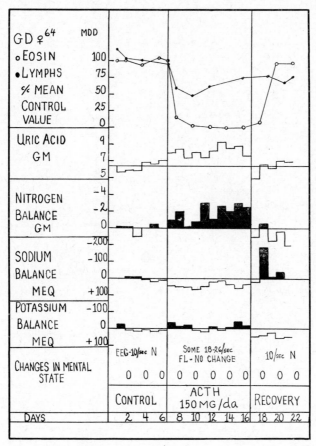

Fig. 211. G.D. 64-year-old woman whose symptoms and frequency of recurrent depressions closely resembled previous patient, G.S. ACTH had no effect on this patient. (See p. 602 for key to changes in mental and motor activity.)

was one of the patients in whom we believed that some correlation of metabolic disturbances and high serum cholesterol with some kind of involution depression could be demonstrated.

It will be noted that there is a marked retention of sodium. I believe that she gained about 20 pounds in weight. In the beginning of the treatment she experienced a feeling of well-being. After she gained weight, however, and could not get into her clothes, she felt uncomfortable and her weight gain dominated the whole picture. She became more overactive, but the group who were observing her felt she was overactive because she was so miserable. Then, when the treatment was terminated, she seemed to feel quite depressed because the treatment had been a failure.

Soon, however, she manifested a mildly euphoric condition, and she has remained well now for over a year. We do not know whether or not the improvement has some relationship to the shock of metabolic imbalance which she went through as in the case of the first patient.

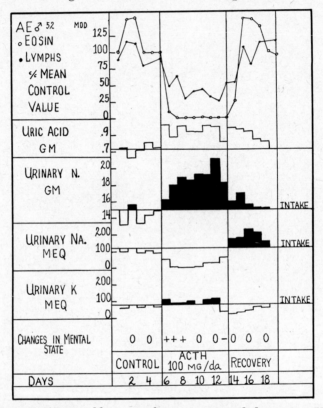

Fig. 212. A.E. 52-year-old man with severe agitated depression. Very slight improvement in symptoms. (See p. 602 for key to changes in mental and motor activity.)

Figure 211 presents the results obtained in another woman of about the same age and, if patients can be duplicated, this one was suffering from the same kind of involution, agitation, and exhausted depression as was the preceding subject. It was her sixth attack and the condition had proved chronic. She responded poorly to electroshock therapy.

This patient received a larger amount of ACTH, 150 mg. daily instead of 100 mg. that were given the previous patients. It will be noted that she did not retain very much sodium, in contrast to the previous patient, G. S.

According to the patient herself, no subjective change was noted; she experienced no feeling of well-being. She complained that we were just giving her placebos. She had been in a number of hospitals and had been subjected to prolonged control periods.

As far as she could tell, in spite of changes in her metabolism, her mental state was unaffected.

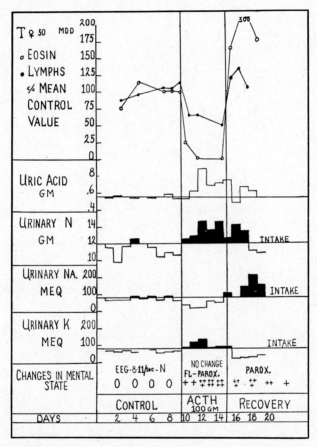

Fig. 213.   T. 50-year-old woman with recurrent attacks of agitated depression. ACTH rapidly increased agitation and anxiety. (See p. 602 for key to changes in mental and motor activity.)

Three or four weeks later we gave her electroshock which resulted in a fair remission.

Figure 212 gives the results on a middle-aged man of 52 years. He is one of the few agitated depressed patients in whom it was difficult to obtain a stable eosinophil count. The patient's cooperation was so uncertain that we went ahead with the experiment before a good control count was obtained. There was the same profound fall in eosinophil count as was observed in the other patients. With institution of ACTH therapy he grudgingly admitted feeling a little better; he became a little more active, but the change in behavior was not really significant. It will be noticed that the favorable effect did not last. The patient was unimproved after the experiment was terminated.

Figure 213 presents data on a patient, a woman 50 years of age, who also has agitated depression and a history of previous attacks. She has been in a chronic state for over a year and a half. She had received electroshock without beneficial results. After the usual control period we started her on ACTH therapy. She was markedly affected by it, was tremendously pleased, and undertook many activities. Then she became progressively more and more restless, overactive, and irritable, and finally she became frantic. We stopped the treatment in a shorter period than we had planned because of the patient's frantic agitation and panic. Within twenty-four hours there was regression to her previous depressed and agitated state.

This patient cooperated poorly and interfered with metabolic studies. From the data in Figure 213 it can be seen that marked changes in eosinophils, uric acid, nitrogen, and sodium occurred in a similar manner to that in patient G. D. (Fig. 211), who experienced no change in mental condition. There is the possibility that this patient was losing potassium more rapidly than were the other patients.

Group II was comprised of diabetics, arthritics, and patients with other medical disorders who were receiving cortisone or ACTH. Out of the thirty who were observed, only two developed states of manic excitement. No schizophrenic episodes were observed. We and Dr. Cyril MacBryde of the Metabolism Service noted that all but two or three patients responded to either hormone with a feeling of well-being and with increased activity which lasted one to three days and then leveled off. Cessation of treatment was followed by mild depression in the majority of patients.

Conclusions

From the point of view of effects of ACTH and cortisone on mental functions, our results appear to be similar to those of other workers with the exception that we have not observed the appearance of schizophrenic-like reactions.

It is our impression that when large enough doses are given, these hormones usually produce a feeling of increased mental activity and well-being and thus increase motor behavior. This speeding up may be sufficient to produce anxiety in patients and ultimately produce manic excitement.

The individual variations in patients' capacities to tolerate the severe metabolic changes are remarkable. This phenomenon is worthy of special study when more hormone becomes available.

The amount of change in metabolic factors did not correspond to presence or absence of change in mental functions of patients.

The favorable effects of ACTH on the mental condition of psychotic patients have proved to be transient.

I believe that we have a slight lead, however, that there may be metabolic substances in the adrenal glands that produce acceleration in mental activity and increase in energy. This possibility should be kept in mind as new extracts and related synthetic products are discovered.

In conclusion, I want to emphasize that in the patients without psychoses whom we have observed, we have not seen any schizophrenic reactions. When reactions occurred in about two-thirds of the patients, they appear to us to have experienced euphoria and increased mental and motor activity. There have been about 5 per cent of the patients who have developed manic psychoses that subsided on withdrawal of hormone.

REFERENCES

1. BOCHNER, A., and BOND, D. M.: Pituitary Adrenocortical Reponses in Normal and Psychotic Subjects. Paper presented at Central Neuropsychiatric Association Meeting, Cleveland, Ohio, October 13, 1950.
2. CLEGHORN, R. A.; GRAHAM, S. M.; and CAMERON, D. E.: *Canadian Medical Association Journal*, 1950, 63, p. 329.
3. HOAGLAND, H., and PINCUS, G.: Proceedings of the First Clinical ACTH Conference (Mote, J. R., ed.), p. 554. The Blakiston Company, Philadelphia, 1950.
4. HOEFER, P. F. A., and GLASER, G. H.: Proceedings of the First Clinical ACTH Conference (Mote, J. R., ed.), pp. 536-543. Philadelphia, The Blakiston Company, 1950.
5. LEHMAN, H. E.; TURSKI, M.; and CLEGHORN, R. A.: *Canadian Medical Association Journal*, 1950, 63, pp. 325.
6. ROME, H. P., and BRACELAND, F. J.: *Proceedings of the Staff Meetings of Mayo Clinic*, 1950, p. 495.
7. SMITH, J. J.: *Quarterly Journal of Studies on Alcohol*, 1950, 11, p. 190.
8. SPRAGUE, R. G.; POWER, M. H.; MASON, H. L.; ALBERT, A.; MATHIESON, D. R.; HENCH, P. S.; KENDALL, E. C.; SLOCUMB, C. H.; and POLLEY, H. F.: *Archives of Internal Medicine*, 1950, 85, p. 119, *Archives of Internal Medicine*, 1950, 85, p. 545.

Hypophyseal-Adrenocortical Dysfunction in Mental Disease

WILLIAM MALAMUD, M.D.

It was a great pleasure to listen to Dr. Gildea's report. It was a concise, clear, well-documented statement of facts that he had observed. I regret that I have not had an opportunity to see his paper. I shall have to confine myself, in my discussion of his material, to a few points I jotted down during its presentation.

I have had some experience, although not extensive, with the therapeutic use of ACTH. As far as the psychoses are concerned, I noted practically the same results as Dr. Gildea did; if anything mine were even less encouraging than his. In some patients (I now refer to schizophrenics), particularly those who in the course of schizophrenia also showed some depressive reactions, we observed a transient euphoria but it was only temporary and did not last too long, whether the treatment was continued or not.

Varied doses were used, from very low ones to as high a level as Dr. Gildea used.

I think Cleghorn's results that he reported at the last meeting of the APA on patients suffering from depressions would correspond to those in our experience; that is, in depressions a relief is experienced during treatment, but there is no carry-over following treatment and the results are not permanent. If that is not so, I would like Dr. Cleghorn to tell me whether or not he has found any different observations later on.

As far as the treatment of other conditions is concerned, i.e., in nonpsychotic patients, I believe that I would again agree with Dr. Gildea. There are, however, some rather unexpected developments taking place in the use of ACTH, and I would like to report one case which I followed recently at the Massachusetts Memorial Hospital.

The patient had severe asthma and also showed a severe reactive depression associated with the asthma. All types of medication were used to relieve the asthma but all were to no avail. Finally, it was decided to try ACTH and after a few administrations the asthma cleared up and, at the same time, the patient developed a state of euphoria, a euphoria which amounted almost to a manic type of excitement. He showed a great deal of activity and experienced a feeling of well-being. As the treatment continued, the euphoria changed into a depression with definite ideas of persecution more or less resembling a type of depression that is found in agitated involutional psychosis. Following that, there was a disappearance of the depression, but a continuation of the paranoid ideas, although no other signs of schizophrenia could be observed. When the treatment was stopped the patient reverted to his asthmatic condition, and when it was resumed the asthma disappeared and psychotic symptoms reappeared again. We finally settled on a very low dose of ACTH, 25 mg., and it was found that with this dose, he maintained a mild degree of asthma and mild personality changes; he could live outside the hospital much better than he could with either the severe asthma or the severe psychosis.

That is a very interesting finding because Funkenstein, at the Boston Psychopathic, reported practically similar experiences in an asthma patient who was treated with electric shock, and I have had two asthma patients who were treated with electric shock in whom the asthma disappeared but a psychosis developed. I do not believe that the psychosis is schizophrenia, but it certainly approaches it, being characterized by ideas of persecution and similar fantasies.

I do not believe, however, that the fact that cortisone may not be effective in the treatment of schizophrenia should at all deter us from continuing our work, which is based on the proposition that in schizophrenia there is a definite disturbance of the hypophyseal-adrenal cortex system. Dr. Hoagland and Dr. Pincus have told us that there are not only two or three or four substances produced by the adrenal cortex, but many more. They have suggested that there are 15 steroids released in response to ACTH. Until we actually find, isolate, and recognize both the nature of all these compounds and their specific effects upon the human being, we should not give up the attempts at using these substances for treatment before we have tried all of them.

If I may have a few more minutes, I would like to say a word or two concerning the question of disturbances of the hypophyseal-adrenal cortex mechanisms in schizophrenia. We have heard Dr. Hoagland present the results of studies at Worcester.

At the same time, we heard one of the discussants of Dr. Hoagland's paper, Dr. Altschule, whose findings as he reported them seemed to cast some doubt, to put it moderately, on the findings that Dr. Hoagland reported. Since, because of time limitations, Dr. Hoagland was given no opportunity to reply to Dr. Altschule's discussion, I wish to take this opportunity to comment upon it.

When investigators disagree as to conclusions, it is usually because they have employed different operational procedures. This is certainly the case in relation to Altschule's disagreement with the Worcester group. Table 45 of Hoagland's paper shows clearly that schizophrenic patients at rest differ little from normal controls but that what differences there are show hypoadrenalism, not hyperadrenalism. In stress experiments, his figures and tables show that the patients as a group give subnormal adrenal responses to stress and to ACTH when sizable populations are compared under standardized conditions.

Hoagland pointed out that the seven available indices of adrenal cortical stress responses display marked differences in their ability to characterize statistically valid group differences between schizophrenic patients and normal controls. Thus, while at rest the patients excrete significantly less corticoids or neutral reducing lipids (Table 45, p. 438). The percent of changes in neutral reducing lipids excreted following stress and ACTH injection are, however, the same in the patient group and in the control group (see Figs. 153 and 154, pp. 439 and 440) and therefore show no separation between the groups in stress tests, as they do at rest. The eosinophils, for reasons that Hoagland mentioned, are not good delineators between groups of psychotics and normals, although following ACTH injection they have been found by the Worcester group to be depressed less in the patients than in the controls. At a recent meeting in Boston, Greenblatt reported similar findings. The absolute cell counts of either eosinophils or lymphocytes are determined by so many factors that their levels are irrelevant to the point at issue. Adrenal cortical activity is only one of many factors determining the resting level of these cells.

Relative changes in lymphocytes with severe stresses have been shown by the Worcester group to differentiate between their normal and schizophrenic population, but they have not found this an index with mild stresses because of the multiplicity of competing factors involved in the regulation of the lymphocyte level. This is clear from Hoagland's paper in which the lymphocyte changes are not significantly different following 25-mg. injections of ACTH in the patient and control groups (see Fig. 154) and if used alone in pursuit meter tests (without anoxia). The patients would appear to be the more responsive (see Fig. 153) in sharp contrast to information furnished by the more reliable urinary signs of adrenal response.

The total response index (TRI), according to these workers, does not change significantly in approximately two-thirds of a sizable group of schizophrenic patients, as compared to a large group of controls, when they are given a variety of stresses, including the injection of 25 mg. of ACTH (see Table 46, p. 442).

The Worcester group has studied in comparable stresses large numbers of patients and normal controls and treated their data statistically, while Altschule has investigated six schizophrenic patients with two of the indices of adrenal response least capable of separating the normal and psychotic populations. Results obtained by such a procedure are meaningless for reasons that are apparent from the data in Hoagland's paper. Since lymphocyte and eosinophil changes would not be definitive under these circumstances, we are left with a few data on uric acid excretion in a heterogenous group of patients which appear to be in disagreement with the extensive findings of the Worcester group using this variable. Altschule's reported absolute values of blood cell levels and his data on sugar tolerance curves are entirely irrelevant to considerations of the role of the adrenal cortex in stress responses in terms of what is known of adrenal physiology.

We should bear in mind that the Worcester results are based on mean and statistically significant changes of indices that Altschule did not use. Changes in a single index on a few patients tell little, if anything, because of the variability involved.

The nature of Altschule's study does not permit any conclusions concerning qualitative differences in adrenal stress responses which are perhaps the most interesting aspect of the Worcester group's findings. The ratios of the components of the special measures of adrenal function statistically separate from the normals not only the two-thirds of schizophrenics who are sluggish responders, but the one-third who fall within the quantitatively normal response range. Statistically significant group differences between alpha and beta ketone excretion as reflecting adrenal steroid metabolites should also be mentioned in this connection. Finally prediction of prognosis with shock treatment was shown by Hoagland to occur in terms of adrenal response level to ACTH as measured before shock, in which patients with the more responsive adrenals are the ones who show the greatest clinical improvement with EST.

Gildea[3] finds that psychologic (though not physiologic) stresses are less effective in lowering lymphocytes in schizophrenics than in other persons. Cleghorn[1] has reported data indicating that adrenal cortical responses to stress were less marked in two schizophrenics who were included in his study than were responses in a large group of psychoneurotics. Finally Hemphill and Reiss[2] of England have reported, at the 1950 Paris International Congress of Psychiatry, extensive data generally confirmatory of the Worcester findings.

REFERENCES

1. CLEGHORN, R. A., and GRAHAM, B. F.: *The American Journal of Psychiatry*, 1950, 106, p. 668.
2. HEMPHILL, R. E., and REISS, H.: ACTH in Psychiatry. Presented at International Congress of Psychiatry, Paris, 1950.
3. PARSONS, E. H., and GILDEA, E.: *American Journal of Psychiatry*, 1949, 105, p. 573.

Discussion

DR. HUDSON HOAGLAND: There is just one point I would like to make with regard to the future of work with adrenal hormones in connection with possible therapeutic approaches.

I mentioned in my paper that perfusion studies in our laboratory of the beef adrenal had led to the development of new methods of analyzing the specific hormones that the gland produces when ACTH acts upon it.

We have evidence that when ACTH reaches the gland, some fifteen specific steroids are produced. We think that in the next year or so we will be able to say what all of them are and from what precursors they are derived. We know what seven of them are at the present time.

This type of analysis is clinically promising because we believe that it can be applied to an unraveling of the nature of secretion of steroid hormones in patients. We hope eventually to perfuse human adrenals, but in the meantime, the technics offer possibilities in relation to blood and urine which have not hitherto been available. What we hope to do is to abandon classifications of types of steroids in terms of metabolic end effects such as uric acid, 17-ketosteroids, sodium, potassium, corticoids, and hematologic effects and be able to say eventually just what and how much individual persons secrete. When this is done we can not only state as we do now that the psychotic patients are deficient in their ability to produce adrenal steroids in adequate amount under stress but what these deficiencies are in terms of steroid molecules. We then can develop a rational therapy, if such a therapy can be had at all, for psychotic patients.

It is possible that there will be no therapeutic action of any of the steroids on schizophrenia, but, in any case, we think we can find out.

We also have used ACTH therapeutically but without effectively improving the patient's symptoms. Because of the qualitative (as well as quantitative) aberrations of steroid production in psychotic patients we would now not expect ACTH to be beneficial therapeutically, assuming for the moment that the adrenal aberrations are causally related to the disorder. Large (100 mg.) doses of ACTH merely accentuate the abnormal ratios of steroid metabolic effects as we measure them in the urine.

DR. ROBERT A. CLEGHORN: I believe that it is significant that the topic of our discussion, the adrenal glands, has long been recognized as being a very important one in respect to all emergency functions of the body. The history of the adrenal glands includes several excellent all-out combats which we need not go into at the present time, but I think the present discussion is continuing, in a very modest way, that excellent tradition.

I would like to say a few words concerning our investigation of eight cases of depression.

We began with a false hypothesis and ended up with a negative result. We thought that since some patients had been reported as showing euphoria when given ACTH, that perhaps depressions would clear following its use. There was some transient improvement during the first few days of treatment in some of these patients, but I do not believe that there was a specific result. The concern felt about this investigation may well have been transmitted to the patients. In any case, they received more attention during the study, which is in itself important.

There is one result which came out of that work which I think is of some significance, however, and that is that we did not observe the electroencephalographic changes which have been reported by other workers in studying patients with arthritis and asthma and other psychosomatic conditions during ACTH therapy.

It is also significant, I believe, that from the Royal Victoria Hospital results have been reported which indicate that in arthritics and asthmatics there may be a lowered excretion of adrenal cortical substances so that when one is dealing with that psychosomatic group one is dealing with a patient population that differs from the group of patients with depression whom we were studying.

As far as the schizophrenics that we studied are concerned, we did not do this purposely, I assure you. We started out by studying psychoneurotics, but somehow or other a couple of schizophrenics crept into our study and we did not know it until we had finished.

I am not getting on either side of this Waverly-Worcester axis, but these two schizophrenic patients did show a lower response to ACTH according to our blood cell findings than did the other patients, that is, in respect to neutrophils, eosinophils, and lymphocytes. However, two swallows do not make a summer.

I wish to refer briefly now to Dr. Liddell's work. It has been a matter of considerable interest to me and of some concern. During the early thirties, I was heartily mixed up in the brewing of adrenals, and I made some calculations, from Dr. Liddell's paper, and came to the conclusion that the sheep that he was treating were getting one to one-half daily dog maintenance doses of adrenal cortical extract a day provided the Hartman extract was about the same potency as those in vogue elsewhere at the time. Therefore, although I could see no flaw in Dr. Liddell's work, I think the sheep must have been allergic to the cortical steroids!

We need more data such as Dr. Gildea has given us this afternoon, and more careful clinical description of the cases which are being studied.

CHAPTER 38

A Final Glance at the Symposium

RALPH W. GERARD, M.D.

THAT the symposium has been a success is most obvious from the exchange of information in and out of the sessions, from the fact that later speakers did actually refer to what was said in the earlier sessions, and, I had hoped to say, from the rearrangement of the seating groups; but I notice everyone is so fed up with everyone else by now that all are as far apart as they can be.

The faith indicated by the planners of this symposium, that somehow or other the mental rests upon the biologic, was clearly indicated by the character of the papers and persons selected. I think everyone here will agree, that in contrast to the blood-brain barrier which God or Nature put there, the mind-brain barrier is largely man-made, and that the two sides must somehow get across to each other. It is only coincidental that the blood-brain barrier does not exist in the epiphysis and that there Descartes thought the mind-brain barrier did not exist.

However, we are not in such good agreement when we come to the exact relations of brains and minds, of heredity and environment, or of the interaction of metabolism and structure and function and pathology; and I shall take the liberty of sketching, as quickly as I can, a blueprint of all this as I have seen it through the week.

It seems to me that "organization" covers both structure and chemistry and function and pathology, because the arrangement of molecules, ions, colloids, and the like, on the one hand, constitutes the chemistry, and, on the other hand, constitutes the structure; and the changes in these constitute the physiology or the pathology, as the case may be.

The job that faces science in this area, the job upon which each of us here is engaged at some level or other, has been first of all to identify the actual components present, find them, show what they are chemically, and measure their quantities. This is the sort of work reported by Folch-Pi, Ball, Meyerhof, Waelsch, Hoagland, Pincus, Jervis, and others during the week. Next, having found out what the particles are, the task is to locate them in space relative to each other and to the visible structures. This has been done in the reports of Manery, Flexner, Pope, Lilienthal, Wolf, Nurnberger, and others. That is the general trend of cytochemical work in this day: the particular localization, practically down to the molecular level, of the various substances present in tissues and cells; in our case, specifically in the nervous system.

Then, while such work is still continuing, because of course it is nowhere near complete, as substances become known and located to some extent, other workers, or sometimes the same ones, begin to look at dynamics instead of the statics: what happens to these materials—how they are formed, from what precursors and with what enzymes, coenzymes, ions, and other agencies; where do they go, how and to what degraded. We have heard much on this from Racker, Sperry, Rittenberg, Ball, Meyerhof, Ochoa, and others.

I also remind you that changes in these particular substances in the brain may not be in chemical character but in position, which is oftentimes just as important. The movements of these substances, particularly the charged ions, constitute electric currents; and their positions, in nonuniform distribution, give electric potentials. The reports of Lloyd, Brazier, and Lilly tie in closely here, and movements are also involved in growth and related changes, as Flexner reported. The experiments here tend to rest more and more on tracer technics, and electrical methods begin to show their importance even at this stage.

Then comes another step upward in our understanding and interpretation, again building upon such knowledge as we have so far acquired of these other things. This involves the relation of the materials and their organizational changes to the functioning of individual neurons, function being manifested by the electrical behavior, discharge, threshold, and such other properties of neurons as we are familiar with. The relation of respiration and glycolysis to function has been amply developed by Elliott, Quastel, Larrabee, and Kety; that of the nitrogen compounds by Lilienthal, Marrazzi, and Waelsch; that of salts particularly by Manery; that of enzymes by Flexner, Pope, Ashby, and others; and so on down the line. As Bishop has already pointed out, the electrical methods are especially effective at this level.

There is not time to elaborate any of these points (although I did have in mind a number of things that seemed to me important to say about them), except for one. I have become unhappy in the last year or so about our universally accepted assumption, that all the metabolic changes which must proceed in neurons to keep them functioning are serving primarily in terms of their energy yield. That still seems reasonably true, but there are a number of observations now that begin to throw doubt upon it, and I am more and more suspecting particular roles of particular molecules as such.

I am thinking of the fact that under azide poisoning a nerve can conduct for many hours full-sized normal impulses without any increase in its oxygen consumption, which, of course, normally should occur. I am thinking of Larrabee's finding reported here that, at physiologically narcotizing doses, physiologic change is not accompanied by a depression in respiratory metabolism. Although, as he pointed out, this is not the case for conducted impulses, the exact one-to-one falling off of oxygen consumption with conduction is to me very strong evidence that the loss of conduction is responsible for the decrease of respiration rather than the reverse. One would not expect a linear relation if the causation were the other way.

I am thinking also of the hypoglycemic effects on neural function and of the ability of certain other substrates to restore function of the sugar-deprived nervous system. There is our extremely disturbing observation that, when succinate is given instead of glucose, it is oxidized in great amounts but does not restore cord reflexes. We have even succeeded in showing—I know how Dr. Quastel felt about it because for a year we also couldn't confirm the reports—that the succinate can lead to the formation of energy-rich phosphate bonds. Nevertheless, succinate will not restore reflex function under conditions where glucose will. Clearly, some very important and basic problems are still present.

Well, let me continue to the next step in the growth of our understanding. Having learned something of the substances and their changes and their relation to the function of individual neurons, the problem of the integrated behavior of neuron groups—as nets, or masses, or whatever the case may be—must be explored. Much of the work here reported has dealt with this level. Woolsey, Bailey, Barron, and Conel have been concerned with the structural aspects; Tschirgi, Craigie, and Taylor with closely related problems of transportation; Jasper, Magoun, Lilly, Chang, and Lloyd with physiologic activity; and Hooker, Liddell, Hoch, Harlow, Teuber, Landis, Flexner, and others with the behavioral and psychologic phenomena. (I would re-emphasize the important point that Dr. Hoch made, that different kinds of drugs can produce qualitatively different effects on the psyche of one individual.)

Now, with all this laid out, we still must face the aberrations. What are the particular alterations which are associated with this or that or the other particular syndrome with which we happen to be concerned? In many instances the disturbing agent is known, yet the sequences must be painfully disentangled. Thus Quastel, Larrabee, Kety, and Himwich were concerned with the action of anesthetics; Windle, McFarland, Nims, Barach, and Kety with hypoxia; Keys, Wilder, and Lehmann with malnutrition; Jarvis, Wolf, Fölling, Hoagland, Altschule, McCulloch, Cleghorn, and Gildea with particular clinical entities; and Himwich, Lorenz, Gildea, and Lehmann with shock and other therapies.

But there is still another step before we are really through with our job: The abnormality in the sequence must be located, not only in its hierarchic level, but also chronologically. Kallmann, Bruetsch, Ingalls, Flexner, and some others were most concerned with this. So concludes the cataloging.

Now, it seems to me that the great argument about hereditary versus environmental causation, with congenital in between, is merely one aspect of this time problem; as indeed is the similar argument of organic versus functional disease.

People do take extreme positions on this matter. Dr. Meyerson, in his posthumous book, says that an environmentalist would maintain that if a cat had kittens in an oven, they would turn out to be biscuits. I suppose the answer—if you take the opposite view—is that if a hot dog had offspring in an oven they would be puppies, or at worst ponies. Or, perhaps, to make a somewhat less fantastic case, one would have his opponents say that an English child brought up in the jungle would somehow learn to make a dress suit out of banana leaves and regularly sing "God Save the King" after eating.

Ridiculously extreme positions are easily taken or ascribed to others. What I, at least, think is the real story—and certainly all physiologic geneticists think this way—is that at any stage in the history of an entity, beginning with a single chromosome and a single germ cell, if you wish, a certain unit system exists (an org of some sort, if I may use my word) which interacts with its environment. This interaction of the then existing org and its surroundings leads to a later stage in the system when it has become something different. The chromosome is now part of a nucleus, and the properties of the cytoplasm around it are determined by the kind and amount of substrate molecules, among other substances, brought from the environment to come under the action of the gene enzymes. The cells so produced, plus new environments, e.g., intrauterine, determine the succession of embryonic stages; and so on through infancy to adulthood. At each stage, whatever has come into being by that time continues still to interact with its environment, on and on; so that the environment of the past is built into the heredity of the future.

An excellent example of the meaninglessness of an artificial dichotomy between heredity and environment is offered by some of the work on the mold, neurospera. A genetic strain can easily be obtained which lacks a particular gene, necessary to develop a particular enzyme, required to oxidize a particular food molecule to some substance essential in building protoplasm for subsequent growth and development. Such a mutation will not survive at all on the ordinary nutrients of the wild form. But if it is offered, not the precursor on which that gene acts, but the product of that particular gene-induced reaction, then the organism shows normal development and is indistinguishable from the wild form. In effect, the situation can be viewed as purely hereditary, a genetic strain that requires an extra essential food component; or as purely environmental, a deficiency disease when an essential component has been omitted.

In general, the earlier and the more severe this abnormal metabolic step, the more structural are the consequences and the more irreversible they tend to be. This was well illustrated by the hypoxia material. With brief hypoxia early *in utero* or severe hypoxia later in life, there results the death of neurons and structural defects—magnified in the former case into developmental anomalies. With a milder hypoxia in later life, all that results is difficulty with behavior, exemplified by the report of the sweater-wearing young woman.

As I have said elsewhere (*American Journal of Psychiatry*, 1949, 106, p. 161), "The meaningful question, which is mostly not asked (in the psychiatric realm also), is a quantitative one. 'Within the permissible limits of variation of the hereditary factors, and of the environmental factors, what is the correlation between hereditary variance and the variance of the somatic character in the organism, and between the environmental variance and the variance of this character.' The answer will be different quantitatively from case to case, probably all the way from 99 per cent to 1 per cent."

The matter of methods deserves a few sentences. Electrical tools have proved enormously useful for functional studies; cytochemical procedure and electron microscopy are closing the gap between micra and angstroms in architecture; and tracer technics are breathing new life into problems of the transformation and translocation of substances. On this latter, Dr. Tschirgi is developing apparatus that will keep the plasma concentration of any desired radioactive substance constant, so that we should be able to follow its penetration into and adventures in the brain with considerable precision. Tracers also bid fair to overcome the great differential in sensitivity and speed between chemical and electrical indices.

Work reported last summer at the International Congress of Physiology in Copenhagen brings this new era of chemical methods to application on peripheral nerve. The tissue sample is placed in a pile or other neutron source to produce radioactive isotopes of the atoms present, and the amounts of these various atoms are inferred from the induced activity and its decay. Keynes, Hodgkin, and their colleagues have thus actually measured the movement of sodium into and potassium out of a single fiber with the passage of impulses, making measurements precise down to tenths of micrograms. So the chemical and electrical methods perhaps will soon be of equivalent utility, at least in some areas, and the correlations of phenomena will rapidly improve.

What happens in the whole development of science, as I see it and as was certainly illustrated here, is the exploitation of such correlations and the multiplication of researches. (Dr. Lewis said to me at the start of the week, "I tried to get a group like this together fifteen years ago, and there just weren't enough people in the country working in this area." He didn't even specify good people!) As each new substance or property or phenomenon is discovered, it becomes not only possible but obviously desirable to follow its variation under every kind of condition. So the bright area of knowledge ever spreads and, although the dark surface of ignorance is presumably decreasing, the perimeter of contact with the unknown also increases. Most of us are adding our little bit at a small segment of line. The lengthening line means a need of ever more workers and more facilities to do the work. That is why every field keeps growing and expanding—and universities go broke.

This is essentially done without plan, ladies and gentlemen. We all make hypotheses and every now and then there is a lucky guess. Still more rarely, there is a brilliant insight. But in our area, in biology, I think there are still so many unknown components and the variables are so great and the correlations so unsure, that it is rarely indeed that we get a truly seminal idea.

So I have to say, surely without hurting the feelings of anybody here, that I suspect every hypothesis advanced during the week is wrong. In fact, if any one of them is right I make the critic's usual offer to eat it, although I am a bit vague as to how you eat someone else's hypothesis. But our being wrong doesn't make a bit of difference. Dr. Hebb said that the main function of psychologists today is to be willing to be wrong, in making concrete hypotheses; and by that I think he meant neurophysiologic hypotheses. Dr. Jasper anticipated him by saying that the only thing worse than psychologists trying to be physiologists is physiologists trying to be psychologists. Perhaps both are right. But it's good clean fun. It keeps us going, and if we didn't have some hypotheses, we could hardly find experiments we wanted to do.

By and large, our work is like the building of a termite nest. We are engaged in a collective job, some working in one gallery, some in another. The individual termites operate without any plan that we are able to divine. As one watches the termites at work building a nest, there appears to be utter confusion. Each rushes around, drops its excreta at some particular point, and rushes around some more. Nevertheless, as the edifice grows, the tunnels and galleries do connect, and the walls coming together from the two sides join perfectly.

I am very optimistic about the future of our scientific nest, and not the infinitely distant future. The walls of understanding of cellular organization and of brain function and of mental behavior are all growing, and, as I see it, they are leaning toward closure very rapidly indeed.